1000 Stories and Rhymes

Every effort has been made to acknowledge the contributors to this book.
If we have made any errors, we will be pleased to rectify them in future editions.

This is a Parragon Book
This edition published in 2002

Parragon
Queen Street House
4 Queen Street
Bath BA1 1HE, UK

Design and project management by Aztec Design

Page make-up by

Mik Martin, Caroline Reeves and Kilnwood Graphics

ISBN 0-75259-095-2
Printed in China

1000 Stories and Rhymes

p

Contents

Polly the Potty Postlady

Polly Postlady worked hard delivering letters, and she was always in a hurry. She hated to keep the people on her round waiting – and Mr Price the Postmaster always expected her back at the post office by 12 o'clock.

One morning Polly was in a bigger hurry than ever. She had overslept and was late for work! "Hurry, hurry, rush and hurry!" Polly muttered to herself as she rushed out the door.

"People are waiting for their letters!" Polly Postlady said to herself, as she sped to the post office on her bike. "And Mr Price will be waiting for me!" She zoomed down the street as fast as her bike would go.

"Sorry I'm late, Mr Price," Polly puffed as she flew through the post office door.

"Good morning, Polly!" said Mr Price. "Your postbag is all ready – and it looks very full today!"

"Thanks, Mr Price," said Polly. "I'll really have to hurry, with all those letters and parcels!"

Polly sped down Main Street and tore around the corner of Jackson Road. She was going so fast that she didn't see the removal van in front of her until it was too late! "LOOK OUT!" shouted the removal men. "Oh dear!" shouted Polly, as she flew off her bike. Everything in Polly's postbag went flying, too!

"Oh no! It will take ages to collect all these!" cried Polly, when she had stood up and dusted herself off, "and I'm in such a hurry today!"

The removal men helped Polly collect all the letters, postcards and parcels and put them back in her bag. It wasn't too long before she was ready to go.

But when Polly picked up her bike, she saw that the tyre was flat! "I've got a puncture!" she cried. "I can't ride this now. What will I do?"

"You'll have to walk your round today, Polly," said one of the removal men.

"Oh no!" said Polly. "I'm late enough as it is! I'd better get going!" Polly ran off to deliver the post as quickly as she could.

But she was in such a hurry that she got all the names and addresses mixed up!

Mr Green, on Jackson Road, was expecting a parcel of books. Instead, he got two letters and a gas bill addressed to Mrs Jackson!

Mrs Jackson, who lived on Holly Drive, got a magazine that was supposed to go to Holly Walker!

And Holly Walker, who lived on Green Street, got the parcel of books meant for Mr Green!

Everybody was terribly confused, especially Polly Postlady!

"I must be going potty!" she exclaimed.

Polly rushed and hurried as quickly as she could to try and sort everything out... but by 11 o'clock her postbag was still half full.

She was beginning to feel hopeless, when suddenly she saw something that gave her a brilliant idea.

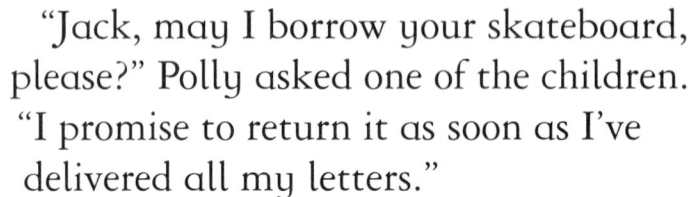

"Jack, may I borrow your skateboard, please?" Polly asked one of the children. "I promise to return it as soon as I've delivered all my letters."

"Sure, Polly," said Jack.

Polly had never been on a skateboard before, but she bravely stepped on. Polly wibbled and wobbled... and teetered and tottered... then she skidded and swayed... and WHOOOOSHED and WHIZZZED down the street.

"Wheeeeeeeee!" cried Polly with glee. "This is just what I need!"

Polly zoomed up and down the street at lightning speed. She had such a good time that the rest of her round seemed to get done very quickly.

"This is much faster than walking," she said, "and much more fun than my bike!"

At last Polly's deliveries were done. She returned the skateboard to Jack, and had just enough time to rush back to the post office.

"I'm back, Mr Price!" she gasped, tripping over her bike as she staggered through the door. "Right on time!"

"I'm glad, Polly," said Mr Price. "And I'm glad you're all right. The removal men brought back your bike. I guess we'll have to mend that puncture right away."

"Oh there's no hurry, Mr Price," said Polly. "I think I've found a much better form of transport for a potty postlady like me!"

Bella Bunny's Bonnet

In pretty Primrose Wood, there was great excitement. It was the Spring Parade. All the animals were joining in because a prize was being given for the best bonnet. "I bet I'll win," said Bella, who was a very vain bunny. "What can I use for my hat?" she wondered, as she skipped through the woods. Bella gathered some pretty Spring flowers, then called her friend, Binky the pigeon, for help. The friends worked hard, weaving daffodils and bluebells into a beautiful display.

"There," said Binky, "perfect." Bella put on the pretty hat and smiled.

"I know I'm going to win!" she cried. Binky just smiled. Bella really was the vainest animal in Primrose Wood! At last, it was time for the parade. The animals from Folly Farm were all wearing jolly bonnets. "There isn't one hat as pretty as mine," giggled Bella. "It looks good enough to eat!" Gordy the goat thought so, too. Trotting behind Bella, he nibbled her bonnet, until he had gobbled up nearly all the flowers!

Then, Holly the horse gave a loud neigh. "The winner of this year's parade is Felicity the fox!" she said.

Everyone cheered – except Bella. "But mine is the best – look!" Bella took the hat off her head. "Aaagghh! My lovely hat!" she cried, looking at a clump of twigs!

"Oops!" said Gordy. "Sorry, Bella."

"But you have won something," sniggered Holly. "The prize for the funniest hat!"

Brave Billy Bunny

At the edge of Frog Pond Wood, there lived a friendly, little bunny called Billy, his brother Bobby and lots of bunny friends. The one thing Billy really, really hated was getting wet! One sunny day, the other bunnies and Bobby hopped off to the stream, to play. "Come on, Billy!" they called.

"No way!" cried Billy. "I hate the water!"

What Billy loved doing most of all was running. So, while the other bunnies played at the stream, Billy ran through the wood, leaping over logs and weaving in and out of the trees – he was very fast! Suddenly, Bouncer Bunny came rushing back from the stream.

"Billy! Come quickly!" he panted. "Bobby's fallen into the water and is being washed away!" Billy rushed off towards the stream, leaving poor Bouncer far behind. When Billy reached the stream, he could just see his little brother, Bobby, splashing away in the rushing water.

"Help!" cried Bobby. "I can't swim!"

Then, Billy began to run! He managed to get ahead of Bobby. Quickly, Billy jumped into the water, swam up to his brother and, coughing and spluttering, dragged poor Bobby to the side.

"Billy!" cried the others. "You're a hero!"

"A wet hero!" said Billy, grinning. "Getting wet wasn't so bad after all. I'm going for another swim!"

Barney the Boastful Bear

Barney was a very boastful bear.

"Look at my lovely soft fur!" he would say to the other toys. "See how it shines!"

Barney loved to talk about himself. "I'm the smartest toy in the playroom!" he would say. "It's a well-known fact."

He didn't know that the other toys all laughed about him behind his back.

"That bear thinks he's so smart," growled Scotty Dog. "But he isn't smart enough to know when everyone's fed up with him!"

"He'll learn his lesson one of these days," said Molly Monkey, and sure enough, that is just what happened...

One hot summer's day, the toys lazed in the warm playroom. "Wouldn't it be lovely if we could all go for a walk outside," said Rag Doll.

"We could have a lovely picnic in the woods!" said Old Bear.

"Even better, we could all go for a drive in the toy car first!" said Rabbit.

"But none of us is big or clever enough to drive the toy car," said Rag Doll, sadly.

"I am!" came a voice from the corner. It was Barney. He had been listening to them talking.

"I can drive the toy car. And I know the best place for a picnic in the woods," he said.

"We've never seen you drive the car," said Rabbit, suspiciously.

"That's because I drive it at night, when you're asleep," said Barney. "I'm a very good driver, in fact."

"Ooh, let's go then!" cried Rag Doll. And in no time they had packed up a picnic and were sitting ready in the car.

"Er, I don't feel like driving today, actually," mumbled Barney. "It's too hot." But the others were not interested in hearing excuses, so rather reluctantly Barney climbed into the driver's seat and started the engine. You see, the truth was, Barney had never really driven the car before, and he was scared. But he wanted to show off, so he pretended to know what he was doing.

Off they set down the garden path. "Toot, toot!" Barney beeped the horn as he turned the little car out into the country lane, and soon they were driving along, singing merrily.

All was going well, until Rag Doll suddenly said, "Hey, Barney, didn't we just miss the turning for the woods?"

"I know where I'm going," said Barney, crossly. "Leave it to me." And he made the little car go faster.

"Slow down a bit, Barney!" called Old Bear, from the back seat. "My fur is getting all ruffled." He was starting to feel anxious.

"I don't need a back-seat driver, thank you," said Barney, with a growl, and made the car go even faster. By now the others were starting to feel scared, but Barney was having a great time.

"Aren't I a wonderful driver!" he chuckled. "Look – no hands!" And he took his paws off the steering wheel. Just then they reached

a sharp corner. The little car went spinning off the side of the road and crashed into a tree, tipping all the toys out into the ditch!

They were a bit dazed, but luckily no one was hurt. They were not pleased with Barney though.

"You're a silly bear!" said Rabbit, crossly. "We could all have been badly hurt!"

"We'll have to walk home now," said Rag Doll, rubbing her head. "Where are we?"

Everyone looked at Barney.

"Don't ask me!" he said, quietly.

"But you told us that you knew the way!" said Old Bear, indignantly.

"I was only pretending," said Barney,

his voice trembling. "I don't really know how to drive, and I don't know where we are!" And he started to cry.

The other toys were furious with Barney.

"You naughty boastful bear!" they scolded. "Now see what trouble your boasting has got us into!"

The lost toys walked through the dark woods all night long, clinging together in fright as shadows loomed around them.

They had never been out at night before. Then just before dawn, they spotted the little house where they lived, and crept back into the playroom.

What a relief it was to be home again!

Luckily their owner had not noticed they were missing, so she never knew what an adventure her toys had been having while she was fast asleep. She often wondered what had happened to her toy car though.

Whale Song

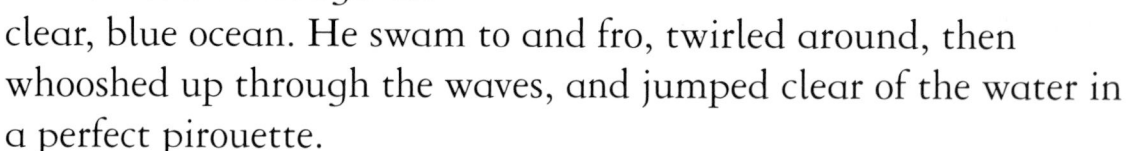

"Oh, what a beautiful morning!" sang Flippy, the whale, as streaks of sunlight filtered down through the clear, blue ocean. He swam to and fro, twirled around, then whooshed up through the waves, and jumped clear of the water in a perfect pirouette.

Flippy loved to sing and dance. The trouble was, although he was a very graceful dancer, his singing was terrible. His big mouth would open wide, as he boomed out song after song – but none of them were in tune! The dreadful sound echoed through the ocean for miles, sending all the fish and other ocean creatures diving into the rocks and reefs for cover, as the waters shook around them. It was always worse when the sun shone, as the bright warm sun made Flippy

want to sing and dance with happiness. It had got so bad that the other creatures had begun to pray for dull skies and rain.

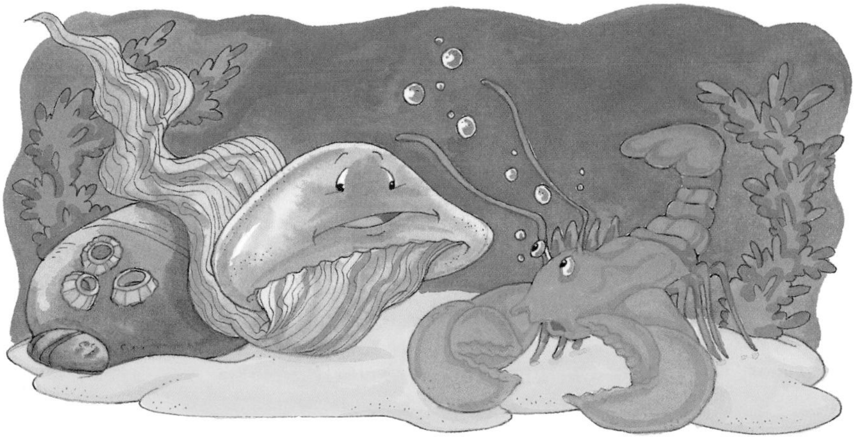

"Something has got to be done!" complained Wobble, the jellyfish. "Flippy's booming voice makes me quiver and shake so much that I can't see where I'm going!"

"Well, I know where I'm going," said Snappy, the lobster. "As far away as possible. My head is splitting from Flippy's awful wailing."

"Someone will have to tell Flippy not to sing any more," said Sparky, the stingray.

"But it will hurt his feelings," said Wobble.

"Not as much as his singing hurts my ears!" snapped Snappy.

And so they decided that Sparky would tell Flippy the next day that they did not want him to sing any more songs. Wobble was right. Flippy was very upset when he heard that the others did not like his singing. He cried big, salty tears.

"I was only trying to enjoy myself!" he sobbed. "I didn't realise I was upsetting everyone else."

"There, there," said Sparky, wishing he had not been chosen to give the little whale the bad news. "You can still enjoy dancing."

"It's not the same without music," said Flippy, miserably. "You can't get the rhythm." And he swam off into the deep waters, saying he wanted to be alone for a while.

As Flippy lay on the bottom of the ocean floor, feeling very sorry for himself, a beautiful sound came floating through the water from far away in the distance. It sounded like someone singing. Flippy wanted to know who was making such a lovely sound so, with a flick of his big tail, he set off in the direction it was coming from.

As he got closer, he could hear a soft voice singing a beautiful melody. Peering out from behind a big rock, he saw that the voice belonged to a little octopus, who was shuffling and swaying about on the ocean floor. His legs seemed to be going in all directions, as he stumbled and tripped along. Then he tried to spin around, but his legs got tangled and he crashed to the ground in a heap.

"Oh, dear," said Leggy, the octopus. "I seem to have eight left feet!"

Flippy looked out shyly from behind the rock.

"What are you trying to do?" he asked.

The little octopus looked rather embarrassed.

"I was trying to dance," he said, blushing pink. "Only I'm not very good at it."

"Well, maybe I could teach you," said Flippy. "I'm a very good dancer. And then, in return, there is something that I would love you to teach me!"

A few weeks later, Wobble, Snappy and Sparky were discussing how they missed having Flippy around, when they heard a strange and beautiful sound floating towards them through the ocean.

"Oh, what a beautiful morning..." came the song, only this time there were two voices singing in perfect harmony!

"Surely that can't be Flippy!" said the others in surprise. But to their amazement, as the voices came closer they saw that, sure enough, it was Flippy, spinning and twirling as he danced gracefully towards them with his new friend!

Harvey the Shyest Rabbit

Harvey the rabbit was the shyest animal in the glade beside Looking-Glass Pond. He was too shy to talk to anyone... too shy to play with the other animals... too shy even to look out from behind his big floppy ears.

"There's no need to be scared," Mama Rabbit told him. "If you want to join in, all you have to do is ask."

But Harvey just hid behind the long grass. No one even noticed that he was there!

One morning, Harvey was sitting beside Looking-Glass Pond – alone, as usual.

"I wish I could make a friend," he sighed. "But how can I, when no one even notices me?"

Harvey gazed down sadly at the pond. He could hardly believe his eyes! There in the water was another little rabbit with big floppy ears, staring back at him.

"He looks just as scared as me!" thought Harvey. He waved shyly at the rabbit in the water. The water rabbit waved too! Harvey did a bunny hop in surprise. The water rabbit did a bunny hop. "Hello!" said Harvey bravely, smiling.

"Hello!" said the rabbit, smiling back. "So that's how you make friends!" cried Harvey, in amazement. "You just need to be a little bit brave."

He was so excited, he forgot all about being shy or scared. Instead, he raced off to tell everyone the good news.

And this time, everyone noticed him! Soon Harvey had lots of new friends to play with. But he never forgot to visit his very first friend in Looking-Glass Pond!

Once I Saw a Little Bird

Once I saw a little bird
  Come hop, hop, hop;
So I cried, "Little bird,
  Will you stop, stop, stop?"
And was going to the window,
  To say, "How do you do?"
But he shook his little tail,
  And far away he flew.

Little Robin Redbreast

Little Robin Redbreast
  Sat upon a rail:
Niddle-noddle went his head!
  Wiggle-waggle went his tail.

Intery, Mintery Cutery, Corn

Intery, mintery, cutery, corn,
  Apple seed and apple thorn.
Wire, briar, limber, lock,
  Three geese in a flock.

One flew east and one flew west;
  One flew over the cuckoo's nest.

The North Wind doth Blow

The north wind doth blow,
  And we shall have snow,
And what will poor Robin do then?
  Poor thing!

He'll sit in a barn,
  And to keep himself warm,
Will hide his head under his wing.
  Poor thing!

Jay-bird

Jay-bird, jay-bird, settin' on a rail,
  Pickin' his teeth with the end of his tail;
Mulberry leaves and calico sleeves –
  All school teachers are hard to please.

Two Little Dicky Birds

Two little dicky birds sitting on a wall,
One named Peter, one named Paul.
  Fly away, Peter!
  Fly away, Paul!
    Come back, Peter!
    Come back, Paul!

The Cuckoo

Cuckoo, Cuckoo,
  What do you do?
In April
  I open my bill;
In May
  I sing night and day;
In June
  I change my tune;
In July
  Away I fly;
In August
  Away I must.

Magpies

One for sorrow, two for joy,
  Three for a girl, four for a boy,
Five for silver, six for gold,
  Seven for a secret never to be told.

Greedy Bear

If there is one thing in the whole wide world that a teddy bear likes more than anything, it is buns – big sticky currant buns with sugary tops, and squishy middles. A teddy bear will do almost anything for a bun. But for one greedy little teddy bear called Clarence, sticky buns were to be his unsticking!

Rag Doll baked the most wonderful buns in the little toy cooker. She baked big buns and small buns, iced buns and currant buns, Bath buns and cream buns, and even hot-cross buns! She shared them out amongst the toys in the playroom, and everybody loved them. But no one loved them as much as Clarence.

"If you will give me your bun, I'll polish your boots!" he'd say to Tin Soldier.

And sometimes, if Tin Soldier was not feeling too hungry, he'd agree. There was always someone who would give Clarence their bun in return for a favour, and sometimes Clarence would eat five or six buns in one day!

Then he'd be busy washing the dolls' dresses, brushing Scotty Dog's fur, or cleaning the toy policeman's car. He would even stand still and let the clown throw custard pies at him!

So you see, Clarence was not a lazy bear, but he was a greedy bear, and in spite of all his busyness, he was becoming a rather plump little greedy bear. All those buns were starting to show around his middle, and his fur was beginning to strain at the seams!

Then one day Clarence rushed into the playroom full of excitement. His owner, Penny, had told him that next week she was taking him on a teddy bears' picnic.

"She says there will be honey sandwiches and ice-cream and biscuits – and lots and lots of buns!" Clarence told the others, rubbing his paws together. "I can hardly wait! In fact all this excitement has made me hungry, so I think I'll have a bun." And he took a big sticky bun out from under a cushion where he'd hidden it earlier.

"Oh, Clarence!" said Rabbit. "One of these days you will simply go pop!"

"Just be happy I don't like carrots!" said Clarence, with a smile.

Well, that week Clarence was busier than ever. Every time he thought about the picnic he felt hungry, and then he'd have to find someone who'd let him have their bun. He ate bun after bun, and would not listen

when Rag Doll warned him that his back seam was starting to come undone.

The day of the teddy bears' picnic dawned, and Clarence yawned and stretched, smiling with excitement. But as he stretched he felt a popping sensation all down his stomach. He tried to sit up in bed, but to his alarm he found he could not move. He looked down to see that the seams around his tummy had popped open, and his stuffing was spilling out all over the bed!

"Help!" he cried. "I'm exploding!"

Just then, Penny woke up. "Oh, Clarence!" she cried when she saw him. "I can't take you to the teddy bears' picnic like that!"

Penny showed Clarence to her mummy, who said he would have to go to the toy hospital.

Clarence was away from the playroom for a whole week, but when he came back he was as good as new. Some of his stuffing had been taken out, and he was all sewn up again.

He had had lots of time to think in the hospital about what a silly greedy bear he had been. How he wished he had not missed the picnic. The other teddies said it was the best day out they had ever had. Penny had taken Rabbit instead.

"It was terrible," moaned Rabbit. "Not a carrot in sight. I did save you a bun though." And he pulled a big sticky bun out of his pocket.

"No thank you, Rabbit," said Clarence. "I've gone off buns!"

Of course, Clarence did not stop eating buns for long, but from then on he stuck to one a day. And he still did favours for the others, only now he did them for free!

A Swarm of Bees in May

A swarm of bees in May
  Is worth a load of hay;
A swarm of bees in June
  Is worth a silver spoon;
A swarm of bees in July
  Is not worth a fly.

Bow, Wow, Wow

Bow, wow, wow,
  Whose dog art thou?
"Little Tom Tinker's dog,
  Bow, wow, wow."

Incey Wincey Spider

Incey Wincey spider
  Climbing up the spout;
Down came the rain
  And washed the spider out.
Out came the sunshine
  And dried up all the rain;
Incey Wincey spider
  Climbing up again.

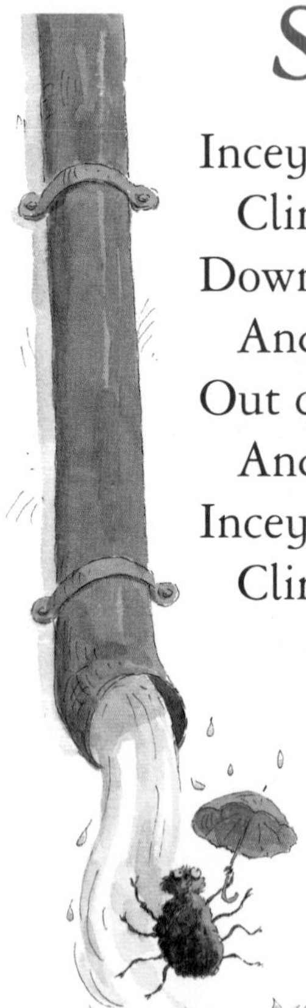

Tinker, Tailor

Tinker, tailor,
  Soldier, soldier,
Rich man, poor man,
  Beggarman, thief!

The Cold Old House

I know a house, and a cold old house,
  A cold old house by the sea.
If I were a mouse in that cold old house
  What a cold, cold mouse I'd be!

Hickory, Dickory, Dock

Hickory, dickory, dock,
  The mouse ran up the clock.
The clock struck one,
  The mouse ran down,
Hickory, dickory, dock.

Bat, Bat

Bat, Bat, come under my hat,
  And I'll give you a slice of bacon,
And when I bake I'll give you a cake,
  If I am not mistaken.

Three Blind Mice

Three blind mice, three blind mice!
  See how they run, see how they run!
They all ran after the farmer's wife,
  Who cut off their tails with a carving-knife,
Did ever you see such a thing in your life,
  As three blind mice?

One Stormy Night

It was Patch's first night outside in his smart new kennel. He snuggled down on his warm blanket and watched as the skies grew dark. Before long he fell fast asleep. As he slept, big spots of rain began to fall. A splash of water dripped from the kennel roof on to his nose.

Just then, there was a great crash and a bright flash of light lit up the sky. Patch woke with a start and was on his feet at once, growling and snarling. "It's just a silly old storm," he told himself. "Nothing to scare a fearless farm dog like me!" But as the lightning flashed again, he saw a great shadow looming against the barn. Patch gulped. Whatever could it be? Patch began to bark furiously, trying to act braver than he felt. Next time the lightning flashed, there was no sign of the shadow. "I soon scared that monster away!" he thought.

But as Patch settled back down in his cosy kennel, the sky outside lit up once more, and there in the doorway towered the monster!

"Just checking you're okay in the storm," said Mummy, giving Patch a lick on the ear.

"A fearless farm dog like me?" said Patch. "Of course I am!" But as the storm raged on, he snuggled up close to her all the same!

The Cow who Jumped over the Moon

Boing, boing, boing! Bouncy Bunny kicked up her heels and bounded happily across the field.

"I can bounce high in the air, watch me!" she called to the other animals on the farm. Her fluffy white tail bobbed up and down.

"Very good!" said Silly Sheep, who was easily impressed.

"Yes, very good," said Swift, the sheepdog. "But not as good as me. I can jump right over the gate." With that, he leapt over the gate and into the field.

"Amazing!" said Silly Sheep.

"Yes, amazing," said Harry Horse, with a flick of his mane. "But not as amazing as me. I can jump right over that hedge. Watch me!" And with that, he galloped around the field, then leapt high into the air, and sailed over the tall hedge.

"Unbelievable!" said Silly Sheep.

"Yes, unbelievable," said Daisy, the cow, chewing lazily on a clump of grass. "But not as unbelievable as me. I can jump right over the moon!"

"Well, I'm afraid that is unbelievable, Daisy," said Harry Horse. "No one can jump over the moon. That's just a fairy story."

"Well, I can," said Daisy, stubbornly. "And I can prove it! You can watch me do it if you like!"

The other animals all agreed that they would very much like to see Daisy jump over the moon.

"Meet me here in the field tonight, then," said Daisy to them. "When the moon is full, and the stars are shining bright."

So that night, when the moon had risen high up in the sky, the excited animals gathered together in the field. The rest of the animals from the farm came along too, for word had soon spread that Daisy, the cow, was going to jump over the moon, and they were all eager to watch.

"Come along then, Daisy," said Swift, the sheepdog, as the animals waited impatiently. "Are you going to show us how you can jump over the moon, or not?"

All the animals laughed because they thought that Daisy was just boasting, and that she would not really be able to do it.

"Yes, I am going to show you," said Daisy, "but, first of all, you will have to come with me. This isn't the right spot." Daisy led the animals across the field, to the far side, where a little stream ran along the edge of the field, separating it from the dark woods on the other side. As they crossed the field, they looked up at the great, yellow moon shining down on them. It looked so very far away. However did Daisy think that she could jump so high?

"Now, stand back everyone, and give me some room," said Daisy. The animals did as they were asked, and watched Daisy with anticipation, giggling nervously. Whatever was she going to do?

Daisy trotted back to the middle of the field, turned, then stopped, shuffling backwards and forwards as she took up her starting position.

"Come on, Daisy," cried the animals, impatiently. Daisy took a deep breath, then ran towards the stream at a great speed.

At the last moment, she sprang into the air, and sailed across the stream, landing safely on the other side.

"I did it!" cried Daisy. "Aren't you going to clap, then?" The other animals looked at each other in confusion.

"But you only jumped over the stream!" said Harry Horse, puzzled.

"Come and take a closer look," called Daisy, still on the far side. The animals gathered close to the water's edge. They looked down, and there reflected in the water, shimmered the great full moon! How the animals laughed when they realised Daisy had tricked them.

"See?" said Daisy. "I really can jump over the moon!" And just to prove it, she jumped back to the field again. The animals all clapped and cheered.

"That was a very good trick!" said Swift, the sheepdog.

"Amazing!" said Silly Sheep. "Could someone explain it to me again, please!"

Katy and the Butterfly

As Katy Kitten lay dozing happily in the sun, something tickled her nose. She opened an eye and saw a butterfly hovering above her whiskers, but as she tapped at it with her soft paw it fluttered away. Katy sprang after the butterfly, missed it and landed with a howl in a bed of thistles. "I'll catch that butterfly!" she said, crossly.

Katy chased the butterfly towards the stream, where it settled on the branch of a tree. She climbed after it, high into the tree, but every time she came near, the butterfly simply flew away – and by now, she was stuck! Nervously, she looked down at the stream swirling below her.

Just then, the butterfly fluttered past her nose. Without thinking, Katy swiped at it with her paw. But as she did so, she lost her balance and went tumbling down through the tree, landing with a great SPLASH! in the water below. "Help!" cried Katy, waving her paws wildly.

Luckily she caught hold of a branch hanging over the stream and clambered onto the bank.

Katy arrived home, cold and wet. She curled up, exhausted, in front of the fire, but just as she started to doze, she felt something tugging at her whiskers. She opened one eye and saw a little mouse.

"Oh no, I've done enough chasing for one day, thank you!" said Katy.

Fred the Fearless Fireman

Fireman Fred hurried to the fire station. It was his turn to cook lunch for the firemen on his shift, and he had just bought some nice, plump sausages at the butcher's.

At the fire station, Fred bumped into Builder Benny, who had come to repair a broken window frame.

"Oops! Hello, Benny!" he said. Then he went straight to the kitchen to start cooking. The smell of sausages wafted through the fire station. "Mmm, those sausages smell good!" said Dan and Mike, the other firemen, as they arrived for work. Suddenly the alarm bell rang – CLANG! CLANG! CLANG!

"Emergency!" cried Fireman Mike. He and Fireman Dan rushed down the pole and into their fire-fighting gear. "What about the sausages?" cried Fireman Fred.

"Don't worry about a thing," said Builder Benny, coming in through the window. "I'll look after them till you get back."

"Thanks, Benny!" said Fireman Fred, trying to get his apron off as he rushed down to join the others. The emergency was in Tony's Pizza

Parlour. One of the ovens had caught fire!

"We'll have that blaze out in a jiffy!" said Fred, rushing in with a big fire extinguisher. Dan and Mike followed with the hose.

With a WHIIISH! and a WHOOOSH! from Fred, and a SPLIISH! and a SPLOOOSH! from Mike and Dan, the fire was soon out.

"WHOOPS!" cried Fireman Fred, slipping on the wet floor. But he was back on his feet in a flash. "Thank you!" said Tony, as the firemen took their equipment back to the truck. "I can get back to baking pizzas now!"

Just when they were ready to go back to the station, the firemen heard a call coming through over their radio. "Emergency! Emergency! Window cleaner in distress on Pine Avenue. Emergency! Over… "

"We're on our way!" said Fireman Fred, starting the engine. "Over and out!"

NEE-NAW! NEE-NAW! With sirens blaring, the fire engine zoomed into Pine Avenue. A crowd had gathered around Tip-Top Towers, the tallest building in town.

"It's Will the window cleaner!" cried Polly Postlady, who had just finished delivering the day's post to the building. "His ladder has broken, and he's hurt his leg. Now he's stuck, and he can't get down! Can you help him?"

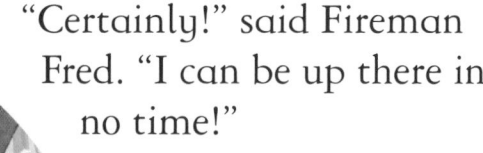

"Certainly!" said Fireman Fred. "I can be up there in no time!"

The firemen put up their tallest ladder. While Mike and Dan held out a net – just in case – Fred fearlessly began scrambling up the ladder. "Here I come, Will!" he shouted.

"I've got you!" said Fred, as he grabbed hold of the window cleaner. The crowd below cheered as Fred carried Will down the ladder and helped him into the fire engine.

Fred drove the fire engine straight to the hospital.

"Thank you for rescuing me," Will said to Fred.

"Don't mention it," said Fred. "I'm sure your leg will be fine– but I think you'll need a new ladder!"

"What a busy day it's been!" said Fireman Fred, as they drove back to the fire station. "I feel really frazzled!"

"Our work's not over yet!" said Fireman Dan. "Look! There's smoke up ahead! NEE-NAW! NEE-NAW! went the siren.

VRROOOM! VRROOOM! went the engine, as it raced to the scene of the fire.

The smoke was coming from the fire station! Dan and Mike unwound the hose, and Fred raced inside. "Oooof!" he gasped, as he tripped over the hose and bumped into Benny – again!

"Sorry, fellows," said a red-faced Builder Benny. "I guess I burnt the sausages. I think your lunch is ruined."

Poor Fred felt really frazzled now – until he had an idea. "I know just the person to rescue us from this situation!" he said.

"Who?" asked the others. "Tony!" said Fireman Fred.

"His pizzas are yummy, and an extra-large one will be a perfect lunch for all of us!"

I Love Little Pussy

I love little pussy, her coat is so warm;
And if I don't hurt her she'll do me no harm.
So I'll not pull her tail nor drive her away,
But pussy and I very gently will play.

Pussycat Mole

Pussycat Mole,
Jumped over a coal,
And in her best petticoat
burnt a great hole.
Poor pussy's weeping,
she'll have no more milk,
Until her best petticoat's
mended with silk.

Pussycat, Pussycat

Pussycat, pussycat, where
have you been?
I've been to London to visit
the Queen.
Pussycat, pussycat, what
did you there?
I frightened a little mouse
under her chair.

Pussycat Sits by the Fire

Pussycat sits by the fire.
How did she come there?
In walks the little dog,
Says, "Pussy! are you there?
How do you do, Mistress Pussy?
Mistress Pussy, how d'ye do?"
"I thank you kindly, little dog,
I fare as well as you!"

Mary had a Little Lamb

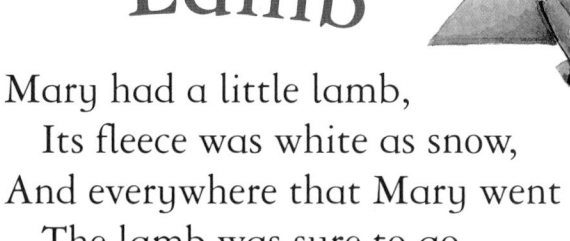

Mary had a little lamb,
Its fleece was white as snow,
And everywhere that Mary went
The lamb was sure to go.

It followed her to school one day,
Which was against the rule;
It made the children laugh and play
To see a lamb in school.

Frisky Lamb

A frisky lamb
And a frisky child
Playing their pranks
In a cowslip meadow:
The sky all blue
And the air all mild
And the fields all sun
And the lanes half-shadow.

Baa, Baa, Black Sheep

Baa, baa, black sheep, have you any wool?
Yes, sir, yes, sir, three bags full;
One for the master, one for the dame,
And one for the little boy that lives down the lane.

On the Grassy Banks

On the grassy banks
Lambkins at their pranks;
Woolly sisters, woolly brothers,
Jumping off their feet,
While their woolly mothers
Watch them and bleat.

The Princess and the Pea

Once upon a time, there was a prince whose dearest wish was to marry a princess – but only a true princess would do. In order to find her, he travelled far and wide, all over the land.

He met young princesses and old ones, beautiful princesses and plain ones, rich princesses and poor ones, but there was always something that was not quite right with each of them.

The prince began to despair. He called together his courtiers and announced, "I have failed to find my dream princess. We will go home to our palace without delay."

One dark night, back at his palace, there was the most tremendous storm. Lightning flashed across the sky and thunder buffeted the thick palace walls.

The prince and his parents were talking in the drawing room. He was telling them all about his hopeless search for a perfect princess to marry. "Don't despair, dear," said his mother, the queen. "Who knows what surprises the future may hold. You could find your perfect princess when you least expect to."

Just then, they heard a tiny tap-tapping at the window. The prince opened it, and standing there before him was a very beautiful, but very wet, young lady. Her hair was dripping, her dress was soaked through, and she was shivering with cold.

"I am a princess," she told the prince, "and I am lost. Please may I come in and shelter from the storm?"

The prince was astonished. He asked the girl into the palace, then he turned to the queen and whispered in her ear, "Oh, Mother, she is enchanting! But how can I be sure she really is a princess?"

"Leave it to me," said his mother, and she hurried off to have a bedroom prepared for the pretty girl.

First, the queen placed a little green pea on the mattress. Then she ordered the servants to bring twenty thick mattresses, and twenty feather quilts, which they piled on top of the pea. The princess needed a very tall ladder to climb into bed that night!

The next morning, at breakfast, the queen asked the princess if she had slept well.

"I had the most awful night!" said the princess. "I don't know what it was, but there was a hard lump under my bed, and it kept me awake all night, and now I'm absolutely covered with bruises!"

"At last!" the queen exclaimed, "our search is over! We have found a true princess for our son. Only a real princess would have skin so tender that she could feel a pea through twenty mattresses and twenty feather quilts!"

The prince was overjoyed, and he and the princess were soon married.

As for the little green pea, the prince had a special cabinet made and it was put on display in the royal museum, where it can still be seen today!

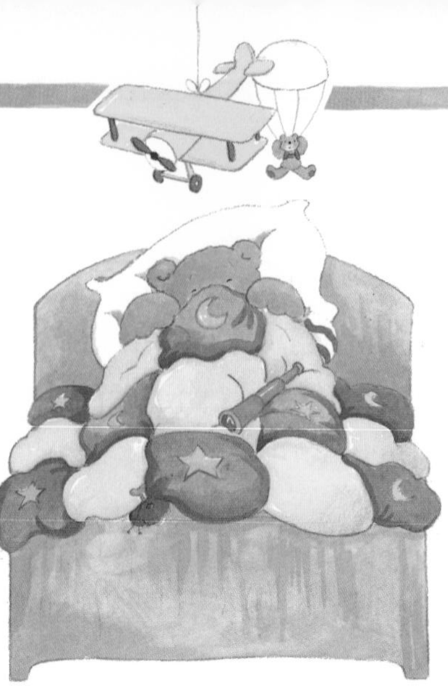

Rise and Shine Bear

"Wakey wakey, rise and shine!" said Mummy Bear, drawing back the curtains.

"I'm still tired!" yawned Teddy Bear, snuggling down in the bed.

"It's time for school! But if you hurry," said Mummy Bear, "you can play your drums while you get ready."

"Hurray!" cried Teddy Bear, suddenly wide awake. He leaped out of bed and strapped on his shiny blue drum kit.

"One beat for getting up!" he said. "And two beats for getting washed. Three beats for getting dressed. Four beats for marching down to breakfast. And five beats because we're having pancakes – yummy!"

"Now put down your drum and eat your breakfast," said Mummy Bear.

Teddy Bear put his drum on the table, but every now and then he gave it a soft tap with his fingers.

"It's getting late," said Mummy Bear, looking at the clock. "Why don't you wake up Daddy Bear?"

"Wakey wakey, rise and shine!" shouted Teddy Bear happily and loudly. Poor Daddy Bear!

Night-night Bear

Teddy Bear had been to the circus. “It’s very late – why don’t you have a nap in the back of the car,” said Mummy Bear kindly.

“I’m not sleepy!” said Teddy Bear, stifling a yawn. “Weren’t the clowns funny? I loved the clowns best.”

“The trapeze artists were amazing,” said Mummy Bear.

“Oh, they were the best of all,” agreed Teddy Bear. “When I grow up I’m going to fly on the trapeze.”

“I thought you were going to be a clown,” said Daddy Bear, smiling.

“I’ll be a clown in my spare time,” yawned Teddy Bear.

“What about the trick riders?” asked a smiling Mummy Bear.

“I’ll do that as well,” sighed Teddy Bear, resting his head against a cushion.

All the way home Teddy Bear dreamed about working in the circus. In his dream he could do everything – he made people laugh and cry and gasp in amazement.

“Night-night Circus Bear,” said Daddy Bear, carrying him upstairs to his bed.

“Night-night Daddy,” mumbled Teddy Bear through his dreams.

Sleeping Beauty

Once upon a time, in a land far, far away, there lived a king and queen who were kind and good. When the queen gave birth to a baby girl, the whole kingdom rejoiced.

When it was time for the baby to be christened, the king and queen arranged a great celebration. They asked the seven good fairies of the kingdom to be the baby's godmothers. But, to their surprise, eight fairies arrived at the feast.

The eighth fairy was ugly and old, and no one had seen her for years. The king and queen, thinking she was dead, hadn't invited her to take part in the ceremony.

Soon it was time for the fairies to give the baby princess their magical presents. The first gave her the gift of beauty, the second gave her wisdom. The third fairy said she would be graceful, the fourth said that she would dance like the wind. The fifth and sixth gave her the gifts of music and song, so that she would sing and play like an angel.

Just before the seventh fairy stepped up to give the princess her gift, the eighth fairy pushed ahead of her. "The princess," she cackled, "will prick her finger on the spindle of a spinning wheel – and die!"

Everyone in the room was horrified, and the queen began to cry. But then the seventh fairy stepped forward. "Here is my gift," she said. "The princess will not die. Instead, when she pricks her finger, she will fall asleep for a hundred years. At the end of that time, a prince will come to wake her up."

The king and queen were relieved, but even so they ordered every spinning wheel in the kingdom to be destroyed. They couldn't bear to think of anything hurting their daughter.

The years passed and the princess grew into a lovely young girl, as wise, beautiful and graceful as the fairies had promised.

On the day of her sixteenth birthday, she was wandering through the castle when she came to a small room in a tall tower. Inside, an old woman sat spinning thread.

"My dear," cackled the old woman, "come here and try this for yourself."

As soon as the princess's hand touched the spindle, she pricked her finger and fell to the floor in a deep sleep.

When they discovered their daughter, the king and queen were heartbroken, for they knew that she would not wake for a hundred years. They called for the palace guards, who gently laid the sleeping princess on a golden stretcher and carried her to the royal bedchamber. There they placed her on a bed with silken pillows and velvet covers. The king and queen watched over her and cried.

"Oh, my dear," said the queen to her husband. "How are we ever going to cope without our darling daughter?"

The fairy who had saved the princess's life heard what had happened. Worried that the princess would wake up in a world where she knew no one, she cast a spell over the whole castle. Everyone, from the guards and the kitchen maids to the gardeners and the cooks – even the princess's pet dog – fell into a deep, deep sleep.

Then the fairy made tall trees and twisting, sharp brambles grow around the castle, surrounding it with a thick thorny wall that no one could get through. Only the very tops of the castle's towers could be seen.

And so a hundred years went by.

One day, a prince from a nearby land was out riding when he saw the tops of the castle towers rising from the middle of the thick, dark wood. He asked some of the country people about it, and they told him the story of the Sleeping Beauty.

"Many people have wanted to get through those thorns," they told him, "but they have all died trying."

The prince was determined to be the one who succeeded and set off towards the mysterious castle. To the prince's amazement, the thorny brambles and the twisting branches of the dark trees let him pass through easily.

He reached the castle door, and went inside.

The prince walked through many halls and chambers where people and animals slept as if they were dead. He searched every room and chamber, until he found the very one where the beautiful princess slept.

"Oh, princess!" cried the prince. "You are more beautiful than the most delicate rose ever found."

The prince moved quietly towards the sleeping princess and gazed down lovingly at her. He gently took her tiny hand in his, and as love filled his heart, he knelt beside her and slowly kissed her red lips. Instantly the princess's eyes opened.

"Is it you, my prince?" she said, when she saw him. "I have waited such a long time for you!"

At that moment the spell was broken, and everyone else in the castle woke up, too.

That evening, the princess's sixteenth birthday was celebrated with a joyous party – just a hundred years too late!

The princess and her prince danced together all evening, and, soon after, they were married. They lived together in happiness for many, many years.

Home Sweet Home

Bella Bunny looked at the sweet green grass growing in the meadow on the far side of the stream. She was tired of eating the rough grass that grew near her burrow. "I'm going to cross the stream!" she said to her brothers and sisters, pointing to a fallen branch that lay across it.

Bella bounced safely across the branch and was soon eating the sweet, juicy grass on the other side of the stream. Her brothers and sisters thought she was very brave and wondered if they should follow. But just then, they saw a sly fox creeping up behind Bella through the grass!

"Look out!" they called.

Bella turned to see the fox just in time! She leapt back onto the branch, but she was in such a hurry that she slipped and fell into the stream. Luckily, Becky Beaver had been watching and she pulled Bella safely to the other side.

"Home sweet home!" gasped Bella, with relief. And she ran off to join her brothers and sisters, vowing never to leave home again.

Benny the Barmy Builder

Benny was a hard-working builder, and he always did his very best. But sometimes he could be forgetful!

One morning, Benny the Builder arrived bright and early at Vicky Vet's surgery. "Benny the Builder at your service!" he announced. "I think you have a job for me to do."

"Not me, Benny," replied Vicky. "But Polly Postlady has!"

"Of course!" said Benny. "Sorry – I really shouldn't be so forgetful!"

And off he went to Polly Postlady's house. "Benny the Builder at your service!" Benny announced. "Woof!" said Benny's dog, Rocky.

"Come in," called Polly.

She took out a drawing to show Benny.

"I want you to build a Wendy house in my garden," Polly said. "It's a surprise for my grandchildren, Peter, Penny and Patty. I did this drawing to

show you just how it should look."

Benny and Polly looked at the drawing together.

"The Wendy house should have two tall doors," said Polly, "one at the front and one at the back, with one small step at the back door. There should be five windows, one at either side of the front door and one on each of the other sides."

"Yes, I see," said Benny.

"And I want a nice sloping roof," said Polly, "not a flat roof!"

"Yes, I see," said Benny. "I will do my very best!"

Polly left for the post office, and Benny went out to start work. But he had barely begun when a gust of wind came along. WHOOSH! went Polly's drawing, up in the air. "WOOF!" barked Rocky, leaping up to catch it.

Oh no! The drawing got caught in the branches of a tree!

Rocky fetched the drawing but, by the time Benny got it back, it was in shreds.

"Oh dear!" moaned Benny the Builder.

"How will I build the Wendy house now?"

Benny tried to remember everything in the drawing. But he quickly got very confused!

"Was it five windows and two doors with one step?" Benny puzzled. "Or was it two windows and five doors with three steps? Was the roof flat and not sloping? Or sloping and not flat? Were the doors tall or small? Oh dear, oh dear!"

Benny decided that he would just have to do the best he could. He got to work measuring… mixing… laying bricks... sawing wood… hammering nails… fixing screws… plastering and painting… and doing his very best to make everything just right.

Late that afternoon, Polly Postlady got home from work. She couldn't wait to see what Benny had done. But, what a surprise she had! The Wendy house's roof was flat. The bottom of the house was sloping. There were two steps leading up to two doors on one side of the house and there were two floors, both different sizes. And there were two windows on one side of the house.

"It's all wrong!" said Polly to Benny. "How will you ever fix it in time?"

But Benny didn't have a chance to answer because, just at that moment, Polly's grandchildren arrived.

"Oooh! Look! A Wendy house!" they cried happily as they rushed towards it. "There's a door for each of us!" they all cried together.

"And we can climb right up to the roof!" said Patty.

"And slide down the other side!" said Peter.

"And there are loads of windows so it's nice and bright inside!" said Penny.

"Granny, it's the best Wendy house ever!" the children told Polly. "It is perfect. Thank you so much!"

"Well, I think you should thank Benny the Builder," said Polly Postlady, smiling. Benny the Builder smiled too. "I just did my very best," he said.

The New Cat

The cats on Old MacDonald's farm like nothing better than dozing. Milly just loves to laze in the sun, and Lazy, as his name suggests, hardly opens his eyes!

One day, Milly was snoozing on a bale of hay, when she heard Old MacDonald talking on the telephone through the open kitchen window. Half-asleep, she heard him say, "The new cat..." Milly was feeling very sleepy. "Yes," continued Old MacDonald, "I need it because the ones I have now are useless."

Milly yawned and stretched, still drowsy and happy. Then she suddenly sat bolt upright. What? The cats were useless? A new one was coming? Oh no!

Milly dashed to where Lazy was fast asleep and eventually woke him up! She hurriedly shouted what she had heard.

"What's the matter with us?" yawned Lazy in a hurt voice. "I don't understand."

"You don't do anything," clucked Henrietta the hen, who liked to put her beak into everybody's business. "You just sleep all day."

Milly and Lazy looked at each other. They knew there was only one thing to do. Ten seconds later, they were tearing around the farmyard, trying to look as busy as possible!

By the end of a week of dashing around all day and miaowing all night, the cats had created quite a stir in the farmyard.

"Look here," said Bruce the sheepdog. "What has got into you both?"

Milly and Lazy explained. Bruce tried not to smile. "Well, you're doing the right thing," he barked. "Impress Old MacDonald like this and you'll be fine. But I would stop the caterwauling at night."

Bruce strolled off chuckling to himself. As Old MacDonald's right-hand dog, he knew that the farmer was waiting for a new CATalogue to order his winter wellies from. But he didn't think he needed to tell Milly and Lazy that – not quite yet anyway!

Poorly Bear

Teddy Bear came home from school feeling tired and poorly. "I don't want my hot chocolate," he told Mummy Bear. Teddy Bear sat on the sofa and closed his eyes. "And I don't want to watch television either," he said.

"Do you want to play your drum?" asked Mummy Bear, looking worried. Teddy Bear shook his head, so Mummy Bear went to fetch the thermometer and she put it under Teddy Bear's tongue. "Oh dear," she said. "I'm afraid you're a very poorly Teddy Bear. Up to bed you go!"

The next morning Teddy Bear was covered all over in bright red spots. "Look at me!" he said proudly, showing off his belly.

"You've got chicken pox," said Mummy Bear. "You'll have to stay home from school today."

"Yippee!" said Teddy Bear. But he said it quietly, because his head was quite sore. Teddy Bear lay on the sofa all day, watching television and colouring some pictures. Mummy Bear read him stories and brought him soup and ice-cream to eat.

After a few days the spots disappeared.

"Can I play my drum?" asked Teddy Bear. Mummy Bear was so glad to see Teddy Bear looking well again, that she let him play his drum for the rest of the afternoon.

Hungry Bear

"I'm hungry!" said Teddy Bear.

"You've just finished your lunch," said Mummy Bear. "You can have something in a little while."

"But I want something now!" wailed Teddy Bear. "I'm starving!"

"If you eat any more you'll go pop!" said Mummy Bear.

"I only want a biscuit! Or ice-cream. Or maybe a piece of cake. I'm really hungry!" grumbled Teddy Bear. He went outside and made hungry faces through the window.

"You don't look hungry," said Betty Bear from next door.

"I am!" said Teddy Bear. Nobody else came by, so Teddy Bear climbed into his sandpit. He dug some roads and built a few houses. He built a huge castle on a hill, with a moat around it. Then he fetched some water from the garden tap and filled the moat.

"Teddy!" called Mummy Bear. "You can come inside now and have some cakes!"

But Teddy Bear just shook his head – he was having far too much fun to feel hungry any more!

Little Dog Lost

"Brrr," shivered Scruffy. "It's cold tonight."
"Well, snuggle up closer to me," said his mum.

"It's not fair," Scruffy grumbled. "Why do we have to sleep outside in the cold? The cats are allowed to sleep inside, and they have nice warm baskets!"

"We're farm dogs, dear," said Mum. "We have to be tough, and work hard to earn our keep."

"I'd rather be a cat," mumbled Scruffy. "All they do is wash themselves, eat and sleep."

"We don't have such a bad life," said Mum. "Now stop feeling sorry for yourself, and get some rest. We've got a lot of work to do tomorrow."

The next day, Scruffy woke early and trotted down the lane for a walk. He ran through the grass, chasing rabbits, and sniffing at the flowers.

Now, usually when he got to the end of the lane he stopped and turned back. But today, he saw a big red van parked outside a house there. The back of the van was open, and Scruffy thought he would just climb inside and take a look.

The van was full of furniture. At the back was a big armchair with soft cushions. Scruffy clambered onto it. "I could doze all day, like a cat!" he told himself. He closed his eyes and before he knew it he had fallen fast asleep.

Scruffy awoke some time later with a sharp jolt.

"Oh, no, I fell asleep!" he groaned. "I'd better hurry back. We've got a busy day ahead!"

But then he saw that the van doors were closed! He could hear voices talking outside.

"Oh, dear, I'll be in trouble if I get found in here," thought Scruffy, and he hid behind the chair.

The back of the van opened and Scruffy peered out. Two men started unloading the furniture.

When Scruffy was sure that no one was looking, he crept out of the van, but he was no longer in the countryside where he lived! He was in a big noisy town, full of buildings and cars.

Poor Scruffy had no idea where he was!

"The van must have carried me away," thought Scruffy, feeling very frightened.

All day long, Scruffy roamed around trying to find his way home, feeling cold, tired and hungry. At last, he lay down and began to howl miserably.

"What's the matter, pup?" he heard a man's kind voice say. "You look lost. Come home with me." Scruffy gave the man's hand a grateful lick, then jumped up and followed him home.

When they arrived at the man's house Scruffy sat on the doorstep, hoping the man might bring out some food for him to eat. But the man said, "Come in, you can't stay out there."

Scruffy followed the man in, and found a little poodle waiting to meet him. Scruffy stared at her in amazement. What ever had happened to her fur?

"You'd better take a bath before supper," said the man, looking at Scruffy's dirty white coat. The man washed him in a big tub, then brushed his tangled coat. Scruffy howled miserably. What had he done to deserve such punishment?

"Don't you like it?" asked the poodle, shyly.

"No, I don't," said Scruffy. "I think that all this washing and cleaning is for cats!"

Next the man gave them supper – small bowls of dry pellets. Scruffy looked at them and sniffed in disgust. He was used to chunks of meat and a nice big bone.

"This looks like cat food," said Scruffy, miserably.

After supper the poodle climbed into a big basket in the kitchen.

"I thought that belonged to a cat," said Scruffy. He tried sleeping in the basket but he was hot and uncomfortable. He missed counting the stars to help him fall asleep, but most of all he missed his mum.

"I want to go home," he cried, and big tears slipped down his nose.

The next day, the man put Scruffy on a lead and took him into town. He hated the way he was dragged along, without being able to stop and have a good sniff at things.

Then, as they crossed the market place, Scruffy heard a familiar bark, and saw his mum's head hanging through the window of the farmer's truck, parked by the side of the road! He started to howl, dragged the man over to the truck, then he leapt up at the window and barked excitedly. The farmer could hardly believe that this little dog was Scruffy – he had never seen him so clean! The man explained how he had found Scruffy, and the farmer thanked the man for taking such good care of him.

Scruffy and his mother leapt into the back of the truck. On the way back home, Scruffy told his mum all about his adventure and what had happened.

"I thought you must have run away because you didn't like being a farm dog," she said gently.

"Oh, no, Mum," said Scruffy, quickly. "I love being a farm dog. I can't wait to get home to a nice big juicy bone and our little bed beneath the stars!"

Webster the Littlest Frog

Webster was the littlest frog on the pond, and he was fed up. Fed up with being bossed about. Fed up with playing on his own. Fed up, in fact, with being the littlest frog. None of the bigger frogs would let Webster play games with them.

"Hop it, Titch!" they croaked. "You're far too small to join in our games."

Every day, Webster sat on his own, watching the other frogs play leap-frog on Looking-Glass Pond.

"You don't have to be a big frog to jump," thought Webster, as he watched. "I can do that."

At last, one bright, moonlit evening Webster found the courage to ask the other frogs if he could join in.

"Please let me play with you," said Webster. "I can jump really high!"

The other frogs just laughed.

"But I can!" he insisted. He took a deep breath. "I can jump… over the moon!"

The other frogs laughed so much, they nearly fell off their lily pads.

"I'll prove it!" he said. "Just watch me."

One... two... three JUMP! Webster leapt off his lily pad and sailed over the moon's reflection in the pond.

The other frogs stared in amazement. It was true. Webster could jump over the moon!

"We're sorry we didn't believe you," said one of the big frogs.

"Of course you can play with us. You might not be the biggest frog on the pond, but you certainly are the cleverest!"

Tiggy-Touchwood

Tiggy-tiggy-touchwood,
my black hen,
She lays eggs for gentlemen.
Sometimes nine and sometimes ten,
Tiggy-tiggy-touchwood,
my black hen.

I had a Little Hen

I had a little hen, the prettiest ever seen,
She washed me the dishes, and kept the house clean;
She went to the mill to fetch me some flour,
She brought it home in less than an hour;
She baked me my bread, she brewed me my ale,
She sat by the fire and told many a fine tale.

Mrs Hen

Chook, chook, chook, chook, chook,
Good morning, Mrs Hen.
How many chickens have you got?
Madam, I've got ten.

Four of them are yellow,
And four of them are brown,
And two of them are speckled red,
The nicest in the town.

I had a Little Cow

I had a little cow;
  Hey-diddle, ho-diddle!
I had a little cow, and it had a little calf;
  Hey-diddle, ho-diddle; and there's my song half.

I had a little cow;
  Hey-diddle, ho-diddle!
I had a little cow, and I drove it to the stall;
  Hey-diddle, ho-diddle; and there's my song all!

The Shortest Tongue Twister

Peggy Babcock

Little Boy Blue

Little Boy Blue,
  Come blow your horn,
The sheep's in the meadow,
  The cow's in the corn.

Where is the boy
  Who looks after the sheep?
He's under a haycock
  Fast asleep.
    Will you wake him?
      No, not I,
    For if I do,
      He's sure to cry.

Princess Petal

Princess Petal lives in a shiny white castle surrounded by beautiful gardens, filled with pretty flowers and colourful butterflies. The Princess's best friend is Sparkle, a sweet little puppy. Every morning, he helps the princess to chose her dress.

"Which one today?" she asks.

Sparkle stands next to a pretty yellow one, wags his tail and barks.

"Perfect," says the Princess.

Then they play games in the garden. They love to run and jump and play "catch the ball".

Today, Princess Petal is very excited. She has just received an invitation to a special party – a ball at the palace.

"The Prince is very handsome," Petal says to her puppy. "I must look my best."

She slips on a beautiful pink dress, trimmed with jewels and satin ribbons. On her feet are dainty gold slippers. Then Petal opens her jewellery box and takes out a pair of crystal earrings and a diamond tiara.

She places the tiara carefully on her head – now she can off to the ball in her beautiful horse-drawn carriage.

As the Princess and Sparkle enter the crowded ballroom, everyone gasps in delight. The handsome Prince takes the Princess's hand.

"You are the loveliest lady here," he says. "May I have this dance?"

"Of course, Your Majesty!" says the Princess.

Princess Petal is the happiest girl in the whole kingdom.

Lazy Teddy

There was nothing Lazy Teddy liked more than to be tucked up snug and warm in Joshua's bed.

Every morning the alarm clock would ring and Joshua would leap out of bed and fling open the curtains. "I love mornings!" he'd say, stretching his arms up high as the sun poured in through the window. "You're crazy!" Teddy would mutter, and he'd burrow down beneath the quilt to the bottom of the bed, where he'd spend the rest of the morning snoozing happily.

"Come out and play, you lazy bear," Joshua would call. But Lazy Teddy wouldn't budge. He would just snore even louder.

Joshua wished that Teddy would be more lively, like his other friends' bears. He loved having adventures, but they would be even better if Teddy would share them with him.

One evening, Joshua decided to have a talk with Teddy before they went to bed. He told him about the fishing trip he'd been on that day with his friends and their teddy bears.

"It was lots of fun, Teddy. I wish you'd been there. It really is time you stopped being such a lazybones. Tomorrow is my birthday, and I'm having a party. There will be games, and presents and ice-cream. Please promise you'll come?"

"It does sound like fun," said Teddy. "Okay, I promise. I'll get up just this once."

The next morning, Joshua was up bright and early. "Yippee, it's my birthday today!" he yelled, dancing around the room. He pulled the covers off his bed. "Come on, Teddy, time to get up!"

"Just five more minutes!" groaned Teddy, and he rolled over and fell straight back to sleep. When Joshua came back up to his room after breakfast, Teddy still wasn't up. Well, by now Joshua was getting quite cross with Teddy. He reached over and poked him in the tummy. Teddy opened one eye and growled. "Wake up, Teddy! You promised, remember?" said Joshua.

Teddy yawned. "Oh, if I must!" he said, and muttering and grumbling he climbed out of bed. He washed his face and paws, brushed his teeth

and put on his best red waistcoat.

"There, I'm ready!" he said.

"Good," said Joshua. "About time too!"

Just then the doorbell rang, and Joshua ran to answer it. "I'll come and fetch you in a minute," he said to Teddy. But when he returned there was no sign of Teddy, just a gentle snoring coming from the bottom of the bed.

Joshua was so cross and upset with Lazy Teddy, that he decided to leave him right where he was.

"He'll just have to miss the party!" he said. Deep down though, he was hurt that Teddy wouldn't keep his promise.

Joshua enjoyed his party, although he wished that Teddy had been there. Later that night when he got into bed, he lay crying quietly into his pillow.

Teddy lay awake in the dark, listening. He knew Joshua was crying because he had let him down, and he felt very ashamed.

"I'm sorry!" whispered Lazy Teddy, and he snuggled up to Joshua and stroked him with a paw until he fell asleep.

The next morning when the alarm clock rang, Joshua leapt out of bed, as usual. But what was this? Teddy had leapt out of bed too, and was stretching his paws up high. Joshua looked at him in amazement.

"What are we doing today, then?" asked Teddy.

"G...g...going for a picnic," stammered Joshua, in surprise. "Are you coming?"

"Of course," said Teddy. And from that day on, Teddy was up bright and early every day, ready to enjoy another day of adventures with Joshua, and he never let him down again.

Moo! Moo! Moo!

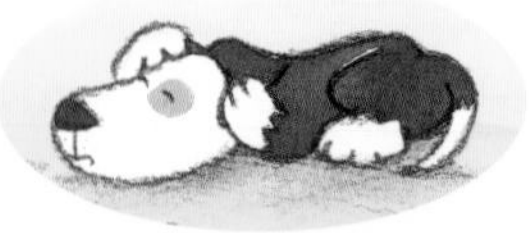

The Meadow Ladies Chorus,
Is something rather new.
You'll hear them all too clearly,
They're singing, "Moo! Moo! Moo!"

They try to trill like budgies,
And copy blackbirds, too.
The only song they really know,
Of course, is, "Moo! Moo! Moo!"

They practise in the morning,
And in the night-time, too.
It doesn't make a difference though,
They still sing, "Moo! Moo! Moo!"

You Need a Cow!

How does fresh milk reach your shake,
The frothy, creamy kind you make?
You ask how? – You need a cow!
How does butter reach your bread,
The slithery, slippery stuff you spread?
You ask how? – You need a cow!
How does your cheese reach your plate,
The yummy, yellow kind you grate?
You ask how? – You need a cow!
How does ice cream reach your spoon,
The kind you cannot eat too soon?
You ask how? – You need a cow!

Counting Sheep

Old MacDonald's counting sheep,
But not because he cannot sleep.
You see, he's wondering if maybe,
Each sheep has now had her baby.
"Stand still!" he cries. "Be still and steady,
I might have counted you already!"
Poor Old MacDonald's feeling dizzy!
Then suddenly he starts to smile.
"Goodbye! I'll see you in a while."
When all the farm is soundly sleeping,
Old MacDonald's softly creeping.
It's really easy to count sheep,
When you're awake and they're asleep!

Woolly Coats

In the middle of the winter,
All the animals complain,
"Our furry coats are much too thin.
They let the icy north wind in.
We want to go indoors again!"
But while the rest all shiver,
Sheep are fine and look quite smug,
"We will not come to any harm.
We are the warmest on the farm.
Our woolly coats will keep us snug!"

Clip, Clop!

Pigs can prance,
And ducks can dance,
Hens flutter in a flurry.
But George plods on and doesn't stop,
Clip, clop! Clip, clop!
He's *never* in a hurry.

"Of course, I know
My horse is slow,
But I will never worry.
For George plods on and doesn't stop,
Clip, clop! Clip, clop!
He doesn't *need* to hurry."

Egg Hatching Dream

When Jenny is sitting,
And sitting, and sitting,
She can't take up knitting,
Or sew a fine seam.

If her eggs are to hatch,
Every one of the batch,
There is nothing to match,
An egg-hatching dream.

Her thoughts travel far and near.
Half-asleep she'll appear,
Until she starts to hear,
Her eggs start to crack!

A Horse, of Course!

Who can you trust when the
tractor breaks down,
And the nearest mechanic is
off in the town?
Who is as big and as strong as a horse?
Oh, silly me, a horse, of course!
Who do you know who can eat
tons of hay,
And even munch ten sacks of oats
in a day?
Who has an appetite large as a horse?
Oh, silly me, a horse, of course!
Who will stick by you when you
need a friend,
And hear all your troubles right through
to the end?
Who is as wise and as kind as a horse?
Oh, silly me, a horse, of course!

One Hen Pecking

One hen pecking in the garden –
Mrs MacDonald shakes her head.
Two hens pecking in the garden –
Makes her shake her fist instead!
Three hens pecking in the garden –
The farmer's wife comes storming out.
Four hens pecking in the garden –
Mrs MacDonald starts to shout.

Vicky the Very Silly Vet

"Good morning!" calls Vicky Vet as she opens the door to her surgery. "How are all my animals today?"

Vicky starts her early morning rounds with the Goldie Goldfish. Vicky Vet loves looking after animals but sometimes she gets very mixed up! She knows she has a busy morning ahead of her, so Vicky wants to get all the cages cleaned, and the animals fed, before her first patient arrives. I'll give you some clean newspaper first, Patch," she says to the messy puppy, "and then I'll give your blanket a good shake, Tabby."

"There you are, Tabby. A nice fluffy bed for you," says Vicky, putting the blanket back into Tabby's basket, when… Brriiing, brriiing! Brriiing, brriiing! "That's the phone, Tabby," she cries.

Vicky Vet drops everything and rushes to answer it. "Now, where was I?" thinks Vicky Vet to herself, coming back to the cages.

"I was just about to give you some fresh wood chips, wasn't I?" she says to Hickory and Dickory, the two mice. Just as she is putting the wood chips in the mouse cage…

Ding dong! goes the doorbell. "Who can that be?" Vicky wonders.

"My first patient's not due for half an hour!" Vicky hasn't noticed that the cage doors are open and Patch is busy chasing Tabby around the room!

It is Polly Postlady with a parcel that is too big to fit through the letterbox. "Thank you, Polly," says Vicky, "but I don't think this parcel is for me. It's addressed to Tony's Pizza Parlour."

"Oh dear!" says Polly Postlady. "How could I be so potty? Sorry, Vicky!"

"Now," says Vicky Vet, "I think I was about to clean Percy Parrot's cage." She has just finished cleaning the cage when she feels something scampering up her leg!

"Oh no!" cries Vicky. "Hickory and Dickory, how did you escape? "And Patch and Tabby! How did you get out?" Very silly Vicky is flapping about trying to catch all the animals, and all the time Percy is hopping closer to the open door of his cage. Vicky dives at Tabby and pounces on Hickory and Dickory and is busy chasing Patch back into his cage when... SUDDENLY there is a loud squawk! Percy Parrot is flying towards the open window!

"Wait! Percy! Stop!" she cries, rushing after the parrot. Luckily, Vicky catches Percy just in time. Once he is safely back in his cage, she manages to round up Hickory and Dickory, get Tabby back into her basket, and shut Patch safely into his cage.

"Phew!" she puffs. "I feel as if I've done a whole morning's work already. "I think after all this, it must be time for some breakfast!"

Vicky lines up the feeding bowls and animal feed on the table. Carefully, she measures out some delicious dog food for Patch and gives him a big juicy bone to chew. Then she spoons out some crunchy bird seed for Percy, some fishy cat food for Tabby, and some tasty sunflower seeds for the mice. Vicky has nearly finished making breakfast for the animals when... Ding dong! It's the doorbell again.

"Oh!" she cries. "My first patient is here already! I'd better hurry!" As quickly as she can, Vicky puts the food bowls in the cages – but she doesn't look to see who is getting what! So Patch the dog gets a bowl of crunchy bird seed. Hickory and Dickory the mice get the dog food and the big juicy bone. Tabby the cat gets the tasty sunflower seeds. And Percy the parrot gets the fishy cat food! What's more, Vicky is in such a rush that she leaves all the cage doors open again!

This time, though, the animals know just what to do. Hickory and Dickory find their sunflower seeds in Tabby's basket. Tabby discovers her fishy cat food in Percy's cage.

Percy pecks at his bird seed in Patch's cage. And Patch finds his delicious dog food in the mouse cage.

Fred Fireman is at the door with his dog Dot for a check-up.

"Come in," says Vicky Vet. "You're right on time."

"We always like coming here," says Fireman Fred. "The animals are so happy and everything seems so relaxed. I'm always so frazzled. What's your secret, Vicky?"

Very silly Vicky thinks about her crazy morning and wonders what dreadful mess will greet Fred as they walk into the surgery. But clever Patch, Tabby, Percy and the mice are back in their own cages. Vicky sees the clean and tidy room and grins at her animals.

"Treats for tea," she whispers!

One Bad Bunny

Barney was a very bad bunny. He liked playing tricks on his friends. Barney hid Squirrel's nut store and it took him all day to find it. He put sticky honey on Badger's walking stick and Badger was chased by bees. And he put black paint on Mole's glasses, so poor Mole got even more lost than usual!

"It's time we taught that bad bunny a lesson!" said Badger crossly. So that night, while Barney was sleeping, Mole and Badger dug a big hole. Squirrel climbed up to the treetops and fetched some branches to put over the hole and they covered it with grass. They set a big juicy carrot on top, then hid behind the trees to wait.

The next morning, Barney came bouncing out of his burrow, spotted the juicy carrot and jumped straight into the trap!

"Help!" he cried, from the bottom of the hole. The others appeared.

"We tricked you!" they laughed. They only let Barney out when he promised to stop playing tricks on them. And from then on he was a very good bunny indeed.

The Fly

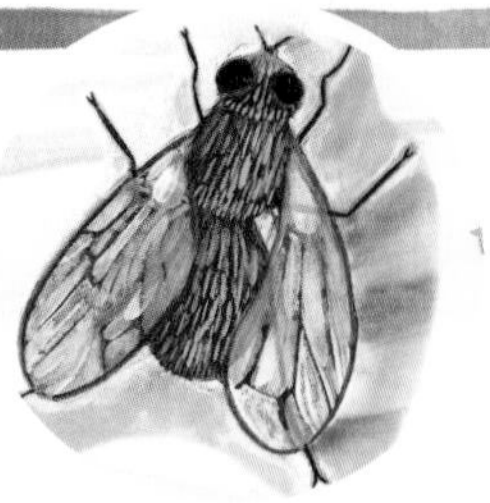

Little Fly,
  Thy summer's play
My thoughtless hand
  Has brushed away.

Am not I
  A fly like thee?
Or art not thou
  A man like me?

For I dance,
  And drink, and sing,
Till some blind hand
  Shall brush my wing.

If thought is life
  And strength and breath,
And the want
  Of thought is death;

Then am I
  A happy fly,
If I live
  Or if I die.

WILLIAM BLAKE

Aiken Drum

There was a man lived in the moon,
  and his name was Aiken Drum
And he played upon a ladle,
  and his name was Aiken Drum.

And his hat was made of good cream cheese,
  and his name was Aiken Drum.

And his coat was made of good roast beef,
  and his name was Aiken Drum.

And his buttons were made of penny loaves,
  and his name was Aiken Drum.

His waistcoat was made of crust of pies,
  and his name was Aiken Drum.

His breeches were made of haggis bags,
  and his name was Aiken Drum.
And he played upon a ladle,
  and his name was Aiken Drum.

Ladybird! Ladybird!

Ladybird! Ladybird! Fly away home,
  Night is approaching, and sunset is come.
The herons are flown to their trees by the Hall;
  Felt, but unseen, the damp dewdrops fall.
This is the close of a still summer day;
  Ladybird! Ladybird! haste! fly away!

EMILY BRONTË

Three Wise Old Women

Three wise old women were they, were they,
Who went to walk on a winter day:
One carried a basket to hold some berries,
One carried a ladder to climb for cherries,
The third, and she was the wisest one,
Carried a fan to keep off the sun.

But they went so far, and they went so fast,
They quite forgot their way at last,
So one of the wise women cried in a fright,
"Suppose we should meet a bear tonight!
Suppose he should eat me!"
"And me!!" "And me!!!"
"What is to be done?" cried all the three.

Whether they ever sailed home again,
Whether they saw any bears, or no,
You must find out, for I don't know.

The Kangaroo

Old Jumpety-Bumpety-Hop-and-Go-One
Was lying asleep on his side in the sun.
This old kangaroo, he was whisking the flies
(With his long glossy tail)
from his ears and his eyes.
Jumpety-Bumpety-Hop-and-Go-One
Was lying asleep on his side in the sun,
Jumpety-Bumpety-Hop!

Ducks' Ditty

All along the backwater,
Through the rushes tall,
Ducks are a-dabbling.
Up tails all!

Ducks' tails, drakes' tails,
Yellow feet a-quiver,
Yellow bills all out of sight
Busy in the river!

Slushy green undergrowth
Where the roach swim –
Here we keep our larder,
Cool and full and dim.

Every one for what he likes!
We like to be
Heads down, tails up,
Dabbling free!

High in the blue above
Swifts whirl and call –
We are down a-dabbling
Up tails all!

Mrs Mouse's Holiday

Mrs Mouse was very excited. All year she had been so busy. First there had been nuts and berries to gather in readiness for winter. Then she had needed to give her little house a big spring clean to make it nice and fresh. Now, as the warm sun shone down on the trees and flowers of her woodland home, she had promised herself a well-deserved holiday. But getting ready for holidays seemed to make one busier than ever! There was so much to do!

First she took out her little case, opened it and placed it carefully on her neatly made bed. Then she rushed to her cupboard and selected some fine holiday dresses. Back to her case she scuttled and laid them in. Now she chose several pairs of shoes – a nice pair of sandals for walking along the front in, a pair of smart shoes for shopping in, an even smarter pair for going to dinner in, and another pair just in case!

"I'll need a couple of sun hats," she thought to herself, and so into the case they went as well. These were followed by a coat, some gloves and a scarf (just in case the breeze got up

and it became cold). Then, in case it became very sunny, in went some sunglasses, some sun cream and a sunshade. But, oh dear, there were so many things in the case that it refused to shut. She tried sitting on it, and bouncing on it, but still it stubbornly would not close.

So out from the case came all the things that she had just put in, and Mrs Mouse scurried to the cupboard again and chose an even bigger case. This time they all fitted perfectly, and she shut the case with a big sigh of relief.

Now she was ready to go to the seaside for her holiday. She sat on the train, with her case on the rack above her head, munching her hazelnut sandwiches and looking eagerly out of the window hoping to see the sea. Finally, as the train chuffed around a bend, there it was! A great, deep blue sea shimmering in the sun, with white gulls soaring over the cliffs and headlands.

"I'm really looking forward to a nice, quiet rest," she said to herself.

Her guesthouse was very comfortable, and so close to the sea that she could smell the clean, salty air whenever she opened her window. "This is the life," she thought. "Nice and peaceful."

After she had put her clothes away, she put on her little swimming costume and her sun hat and packed her beach bag. Now she was ready for some peaceful sunbathing!

At the beach, she found herself a quiet spot, closed her eyes and was soon fast asleep. But not for long! A family of voles had arrived on the beach, and they weren't trying to have a quiet time at all. The youngsters in the family yelled at the top of their voices, splashed water

everywhere, and sent their beach ball tumbling all over Mrs Mouse's neatly laid out beach towel.

Just as Mrs Mouse thought that it couldn't get any noisier, along came a crowd of ferrets. Now if you've ever sat on a beach next to a crowd of ferrets, you'll know what it's like. Their noisy shouting and singing made Mrs Mouse's head buzz.

Mrs Mouse couldn't stand it a moment longer. She was just wondering where she might find some peace and quiet when she spotted a rock just a little way out to sea.

"If I swim out to that rock," she thought, "I will surely have some peace and quiet there." She gathered up her belongings and swam over to the rock. It was a bit lumpy, but at least it was quiet. Soon she was fast asleep again.

Just then the rock started to move slowly out to sea! It wasn't really a rock at all, you see, but a turtle which had been dozing near the surface. Off into the sunset it went, with Mrs Mouse dozing on its back, quite unaware of what was happening.

Eventually, the turtle came to a deserted island. At that moment, Mrs Mouse woke up. She looked at the empty beach, and, without even knowing she had been sleeping on a turtle, she jumped off and swam to the shore, thinking it was the beach that she had just left.

Just then, the turtle swam off, and Mrs Mouse suddenly realised what had happened. For a moment she was horrified. But then she looked at the quiet, palm-fringed beach with no one about but herself, and thought of the noisy beach she had just left.

"Well, perhaps this isn't such a bad place to spend a quiet holiday after all," she thought.

And that's just what she did. Day after day she lazed on her own private beach with no one to disturb her. There were plenty of coconuts and fruits to eat, and she wanted for nothing. She even made herself a cosy bed from palm leaves.

Eventually, though, she started to miss her own little house in the woods and decided it was time to get back home. First she took half a coconut and nibbled out the tasty inside. "That will make a fine boat to sit in," she said.

Next she found a palm leaf and stuck it in the bottom of the shell. She took her little boat to the water's edge and, as the wind caught her palm leaf sail, off she floated back to the boarding house to get her belongings. As she sailed slowly back she thought, "This is the quietest holiday I've ever had. I may come back here next year!"

I Love my Puppy

I love my puppy because he wags his tail and comes to meet me.

He barks and jumps in the air when he wants to play, and chases my big bouncy ball.

He fetches a stick for me to throw.

He scampers beside me when we go for walks in the park.

But I love him most when he is sleepy and we snuggle up close.

I Love my Kitten

I love my kitten because she purrs softly when I stroke her.

She pounces on a ball of wool and rolls it between her paws.

She runs along the garden wall and leaps over the gate.

She washes her face by licking her soft padded paws.

She peeps through the cat flap to see if her dinner is ready.

But I love her most of all when she sits with her tail curled all around her.

I Love my Pony

I love my pony because he neighs hello when I come to visit him.

He lets me sponge him and brush his soft shiny mane.

He eats a shiny green apple right out of my hand.

He's fun to be with when we go for long rides.

He jumps at the show and wins a bright red rosette.

But I love him most of all when I talk to him and he nuzzles up close.

I Love my Bunny

I love my bunny because he twitches his nose, and has smooth silky fur.

Bunny nibbles a carrot with his bright white teeth.

He runs in the garden and his fluffy white tail bobs up and down.

He digs a hole in the lawn with his big soft paws.

He sits quietly as I stroke his big floppy ears, and his whiskers twitch up and down.

But I love him most when he dozes off to sleep sitting on my lap.

Crocodile Smiles

"Say cheese!" said the photographer.

"CHEESE!" grinned Snappy, the crocodile. Lights flashed, and cameras clicked as he gave his most winning smile.

"You're a natural!" cried the expedition leader. He was with a team of wildlife photographers. Snappy smiled at his reflection in the river.

"Ooh, you are a handsome chap!" he preened, gnashing his fine set of teeth together with glee.

Snappy was terribly proud of his sharp fangs, and fine good looks. He strutted up and down the river bank for all to see.

"I'm a star!" he said. "My face will be known throughout the world!"

"Thanks for letting us take your picture," said the expedition leader.

"No problem," said Snappy. "Any time!"

"And, as your reward, here's the truck load of chocolate you asked for," said the leader.

"How delicious!" said Snappy. "Most kind of you. Thank you so much."

When they had gone, Snappy lay sunning himself on the river bank, daydreaming of fame and fortune, and popping chocolate after chocolate into his big, open mouth.

Just then, along slithered Snake.

"What's thissss?" he hissed. "A crocodile eating chocolate? How very sssstrange!"

"Not at all!" snapped Snappy. "All crocodiles love chocolate. It's just that most of them aren't clever enough to know how to get hold of it."

"Well, if you're so sssmart, you ssshould know that too much chocolate will make your teeth fall out!" hissed Snake.

"What rot!" said Snappy, crossly. "For your information, I've got perfect teeth."

"Lucky you!" said Snake, and slithered off into the bushes.

So Snappy carried on munching happily, eating his way through the mound of chocolate. He had chocolate for breakfast, chocolate for lunch and chocolate for dinner.

"Ooh, yummy!" he grinned, licking his lips and smiling a big, chocolatey smile. "This is heaven."

"You won't be saying that when you are too fat to float in the river," said Parrot, who had been watching him from a tree.

"Nonsense!" scoffed Snappy. "I've got a very fine figure, I'll have you know!"

"If you say so," said Parrot, and flew off into the jungle.

Days and weeks passed, and Snappy happily carried on eating chocolate after chocolate, until at last it was all gone.

"Back to the river to catch my next meal, then," Snappy thought miserably. "Though I'd much rather have more chocolate!"

But, when Snappy slid into the river, instead of bobbing gently at the surface, he sank straight to the bottom, and his stomach rested in the mud.

"Oh dear, what's happened to the river?" Snappy wondered aloud to himself. "It's very hard to float in today."

"Even for someone with such a fine figure as you?" jeered Parrot, watching from the trees. Snappy didn't answer. He just sank further beneath the water so that only his two beady eyes could be seen, and gave Parrot a very hard stare.

The next morning when he awoke there was a terrible pain in his mouth. It felt like someone was twisting and tugging on his teeth. "Oww, my teeth hurt!" he cried.

"Sssurely not!" hissed Snake, dangling down from a tree. "After all, you have sssuch perfect teeth!" and he slunk away again, snickering.

Snappy knew what he had to do. He set off down the river to visit Mr Drill the dentist.

It seemed such a long, hard walk, and by the time he got there he was puffing and panting.

"Open wide!" said Mr Drill, an anteater, peering down his long nose into Snappy's gaping mouth. "Oh dear. This doesn't look good at all. What have you been eating, Snappy? Now show me where it hurts."

"Here," said Snappy pointing miserably into his mouth, and feeling rather ashamed, "and here, and here, and here..."

"Well, there's nothing for it," said Mr Drill, "they'll have to come out!" And so out they came!

Before long, another photography expedition arrived in the jungle.

"Say cheese!" said the expedition leader.

"CHEESE!" smiled Snappy, stepping out from behind a tree. But, instead of a flash of cameras, Snappy met with howls of laughter, as the photographers fell about holding their sides.

"I thought you said Snappy was a handsome crocodile with perfect teeth!" they cried, looking at the leader. "He should be called Gappy, not Snappy!"

Poor Snappy slunk away into the bushes and cried. It was all his own fault for being so greedy and eating all that chocolate.

"There, there," said Mr Drill, patting his arm. "We'll soon fit you out with some fine new teeth."

And from then on, Snappy vowed he would never eat chocolate again!

Smelly Pup

All the animals were gathered in the barn. "It has come to our attention," said Mrs Hen to Smelly Pup, "that you are in need of a bath. You haven't had one all summer. Even the pigs are complaining!"

Smelly Pup just laughed. "Take a bath? That'll be the day!" he said, and off he went.

Outside Smelly Pup strolled through the farmyard, muttering, "What a crazy idea. I'm a dog. I do dog things… like chasing cats!" The farm cat leapt up hissing as Smelly Pup came racing towards her. He chased her all around the farmyard. Then, just as he was about to catch up, she sprang into the air. Smelly Pup took a great leap after her… and landed in the pond with a SPLASH!

"Silly Pup!" smirked the cat as she watched, perched on the branch of a nearby tree.

The ducks quacked as he spluttered and splashed, chasing them through the shallows! The water felt cool and refreshing on his fur. After a while, he came out and rolled on the nice muddy bank. "That was fun," he said. "Maybe I could get used to baths after all!"

Jelly on the Plate

Jelly on the plate,
  Jelly on the plate,
Wibble, wobble,
  Wibble, wobble,
Jelly on the plate.

Sweeties in the jar,
  Sweeties in the jar,
Shake them up,
  Shake them up,
Sweeties in the jar.

Candles on the cake,
  Candles on the cake,
Blow them out,
  Blow them out,
Puff, PUFF, PUFF!

Polly Put the Kettle On

Polly put the kettle on,
  Polly put the kettle on,
Polly put the kettle on,
We'll all have tea.

Sukey take it off again,
  Sukey take it off again,
Sukey take it off again,
  They've all gone away.

I Scream

I scream, you scream,
We all scream for ice cream!

Little Jack Horner

Little Jack Horner,
  Sat in a corner,
Eating a Christmas pie.
  He put in his thumb,
And pulled out a plum,
  And said, "What a good boy am I!"

Ten Green Bottles

Ten green bottles, standing on a wall,
Ten green bottles, standing on a wall,
And if one green bottle should accidentally fall,
There'd be nine green bottles, standing on a wall.

Nine green bottles, standing on a wall,
Nine green bottles, standing on a wall,
And if one green bottle should accidentally fall,
There'd be eight green bottles, standing on a wall.

Eight green bottles, standing on a wall,
Eight green bottles, standing on a wall,
And if one green bottle should accidentally fall,
There'd be seven green bottles, standing on a wall.

(continue with seven green bottles etc...)

A Peanut

A peanut sat on the railroad track,
His heart was all a-flutter;
Along came a train – the 9:15 –
Toot, toot, peanut butter!

Dibbity, Dibbity, Dibbity, Doe

Dibbity, dibbity, dibbity, doe,
Give me a pancake
And I'll go.
Dibbity, dibbity, dibbity, ditter,
Please to give me
A bit of a fritter.

Pat-a-Cake

Pat-a-cake, pat-a-cake, baker's man,
Bake me a cake, as fast as you can.
Pat it and prick it and mark it with B,
And put it in the oven for Baby and me.

Hazel Squirrel Learns a Lesson

Hazel Squirrel had the finest tail of all the animals that lived beside Looking-Glass Pond.

It was fluffier than Dilly Duck's tail… bushier than Harvey Rabbit's tail... and swooshier than everybody's!

Each morning Hazel groomed her tail and admired her reflection in the pond."I really do have a beautiful tail!" she would say, smiling at herself in the silvery water.

Sometimes Hazel played with her friends, but it usually ended in tears.

"You splashed my lovely tail!" Hazel would shout crossly, when she played leap-frog with Webster. "You're getting my tail dirty, Harvey!" she would moan very grumpily, when they played digging.

Soon, Hazel stopped playing with her friends altogether.

"I'm far too busy brushing my tail!" she said when they came to call. "Come back some other time."

One morning as usual, Hazel was admiring her tail by the pond. Suddenly, she had a funny thought. She couldn't remember the last time she had seen her friends.

Hazel looked at her reflection in the pond. Staring back was a strange face… a cross face… a grumpy face. It was Hazel's face! Hazel couldn't believe her eyes. "No wonder my friends don't visit me any more," she cried. "I've forgotten how to smile!"

The next day Hazel called for her friends. They had such fun playing leap-frog and digging muddy holes that she forgot all about her tail. "From now on," she laughed, "the only time I'll look at my reflection is to practise smiling!"

Teddy Bear Tears

"Boo hoo! I want to go home!"
As a little fairy called Mavis flew past the rubbish dump, holding her nose, she heard an unmistakable sound coming from the other side of a very smelly pile of rubbish.

"Oh dear. Those sound like teddy bear tears," she said to herself. "I'd better go and see if I can help."

She flew down to take a look, and, sure enough, there amongst a heap of old potato peelings and banana skins sat a very old, very sad teddy indeed. Mavis sat and held his paw, while he told her tearfully what had happened:

"My owner, Matilda, was told to clean out her room. She's terribly messy, but she's sweet and kind," Teddy sniffed. "She threw me out with an old blanket by mistake – she didn't realise I was tucked up having a sleep inside it. Then some men in a big, dirty truck came and emptied me out of the dustbin and brought me here. But I want to go home!" And with that poor Teddy started to cry again.

"There, there," said Mavis. "I'll help to get you home. But first I'll need two teddy bear tears." She unscrewed the lid of a little jar, and scooped two big salty tears into it from Teddy's cheeks.

"What do you need those for?" asked Teddy, feeling rather bewildered.

"Just a little fairy magic!" said Mavis. "Now wait here, and I promise I'll be back soon." And with a wave of her wand, she disappeared.

Teddy pulled the blanket around him, and sat trying to be brave, and not to cry. He stayed like that all night, feeling cold and alone and frightened. How he wished he was back in his warm, cosy home.

Meanwhile Mavis was very busy. She flew back and forth around the neighbourhood, until she heard the sound of sobbing coming from an open window. She flew down onto the windowsill and peered inside. A little girl was lying on the bed, with her mummy sitting beside her.

"I want my teddy!" she cried.

"Well if you weren't so messy, Matilda, you wouldn't lose things," said Mummy gently.

"But I cleaned my room today!" said Matilda.

"Well, try and go to sleep now," said Mummy, kissing her goodnight, "and we'll look for Teddy in the morning."

Mavis watched as poor Matilda lay sobbing into her pillow, until at last she fell fast asleep. Then Mavis flew down from the windowsill, took out the little jar, and rubbed Teddy's tears onto Matilda's sleeping eyes. With a little fizzle of stars, the fairy magic began to work, and Matilda started to dream. She could see an old tyre, a newspaper, some tin cans, some orange peel, a blanket... wait a minute, it was her blanket, and there, wrapped inside it was her teddy, with a big tear running down his cheek! Teddy was at the rubbish dump!

The next morning, Matilda woke with a start, and remembered her dream at once. She ran downstairs to the kitchen, where Mummy was making breakfast, and told her all about it.

"We have to go to the rubbish dump! We have to save Teddy!" said Matilda.

Mummy tried to explain that it was just a dream, but Matilda wouldn't listen, she was sure she was right. So in the end they set off to take a look.

They arrived just as a big machine was scooping up the rubbish and heading for the

crusher. And there, on top of the scoop, clinging to the edge, was Teddy!

Mavis appeared, hovering in the air above him.

"Don't worry, we'll save you!" she said. She waved her wand in a bright flash above Teddy. Matilda looked up and spotted him at once.

"There he is!" she cried, pointing frantically at Teddy. "He's going to be squashed! Mummy, do something, quick!" Mummy ran up to the man driving the machine, waving her arms in the air.

He stopped his machine just in time.

Soon Teddy and Matilda were reunited, and there were more tears, although this time they were happy ones. And from then on, Matilda's room was the tidiest room you have ever seen.

Terrible Tongue Twisters

A bitter biting bittern
  Bit a better brother bittern,
And the bitter better bittern
  Bit the bitter biter back.
And the bitter bittern, bitten,
  By the better bitten bittern,
Said: "I'm a bitter biter bit, alack!"

Ruby Rugby's brother bought
and brought her back some
rubber baby-buggy bumpers.

Three free throws.

Silly Sally swiftly shooed seven silly sheep.
  The seven silly sheep Silly Sally shooed
shilly-shallied south.
  These sheep shouldn't sleep in a shack;
sheep should sleep in a shed.

Lily ladles little
Letty's lentil soup.

Six short slow shepherds.

I saw Esau kissing Kate. I saw Esau,
he saw me, and she saw I saw Esau.

The sixth sick sheik's
sixth sheep's sick.

A flea and a fly flew up in a flue.
Said the flea, "Let us fly!"
Said the fly, "Let us flee!"
So they flew through a flaw in the flue.

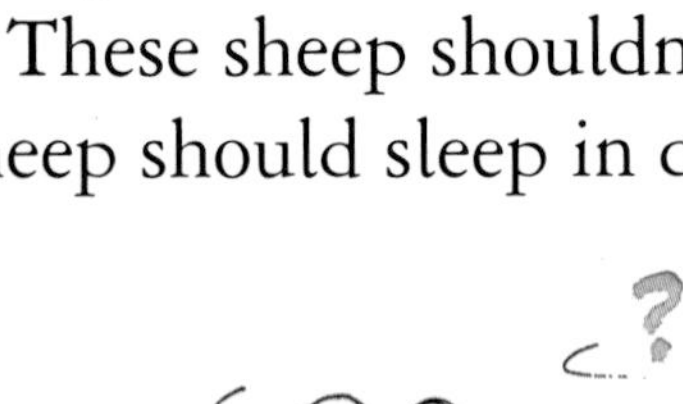

How much wood would a woodchuck chuck
  if a woodchuck could chuck wood?
He would chuck, he would, as much as he could,
  and chuck as much wood as a woodchuck would
if a woodchuck could chuck wood.

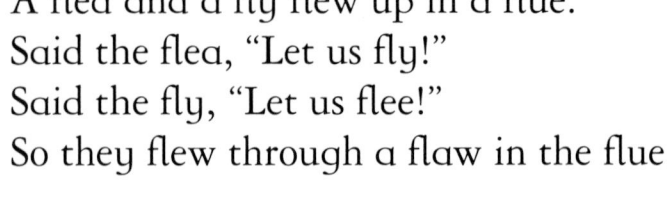

Betty and Bob brought
back blue balloons
from the big bazaar.

Timothy Titus took two ties
To tie two tups to two tall trees,
To terrify the terrible Thomas a Tullamees.
How many T's in *that*?

Red lorry,
yellow lorry,
red lorry,
yellow lorry.

Betty Botter bought some butter,
"But," she said, "this butter's bitter.
If I put it in my batter,
It will make my batter bitter.
But a bit of better butter,
That would make my batter better."
So she bought a bit of butter,
Better than her bitter butter,
And she put it in her batter,
And the batter was not bitter.
So 'twas better Betty Botter
Bought a bit of better butter.

Of all the felt I ever felt,
I never felt a piece of felt
Which felt as fine as that felt felt,
When first I felt that felt hat's felt.

I need not your needles, they're needless to me;
For kneading of noodles, 'twere needless, you see;
But did my neat knickers but need to be kneed,
I then should have need of your needles indeed.

Three grey geese in a green field grazing,
Grey were the geese and green was the grazing.

Six thick thistle sticks.
Six thick thistles stick.

A skunk sat on a stump and
thunk the stump stunk, but the
stump thunk the skunk stunk.

Moses supposes his toeses are roses,
But Moses supposes erroneously;
For nobody's toeses are posies of roses
As Moses supposes his toeses to be.

Mermaid Marina

In a magical cave, down at the bottom of the deep blue sea, lives Marina, a beautiful mermaid with a shimmering tail. She glides through the water, searching for shiny pearls and sparkling shells.

Coral the dolphin is Marina's very best friend. They love to twirl and dive through the crystal blue waters, and play hide-and-seek amongst the colourful seaweed.

Today there is great excitement at the bottom of the sea. It's the Sea King's birthday and there will be a party.

Marina is getting ready. She puts on a pretty necklace made from glistening pearls, a bracelet and some tiny starfish earrings.

"How do I look, Coral?" she asks her friend. Coral flaps her fins and does a special dolphin twirl – Marina looks wonderful! Finally, the mermaid brushes her beautiful long hair and weaves some tiny blue sea-flowers into it. Then, with a flick of their tails, Marina and Coral head off for the party.

When they arrive at the palace, the other mermaids are amazed – Marina looks so pretty!

"Happy Birthday, Your Majesty!" she says, and gives the king her present – a precious pearl.

"Thank you, Marina," says the king, "it's almost as lovely as you are."

Granny Casts a Spell

Susie was very fond of her Granny. Each day, when Susie got home from school, Granny was always there, sitting by the fire, knitting. Granny knitted so fast that sometimes it seemed as though the knitting needles sparked in the firelight.

"Do you know," Granny would say, "that I'm really a witch?" Susie always laughed when Granny said that because she didn't look at all like a witch. She had a smiling face and kind eyes and she never wore black. Not ever. When Granny wasn't looking, Susie would take a peek inside her wardrobe just in case she might find a broomstick or a witch's hat. But she never found so much as a book of spells.

"I don't believe you're a witch," said Susie.

"I am," replied Granny, "and I'll cast a spell one day. You'll know when that day comes, for my needles will start to knit by themselves."

After that, Susie kept a careful watch over Granny's needles, but they always lay quite still in the basket of knitting.

One day, Susie was playing in her garden when she heard the sound of weeping. The sound seemed to be coming from under the old tree in the corner.

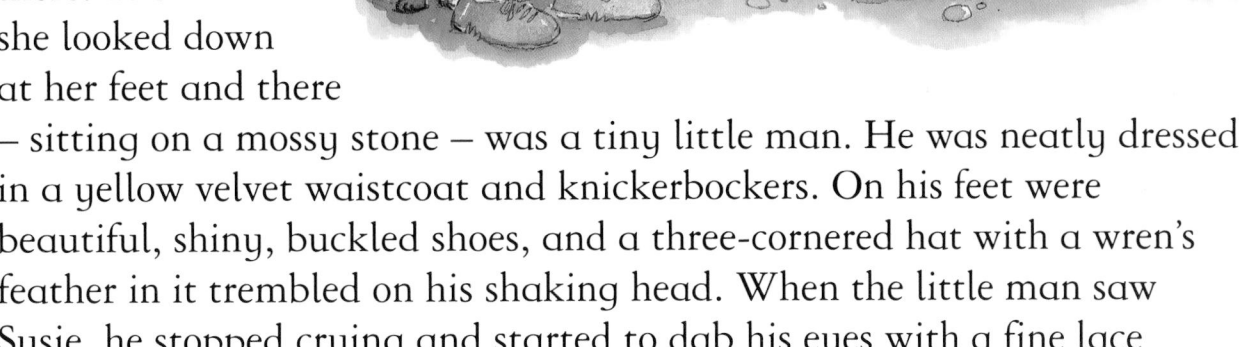

She walked towards the tree and as she did so the crying noise got louder, but she could not see anyone there. Then she looked down at her feet and there – sitting on a mossy stone – was a tiny little man. He was neatly dressed in a yellow velvet waistcoat and knickerbockers. On his feet were beautiful, shiny, buckled shoes, and a three-cornered hat with a wren's feather in it trembled on his shaking head. When the little man saw Susie, he stopped crying and started to dab his eyes with a fine lace handkerchief.

"Whatever can the matter be?" asked Susie, crouching down.

"Oh dear, oh dear!" sobbed the little man. "I am the fairy princess's tailor and she has asked me to make her a lovely gown to wear to the May Ball tonight, but a wicked elf has played a trick on me and turned all my fine gossamer fabric into bats' wings. Now I shall never be able to make the princess's gown and she will be very angry with me." He started to cry again.

"Don't cry!" said Susie. "I'm sure I can help. My Granny's got a sewing basket full of odds and ends. I'll see if she's got anything nice for a party dress. I'm sure she won't mind sparing some – after all, you won't need much," she said. At that, the little man looked a bit more cheerful.

"Wait here," said Susie, "while I run indoors and see." She ran up the garden path and in through the back door.

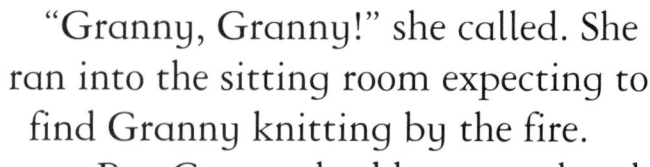

"Granny, Granny!" she called. She ran into the sitting room expecting to find Granny knitting by the fire. But Granny had her eyes closed and she was whispering to herself. On her lap was her knitting – and the needles were moving all by themselves, so that the yarn danced up and down on the old lady's knees.

At first Susie was too astounded to move. Then she thought, "I hope Granny's not casting a bad spell. I must see if the little tailor is alright."

She ran back down the garden path and there sat the tailor, surrounded by a great pile of gorgeous gossamer, shining in the sunlight.

"I've never seen such fine material – ever!" he exclaimed. "But where did it come from? I just closed my eyes to dab them with my hanky and when I opened them again – there it was!"

"I don't know," said Susie, "but I think my Granny might have had something to do with it."

"Well, I'd never be able to thank her enough," said the tailor. "I shall be able to make the finest gown in the whole of fairyland. The princess will dance all night in the prettiest dress there ever was. I'm also indebted to you, for it was you who helped me in the first place. I would like it very much if you came to the May Ball, too."

"Why, thank you so much," Susie replied, "I should like that very much." She didn't want to hurt the tailor's feelings but she knew she couldn't go – she was far too big to go to a fairy ball!

"Well, I must get on with the dress now," said the little man, reaching for a pair of fairy scissors. "See you tonight!" And with that he vanished.

That night, Susie wondered if the fairies really were having a ball. How she longed to be there! Once she thought she heard a tapping at the window. Was that the fairy tailor she saw through the glass – or was she imagining it? In the middle of the night she awoke with a start. There was a click, clicking noise at the end of her bed.

"Granny is that you?" asked Susie.

"Yes, dear," replied Granny. "I couldn't sleep, so I decided to do some knitting. All at once the needles started twitching, so I knew it was time to cast a spell. What is your wish, Susie?"

"I... I..." stammered Susie, "I want to go to the May Ball," she blurted.

"Then you shall, my dear," said Granny.

In an instant, Susie felt herself shrinking and when she looked down she saw she was wearing a beautiful gown and tiny satin slippers. Then she floated on gossamer wings out through the window and off to the Ball.

The next morning, Susie woke up in her bed. Had it all been a dream – the revelry, the fairy food, the frog band, the dance with the fairy prince? Then she saw something peeping out from under her pillow. And what do you think it was? It was a tiny, tiny shred of the finest gossamer fabric.

Little Jack Jingle

Little Jack Jingle,
  He used to live single:
But when he got tired of this kind of life,
  He left off being single, and lived with his wife.

Harry Parry

O rare Harry Parry,
  When will you marry?
When apples and pears are ripe.
  I'll come to your wedding,
Without any bidding,
  And dance and sing all the night.

Young Roger Came Tapping

Young Roger came tapping at Dolly's window,
  Thumpaty, thumpaty, thump!
He asked for admittance, she answered him "No!"
  Frumpaty, frumpaty, frump!

"No, no, Roger, no! as you came you may go!"
  Stumpaty, stumpaty, stump!

Jack, Jack, the Bread's A-burning

Jack, Jack, the bread's a-burning,
  All to a cinder;
If you don't come and fetch it out
  We'll throw it through the window.

Robin and Richard

Robin and Richard were two pretty men;
  They laid in bed till the clock struck ten;
Then up starts Robin and looks at the sky,
  Oh! brother Richard, the sun's very high:

The bull's in the barn threshing the corn,
  The cock's on the dunghill blowing his horn,
The cat's at the fire frying of fish,
  The dog's in the pantry breaking his dish.

Little Tommy Tittlemouse

Little Tommy Tittlemouse
  Lived in a little house;
He caught fishes
  In other men's ditches.

Tom, Tom, the Piper's Son

Tom, Tom, the piper's son,
  Stole a pig, and away he run.
The pig was eat, and Tom was beat,
  And Tom went roaring down the street.

Jack and Guy

Jack and Guy went out in the rye,
  And they found a little boy with one black eye.
Come, says Jack, let's knock him on the head.
  No, says Guy, let's buy him some bread;
You buy one loaf and I'll buy two,
  And we'll bring him up as other folk do.

A Hat Like That

Heather the cow took great care of her appearance. She had the shiniest hooves and the glossiest coat. She had already won three rosettes at the County Show, and she wanted to win more.

One windy afternoon, when Heather was standing near a hedge, she found a beautiful straw hat on a branch. It had a couple of holes in it, but an elegant cow has to put her ears somewhere!

She strolled back across the field with her nose in the air, and the hat placed firmly on her head. Heather couldn't wait to show it off to her friends.

But Poppy, Annabel and Emily simply carried on munching. Heather tried a tiny ladylike cough. The munching didn't stop

for a second. So Heather coughed a little louder. The munching grew louder.

Heather couldn't bear it any longer. "Haven't you noticed it?" she mooed.

"Did I hear something?" asked Emily.

"It was me!" cried Heather, stamping her hoof crossly.

"Oh, so it was," said Annabel, and returned to a particularly juicy clump of green grass.

"Oh dear! I'm feeling rather sleepy, I think I'll just have a little snooze," said Poppy.

"And I'm going for a walk," said Emily.

Heather was not a patient cow."Look at my hat!" she cried.

Of course, the other cows had noticed the hat, but they loved to tease their friend.

"I always think," said Poppy, "that hats are rather… old-fashioned."

"Nonsense," Heather replied. "Only the most fashionable cows are wearing them."

"It's new then, is it?" asked Annabel.

"Certainly!" Heather replied. "It's the very latest style."

"Didn't Mrs MacDonald have a hat like that a few years ago?" asked Emily.

"I don't think so!" Heather said firmly. "Mrs MacDonald is lovely, but she's not what you would call stylish. Only a prize-winning cow could carry off a hat like this."

"If you say so, dear," mooed Annabel.

That evening, the cows ambled into the farmyard to be milked. Before long, all the other animals had gathered round.

"They're admiring my hat!" whispered Heather to Poppy.

But the giggling and chuckling didn't sound as if they thought Heather looked beautiful. It sounded more like animals who thought she looked rather silly.

"Well, well! So that's what happened to Scarecrow Sam's hat!" cried Old MacDonald.

Nowadays, if Heather starts putting on airs and graces, Poppy, Emily and Annabel know just what to do – they start talking about hats, and Heather tiptoes away.

Elephant

Here is Baby Elephant. Baby Elephant plays with his friends, and he helps them, too.

"Giraffe, you've lost your patterns in the mud," said Baby Elephant. "I'll spray you with my trunk."

"Lion, you look too hot," said Baby Elephant. "I'll shade you with my big ears."

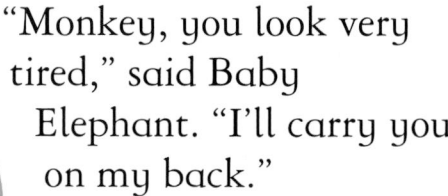

"Monkey, you look very tired," said Baby Elephant. "I'll carry you on my back."

"Oh no. Rhino! You've fallen in the river," said Baby Elephant. "Hold on to my tail very tightly, and I will pull you out."

After his hard work helping his friends, Baby Elephant decided to have a rest under a tree.

"We'll all stay close to Baby Elephant," said his friends, "to make sure he is safe while he rests."

Tiger

Baby Tiger lived in the jungle. One day he fell fast asleep, and his friends could not find him.

"Where is Baby Tiger?" they asked.

Monkey climbed to the top of the highest tree. Rhino ran fast along the riverbank. Elephant searched deep in the jungle.

"Where are you, Baby Tiger?" they called, as loudly as they could.

Then Elephant gave such a loud trumpet that Baby Tiger was woken up.

"Here I am," called Baby Tiger, and with a sleepy yawn and a stretch he waved a stripy paw.

"Baby Tiger! We've been looking everywhere for you," said the animals.

"We couldn't see you because of your stripes," said Monkey.

"We missed you, Baby Tiger," they said, giving him a great big hug.

Jack and the Beanstalk

Jack was a lively young boy who lived with his mother in a tiny little cottage in the country.

Jack and his mother were very poor. They had straw on the floor, and many panes of glass in their windows were broken. The only thing of value that was left was a cow.

One day, Jack's mother called him in from the garden, where he was chopping logs for their stove. "You will have to take Daisy the cow to market and sell her," she said sadly.

As Jack trudged along the road to market, he met a strange old man.

"Where are you taking that fine milking cow?" asked the man.

"To market, sir," replied Jack, "to sell her."

"If you sell her to me," said the man, "I will give you these beans. They are special, magic beans. I promise you won't regret it."

When Jack heard the word "magic", he became

very excited. He quickly swapped the cow for the beans, and ran all the way home.

Jack rushed through the cottage door. "Mother! Mother!" he called. "Where are you?"

"Why are you home so soon?" asked Jack's mother, coming down the stairs. "How much did you get for the cow?"

"I got these," said Jack, holding out his hand. "They're magic beans!"

"What?" shrieked his mother. "You sold our only cow for a handful of beans? You silly boy, come here!"

Angrily, she snatched the beans from Jack's hand and flung them out of the window and into the garden. Jack was sent to bed with no supper that night.

The next morning, Jack's rumbling stomach woke him early. His room was strangely dark. As he got dressed, he glanced out of his window – and what he saw took his breath away.

Overnight, a beanstalk had sprung up in the garden. Its trunk was almost as thick as Jack's cottage and its top was so tall that it disappeared into the clouds.

Jack yelled with excitement and rushed outside. As he began to climb the beanstalk, his mother stood at the bottom and begged for him to come back down, but he took no notice.

At last, tired and very hungry, Jack reached the top. He found himself in a strange land full of clouds. He could see something glinting in the

distance and began walking towards it.

Eventually he reached the biggest castle he had ever seen. Maybe he could find some food in the kitchen there?

He crept carefully under the front door and ran straight into an enormous foot!

"What was that?" boomed a female voice, and the whole room shook. Jack found himself looking into a huge eye. Suddenly, he was whisked into the air by a giant hand!

"Who are you?" roared the voice.

"I'm Jack," said Jack, "and I'm tired and hungry. Please can you give me something to eat and a place to rest for a while?"

The giant woman was a kind old lady and took pity on the tiny boy. "Don't make a sound," she whispered. "My husband doesn't like boys and will eat you if he finds you." Then she gave Jack a crumb of warm bread and a thimble full of hot soup.

He was just eating the last drop when the woman said,

"Quick! Hide in the cupboard! My husband's coming!"

From inside the dark cupboard, Jack could hear the approach of thundering footsteps. Then a deep voice bellowed, *"Fee, fie, foe, fum, I smell the blood of an Englishman! Be he alive or be he dead, I'll grind his bones to make my bread!"*

Jack peeped out through a knothole in the cupboard door, and saw a huge giant standing beside the table.

"Wife!" shouted the giant. "I can smell a boy in the house!"

"Nonsense, dear," said the giant's wife soothingly. "All you can smell is this lovely dinner I have made for you. Now sit down and eat."

When the giant had gobbled up his dinner and a huge bowl of pudding, he shouted, "Wife! Bring me my gold! I wish to count it!"

Jack saw the giant's wife bring out several enormous sacks of coins. The giant picked one up

and a cascade of gold fell onto the table top.

Then Jack watched the giant count the coins, one by one. The giant began to stack them up in piles as he worked.

After a while, he started to yawn, and, not long after, Jack saw that he had fallen asleep. Soon Jack heard very loud snoring!

"It's time I made a move!" Jack said to himself. And, quick as a flash, he leapt out of the cupboard, grabbed a sack of gold, slid down the table leg and ran for the door.

But the giant's wife heard him. "Stop, thief!" she screamed at the top of her voice, which woke her husband. He jumped up in a hurry and ran after Jack, shouting loudly, "Come back!"

Jack ran until he came to the top of the beanstalk. Then, with the giant still after him, he scrambled down as fast as he could.

"Mother!" he called, as he got closer to the ground. "Mother, get the axe, quickly!"

By the time Jack reached the bottom, his mother was there with the axe. She chopped down the beanstalk, and the giant came crashing down with it – he never got up again!

Now that they had the gold, Jack and his mother were very rich. They wouldn't have to worry about anything ever again and they lived happily ever after.

The Apple Tree

Here is the tree with leaves so green.
Here are the apples that hang between.
When the wind blows the apples fall.
Here is a basket to gather them all.

The Cherry Tree

Once I found a cherry stone,
I put it in the ground,
And when I came to look at it,
A tiny shoot I found.

The shoot grew up and up each day,
And soon became a tree.
I picked the rosy cherries then,
And ate them for my tea.

Here We Go Round the Mulberry Bush

Here we go round the mulberry bush,
The mulberry bush, the mulberry bush,
Here we go round the mulberry bush,
On a cold and frosty morning.

This is the way we wash our hands,
Wash our hands, wash our hands,
This is the way we wash our hands,
On a cold and frosty morning.

Here we go round the mulberry bush,
The mulberry bush, the mulberry bush,
Here we go round the mulberry bush,
On a cold and frosty morning.

This is the way we wash our clothes,
Wash our clothes, wash our clothes,
This is the way we wash our clothes,
On a cold and frosty morning.

Here we go round the mulberry bush,
The mulberry bush, the mulberry bush,
Here we go round the mulberry bush,
On a cold and frosty morning.

Lavender's Blue

Lavender's blue, dilly, dilly, lavender's green,
When I am king, dilly, dilly, you shall be queen;
Call up your men, dilly, dilly, set them to work,
Some to the plough, dilly, dilly, some to the cart;
Some to make hay, dilly, dilly, some to thresh corn;
Whilst you and I, dilly, dilly, keep ourselves warm.

Dancing Round the Maypole

Dancing round the maypole,
Dancing all the day,
Dancing round the maypole,
On the first of May,
Dancing round the maypole,
What a merry bunch,
Dancing round the maypole,
Till it's time for lunch.

Dancing round the maypole,
Shouting out with glee,
Dancing round the maypole,
Till it's time for tea.
Dancing round the maypole,
Blue and white and red,
Dancing round the maypole,
Till it's time for bed.

I Had a Little Nut Tree

I had a little nut tree, nothing would it bear,
But a silver nutmeg, and a golden pear;
The King of Spain's daughter came to visit me,
And all for the sake of my little nut tree.
I skipped over water, I danced over sea,
And all the birds of the air
couldn't catch me.

The Littlest Pig

Little Pig had a secret. He snuggled down in the warm hay with his brothers and sisters, looked up at the dark sky twinkling with stars, and smiled a secret smile to himself. Maybe it wasn't so bad being the littlest pig after all...

Not so long ago, Little Pig had been feeling quite fed up. He was the youngest and the smallest pig in the family. He had five brothers and five sisters who were all much bigger and fatter than him. The farmer's wife called him Runt, because he was the smallest pig of the litter.

His brothers and sisters teased him terribly. "Poor little Runtie," they said to him, giggling. "You must be the smallest pig in the world!"

"Leave me alone!" said Little Pig, and he crept off to the corner of the pigpen, where he curled into a ball, and started to cry. "If you weren't all so greedy, and let me have some food, maybe I'd be bigger!" he mumbled, sadly.

Every feeding time was the same – the others all pushed and shoved, until all that was left were the scraps. He would never grow bigger at this rate.

Then one day Little Pig made an important discovery. He was hiding in the corner of the pen, as usual, when he spied a little hole in the fence tucked away behind the feeding trough.

"I could fit through there!" thought Little Pig.

He waited all day until it was time for bed, and then, when he was sure that all of his brothers and sisters were fast asleep, he wriggled through the hole. Suddenly he was outside, free to go wherever he pleased. And what an adventure he had!

First, he ran to the henhouse and gobbled up the bowls of grain. Then he ran to the field and crunched up Donkey's carrots.

He ran to the vegetable patch and munched a row of cabbages. What a feast! Then, when he was full to bursting, he headed for home. On the way he stopped by the hedgerow. What was that lovely smell? He rooted around and found where it was coming from – a bank of wild strawberries.

Little Pig had never tasted anything quite so delicious.

"Tomorrow night, I'll start with these!"

he promised himself as he trotted back home to the pigpen. He wriggled back through the hole, and fell fast asleep snuggled up to his mother, smiling very contentedly.

Every night Little Pig continued his tasty adventures. He didn't mind when they pushed him out of the way at feeding time, he knew that a much better feast awaited him outside. Sometimes he would find the dog's bowl filled with scraps from the farmer's supper, or buckets of oats ready for the horses. "Yum, yum – piggy porridge!" he would giggle, and gobbled it up.

But, as the days and weeks went by, and Little Pig grew bigger and fatter, every night it became more of a squeeze to wriggle and push his way through the hole.

Little Pig knew that soon he would no longer be able to fit through the hole, but by then he would be big enough to stand up to his brothers and sisters. And for now he was enjoying his secret!

Loves to Sing!

Old MacDonald loves to sing,
  Whilst doing all his chores.
His wife just thanks her lucky stars,
  He does it when outdoors!

It's rather like a lost lamb's bleat,
  A hungry horse's neigh.
The kind of snort a piglet makes,
  When rolling in the hay!

So Old MacDonald's wife just cooks,
  Her husband gets no thinner,
Because MacDonald cannot sing,
  With his mouth full of dinner!

Did You Know?

Did you know ducks like to dance?
  Their pirouettes are grand.
And what is more,
  They can perform
On water or on land.

Did you know ducks like to dance?
  They shimmy and they shake.
And what is more,
  They can perform
A very fine Swan Lake!

Busy Farmer

When a very busy farmer,
  Goes upstairs to bed at night,
He simply can't stop wondering,
  If everything's all right.

Are the cows asleep and dreaming?
  Are they trotting down the lane?
Is the cockerel in the kitchen,
  Pecking at the pies again?

So a very busy farmer,
  Always rises at first light.
He simply cannot wait to check
  That everything's all right.

Where are You?

Doris Duck, Doris Duck,
  Where are you?
Here I am! Here I am!
  Dabbling in the dew.
Dora Duck, Dora Duck,
  Where are you?
Here I am, diving down,
  Which I love to do!
Ducklings all, ducklings all,
  Where are you?
Here we are, swimming round,
  Coming to splash YOU!

Watch Out!

When Percy the pig feels peckish,
There's very little doubt,
That he will gobble anything,
Animals, watch out!

He nibbles straw
At the stable door.
He chomps on weed
Where the ducklings feed.
He munches hay
When the cows are away.

He snacks on corn
If a sack is torn.
When Percy the pig feels peckish,
There's very little doubt,
That even Old MacDonald
Shouldn't leave his lunch about!

Kittens are Cuddly

Kittens are cuddly,
Kittens are sweet,
They dash round the farmyard,
On soft, furry feet.

And before very long,
They are kittens no more,
But cats who do nothing,
But stretch out and snore!

Back to the Farm

Old MacDonald went to town,
Three pigs under his arm.
One didn't want to go there,
So he ran back to the farm.

Old MacDonald went to town,
Two pigs under his arm.
One kicked the farmer on his knee,
And ran back to the farm.

Old MacDonald went to town,
One pig under his arm.
He bit the farmer on the nose,
Then ran back to the farm.

The piglets didn't want to go,
They said, "We like it here!"
MacDonald said, "Oh, all right then!"
And the pigs began to cheer!

Without a Growl

When Old MacDonald's work is done,
And twilight falls with the setting sun,
He sits down in his chair.
For he knows that he has a friend,
From day's beginning to day's end,
Bruce the sheepdog
is there.

One Dark Night

Paws tiptoed out into the dark farmyard. Mummy had told him to stay in the barn until he was old enough to go out at night. But he was impatient. He had not gone far when something brushed past his ears. He froze as the fur on his neck began to rise. To his relief it was only a bat – there were plenty of those in the barn.

A loud hoot echoed through the trees – "Toowhit, Toowhoo!" and a great dark shape swooped down and snatched something up. "Just an owl," Paws told himself. "Some of those in the barn too. Nothing to be afraid of!" Creeping nervously on into the darkness, he wondered if this was such a good idea after all. Strange rustlings came from every corner, and he jumped as the old pig gave a loud grunt from the pigsty close by.

Then, all of a sudden, Paws froze in his tracks. Beneath the henhouse two eyes glinted in the darkness, as they came creeping towards him. This must be the fox Mummy had warned him of! But to his amazement he saw it was Mummy!

"Back to the barn!" she said sternly and Paws happily did as he was told. Maybe he would wait until he was older to go out at night, after all!

The Bear Will Have to Go

While Lucy slept in the shade of a tree, Cuthbert went for a walk into the woods and was soon quite lost. He had no idea which way was back, so he sat down and thought about what to do next.

When Lucy awoke, she looked around in surprise. Her teddy bear, Cuthbert, was missing. She thought someone had taken him, for she didn't know that when people are asleep their teddy bears come to life and like to go exploring.

"Cuthbert!" she called. "Cuthbert, where are you?"

He wasn't very far away. Lucy soon found him sniffing at a clump of moss.

"There you are!" she sighed. "I thought I'd lost you. What have you done with your waistcoat?"

In fact, Lucy really had lost Cuthbert, for the bear she was now taking home was not a teddy bear at all, but a real baby bear cub! As they ran back through the woods, the bear in Lucy's arms kept very still. He stared straight ahead without blinking, and tried not to sneeze. Soon they were back home in Lucy's bedroom.

Lucy flung the bear on her bed, then went to run a bath.

"Time to escape!" thought the bear. He slid off the bed, pulling the covers after him. He ran over to the window and tried to climb up the curtains. They tore down and tumbled to a heap on the floor. Just then Lucy's mother came into the room. The bear froze. Then Lucy appeared.

"Look at this mess," said Lucy's mother. "You've been playing with that bear again. Please tidy up."

Lucy had no idea how her room had got in such a mess, but she quickly tidied up, took the bear into the bathroom and put him on the edge of the bath.

"Don't fall in," she said, and went to fetch a towel. The bear jumped into the bath with a great splash. He waved his paws wildly, sending sprays of soapy water across the room. When he heard footsteps, he froze and floated on his back in the water as if nothing was wrong. It was Lucy, followed by her mother. "Oh, Lucy! What a mess!"

"Cuthbert must have fallen in," cried Lucy, rubbing his wet fur with a towel.

"A teddy bear couldn't make all this mess on its own," said Lucy's mother. "Please clean it up."

Lucy looked carefully at Cuthbert. Something was different about him, but she just couldn't work out what it was.

That night, while Lucy slept, the bear tiptoed downstairs. He needed to get back to the woods where he belonged, but he was hungry. In the kitchen he found lots of food, and he had a feast.

When Lucy came down for a glass of milk she found him with food all over his paws. The bear froze. Then her mother appeared in the doorway, looking really angry.

"This is the last straw, Lucy," said her mother, crossly. "You have been very naughty today, and every time something happens you've got that bear with you. If there is any more bad behaviour like this, then the bear will have to go."

When her mother had gone back upstairs, Lucy looked carefully at the little furry bear.

"You're not Cuthbert are you?" she said. The bear looked back at her and blinked. Lucy gasped. "You're a real bear!"

Now all the mess made sense! Lucy could hardly believe she had made such a mistake. She stroked the bear gently and he licked her finger.

"I'd better get you back to

the woods before there's any more trouble," she said. "And I'd better try to find the real Cuthbert."

So early next morning, before her parents were awake, she crept out of the house carrying the bear. Out in the woods she put the bear on the ground. He licked her hand and padded away.

Lucy was sad to see the little bear go. She wiped a tear from her eye as she turned away... and there at the foot of a tree sat her teddy bear, Cuthbert! Lucy picked him up and hugged him.

"Where have you been?" she asked. "You'll never guess the trouble I've been in. What have you been doing all night?"

Cuthbert said nothing. He just smiled. What had he been doing all night? Well, that's another story!

Monday's Child is Fair of Face

Monday's child is fair of face,
Tuesday's child is full of grace,
Wednesday's child is full of woe,
Thursday's child has far to go,
Friday's child is loving and giving,
Saturday's child works hard for his living,
And the child that is born on the Sabbath day
Is bonny and blithe, and good and gay.

Little Jumping Joan

Here am I, little jumping Joan.
When nobody's with me,
I'm always alone.

There Was a Little Girl

There was a little girl, and she had a little curl
Right in the middle of her forehead;
When she was good she was very, very good,
But when she was bad she was horrid.

Anna Maria

Anna Maria she sat on the fire;
The fire was too hot, she sat on the pot;
The pot was too round, she sat on the ground;
The ground was too flat, she sat on the cat;
The cat ran away with Maria on her back.

A Pretty Little Girl in a Round-eared Cap

A pretty little girl in a round-eared cap
I met in the streets the other day;
She gave me such a thump,
That my heart it went bump;
I thought I should have fainted away!
I thought I should have fainted away!

Goldy Locks, Goldy Locks

Goldy locks, goldy locks,
Wilt thou be mine?
Thou shall not wash dishes,
Nor yet feed the swine;

But sit on a cushion,
And sew a fine seam,
And feed upon strawberries,
Sugar and cream.

Gilly Silly Jarter

Gilly Silly Jarter,
Who has lost a garter?
In a shower of rain,
The miller found it,
The miller ground it,
And the miller gave it
To Silly again.

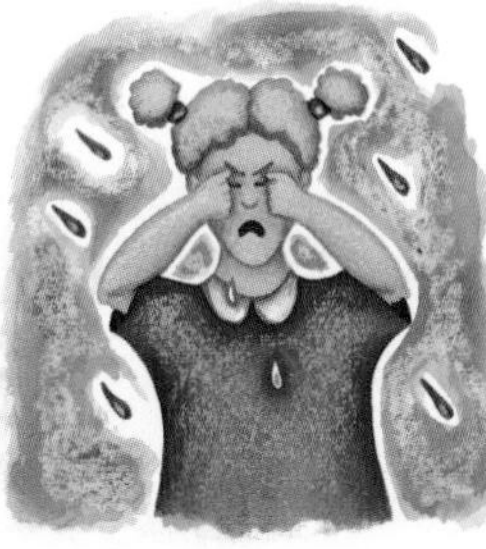

Mr Punchinello

Oh! mother, I shall be married
To Mr Punchinello.
To Mr Punch,
To Mr Joe,
To Mr Nell,
To Mr Lo,
Mr Punch, Mr Joe,
Mr Nell, Mr Lo,
To Mr Punchinello.

You Can Do It, Dilly Duck!

It was the night before Dilly's first swimming lesson.
"I've got a funny feeling in my tummy," said Dilly, as Mamma Duck kissed her goodnight.

"Don't worry!" replied her mother. "Just close your eyes tightly and you'll soon fall asleep." Dilly shut her eyes and tried to go to sleep. But all she could think about was the lesson.

"What if I sink?" she worried. Dilly pictured Mamma Duck's smiling face. "If Mamma Duck can float, perhaps I can, too," she thought. Then she snuggled down to go to sleep.

Suddenly Dilly opened her eyes. "But I'll get all wet!" she quacked, shaking her feathers. Dilly thought about her friend Webster the frog. "Webster loves getting wet," she remembered. "He says it's fun!"

Dilly closed her eyes again, but just as she was about to fall asleep she had a horrible thought.

"What if something nibbles my toes?" Dilly pictured all the bigger ducks

doing duck-dives in the pond. "They're not afraid of what's under the water," she quacked, "so why should I be?" Dilly was wide awake early the next morning, and so were all her friends.

"You can do it, Dilly!" they cheered as she waddled slowly to the edge of the pond. She leaned forward and looked in, very timidly. There in the water was another little duckling gazing back at her. Dilly looked at the other little duckling. She was small and yellow with downy feathers, just like Dilly.

"Well, if you can do it, I guess I can too!"quacked Dilly bravely. SPLASH! She jumped right into the pond. "I can float!" cried Dilly, paddling along. "It's fun getting wet!" Then Dilly did a duck-dive.

"There's nothing scary under the water either!" she added, bobbing up again. "In fact, you are all right! I CAN do it!"

The Very Big Parcel

Once upon a time there lived an old man and his wife. They dwelled in a small house with a small, neat garden and they were very contented. What's more, they had very good friends and neighbours, with whom they shared everything. One day, there was a knock at the door and there stood the postman with a huge parcel in his arms.

"My, oh my!" exclaimed the old man to his wife as he staggered into the kitchen with the enormous load.

"Whatever can it be?" wondered the old woman as the two of them stared at the parcel. "Perhaps it's a new set of china," she said.

"Or a new wheelbarrow," he said – and they began to think about all the fancy things there might be inside the parcel.

"Well, why don't we open it and see?" said the old lady at last – and so they did. They looked into the box and at first it seemed to be totally empty.

"Well, I never did!" cried the old man. And then he spotted something right in the corner of

the box. He lifted it out into the light to examine it more carefully and discovered it was a single seed.

Well, the old man and his wife were most upset. Whereas before they were quite content, now that they had thought about all the things that might have been in the box they were bitterly disappointed by the seed. "Still," said the old man at last, "we'd better plant it anyway. Who knows, maybe we'll get a nice fresh lettuce from it."

So he planted the seed in the garden. Every day he watered the ground and soon a shoot appeared. The shoot grew into a strong young plant and then it grew taller and taller. Higher and higher it grew until it was a handsome tree. The man and his wife were excited to see fruits growing on the tree.

"I wonder if they're apples," the old man said. Each day he watered the tree and examined the fruits. One day he said to his wife, "The first fruit is ready to pick." He carefully reached up into the tree and picked the large red fruit. He carried it into the kitchen and put it on the table. Then he took a knife and cut the fruit in half. To his astonishment out poured a pile of gold coins. "Come quickly!" he called to his wife. Well, the pair of them danced around the kitchen for joy.

The old couple decided to spend just one gold coin and keep the rest. "After all," said the woman wisely, "we don't know what's in the other fruits. They may be full of worms." So they spent one golden penny in the town and put the rest aside.

The next day the old man picked another big red fruit and this, too, was full of gold. After

that the old couple were less careful with their money, thinking all the fruits must be full of gold. They had a wonderful time buying fine clothes and things for the house and garden. Each day the man picked another fruit. Each day it was full of gold and each day they went into town and had a grand time spending the money. But all the while the man forgot entirely to water the tree.

Meanwhile, the old couple's friends and neighbours started to gossip among themselves. They wondered where all the money was coming from and they began to resent the old couple. They noticed that they didn't buy anything for their friends, or even throw a party. Gradually their friends ignored them until the old couple were left with no friends at all. But they didn't even notice because they were so busy spending the gold coins.

Then one day the old man looked out into the garden and saw that the tree was all withered. He rushed outside and threw bucket after bucket of water over the tree, but all to no avail. He and his wife frantically picked the fruits left on the tree, but when they took them indoors they found to their dismay that they were cracked and gnarled. When they broke open the fruits they were full of dust.

"If only I had not been so thoughtless and remembered to water the tree!" cried the old man in anguish.

The next day the old couple looked out of the window to find that the tree had vanished. Now what were they to do? They had neglected their garden and now they had nothing to eat. They realised that they would have to sell their riches to buy food. Then they also needed new gardening tools, for theirs had grown rusty with neglect.

As the weeks passed, the old man and his wife gradually sold all the fine things they had bought, just to keep body and soul together. They felt truly miserable and sorry for the way they had treated their neighbours. They realised just how lonely they were without their friends.

"We have no money now," said the wife one day, "but let's have a party anyway – friendship is more valuable than any amount of gold coins."

So the old couple invited all their friends and neighbours round and they had a grand party. The friends wondered what had happened to all the old couple's riches and what had happened to make the old couple so friendly once more, but I don't think they ever found out, do you?

Honey Bear and the Bees

One day, as Honey Bear woke from her dreams, her furry little nose started to twitch with excitement. She could smell her most favourite thing in the world – sweet, yummy honey! The smell was coming from a hollow tree stump nearby. She padded over and dipped in a large paw. How delicious the sweet, sticky honey tasted!

Honey Bear dipped her paw in again and again, digging deep into the tree stump to reach more of the lovely, sticky honey. This was the life! In fact, she dug so deep that, when she tried to take her great paw out, she found it was stuck fast! Just then, she heard a loud buzzing noise and looked up to see a huge swarm of angry bees returning to their hive!

Poor Honey Bear hollered as the bees flew around, stinging her all over! She tugged and tugged and at last she pulled her paw free. The angry bees chased her all the way to the river where she sat cooling her burning skin. Just then an irresistible smell reached her furry nose. It was coming from a hollow tree nearby.

"Mmm, honey!" said Honey Bear. "I'll just go and take a look... "

The Great Brown Owl

The brown owl sits in the ivy bush,
  And she looketh wondrous wise,
With a horny beak beneath her cowl,
  And a pair of large round eyes.

She sat all day on the selfsame spray,
  From sunrise till sunset;
And the dim, grey light it was all too bright
  For the owl to see in yet.

"Jenny Owlet, Jenny Owlet," said a merry little bird,
  "They say you're wondrous wise;
But I don't think you see, though you're looking at *me*
  With your large, round, shining eyes."

But night came soon, and the pale white moon
  Rolled high up in the skies;
And the great brown owl flew away in her cowl,
  With her large, round, shining eyes.

The Eagle

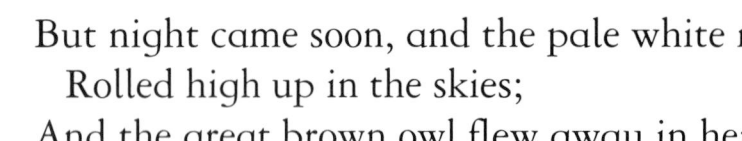

He clasps the crag with crooked hands;
  Close to the sun in lonely lands,
Ring'd with the azure world, he stands.

The wrinkled sea beneath him crawls;
  He watches from his mountain walls,
And like a thunderbolt he falls.

ALFRED, LORD TENNYSON

The Owl

When cats run home and light is come,
  And dew is cold upon the ground,
And the far-off stream is dumb,
  And the whirring sail goes round,
And the whirring sail goes round;
  Alone and warming his five wits,
The white owl in the belfry sits.

ALFRED, LORD TENNYSON

Little Trotty Wagtail

Little Trotty Wagtail, he went in the rain,
  And twittering, tottering sideways, he ne'er got straight again;
He stooped to get a worm, and looked up to get a fly,
  And then he flew away 'ere his feathers they were dry.

Little Trotty Wagtail, he waddled in the mud,
  And left his little foot-marks, trample where he would,
He waddled in the water-pudge, and waggle went his tail,
  And chirrupped up his wings to dry upon the garden rail.

Little Trotty Wagtail, you nimble all about,
  And in the dimpling water-pudge you waddle in and out;
Your home is nigh at hand and in the warm pig-stye;
  So, little Master Wagtail, I'll bid you a good-bye.

Monkey Mayhem

Mickey and Maxine Monkey had finished their breakfast of Mango Munch. Now they were rushing off to play.

"Be careful!" called their mum. "And please DON'T make too much noise!"

"We won't!" the two mischievous monkeys promised, leaping across to the next tree.

"Wheeee," screeched Mickey, and "Wa-hoooo!" hollered Maxine.

The noise echoed through the whole jungle – Mickey and Maxine just didn't know how to be quiet!

Ka-thunk! Mickey landed on a branch. Ka-clunk! Maxine landed beside him. Ker-aack!

"Ooohh noooo!" the monkeys hollered as the branch snapped.

"Yi-i-i-kes!" they shrieked, as they went tumbling down. Ker-thumpp! The jungle shook as the two monkeys crashed to the ground.

"Yipppeeee!" the monkeys cheered, jumping up happily.

"That was so much FUN!" exclaimed Maxine. "Let's go and get Chico Chimp and see if he wants to do it, too!" And the two monkeys scrambled back up to the tree tops, bellowing, "HEY, CHICO! COME AND PLAY WITH US!" as they swung through the branches.

All over the jungle, animals shook their heads and covered their ears. Couldn't anyone keep those naughty, noisy monkeys quiet?

Chico Chimp arrived to play with his friends. The three of them were having a great time swinging, tumbling and bouncing together when suddenly they stopped short. Grandpa Gorilla was standing in their path, glaring at them angrily.

"Go away, you mischief-makers," he said. "You've given us all enough headaches today. My grandson Gulliver is fast asleep by the river and, if you wake him up, I will be very, very upset!"

"Sorry," whispered Maxine, looking down at the ground. Everyone in the jungle knew it was a big mistake to upset Grandpa Gorilla!

"We'll be quiet," they promised.

Mickey, Maxine and Chico didn't know what to do until Mickey said, "Let's climb the coconut palm tree. We can do that quietly."

"Okay," the others agreed half-heartedly.

"I suppose it's better than doing nothing," said Maxine.

From their perch among the coconuts, the three friends could see right over the jungle.

They saw Jerome Giraffe showing his son Jeremy how to choose the juiciest, most tender leaves on a tree… and they saw Portia Parrot giving her daughter Penelope her first flying lesson. And right down below them, they saw little Gulliver Gorilla sleeping contentedly in the tall grass beside the river.

And – uh-oh! They saw something else, too… Claudia Crocodile was in the river. She was grinning and snapping her big, sharp teeth – and heading straight for Gulliver!

The friends didn't think twice. Maxine shouted, "GET UP, GULLIVER! GET UP RIGHT NOOOOOOWW!"

Then Mickey and Chico began throwing coconuts at Claudia.

SMAACCCK! they went, on Claudia's hard crocodile head.

"OWW-WOOW!" moaned Claudia.

"What's going on here?" Grandpa Gorilla shouted up into the coconut tree. "I thought I told you three to keep quiet!"

All the noise woke Gulliver. The little gorilla sat up, looked around, and ran to his grandpa, who was hurrying towards the river.

When Grandpa saw Claudia he realised what had happened. "I am so glad you're safe!" he said, giving Gulliver a great big gorilla hug. The three monkeys came down from the tree.

"We're sorry we made so much noise," Chico said.

By this time all the gorillas had gathered around, and so had most of the other animals.

"What's going on?" squawked Portia Parrot.

"Yes, what's all the commotion about?" asked Jerome Giraffe.

"These three youngsters are heroes," said Grandpa. "They have saved my grandson from being eaten by Claudia Crocodile!"

"I think you all deserve a reward," said Grandpa. "And I think it should be..."

"Hurrah!" cheered all the other animals and then they held their breath in anticipation.

"...permission to be just as noisy as you like, whenever you like!" Grandpa Gorilla announced.

"YIPPEEE!" cheered Mickey, Maxine and Chico, in their loudest, screechiest voices. Their grins were almost as wide as the river.

"OH, NOOOOO!" all the other animals groaned together – but they were all smiling, too.

Bears Ahoy!

One summer's day, three little boys went for a picnic by the bank of a river. They took with them their swimming things, some cheese and pickle sandwiches and, of course, their teddy bears.

When they arrived, they found a small boat tied to a tree. The boys climbed on board, taking their teddies with them, and had a great game of pirates. The boys pretended to walk the plank, and soon they were all splashing about, playing and swimming in the river. They chased each other through the shallow water, and disappeared along the river and out of sight.

Now, the three bears left on board the boat did not get on very well together. Oscar was a small, honey-coloured bear. He was good friends with Mabel, who had shaggy brown fur, but neither of them liked Toby. He was bigger than they were and he was a bully. He was always growling at the other bears and telling them what to do.

As soon as the boys were out of sight, Toby leapt to his feet. The boat rocked. Oscar and Mabel begged him to sit down.

"I'm a fearless sailor," cried Toby. "I've sailed the seven seas and now I'm going to sail them again."

Before the others realised what he was doing, Toby had untied the boat, and pushed it away from the bank. The boat lurched from side to side.

"Come on, crew. Look lively!" shouted Toby. "Do as I say or I'll make you walk the plank." Now that it was untied, the little blue boat began to drift out into the river. It turned sideways gently, then caught the main current and began to gather speed.

"Toby!" cried Oscar. "We're moving!"

"Of course we are, you big softie," growled Toby. "We're bold and fearless pirates on the high seas."

Oscar and Mabel clung together in fright, as the little boat sailed down the river, past fields and houses. "Help!" they shouted. "Toby, make it stop!" But Toby was having a great time.

"Ha, ha," shouted Toby. "This is the life!"

Oscar glanced over the side. He wished he hadn't. The sight of everything passing by so quickly made him feel seasick.

"Look out, Toby!" he cried. "We're going to hit the bank. Quickly, steer it away before we crash!"

But Toby did nothing. He simply sat and watched as the little boat careered along, gathering speed as it headed for the bank. Oscar and Mabel clutched the sides of the boat tightly, and clung on fast. They were feeling very frightened. The boat hit the bank with a thump and Toby fell forward. The boat swung round and headed for the middle of the river once more.

"Toby!" shouted Mabel. "Save us!"

But Toby was sitting in the bottom of the boat, rubbing a big bump on his head.

"I can't. I don't know how to sail a boat," he whimpered, feebly. He hid his face in his paws and began to cry. The boat zig-zagged on down the river, with the little bears clinging on to the sides in fright. In time, the river became wider and they could hear the cry of seagulls.

"Oh, Toby," cried Mabel. "We're heading for the sea. Do something!"

"Nobody likes me," wailed Toby. "Now we're going to sink to the bottom of the sea, and you won't like me either!"

Oscar wasn't listening. He had found a rope hanging from the sail. "Let's put the sail up and see if it will blow us to shore," he said.

"We'll be blown out to sea," wailed Toby, but Oscar ignored him, and carried on. The wind filled the sail and the little boat started moving forward. They sailed right across the bay to the far side, and blew up on to the beach.

"Oh, Oscar, you are a hero!" sighed Mabel, hugging him tight. "You saved us!"

Imagine the bears' surprise to see the three little boys running towards them along the beach – they had gone to find the coastguard and raise the alarm. There were hugs and kisses all round when they found the bears safe and sound. And you can be sure that, from that day on, Toby was a much wiser and kinder bear, and he never bullied the others again.

Fairy Fern

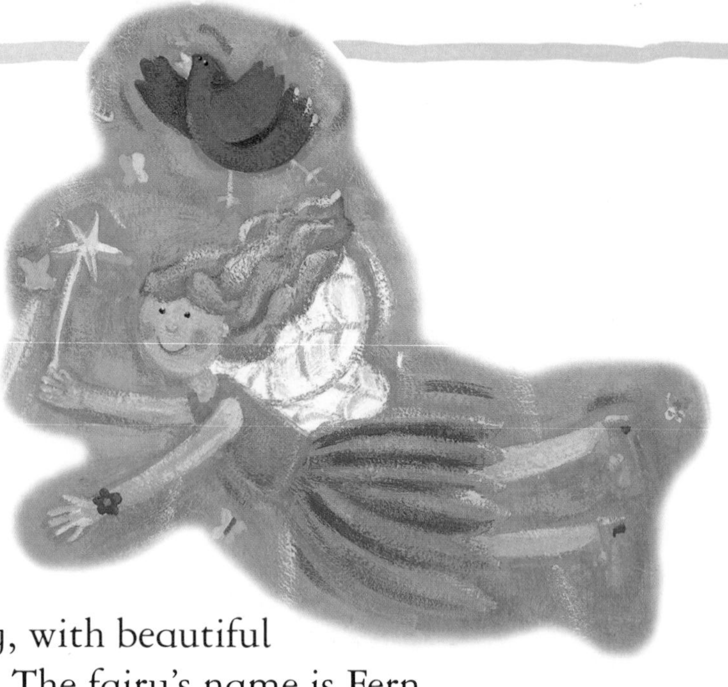

Deep in the heart of Rosebud Forest lives a tiny little fairy, with beautiful cobweb wings and a magic wand. The fairy's name is Fern, and her home is among the wild flowers that grow in a secret glade.

Fern has a special friend – Sapphire the bluebird. They love to fly through the forest, leaping over rays of sunlight, chasing pretty butterflies. Then, by the light of the moon, Sapphire and Fern dance and sing around a "fairy ring" with all their friends.

Today, Fairy Fern is really excited! There's to be a fairy parade. Flora, the Fairy Queen, will choose the prettiest fairy dress.

With a tap-tap of her wand, Fern magically changes into a dress of velvety rose petals and bluebells. Then, with a sprinkling of fairy dust, Fern makes a secret wish…

"Please let Queen Flora choose me!" she whispers.

But Fern has forgotten to get her friend ready! She weaves some flowers through Sapphire's feathers and adds a sprinkling of fairy dust.

Now for the final touch! Fairy Fern twists her hair up and pins it into place with a golden flower. Then, with a flutter of wings, they fly off to the parade.

Fairy Fern arrives just as Queen Flora is announcing the winner… "and the Golden Crown goes to… Fairy Fern!"

All the fairies cheer and flutter their wings. Fairy Fern smiles as the crown is placed on her head. She is the happiest fairy in the forest – her secret wish has come true.

Hot Cross Buns!

Hot cross buns!
  Hot cross buns!
One a-penny, two a-penny,
  Hot cross buns!
If you have no daughters,
  Give them to your sons,
One a-penny, two a-penny,
  Hot cross buns!

Pease Pudding Hot

Pease pudding hot,
  Pease pudding cold,
Pease pudding in the pot,
  Nine days old.

Some like it hot,
  Some like it cold,
Some like it in the pot,
  Nine days old.

Pop Goes the Weasel

Half a pound of tu'penny rice,
  Half a pound of treacle.
That's the way the money goes,
  POP! goes the weasel.

Oats and Beans

Oats and beans and barley grow,
  Oats and beans and barley grow,
Do you or I or anyone know,
  How oats and beans and barley grow?

First the farmer sows his seeds,
  Then he stands and takes his ease,
Stamps his feet and claps his hands,
  Turns around to view the land.

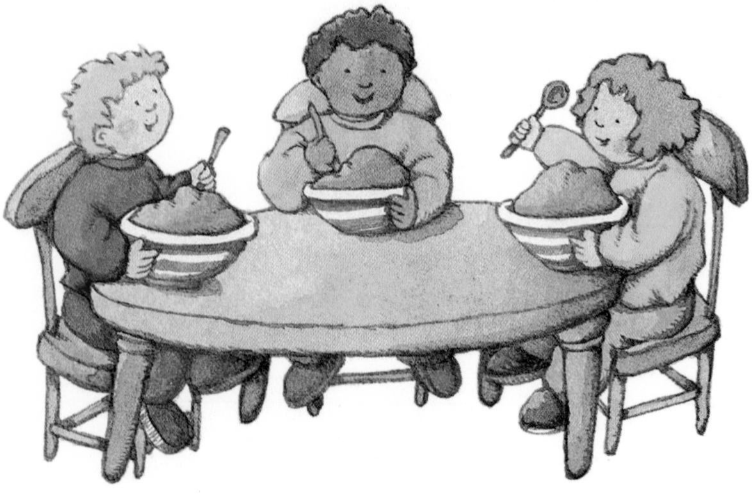

Sing a Song of Sixpence

Sing a song of sixpence,
  A pocket full of rye;
Four-and-twenty blackbirds
  Baked in a pie;
When the pie was opened,
  The birds began to sing;
Wasn't that a dainty dish,
  To set before a king?

Five Little Peas

Five little peas in a pea-pod pressed,
  One grew, two grew, and so did all the rest.
They grew, and they grew, and they did not stop,
  Until one day the pod went ... POP!

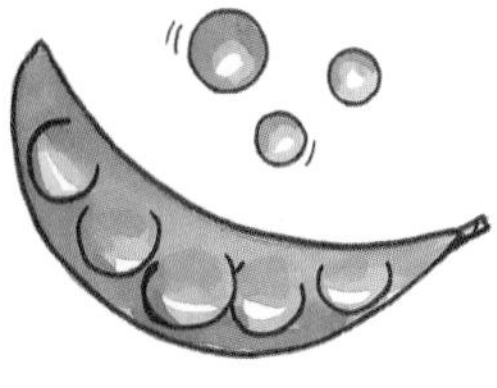

Five Fat Sausages

Five fat sausages frying in a pan,
  All of a sudden one went "BANG!"
Four fat sausages, etc.
  Three fat sausages, etc.
Two fat sausages, etc.
  One fat sausage frying in a pan,
All of a sudden it went "BANG!"
  and there were NO sausages left!

Robin the Bobbin

Robin the Bobbin, the big-bellied Ben,
  He ate more meat than fourscore men;
He ate a cow, he ate a calf,
  He ate a butcher and a half;
He ate a church, he ate a steeple,
  He ate the priest and all the people!
    A cow and a calf,
      An ox and a half,
    A church and a steeple,
      And all the good people,
And yet he complained that his stomach wasn't full.

Chasing Tails

Barney had been chasing his tail all morning. Round and round he went, until he made himself feel quite dizzy.

"Can't you find something useful to do?" asked the cat, from where she sat watching him on the fence.

"What? Like chasing lazy cats?" said Barney, as he leapt towards her, barking fiercely.

Later, as he trotted around the farmyard, Barney thought about what the cat had said. He wished he could be more useful, but he was only a little pup. When he grew up, he would be a fine, useful farm dog, like his mum. Just then, he rounded the barn, and there in front of him waved a big bushy tail...

"Here's a tail I can catch!" thought Barney playfully, and he sprang forward and sank his sharp little puppy teeth into it!

Now, the tail belonged to a sly fox, who was about to pounce on Mrs Hen and her chicks! The fox yelped in surprise, and ran away across the fields.

"Ooh, Barney, you saved us!" cried Mrs Hen.

The cat was watching from the fence. "Maybe all that practice chasing tails has come in useful after all!" she said.

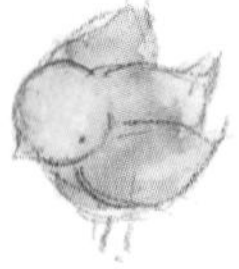
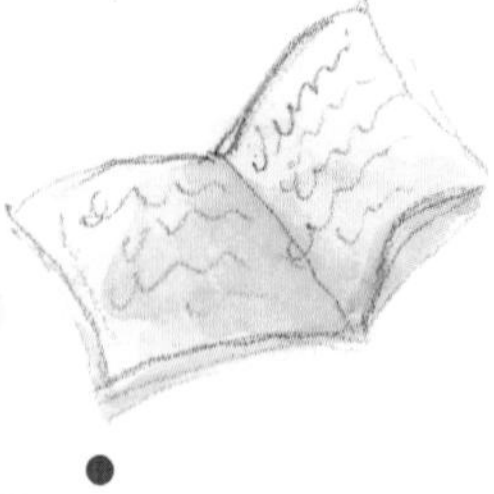
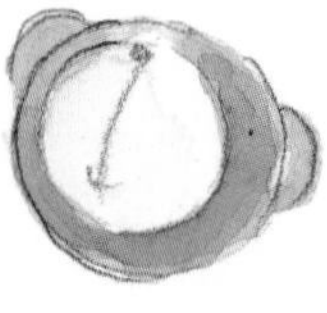

Staying at Grandma's

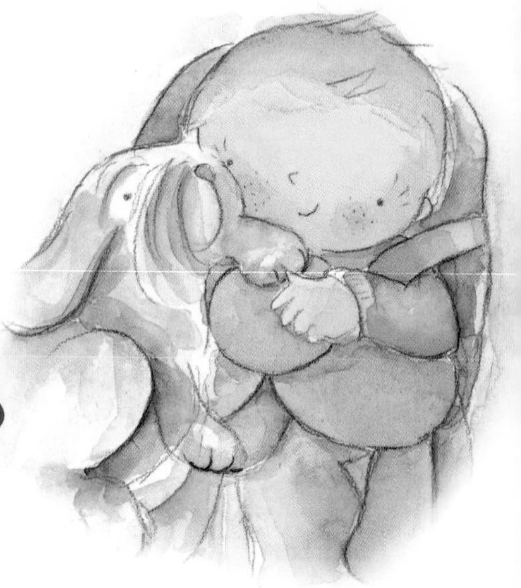

Jack hugged his teddy bear tightly, while Mum packed his slippers and pyjamas into a bag.

"Why can't I come with you?" he asked.

"Because Dad and I have to go away for one night," said Mum. "You're going to stay with Gran and Grandad. They can't wait to see you."

"But I'll be scared without you and Dad," whispered Jack.

"Don't worry," said Mum. "You'll have such a good time, you won't want to come home!"

Later that day, Gran and Grandad opened their front door, as Mum, Dad and Jack arrived in their car. Holly, Gran's little dog, peeped through her legs, wagging her tail with excitement. But soon, it was time for Jack to say goodbye to his mum and dad. Jack felt really sad. He didn't want them to leave. He hugged his mum tightly. "I'll miss you," he said.

Mum gave Jack a big hug. "We'll be back tomorrow morning, I promise," she smiled. Then, she and Dad got into the car.

As they drove away, Jack waved until he couldn't see the car any-more. His eyes filled with tears. "Come on, Jack," said Gran, giving him a big cuddle. "We're going to have

such a good time. Guess where Grandad's taking us this afternoon?" Jack wiped his eyes and shook his head.

"Um... I don't know," he sniffed. Grandad gave him a tissue. Just then, Holly came bounding over. "Hello, Holly," said Jack, looking more cheerful. He rubbed her big, floppy ears. Jack loved Holly and, just for tonight, he could pretend she was his dog.

"Grandad," asked Jack, "where are we going this afternoon?"

"It's a surprise," said Grandad. "But we'll need the car. Why don't we give it a good clean?" So, Grandad gave Jack a big, yellow sponge and a bucket of soapy water. Soon, bubbles filled the air. They even went on Holly's nose!

Just then, Gran called to Jack from the kitchen. "I'm going to make a lovely picnic to take with us," said Gran. "Would you like to help me, Jack?" Jack nodded. At home, he liked to help his mum, too. "Grandad likes sausage rolls and I like cheese and tomato sandwiches," said Gran. "What's your favourite food?"

"Chocolate spread sandwiches!" said Jack, licking his lips. "Can we take something for Holly, too?"

"Of course," said Gran, smiling. "She can have one of her crunchy biscuits."

When the car was clean and the picnic was ready, Jack and Grandad packed everything for their trip into the boot.

Then, Gran strapped Jack into his car seat and they all set off.

"Here we are," said Grandad. "The park."

"Great!" said Jack. He couldn't wait to get out and explore. They soon found the perfect place for their picnic. Jack hungrily ate his chocolate sandwiches.

Afterwards, Grandad took Jack and Holly for a walk in the woods, while Gran had a little nap. On the way, Jack saw a playground. "Can we go there, Grandad?" he asked.

"Of course, we can," said Grandad. First, Grandad pushed Jack on the swings and then watched him zoom down the slide.

"Wheee!" cried Jack. "This is great fun!" Soon, he was laughing and playing with all the other children, while Grandad watched, just like Jack's mum and dad would do.

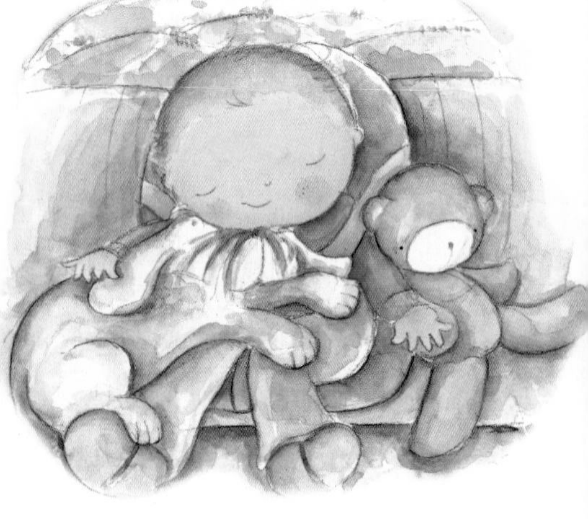

When it was time to go home, Gran packed up the picnic things and Grandad put them back in the car. Jack was very tired and soon fell asleep. What a fun day they'd had.

That evening, Gran made Jack a special dinner – sausages and mash, followed by apple pie and ice cream.

Afterwards, they watched Jack's favourite television programmes, until it was time for bed. As Jack settled himself in bed, with his teddy bear beside him, Grandad asked him

what story he would like. "Mum usually reads me this one," said Jack, picking up a book and handing it to Grandad.

"Once upon a time… " began Grandad. Jack knew the story off by heart. It was nice to hear it again, and soon he was drifting off to sleep. It was just like being at home.

When Jack woke up, he couldn't understand why his room felt so strange. Then, he remembered. He was staying with Gran and Grandad!

"Breakfast, Jack," said Gran, as she came in to help him dress. "Did you sleep well?"

"Yes, thank you, Gran," he said.

For breakfast, Gran cooked Jack a boiled egg, with toasted bread soldiers, milk and fresh orange juice. Delicious!

Afterwards, Jack helped Gran to pack his bag, ready for when Mum and Dad came to collect him. Jack was really excited when he saw his mum and dad arrive. He ran out to meet them and gave them both a giant hug. "Jack!" cried Mum. "Have you had a good time?"

"Yes," laughed Jack. "We went to the park and had a picnic and I played on a slide and had chocolate sandwiches and we took Holly for a walk… and Grandad read me my favourite story. Can I stay again?" Everyone laughed and Holly barked.

"Of course, you can!" said Mum and Dad.

There Were Two Birds Sat on a Stone

There were two birds sat on a stone,
Fa, la, la, la, lal, de;
One flew away, then there was one,
Fa, la, la, la, lal, de;
The other flew after, and then there was none,
Fa, la, la, la, lal, de;
And so the poor stone was left all alone,
Fa, la, la, la, lal, de!

I am a Pretty Little Dutch Girl

I am a pretty little Dutch girl,
As pretty as I can be.
And all the boys in the
neighborhood
Are crazy over me!

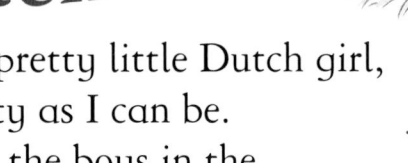

Five Little Ducks

Five little ducks went swimming one day,
Over the hills and far away,
Mother Duck said, "Quack, quack, quack, quack,"
But only four little ducks came back.
One little duck went swimming one day,
Over the hills and far away,
Mother Duck said, "Quack, quack, quack, quack,"
And all the five little ducks came back.

There Was an Old Crow

There was an old crow
Sat upon a clod:
There's an end of my song,
That's odd!

The Wise Old Owl

There was an old owl who lived in an oak;
The more he heard, the less he spoke.
The less he spoke, the more he heard.
Why aren't we like that wise old bird!

The Ostrich

Here is the ostrich straight and tall,
Nodding his head above us all.
Here is the hedgehog prickly and small,
Rolling himself into a ball.
Here is the spider scuttling around,
Treading so lightly on the ground.
Here are the birds that fly so high,
Spreading their wings across the sky.
Here are the children fast asleep,
And in the night the owls do peep,
"Tuit tuwhoo, tuit tuwhoo!"

Billy Booster

Billy Billy Booster,
Had a little rooster,
The rooster died
And Billy cried.
Poor Billy Booster.

Birds of a Feather

Birds of a feather flock together
And so will pigs and swine;
Rats and mice shall have their choice,
And so shall I have mine.

Chalk and Cheese

Chalk and Cheese were as different as two kittens can be. Chalk was a fluffy white kitten, who liked dishes of cream and lazing in the sun. Cheese was a rough, tough black kitten, who liked chewing on fish tails and climbing trees. Their mother puzzled over her odd little pair of kittens, but she loved them both the same.

One day, Cheese climbed high up on the barn and got stuck. "Help!" he cried to his sister.

"I don't like climbing!" she said, opening one eye.

"If only you were more like me!" said Cheese, "you'd be able to help!"

"If only you were more like me," said Chalk, "you wouldn't have got stuck in the first place!" And with that she went back to sleep. Just then, the farm dog came by. Chalk sprang up as he gave a loud bark and began to chase her.

"Help!" she cried to Cheese, up on the barn.

“I’m stuck, remember?” he cried. “You shouldn’t lie where dogs can chase you.”

Then Mummy appeared. She swiped the dog away with her claws, then climbed up and rescued Cheese.

“If only you were more like me,” she said, “you’d keep out of danger and look after each other.” And from then on, that’s just what they did.

The Toys that Ran Away

"Put your toys away, Lucy," said Lucy's mother, "it's time for bed." Lucy gave a great big sigh. "Do I really have to?" she asked, knowing full well what the answer was going to be.

"Of course you do," said her mother. "You shouldn't have to be told to put your toys away. You really don't look after them properly."

It was true. Lucy never had been very good at looking after her toys. Once she left her beautiful new doll outside in her pram and she had become ruined after it rained. Then she had carelessly dropped her tea set on the floor and some of the cups had broken. And she was forever just pushing all her toys back in the cupboard in a hurry, instead of putting them away carefully. Worse still, when she was in a temper, she would throw her toys, and sometimes she would even kick them.

Tonight Lucy was in another of her "can't be bothered" moods. She grabbed some dolls and a teddy and threw them into the cupboard. Without even looking behind her, Lucy picked up some puzzles and a skipping rope, and tossed them into the cupboard, too. They landed with a crash on top of the other toys. Then Lucy closed the cupboard door, squashing the toys even more, and went to have her bath.

Inside the toy cupboard Teddy said, "I'm not going to stay here a moment longer. I'm leaving for good."

"So am I!" said Katie, the ragdoll.

"I want to be somewhere where I'm not thrown around," said one of the puzzles.

One after another the toys decided they would all go back to Toyland and wait to be given to some children who would love them more.

The next morning, Lucy decided to play with some toys but, when she opened the toy cupboard, she couldn't believe her eyes!

All the toys had vanished. The shelves were completely empty. All day, Lucy searched high and low for her missing toys, but they were nowhere to be found. She went to bed in tears, and wondered if she would ever be able to play with her toys again.

That night, Lucy was suddenly woken by a noise in her bedroom. Was she seeing things or was that a little fairy at the bottom of her bed? "Who are you?" asked Lucy.

"I am the special messenger from Toyland," replied the fairy. "I have been sent to tell you that all your toys have run away back to Toyland, because you treated them badly."

"Oh, I do miss my toys so much," cried Lucy.

With that, the fairy floated over to Lucy, took her hand and lifted Lucy off her bed. They both flew out of Lucy's bedroom window, across fields and forests, until it became too misty to see anything at all. Then they floated down to the ground and the mist lifted, and Lucy found herself in the grounds of a huge fairy-tale castle.

"This is Toyland Castle," explained the fairy. Lucy found herself in a large, cosy room with a huge log fire. Sitting in the corner was a kindly looking little man wearing a carpenter's apron and holding a broken wooden doll. "Hello," he said, "you've come to ask your toys to return, haven't you?"

"Well... er... yes," said Lucy, not really knowing what to say.

"It's up to them to decide, of course," said the little man. "They only come back here if they are mistreated. If they are broken, I repair them, and then they go to other children who love them more."

"But I do love my toys," wept Lucy.

"Then come and tell them yourself," smiled the little man, and he led Lucy into another room. There, to her surprise, were all her toys. Not only that, but they were all shiny and new again. Nothing was broken or chipped or scratched.

Lucy ran up to her toys. "Please, toys, please come home again. I really do love you and miss you, and I promise I shall never mistreat you again," she cried, and then she hugged all the toys.

"Well, it's up to the toys now," said the little man. "You must go back home again with the fairy messenger and hope that they will give you another chance."

With that, the fairy messenger took Lucy's hand. Soon they were floating over her own garden and through her bedroom window. Lucy was so tired she fell asleep as soon as she got into bed.

In the morning she awoke, still rather sleepy, and rushed to the toy cupboard. There, neatly lined up on the shelves, were all her toys. Lucy was overjoyed. From that day on, she always treated her toys well and took great care of them.

Lucy never was quite sure whether the whole thing was a dream or not, but it certainly did the trick whatever it was. There was one thing that really puzzled her though. If it had just been a dream, why were all the toys so shiny and new again?

Willie Wastle

I, Willie Wastle,
Stand on my castle,
An' a' the dogs o' your toon,
Will no' drive Willie Wastle down.

Bow-wow

Bow-wow, says the dog,
Mew, mew, says the cat,
Grunt, grunt, goes the hog,
And squeak goes the rat.
Tu-whu, says the owl,
Caw, caw, says the crow,
Quack, quack, says the duck,
And what cuckoos say you know.

Parliament Soldiers

High diddle ding, did you hear the bells ring?
The parliament soldiers are gone to the king.
Some they did laugh, and some they did cry,
To see the parliament soldiers go by.

Ride Away

Ride away, ride away,
Johnny shall ride,
He shall have a pussy cat
Tied to one side;
He shall have a little dog
Tied to the other,
And Johnny shall ride
To see his grandmother.

Spin Dame

Spin, Dame, spin,
Your bread you must win;
Twist the thread and break it not,
Spin, Dame, spin.

The Robin and the Wren

The robin and the wren,
They fought upon the porridge pan;
But before the robin got a spoon,
The wren had eaten the porridge down.

On Oath

As I went to Bonner,
I met a pig
Without a wig,
Upon my word and honour.

Richard Dick

Richard Dick upon a stick,
Sampson on a sow,
We'll ride away to Colley fair
To buy a horse to plough.

Punctuality

Be always in time,
Too late is a crime.

Diddlety, Diddlety

Diddlety, diddlety, dumpty,
The cat ran up the plum tree;
Half a crown to fetch her down,
Diddlety, diddlety, dumpty.

Greedy Tom

Jimmy the Mowdy
Made a great crowdy;
Barney O'Neal
Found all the meal;
Old Jack Rutter
Sent two stone of butter;
The Laird of the Hot
Boiled it in his pot;
And Big Tom of the Hall
He supped it all.

Bless You

Bless you, bless you, burnie-bee,
Tell me when my wedding be;
If it be tomorrow day,
Take your wings and fly away.
Fly to the east, fly to the west,
Fly to him I love the best.

A Rat

There was a rat,
for want of stairs,
Went down a rope
to say his prayers.

Milking

Cushy cow, bonny, let down thy milk,
And I will give thee a gown of silk;
A gown of silk and a silver tee,
If thou wilt let down thy milk for me.

Missing Mouse

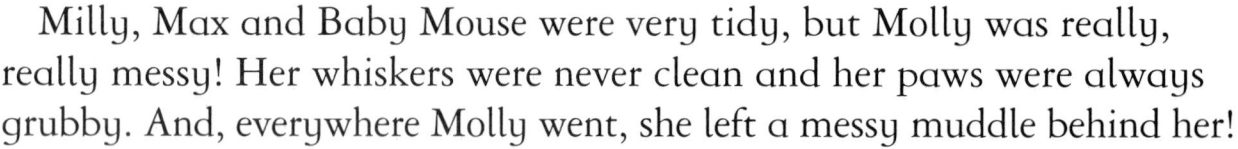

In some ways, Molly Mouse was just like her brother and sisters. She had soft, pink ears and a cute, little nose. But, in other ways, she was very different…

Milly, Max and Baby Mouse were very tidy, but Molly was really, really messy! Her whiskers were never clean and her paws were always grubby. And, everywhere Molly went, she left a messy muddle behind her!

After breakfast, Milly and Max never forgot to make their beds. Each and every morning, they threw out their old bedding and made new beds with fresh, clean hay. But Molly wasn't bothered! She just jumped out of bed and left everything in a tangled, untidy heap!

"How can you sleep in that mess?" asked Milly, her sister.

At lunch time, the rest of the family nibbled their food carefully and always cleaned up after themselves. They brushed up their crumbs and cleared away their bowls. But Molly wasn't bothered! She just munched away merrily, scattering food everywhere!

"Why do you make such a mess?" asked Daddy Mouse.

At playtime, Milly and Max would carefully scamper up cornstalks. But Molly couldn't be bothered! She rushed up the stalks so fast, that she snapped them in two and fell to the ground in a messy heap!

"Why are you so clumsy?" asked Max.

And when Max and Milly collected nuts and seeds for their tea, they always stacked them in neat, little piles. But Molly couldn't be bothered! Her heaps always toppled over.

"Why are you so untidy?" asked Milly.

Everyone was really fed up with Molly and her messy ways. "Why can't you eat properly?" said Daddy Mouse.

"Why can't you keep yourself clean and tidy?" said Mummy Mouse.

"Why can't you be quieter?" said Baby Mouse.

"Oh, Molly," groaned Milly and Max.

"I can't do anything right," Molly sniffed. "It's not fair." And, with her messy tail in her paw, she said "Goodnight" and went to bed.

But Molly had a plan. She was fed up with all the grumbling and she wasn't going to put up with it any longer! So, when Max and Milly came to bed, Molly was already fast asleep – at least, that's what they thought. Molly was really wide awake!

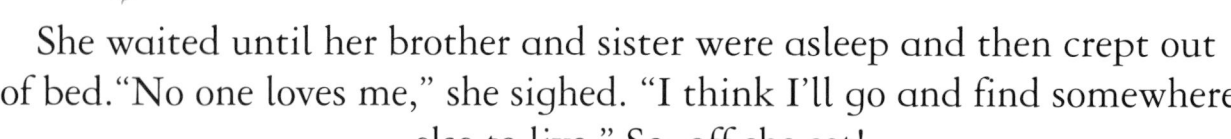

She waited until her brother and sister were asleep and then crept out of bed."No one loves me," she sighed. "I think I'll go and find somewhere else to live." So, off she set!

Molly had no idea where she was going. She scurried along the hedgerow and scampered through the cornstalks. And, as the sun began to rise, she slipped out of the field and happily skipped down the lane.

"I'll show them!" she said. "Why should I stay at home to be grumbled and moaned at? I'm going to find a home where people want me."

But, as the morning went on and Molly got further and further away from home, she became very tired. She sat down by a farmyard gate. "I'm really sleepy," she said and gave a big yawn! Then Molly noticed the barn door slightly open. Inside was a warm and comfy pile of hay – perfect for a little nap! She snuggled up in the hay and fell fast, fast asleep.

Back at home, when Mummy Mouse came to wake up her little ones, Molly's bed was empty. "Where's Molly?" she asked Milly and Max.

The two little mice rubbed their eyes and looked around. "We don't know," they said. "She was here last night, fast asleep."

"Daddy! Daddy! Come quick!" called Mummy Mouse. "Our Molly's missing!" So, they searched the house, but Molly was not

there. They went outside and looked through the cornfield, combed the hedgerows, searched under and over toadstools, in fact, they didn't leave a leaf unturned! They even went down the lane.

Suddenly, Milly started jumping up and down. "Look!" she squealed, pointing at the muddy path that led into the farmyard.

There, right in front of Milly, was a set of tiny mouse footprints.

Milly and Max followed the footprints across the farmyard and into the barn. And there, fast asleep in a messy pile of hay, was Molly.

"We've found her!" they shouted.

Molly slowly opened her eyes. There were bits of straw sticking to her fur, her whiskers were crumpled and her paws were muddy. "Oh, Molly!" yelled Milly and Max. "We've missed you so much."

"How can you have missed *me*?" said Molly. "I'm always such a mess!"

"You might be messy," said her mummy, "but we love you just the same!" Everyone cheered and Molly smiled – they really did love her!

And with that, they set off home.

Don't be Shy, Kitty

Kitty is playing with a yo-yo. "Watch me, Mum," she says. "I can make it go up and down." Suddenly, from the farmyard, Kitty hears laughing. "What is it, Mum?" she asks Cat.

"There's a big game going on," says Cat. "It looks fun, doesn't it, Kitty?"

Just then, Parsnip the pig spots Kitty. "Hello, Kitty! Come and join in!" he says. But Kitty hides behind Cat instead.

"What's the matter, Kitty?" asks Cat gently.

"The game is so loud. It makes me feel shy," Kitty says sadly.

"There's no need to be shy," says Cat. "All your friends are here."

But Kitty still feels shy. "I think I'll just watch for a bit," she says. The animals are having a wonderful time.

Then, Dennis the donkey gives the ball a big kick. "Whoops!" says Dennis. "Did anyone see where the ball went?" Quick as a flash, Kitty leaps up and races up the tree.

"I can see the ball, Mum!" she shouts. "Here it is!" Kitty laughs, throwing it down from the tree. "You're a hero, Kitty!" the animals shout. The game starts again and now Kitty is right in the middle of things.

"Great kick, Kitty," shouts Parsnip.

"You were right, Mum," she says. "I didn't need to feel shy at all."

Kitty and Cat Help Out

Kitty and Cat are going for a walk around the farm. "Look at the bees, Kitty," says Cat. "They're very busy." Suddenly Cat hears another noise. "Someone's crying," she says. "What's the matter, Little Rabbit?" asks Cat. "Why are you crying?"

"I've lost my teddy bear," sniffs Little Rabbit. "It's my favourite toy."

"Don't worry," says Kitty. "We'll help you look for it. Perhaps it's behind the haystack. I'm going to look inside the tractor," says Kitty.

"Well, I can't see your teddy," calls Kitty. "But here's my ball of wool!"

Cat points to the gate. "Perhaps you left your teddy in the field, Little Rabbit," she says. Little Rabbit begins to cry again.

"I'll never find my teddy," he wails.

"Don't give up," says Kitty kindly. "I'm sure we'll find it soon."

"Have you looked for your teddy at home, Little Rabbit?" asks Cat. "It could be there, you know. We've looked everywhere else."

So they walk slowly to Little Rabbit's home, carefully looking for teddy on the way. But, when they arrive, they find teddy! He is tucked right down inside Little Rabbit's bed.

Little Rabbit gives Kitty a big hug. "Thank you, Kitty and Cat," he says. "I'd never have found my teddy without you!"

Birthday Bunnies

"It's my first birthday tomorrow!" announced Snowy, a little white rabbit, very proudly. "Isn't that exciting?"

"Yes, very exciting!" said Whiskers, her brother. "Because it's my birthday too!"

"And mine!" said Patch.

"And mine!" said Nibble.

"And mine!" said Twitch.

"Do you think mummy and daddy have got a surprise for us?" asked Snowy.

"I hope so!" said Whiskers, giggling.

Mrs Rabbit was listening outside the door, as her children were getting ready for bed. She heard the little bunnies chattering excitedly about their birthdays the next day.

Whatever could she do to make it a special day for them? She sat and thought very hard, and later that evening, when Mr Rabbit came home, she said: "It is the children's first birthday tomorrow, and I'm planning a surprise for them. I want to make them a carrot cake, but I will need some carrots. Could you go and dig up some nice fresh ones from your vegetable garden?"

"Certainly, dear," said Mr Rabbit, and off he went back outside.

Mr Rabbit was proud of the carrots he grew. They were very fine carrots – crunchy and delicious. Every year he entered them in the Country Show, and they nearly always won first prize. So you can imagine his dismay when he arrived at his vegetable patch to find that every single carrot had been dug up and stolen!

He marched back to the burrow. "Someone has stolen my carrots!" he told his wife, crossly. "And I am going to find out just who it is!"

And, although it was getting late, he went back outside, and set off to find the naughty person.

First of all he stopped at Hungry Hare's house, and knocked loudly.

"Someone has stolen all my carrots!" Mr Rabbit said. "Do you know who?"

"Oh, yes," said Hungry Hare. "But it wasn't me." And, although Mr Rabbit pressed him, Hungry Hare would say no more.

Next Mr Rabbit went to Sly Fox's house.

"Someone has stolen my carrots!" he said. "Do you know who?"

"Oh, yes," said Sly Fox. "But it wasn't me." And, although Mr Rabbit begged and pleaded with him, Sly Fox would say no more.

So Mr Rabbit marched to Bill Badger's house, and asked if he knew who had taken the carrots.

"Why, yes, in fact I do," said Bill Badger. "But it wasn't me."

And just like the others, he would say no more. It was the same wherever Mr Rabbit went, and, although he got very cross, and stamped his foot, no one would tell him who had stolen his carrots!

"You'll find out soon enough," said Red Squirrel.

So Mr Rabbit went home feeling very puzzled.

"It seems that everyone knows who it was, but no one will tell me!" said Mr Rabbit to his wife.

"Not everyone, dear," she said. "I don't know who it was either. All I know is that it's our children's first birthday tomorrow, and we have no surprise for them." And, feeling very miserable and confused, they went to bed, determined to get to the bottom of the mystery in the morning.

Next day the little bunnies came running into the kitchen, where their parents were having breakfast.

"Happy birthday, everyone!" called Snowy.

"Happy birthday!" cried the other little bunnies.

"Now, it's not much, but I wanted to give each of you a surprise!" Snowy went on. "By the way, I hope you don't mind, Dad." And with that Snowy pulled out a box of juicy carrots, each tied with a bow, and handed one to each of her brothers and sisters.

"Snap!" cried Whiskers, "I had just the same idea!" and he pulled out another box of carrots.

"Me too!" said Patch, and "Me too!" said Nibble. Soon there was a great pile of juicy carrots heaped on the kitchen table.

"So that's what happened to my carrots!" cried Mr Rabbit, in amazement. "I thought they had been stolen! And when he told the little bunnies the story they laughed till their sides ached. Then Mrs Rabbit put on her apron and shooed them outside.

"Just leave the carrots with me," she said. "I have a birthday surprise of my own in store!"

And so the mystery was solved. It turned out that Hungry Hare had seen the little bunnies creep out one by one, and each dig up a few carrots when they thought no one was looking. He knew it was their birthdays and he guessed what they were doing. He had told the other forest folk, and everyone thought it was a great joke.

Mr Rabbit felt very ashamed that he had been so cross with everyone, when they were really just keeping the secret. And so he invited them for a special birthday tea that afternoon, which the little bunnies thought was a great surprise.

And of course the highlight of the day was when Mrs Rabbit appeared from the kitchen carrying, what else, but an enormous carrot cake!

One Snowy Day

One snowy day, Old Bear poked his nose out of his den, and saw the deep snow that had fallen while he slept. "I'll take a stroll in the woods," he said. Off he went, his great paws padding along, as big white snowflakes tickled his nose. How he loved the snow! He walked far into the woods, deep in thought, and quite forgot to look where he was going.

After a while, Old Bear stopped and looked around. To his dismay, he realised he was quite lost. Then he spied the trail of pawprints behind him. "Ho, ho!" he chuckled. "I'm not lost at all! I can follow my pawprints home!" And, thinking what a clever old bear he was, he carried on walking, until at last he began to feel tired. "I'll just take a rest," he said to himself. He closed his eyes, and soon fell fast asleep. Meanwhile, the snow kept on falling...

By the time Old Bear woke up his trail of pawprints had disappeared! "Now I'll never find my way home!" he groaned. Then, he noticed an old tree stump nearby.

"That looks familiar. And so does that fallen log over there. If I'm not mistaken, I've walked in a big circle, and ended up at home!" he chuckled, turning towards his den. "What a clever old bear I am, after all!"

See a Pin and Pick It Up

See a pin and pick it up,
All the day you'll have good luck;
See a pin and let it lay,
Bad luck you'll have all the day!

Miss Mary Mack

Miss Mary Mack, Mack, Mack,
All dressed in black, black, black,
With silver buttons, buttons, buttons,
All down her back, back, back.
She went upstairs to make her bed,
She made a mistake and bumped her head;
She went downstairs to wash the dishes,
She made a mistake and washed her wishes;
She went outside to hang her clothes,
She made a mistake and hung her nose.

Ring-a-Ring O'Roses

Ring-a-ring o'roses,
A pocket full of posies,
A-tishoo! A-tishoo!
We all fall down!

Mr Nobody

Mr Nobody is a nice young man,
He comes to the door with his hat in his hand.
Down she comes, all dressed in silk,
A rose in her bosom, as white as milk.
She takes off her gloves, she shows me her ring,
Tomorrow, tomorrow, the wedding begins.

Little Sally Waters

Little Sally Waters,
  Sitting in the sun,
Crying and weeping,
  For a young man.
Rise, Sally, rise,
  Dry your weeping eyes,
Fly to the east,
  Fly to the west,
Fly to the one you love the best.

Oliver Twist

Oliver Twist
  You can't do this,
So what's the use
  Of trying?
Touch your toe,
  Touch your knee,
Clap your hands,
  Away we go.

Three Children

Three children sliding on the ice
  Upon a summer's day,
As it fell out, they all fell in,
  The rest they ran away.

Now had these children been at home,
  Or sliding on dry ground,
Ten thousand pounds to one penny
  They had not all been drowned.

You parents all that children have,
  And you that have got none,
If you would have them safe abroad,
  Pray keep them safe at home.

Georgie, Porgie

Georgie, Porgie, pudding and pie,
  Kissed the girls and made them cry;
When the boys came out to play
  Georgie Porgie ran away.

A Perfect Puppy

Molly had wanted a puppy for a long time, so when Mummy and Daddy said yes, she couldn't wait to get to the pet shop.

At the pet shop, Polly inspected the puppies one by one. After all, her puppy had to be perfect.

"That one's too big," said Polly, pointing to a Great Dane. "And that one's too small." She pointed to a tiny Chihuahua.

"This one's nice," said the shopkeeper, patting a Poodle.

"Too curly," Polly declared.

Another puppy was too noisy. And one was too quiet. Before long, there weren't many puppies left. Polly was about to give up, when something soft rubbed against her leg.

"Ah, perfect," she cried, picking up a small bundle of black and white fur.

"Err, what kind of puppy is it?" asked Daddy.

"It's my puppy," sighed Polly.

"It's a mongrel," said the shopkeeper. "I think it's part Spaniel and part Collie. We're not really sure."

"I don't care what he is," smiled Polly. "He's just perfect. I'm going to call him Danny."

Danny whined as he left the pet shop. And he whined all the way home. He stopped whining when he saw the cat and barked instead.

"He'll be okay once he gets used to us," said Mummy. Polly hoped she was right.

In the afternoon, they took Danny for a walk. Polly took some bread to feed the ducks, but as soon as Danny saw the ducks he started to bark. Then he began to chase them and didn't stop until they had all flown away.

Daddy bought Polly an ice cream to cheer her up.

"He's just a puppy. He's got a lot to learn," explained Daddy as Danny jumped up and stole her ice cream. Polly was beginning to wonder if she'd chosen the right puppy.

When they got home, Polly decided to introduce Danny to all her dolls and cuddly toys, but Danny pounced on her favourite teddy.

"He's got Mr Fluffy," cried Polly, as Danny raced from the room into the garden. When he came back, Mr Fluffy was gone.

Polly was furious. She waved an angry finger at Danny. "You're not a perfect puppy," she said. "I don't think you'll ever learn."

Poor Danny, he hung his head and slunk away under the table and wouldn't come out all evening.

The next morning, Polly was woken up by something wet pressed against her cheek. It was Danny, and in his mouth was Mr Fluffy! Danny dropped Mr Fluffy on the floor for Polly to pick up.

"Good boy, Danny," laughed Polly, tickling his ears. "You are a perfect puppy, after all!"

The Red Daffodil

It was spring time and all the daffodils were pushing their heads up towards the warmth of the sun. Slowly, their golden petals unfolded to let their yellow trumpets dance in the breeze. One particular field of daffodils was a blaze of gold like all the others – but right in the middle was a single splash of red. For there in the middle was a red daffodil.

From the moment she opened her petals, the red daffodil knew she was different from the other flowers. They sneered at her and whispered to each other. "What a strange, poor creature!" said one.

"She must envy our beautiful golden colour," said another.

And indeed it was true. The red daffodil wished very much that she was like the others. Instead of being proud of her red petals, she was ashamed and hung her head low. "What's wrong with me?" she thought. "Why aren't there any other red daffodils in the field?"

Passers-by stopped to admire the field of beautiful daffodils. "What a wonderful sight!" they exclaimed. And the daffodils' heads swelled with pride and danced in the breeze all the more merrily.

Then someone spotted the red daffodil right in the middle

of the field. "Look at that extraordinary flower!" the man shouted. Everyone peered into the centre of the field.

"You're right," said someone else, "there's a red daffodil in the middle." Soon a crowd had gathered, all pointing at the red daffodil.

She could feel herself blushing even redder at the attention. "How I wish my petals would close up again," she said to herself in anguish. But, try as she might, her fine red trumpet stood out for all to see.

Now, in the crowd of people gathered at the edge of the field was a little girl. People were pushing and shoving and she couldn't see anything at all. At last, her father lifted her high upon his shoulders so that she could see into the field. "Oh!" exclaimed the little girl in a very big voice. "So that's the red daffodil. I think it's really beautiful. What a lucky daffodil to be so different."

And, do you know, other people heard what the little girl said and they began to whisper to each other, "Well, I must say, I actually thought myself it was rather pretty, you know." Before long, people were praising the daffodil's beauty and saying it must be a very special flower. The red daffodil heard what the crowd was saying. Now she was blushing with pride and held her head as high as all the other daffodils in the field.

The other daffodils were furious. "What a foolish crowd," said one indignantly. "We are the beautiful ones!" They turned their heads away from the red daffodil and ignored her. She began to feel unhappy again.

By now word had spread far and wide about the amazing red daffodil and people came from all over the land to see her.

Soon, the king's daughter got to hear about the red daffodil. "I must see this for myself," said the princess. She set off with her servants, and eventually they came to the field where the red daffodil grew. When the princess saw her, she clapped her hands and jumped up and down with excitement.

"The red daffodil is more beautiful than I ever imagined," she cried. Then she had an idea. "Please bring my pet dove," she said to her servant. The man looked rather puzzled, but soon he returned with the bird. "As you know," said the princess to the servant, "I am to be married tomorrow and I would dearly love to have that red daffodil in my wedding bouquet."

The princess sent the dove into the middle of the field and it gently picked up the daffodil in its beak and brought her back to where the princess stood. The princess carried the daffodil back to the palace. She put the daffodil in a vase of water and there she stayed until the next day.

In the morning, the princess's servant took the red daffodil to the church. The daffodil could hear the bells and see all the guests assembling for the wedding ceremony. Then she saw the princess arrive in a gorgeous coach pulled by four white horses.

How lovely the princess looked in her beautiful gown and her head crowned with deep red roses.

As the servant reached the church door, the princess's lady-in-waiting stepped forward holding a huge bouquet of flowers. Just as the flowers were handed to the princess the servant placed the red daffodil among the other flowers in the bouquet. For a while, the red daffodil was overcome by the powerful scents of the other flowers in the bouquet, but when at last she looked around her she realised, with astonishment, that all of them were red. There were red daisies, red lilies, red carnations and red foxgloves. "Welcome," said one of the daisies, "you're one of us." And, for the first time in her life, the red daffodil felt really at home.

After the wedding, the princess scattered the flowers from her bouquet among the flowers in her garden. Every spring, when she opened her petals, the red daffodil found she was surrounded by lots of other red flowers, and she lived happily in the garden for many, many years.

As I was Going to St Ives

As I was going to St Ives,
I met a man with seven wives.
Each wife had seven sacks,
Each sack had seven cats,
Each cat had seven kits.
Kits, cats, sacks, and wives,
How many were going to St Ives?

The Little Turtle Dove

High in the pine tree,
The little turtle dove
Made a little nursery
To please her little love.

"Coo," said the turtle dove,
"Coo," said she;
In the long, shady branches
Of the dark pine tree.

Dickery Dickery Dare

Dickery, dickery dare,
The pig flew up in the air.
The man in brown
Soon brought him down!
Dickery, dickery, dare.

Hey, my Kitten

Hey, my kitten, my kitten,
And hey my kitten, my deary,
Such a sweet pet as this
There is not far not neary.
Here we go up, up, up,
Here we go down, down, downy;
Here we go backwards and fowards,
And here we go round, round, roundy.

Clap Hands

Clap hands, Daddy's coming
Up the waggon way,
His pockets full of money
And his hands full of clay.

Pussycat Ate the Dumplings

Pussycat ate the dumplings,
Pussycat ate the dumplings,
Mamma stood by,
And cried, "Oh fie!
Why did you eat the dumplings?"

There Was...

There was a girl
  in our town,
Silk an' satin was
  her gown,
Silk an' satin, gold an'
  velvet.
Guess her name, three
  times I've telled it.

The Mischievous Raven

A farmer went trotting upon his grey mare,
  Bumpety, bumpety, bump!
With his daughter behind him so rosy and fair,
  Lumpety, lumpety, lump!

A raven cried, "Croak!" and they all tumbled down,
  Bumpety, bumpety, bump!
The mare broke her knees and the farmer his crown,
  Lumpety, lumpety, lump!

The mischievous raven flew laughing away,
  Bumpety, bumpety, bump!
And vowed he would serve them the same next day,
  Lumpety, lumpety, lump!

Cats and Dogs

Hodley, poddley, puddle and fogs,
  Cats are to marry the poodle dogs;
Cats in blue jackets and dogs in red hats,
  What will become of the mice and the rats?

Mrs White

Mrs White had a fright
  In the middle of the night.
She saw a ghost, eating toast,
  Halfway up a lamp post.

I Bought an Old Man

Hey diddle diddle,
  And hey diddle dan!
And with a little money,
  I bought an old man.
His legs were all crooked
  And wrong ways set on,
So what do you think
  Of my little old man?

The New Arrival

All day long, Old MacDonald's cows grazed in the green meadow and chatted. Nothing happened on the farm that Poppy, Annabel, Emily and Heather didn't know about.

One morning Old MacDonald visited the horses in the field next door.

"Here's an apple for you and George, Tilly," he said. "I wanted you to be the first to hear – we're expecting a new baby on the farm. You can imagine Mrs MacDonald is very excited about it because..."

But, before he could finish, there was the sound of thundering hooves from the field next to them as a cow, bursting with news, dashed off to find her friends.

"Are you sure?" mooed Annabel, as Poppy panted out what she had heard.

"Positive," gasped Poppy.

"Old MacDonald and Mrs MacDonald, aren't they, well, a bit old to be having a baby?" asked Emily.

"Yes, I thought that," said Poppy. "But I heard it from Old MacDonald himself."

"But if Mrs MacDonald has a baby to look after," said Heather, "who will give me my beauty treatments before the County Show? I simply must win a rosette again this year."

There was silence. Then Annabel said what the animals had all been thinking.

"Ladies! This news is far too important to keep to ourselves! We must tell the others immediately!" And off the four cows dashed.

So, leaning over the gate, Emily mumbled to Jenny the hen. "What?" she squawked. "If Mrs MacDonald has a baby to look after, who is going to collect my eggs? I will tell Henry!"

Henry the cockerel crowed when he heard the news. "Well, cock-a-doodle-doo!" he cried. "If Mrs MacDonald has a baby to look after, who will throw me my corn to peck?" So Henry hurried off to talk to Debbie the duck.

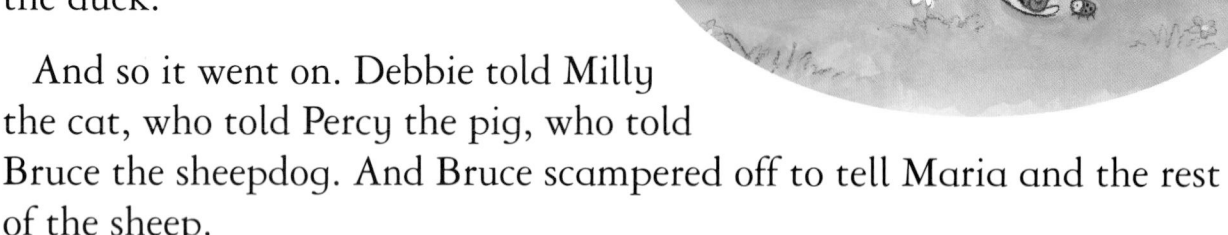

And so it went on. Debbie told Milly the cat, who told Percy the pig, who told Bruce the sheepdog. And Bruce scampered off to tell Maria and the rest of the sheep.

By lunch time, every animal on the farm was worried. Things simply wouldn't be the same if Mrs MacDonald was looking after a baby. In fact, the animals were all so busy and bothered, they didn't notice a truck pulling into the farmyard.

"The new arrival!" called Old MacDonald.

"What, already?" squawked Jenny. "But I thought... oh!"

Out of the truck trotted a beautiful little foal, a new friend for Tilly and Old George.

"It's so lovely to have another baby animal on the farm!" cried Mrs MacDonald.

She was too excited to hear the sigh of relief from all the animals, or the mooing from the meadow, as the other cows had a few well-chosen words with Poppy!

Baby Bear finds a Friend

Baby Bear stretched as he woke from his long winter sleep. He took a deep breath of fresh spring air and smiled at the warm sun on his back. He was bursting with energy. Now he needed someone to play with.

"Come and play with me," he called to Owl.

"I only play at night!" said Owl, sleepily.

Nearby some little bunnies were playing. Baby Bear bounded over to join the fun, but Mrs Rabbit shooed him off. "Your paws will hurt my babies," she said. "You can't play with them."

Baby Bear wandered down to the river, where some beavers were hard at work building a dam. "Come and play with me," called Baby Bear.

But the beavers were too busy. So he sat watching Kingfisher diving into the water.

"That looks like fun!" he said, jumping in with a splash!

"Go away!" said Kingfisher. "You will disturb the fish!"

By now Baby Bear was feeling fed up and tired. He lay down in a hollow and closed his eyes. Then, just as he was drifting to sleep, a voice said, "Will you come and play with me?" He opened his eyes to see another bear cub. Baby Bear smiled. "I'm too tired to play now," he said. "But I'll play with you tomorrow!" And from then on, he was never lonely again.

Gee Up, Neddy

Gee up, Neddy,
  Don't you stop,
Just let your feet go
  Clippety clop.
Clippety clopping,
  Round and round.
Giddy up,
  We're homeward bound.

Hark! Hark!

Hark, hark,
  The dogs do bark,
Beggars are coming to town:
  Some in rags,
Some in tags,
  And some in velvet gowns.

Three Little Kittens

Three little kittens they lost their mittens,
  And they began to cry,
Oh, mother dear, we sadly fear
  That we have lost our mittens.

What! lost your mittens, you naughty kittens!
  Then you shall have no pie.
Mee-ow, mee-ow, mee-ow.
  No, you shall have no pie.

The three little kittens they found their mittens,
  And they began to cry,
Oh, mother dear, see here, see here,
  For we have found our mittens.

Put on your mittens, you silly kittens,
  And you shall have some pie.
Purr-r, purr-r, purr-r,
  Oh, let us have some pie.

Slowly, Slowly

Slowly, slowly, very slowly
  Creeps the garden snail.

Slowly, slowly, very slowly
  Up the garden rail.

Quickly, quickly, very quickly
  Runs the little mouse.

Quickly, quickly, very quickly
Round about the house.

A Cat Came Fiddling

A cat came fiddling out of a barn,
With a pair of bagpipes under her arm;
She could sing nothing but fiddle cum fee,
The mouse has married the humble-bee.
Pipe, cat – dance, mouse,
We'll have a wedding at our good house.

There Was a Little Turtle

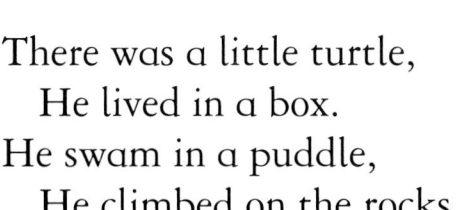

There was a little turtle,
He lived in a box.
He swam in a puddle,
He climbed on the rocks.

He snapped at a mosquito,
He snapped at a flea.
He snapped at a minnow,
He snapped at me.

He caught the mosquito,
He caught the flea.
He caught the minnow,
But... he didn't catch me!

The Little Bird

This little bird flaps its wings,
Flaps its wings,
flaps its wings,
This little bird flaps its wings,
And flies away
in the morning!

As Small as a Mouse

As small as a mouse,
As wide as a bridge,
As tall as a house,
As straight as a pin.

The Magic Tree

Tommy rubbed his eyes, blinked hard, and looked out of his bedroom window again. But it was still there – an enormous oak tree that definitely hadn't been there yesterday! If it had been there, he'd have known all about it for sure. For a start he would have climbed up it, for Tommy loved nothing better than climbing trees.

No, this tree was definitely not there yesterday! Tommy sat staring at the tree in wonder and disbelief. The tree stood there, outside his bedroom window, with its huge, spreading branches almost asking to be climbed. Tommy wondered how on earth it had suddenly got there, but he decided that, before he wondered about that too much, he had better go and climb it first. After all, there was always time later to wonder about things but never enough time to do things, he thought.

As soon as he was dressed, he ran outside to take a closer look at the new tree. It seemed just like any other big oak tree. It had lots of wide, inviting branches and lots of green, rounded leaves. And it had deep, furrowed bark just like any other oak tree.

Tommy couldn't resist any longer – he began to climb. In no time at all, he was in a green, leafy canopy. He couldn't see the ground any more, but something was not quite right. The branches beneath his feet seemed to be so big that he could stand up on them and walk in any direction. And the branches around him were just like trees themselves. In fact, he suddenly realised that he wasn't climbing a tree any longer, but standing in a whole forest full of trees.

Tommy thought he had better get down. But where was down? All he could see were tall, swaying trees with twisty paths leading off even deeper into the forest. Tommy didn't know how he had done it, but he had got himself lost in a forest, and he hadn't even had breakfast yet!

Worse still, it seemed to be getting dark. "Quick, over here!" a voice suddenly called out. Tommy was very startled, but he was even more startled when he saw that the voice belonged to a squirrel.

"You can speak!" blurted out Tommy.

"Of course I can speak!" snapped the squirrel. "Now listen. You are in great danger, and there's no time to lose if we are to save you from the clutches of the evil Wizard of the Woods."

The squirrel quickly explained that, long ago, a spell had been cast on the forest and it had become enchanted. Every now and again, the

Wizard of the Woods lured an unsuspecting person into his realm by making a tree appear. Once you climbed the tree, you entered the forest. Escape was almost impossible.

"But why does the Wizard of the Woods want to lure people into the forest?" asked Tommy, knowing that he wouldn't like the answer.

"To turn them into fertiliser to make the trees grow," said the squirrel.

Tommy didn't really know what fertiliser was, but it sounded nasty. He was pleased when the squirrel suddenly said, "There is just one way to get you out of here. But we must hurry. Soon it will be dark and the Wizard of the Woods will awake. Once he awakes, he will smell your blood and he will capture you."

Jumping up the nearest tree, the squirrel called, "Follow me."

Tommy immediately climbed after the squirrel. "Where are we going?" he panted as they climbed higher and higher.

"To the top of the tallest tree in the forest," the squirrel answered as they clambered from tree to tree, climbing ever higher. "It's the only way to escape. You'll see!" said the squirrel.

Eventually they stopped climbing. Below them and around them was nothing but more trees. Tommy looked up, and at last he could see the clear, twilight sky. He also noticed something rather strange. All the leaves at the top of the tallest tree were enormous.

"Quick, time is running out," said the squirrel. "Sit on this leaf and hold tight."

Tommy sat on one of the huge leaves. The squirrel whistled, and before Tommy could blink he had been joined by a hundred more squirrels. They each took hold of the branch to which the leaf was attached. With a great heave, they pulled and pulled until the branch was bent backwards. Suddenly they let go. With a mighty "TWANG", the branch, with Tommy and the leaf attached, sprang forward. As it did so Tommy and the leaf were launched into the air. High above the trees they soared until, ever so slowly, they began to float down to earth. Down, down, they went, until they landed with a bump.

Tommy opened his eyes to find himself on his bedroom floor. He ran over to the window and looked out. The magic tree was nowhere to be seen. It had gone as quickly as it had appeared – perhaps it had never been there at all. Perhaps it had just been a dream... What do you think?

Bear Finds a Friend

Sally found the teddy bear in the park. She might not have noticed it, but her ball rolled under a bush and she had crawled beneath it to get it back. It was a small, light brown bear, wearing pale blue dungarees and a red and white striped shirt. "Look, Mum," said Sally, "Someone's left their teddy here. What shall we do with it?"

"We'd better take it home with us," said Mum. "We'll put a notice up to say we found it." Sally made a notice and Mum helped her to spell the words, "Teddy bear found. Please ring this number." Sally wrote her telephone number. Then she brushed the leaves from the bear and sat it next to her own teddy. She put her teddy's arm round it. "Look after him," she told her teddy. "He must be feeling very frightened."

Sally and Mum took the notice to the park, and pinned it to a tree near the playground. "Now we'll have to wait and see," said Mum.

The telephone rang just before tea time. "Yes, you can come and get it straightaway," Mum said. She turned to Sally. "The little girl who lost the teddy bear is coming to fetch it." The doorbell rang and a small girl was standing on the step with her mother. She smiled at Sally, "Thank you for looking after my teddy," she said.

"He made friends with my teddy," said Sally. The girl picked up her bear and hugged him tight.

"Perhaps we could be friends, too," she said.

Bears Picnic

In a sunny clearing in the wood, Ellie, her brother Alex, and Ellie's teddy bear were playing hide and seek. "Sit quietly," said Ellie to her teddy, as she placed him carefully behind a tree. "Alex won't find you there." Then she ran off to hide.

"Time to pack up the picnic things," called Ellie's mother. "We need to hurry before it starts to rain." Ellie and Alex collected the plates and cups.

"Race you back to the car," yelled Alex, charging off through the trees.

"I can beat you!" cried Ellie, following. But no one thought of Teddy.

Teddy sat under the tree. A huge leaf drifted down, and landed in front of him. A squirrel hopped along the branch above, dropping the nut he was carrying, and it plopped down onto the leaf in front of the bear. High above, a bird flew past, carrying a blackberry. The blackberry slipped from its beak and fell down onto the leaf, too.

"We've forgotten Teddy!" screamed Ellie in the car. As she and Alex ran through the trees, they startled a mouse, who'd stopped to look at the strange creature sitting under the tree. The mouse opened his mouth to squeak and dropped a seed onto the leaf at the furry creature's feet.

"Look," said Ellie, peering round the tree. "Here he is. He stayed behind to eat his own picnic." She hugged her teddy bear tightly.

"We'll take your plate home with us," she smiled, picking up the leaf.

Beauty and the Beast

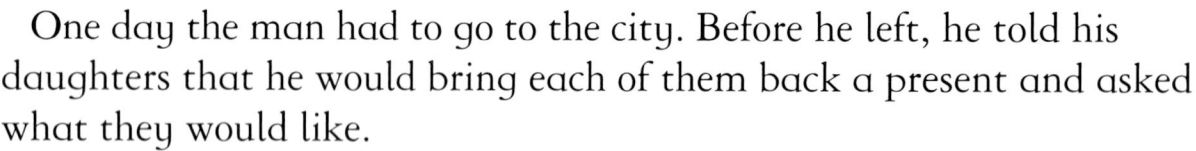

Once upon a time there was a man who lived in a cottage in the country with his three daughters. His youngest daughter was so pretty that everyone called her "Beauty", which made her two sisters very angry and jealous.

One day the man had to go to the city. Before he left, he told his daughters that he would bring each of them back a present and asked what they would like.

"Jewels!" the eldest daughter demanded. "Silk dresses!" said the second daughter. But all Beauty asked for was a single white rose.

On his return home, the father was caught in a snowstorm and lost his way. The blizzard was so thick and fierce and the forest so large and dark that he nearly gave up hope of ever finding his home. Then, through the mist, he glimpsed a grand palace.

He staggered to the great door – there seemed to be no one about. Inside, he found a table laid with a magnificent dinner. The man ate hungrily, then searched the house. Upstairs, he found a huge bed where he gratefully fell into an exhausted sleep. In the morning, when he awoke, breakfast was waiting beside the bed.

As he set off on his way home he noticed a wonderful rose garden. Remembering Beauty's request, he stopped to pick a white rose. Suddenly, with a mighty roar, a terrifying, snarling Beast appeared.

"I have welcomed you with every comfort," he growled, "and in return you steal my roses!"

Shaking with fear, the man begged for forgiveness. "I only wanted the rose as a present for my daughter!"

"I will spare you," said the Beast, "but only if your daughter comes to live here of her own free will. If not, you must return in three months."

Back home, the man tearfully told his daughters what had happened. To his surprise, Beauty agreed to go.

When she arrived at the palace, a glorious meal was waiting for her.

"The Beast must want to fatten me," she thought. But she sat and ate.

As soon as Beauty finished her meal, the Beast appeared. He was truly horrifying, and she was frightened.

"Your room is all ready," said the Beast, and he led her to a door that said "Beauty's Room" in gold letters.

The room was everything Beauty could have wished for. She saw a little piano, beautiful silk dresses and fresh, fragrant roses. On the dressing table was a mirror with these words on it:

If anything you long to see,
Speak your wish, and look in me.

"I wish I could see my father," said Beauty, and instantly saw her father in the mirror, sitting sadly beside the fire at home.

"Perhaps the Beast doesn't mean to kill me after all," Beauty thought. "I wonder what he does want?"

The next evening the Beast joined Beauty for supper. "Tell me," he said, "am I truly horrible to look at?"

Beauty could not lie. "You are," she said. "But I know you are very kind-hearted."

"Then," said the Beast, "will you marry me?"

Beauty was surprised. She knew he might be angry if she refused, but she couldn't say yes because she didn't love him. "No," she said, "I will not marry you."

The Beast sighed so heavily that the walls shook. "Good night, then," he said sadly. And he left her to finish her dinner alone.

Months passed, and the Beast gave Beauty everything she could want. She was very happy in the palace.

Every evening, the Beast asked the same question: "Will you marry me?" And Beauty always said no. But she was growing very fond of him.

One day, Beauty looked in the magic mirror and saw that her father was ill. She begged the Beast to let her go home, and sadly he agreed.

"Take this magic ring," he told her. "If you ever want to come back, put it by your bedside, and when you wake up, you will be here."

"I will come back," Beauty promised.

So Beauty went home to look after her father. He was soon well again, and she was ready to go back to the Beast. But her jealous sisters hated to think of Beauty going back to a palace while they lived in a small cottage. So they convinced her to stay a while longer.

One night, Beauty dreamt that the Beast was lying dead in his garden, and she woke up in tears. She knew then that she loved the Beast, and had to return to him.

Putting the magic ring by her bedside, Beauty lay down again and closed her eyes.

When she opened them again, Beauty was back in the Beast's garden – and, true to her dream, he was lying lifeless on the ground.

"Oh, Beast," she cried, taking him in her arms, "please don't die! I love you, and I want to marry you!"

All at once light and music filled the air, and the Beast vanished. In his place stood a handsome prince.

"Who are you?" cried Beauty.

"I was your Beast," said the prince. "An evil witch cast a spell on me and turned me into that poor animal. The spell could only be broken when a beautiful girl agreed to marry me."

A few days later they were married, and Beauty's family came to join in the joyous celebrations at the palace.

Beauty had never been so happy. She loved the prince with all her heart, and they lived in their rose palace happily ever after.

Ballerina Belle

Belle the ballerina is a beautiful ballet dancer. She loves to dance in her frilly tutu and satin ballet shoes. She has a best friend – Pearl, a fluffy white kitten with big blue eyes. Pearl enjoys watching Belle dance, spinning and twirling across the floor.

Today Belle is getting ready for a very special show. The little kitten sits on her friend's pink dressing table. purring with delight, as Belle carefully dusts a sprinkling of powder over her face.

Belle is so excited and nervous. Tonight, she will dance for the King and Queen.

Pearl purrs her approval as the little ballerina puts on a blue tutu that glistens with jewels. Then she ties the pretty ribbons on her shoes. Finally, Belle puts up her lovely long hair with silver hairpins. Pearl thinks she looks wonderful. Now Belle is all ready for the show and tiptoes to the stage...

The music starts and Belle begins to twirl gracefully across the floor. The King and Queen love to watch her dance – she is the most beautiful ballerina ever.

As the audience cheers, Pearl purrs with delight. Belle's the happiest ballerina in the world.

The Snake

A narrow fellow in the grass
  Occasionally rides;
You may have met him, – did you not?
  His notice sudden is.

The grass divides as with a comb,
  A spotted shaft is seen;
And then it closes at your feet
  And opens further on.

He likes a boggy acre,
  A floor too cool for corn.
Yet when a child, and barefoot,
  I more than once, at morn,

Have passed, I thought, a whip-lash
  Unbraiding in the sun, –
When, stooping to secure it,
  It wrinkled, and was gone.

EMILY DICKINSON

Calico Pie

Calico Pie,
  The little Birds fly
Down to the calico tree,
  Their wings were blue,
And they sang "Tilly-loo!"
  Till away they flew, –
And they never came back to me!
  They never came back!
They never came back!
  They never came back to me!

Calico Jam,
  The little Fish swam,
Over the syllabub sea,
  He took off his hat,
To the Sole and the Sprat,
  And the Willeby-wat, –
But he never came back to me!
  He never came back!
He never came back!
  He never came back to me!

Caterpillar

Brown and furry
  Caterpillar in a hurry,
Take your walk
  To the shady leaf, or stalk,
Or what not,
  Which may be the chosen spot.

No toad spy you,
  Hovering bird of prey pass by you;
Spin and die,
  To live again a butterfly.

The Cow

The friendly cow all red and white,
  I love with all my heart:
She gives me cream with all her might,
  To eat with apple-tart.

She wanders lowing here and there,
  And yet she cannot stray,
All in the pleasant open air,
  The pleasant light of day.

And blown by all the winds that pass
  And wet with all the showers,
She walks among the meadow grass
  And eats the meadow flowers.

To a Butterfly

I've watched you now a full half-hour,
  Self-poised upon that yellow flower;
And, little Butterfly! indeed
  I know not if you sleep or feed.
How motionless! – not frozen seas
  More motionless! And then
What joy awaits you, when the breeze
  Hath found you out among the trees,
And calls you forth again!

This plot of orchard-ground is ours;
  My trees they are, my Sister's flowers.
Here rest your wings when they are weary;
  Here lodge as in a sanctuary!
Come often to us, fear no wrong;
  Sit near us on the bough!
We'll talk of sunshine and of song,
  And summer days, when we were young;
Sweet childish days, that were as long
  As twenty days are now.

The Fairies

Up the airy mountain,
  Down the rushy glen,
We daren't go a-hunting
  For fear of little men;
Wee folk, good folk,
  Trooping all together;
Green jacket, red cap,
  And white owl's feather!

Down along the rocky shore
  Some make their home;
They live on crispy pancakes
  Of yellow tide-foam;
Some in the reeds
  Of the black mountain lake,
With frogs for their watch-dogs,
  All night awake.

Monty the Mongrel

Monty was a very curious puppy. He liked nothing better than exploring the garden.

"Don't go far," Mummy would say. But Monty wasn't worried about getting lost. He was a very good explorer.

One day, a big lorry pulled up outside the house where Monty and his family lived. Men began carrying things out of the house. One of them said something about moving, but Monty was just a puppy and didn't know what that meant.

One of the men left the gate open so, when no one was looking, Monty crept out and he had a wonderful time sniffing around other people's gardens. He found lots of yummy things to eat. And some really lovely things to roll in.

After a while, Monty began to feel tired. He was such a good explorer that he sniffed his way home with no trouble.

But when he got there, he couldn't believe his eyes. Everyone, including Mummy and all his brothers and sisters, had gone.

Monty was very surprised but he wasn't too worried. After all, he was a very good explorer. He began sniffing at once.

He soon found himself in the park where he met a group of dogs.

"Who are you?" asked one, and, "What are you?" asked another.

"Well, he's not a Poodle," sniffed the first dog, who Monty couldn't help thinking looked like a ball of cotton wool. "He's far too rough."

"He's definitely not a Dachshund," said another dog.

"He's certainly not an Old English Sheepdog," barked a third dog. "He's just not hairy enough."

"Hmm!" grunted a fourth dog, who had the flattest nose Monty had ever seen. He walked around Monty and stared at him from all sides. Then he stopped and shuddered. "Do you know what I think? I think he's a MONGREL."

"Well, if that's the case," sniffed the cotton wool dog, "he'd better hang out with Tinker."

"Take no notice of them," said Tinker. "They're just trying to help."

Monty gave Tinker a lick, and before long he was telling Tinker about his family.

"Let's walk around the park," said Tinker. "If we follow our noses, we might find your family."

In the park, Monty sniffed the air. He could smell a very familiar smell. Then, he heard a very familiar bark. Suddenly, a huge brown dog bounded out of one of the houses on the other side of the park.

"Run for your lives," yelped the cotton wool dog.

"Help! It's a giant," barked the flat-nosed dog.

"Mummy!" shouted Monty.

"Monty!" barked Mummy. "Thank goodness you're safe."

"So you're a Great Dane puppy," laughed Tinker. "Not a mongrel, after all."

The Good Old Days

On cold, wet and windy afternoons, when Old MacDonald lets his animals shelter in the warm barn, they like listening to stories. But, it does depend who's telling the story!

The pigs tell tales about food. The hens' stories usually concern the ducks, and the cows are terrible gossips – they repeat things they have half-heard over the hedge!

But Old George and Tilly, the oldest animals on the farm, always talk about how much better it was in days gone by. This bores the other animals. They have heard them many times before.

One very cold spring day the farm was full of newborn chicks.

Old MacDonald went to the henhouse and told Henrietta, "Take your babies into the barn. It will be much cosier there than in here."

"Baaa!" bleated Maria the sheep, who was standing near the barn door. "Did you hear that? Henrietta is bringing her chicks in. There'll be no peace now!"

Suddenly, there was mooing, neighing, snorting and quacking as the other animals all agreed. Those tiny chicks were the most troublesome little creatures on the farm. And the animals all stared in dismay as, one by one, the chicks filed in.

It was Percy the pig's turn to tell a story. "Once upon a time," he began, "there lived a pig who was very hungry…"

Although the animals tried to concentrate, the lively little chicks made it difficult to listen. They pecked at Heather the cow's nose, making her sneeze. They scratched at Bruce the sheepdog's tail until he was forced to bark quite sharply at them. One chick even tried to go to sleep in Maria the sheep's woolly ear. It was very distracting and it made all the animals cross.

"... something very, very delicious. The end," said Percy, aware that no one had been able to listen to his story. He oinked loudly at the chicks and stomped off into a corner to sulk.

Next, it was Old George the horse's turn. "My tale," he said, "is about the good old days..."

All the animals, except Tilly, groaned quietly. A boring story and a barn full of troublesome chicks was a recipe for a dreadfully dull afternoon.

However, as Old George droned on and on and on, an amazing thing happened. Each and every chirping chick began to fall asleep snug in the warmth of Henrietta's feathers.

"... and that reminds me of another story," said Old George, "but I don't expect you want to hear that today."

"Oh, yes! Yes, we do!" chorused the other animals. "We love your stories, George!" And this time they meant every word of it!

Oh Dear, What Can the Matter Be?

Oh dear, what can the matter be?
Dear, dear, what can the matter be?
Oh dear, what can the matter be?
Johnny's so long at the fair.

He promised he'd buy me a basket of posies,
A garland of lilies, a garland of roses,
A little straw hat to set off the blue ribbons
That tie up my bonny brown hair.

Oh dear, what can the matter be?
Dear, dear, what can the matter be?
Oh dear, what can the matter be?
Johnny's so long at the fair.

Goosey Goosey Gander

Goosey, goosey, gander,
Whither shall I wander?
Upstairs and downstairs,
And in my lady's chamber.
There I met an old man
Who would not say his prayers.
I took him by the left leg
And threw him down the stairs.

Knick Knack Paddy Whack

This old man, he played one,
He played knick knack on my drum.
With a knick knack paddy whack, give a dog a bone,
This old man went rolling home.

This old man, he played two,
He played knick knack on my shoe.
With a knick knack paddy whack, give a dog a bone,
This old man went rolling home.

Jack and Jill

Jack and Jill went up the hill
  To fetch a pail of water;
Jack fell down and broke his crown
  And Jill came tumbling after.

Up Jack got and home did trot
  As fast as he could caper;
He went to bed to mend his head
  With vinegar and brown paper.

Cock-a-Doodle-Doo

Cock-a-doodle-doo!
  My dame has lost her shoe,
My master's lost his fiddling stick,
  And doesn't know what to do.

Cock-a-doodle-doo!
  What is my dame to do?
Till master finds his fiddling stick,
  She'll dance without her shoe.

Cock-a-doodle-doo!
  My dame has found her shoe,
And master's found his fiddling stick,
  Sing cock-a-doodle-doo!

Girls and Boys Come Out to Play

Girls and boys, come out to play;
  The moon doth shine as bright as day;
Leave your supper, and leave your sleep,
  And come with your playfellows into the street.

Come with a whoop, come with a call,
  Come with a good will or not at all.
Up the ladder and down the wall,
  A halfpenny roll will serve us all.
You find milk, and I'll find flour,
  And we'll have a pudding in half-an-hour.

The Clumsy Fairy

Did you know that all fairies have to go to school to learn how to be fairies? They have to learn how to fly, how to be graceful and how to do magic. Clementine found it difficult! Poor Clementine. She was the worst in the class. She was clumsy and awkward. When they were dancing she was the only fairy who tripped over her own feet.

"Clementine! Think of feathers, not elephants," Madam Bouquet, the fairy dance teacher, was forever saying. At the end of term all the fairies were given a special task for the holidays. But there was one task that no one wanted. This was to help a little girl who had measles.

"Clementine," said Madam Bouquet, "I want you to paint this rose petal lotion on the little girl's spots every night when she is asleep," said Madam Bouquet. "If you do this for one week, the spots will disappear."

That night Clementine flew in through the little girl's window. So far so good! The little girl's name was Alice, and Clementine could see her fast asleep in bed. She was holding a fat, round teddy in her arms.

Clementine crept towards the bed. Then a toy clown, with a silly face, pinched her bottom! "Ouch!" she yelled.

Alice woke up. "Who's there?" she asked sleepily.

"It's Clementine," said the fairy. "Your clown pinched my bottom!"

Then Clementine overbalanced and sat down quickly on Alice's hot water bottle which was lying on the floor. It was so bouncy she shot straight up in the air and landed with a plop on Alice's bed.

"Are you alright?" asked Alice, rubbing her eyes again, to make sure she wasn't seeing things.

Clementine explained to Alice why she had come. "I'm sorry I woke you," she added. "You're not really supposed to see me."

Alice didn't mind. It was lovely to be able to talk to a real fairy. "Can you really do magic?" she asked Clementine.

"Yes," Clementine told her. "I'm quite good at magic. I just wish I wasn't so clumsy." She told Alice about her dance classes and Alice told Clementine about her ballet lessons.

"If you are helping me get rid of my measles," she said to Clementine, "I'll help you with your ballet." Each night Alice taught Clementine how to point her toes, keep her balance on one foot and curtsy gracefully. But it was the pirouette that Clementine did best of all. Holding her arms high above her head she twirled and twirled round Alice's bedroom.

Each day Clementine painted Alice's spots and by the end of the week they had gone.

After the holidays the fairies went back to school. And, do you know, Clementine was the best dancer in the class. Madam Bouquet couldn't believe her eyes.

"Why, Clementine," she gasped, "you're my prima ballerina!" And "prima", as I'm sure you know, means "first and best"!

Clementine was the happiest fairy in the world!

Wonky Bear

Mr and Mrs Puppety owned an old-fashioned toy shop. They made toys by hand in a room at the back of the shop. But they were getting old and their eyesight was bad.

"It's time we got an apprentice toymaker," said Mr Puppety to his wife. They soon found a young lad called Tom to work for them. He worked hard and carefully. He spent his first week making a teddy bear. When he had finished he showed the bear to Mr and Mrs Puppety.

"He looks very cuddly," said Mrs Puppety.

Tom was pleased that they liked his bear and he went off home whistling happily.

"He really is a lovely bear," said Mr Puppety, "but his head is a bit wonky."

"I know," said his wife, "but it's Tom's first try. Let's just put him up there on the shelf with the other teddy bears."

That night Wonky Bear sat on the shelf and started to cry. He had heard what Mr and Mrs Puppety had said about him.

"What's wrong?" asked Brown Bear, who was sitting next to him.

"My head is on wonky," sobbed Wonky Bear.

"Does it hurt?" asked Brown Bear.

"No," replied Wonky Bear.

"Well then, why are you crying?" asked Brown Bear.

"Because nobody will want to buy a wonky bear. I'll be left in this shop forever and nobody will ever take me home and love me," he cried.

"Don't worry," said Brown Bear. "We've all got our faults, and you look fine to me. Just try your best to look cute and cuddly and you'll soon have someone to love you." This made Wonky Bear feel much happier and he fell fast asleep.

The next day the shop was full of people, but nobody paid any attention to Wonky Bear. Then a little boy looked up at the shelf and cried, "Oh, what a lovely bear. Can I have that one, Daddy?"

Wonky Bear's heart lifted as the little boy's daddy reached up to his shelf. But he picked up Brown Bear instead and handed him to the little boy. Wonky Bear felt sadder than ever. Nobody wanted him. All of his new friends would get sold and leave the shop, but he would be left on the shelf gathering dust. Poor old Wonky Bear!

Now, Mr and Mrs Puppety had a little granddaughter called Jessie who loved to visit the shop and play with the toys. All the toys loved her because she was gentle and kind. It so happened that the next time she came to visit it was her birthday, and her grandparents told her she could choose any toy she wanted as her present.

"I know she won't choose me," thought Wonky Bear sadly. "Not with all these other beautiful toys to choose from."

But, to Wonky's amazement, Jessie looked up and pointed at his shelf and said, "I'd like that wonky bear please. No one else will have a bear quite like him."

Mr Puppety smiled and gave Wonky to Jessie. She hugged and kissed him, and Wonky felt so happy he almost cried. She took him home and put a smart red bow around his neck ready for her birthday party.

He felt very proud indeed.

Soon the other children arrived, each carrying their teddy bears under their arms.

Wonky Bear could not believe his eyes when he saw the little boy with his friend Brown Bear!

"I'm having a teddy bears' picnic," Jessie explained to him, hugging him tight. All of the children and the bears had a wonderful time, especially Wonky. He had found a lovely home, met his old friend and made lots of new ones.

"See, I told you not to worry," said Brown Bear.

"I know," said Wonky. "And I never will again."

More Terrible Tongue Twisters

My dame hath a lame tame crane,
My dame hath a crane that is lame.
Pray, gentle Jane, let my dame's tame crane
Feed and come home again.

She sifted
thistles through
her thistle-sifter.

Cows graze in groves
on grass which grows
in grooves in groves.

Six sick slick
slim sycamore
saplings.

She sells sea shells by the sea shore.
The shells she sells are surely seashells.
So if she sells shells on the seashore,
I'm sure she sells seashore shells.

Sure the ship's
shipshape, sir.

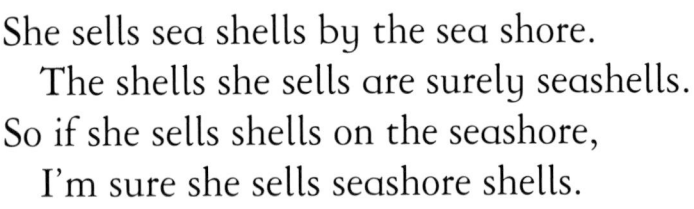

A big black bug bit a big
black bear, made the big
black bear bleed blood.

"Surely Sylvia swims!" shrieked Sammy, surprised.
"Someone should show Sylvia some strokes so she shall not sink."

Chop shops stock chops.

Can you imagine an imaginary
menagerie manager imagining
managing an imaginary menagerie?

Six sharp smart sharks.

One-One was a racehorse.
Two-Two was one, too.
When One-One won one race,
Two-Two won one, too.

I thought a thought.
But the thought I thought wasn't
the thought I thought I thought.

Three twigs twined tightly.

Are our oars oak?

Six slippery snails, slid slowly seaward.

The Leith police dismisseth us,
I'm thankful, sir, to say;
The Leith police dismisseth us,
They thought we sought to stay.
The Leith police dismisseth us,
We both sighed sighs apiece,
And the sigh that we sighed as we said goodbye
Was the size of the Leith police.

The soldiers shouldered shooters on their shoulders.

Fred fed Ted bread,
and Ted fed Fred bread.

Freshly-fried flying fish.

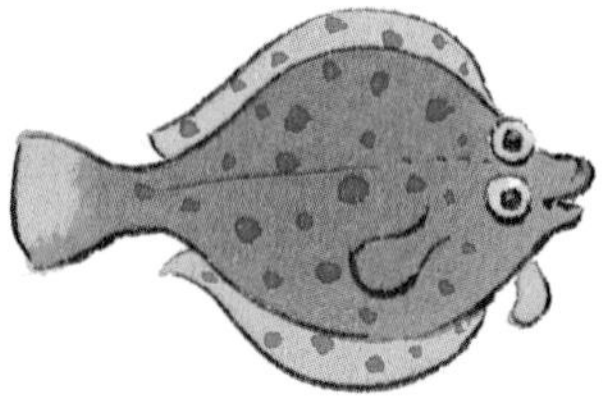

A pleasant place to place a plaice is a place where a plaice is pleased to be placed.

Susan shineth shoes and socks;
Socks and shoes shines Susan.
She ceased shining shoes and socks,
For shoes and socks shock Susan.

Once upon a barren moor
There dwelt a bear, also a boar.
The bear could not bear the boar.
The boar thought the bear a bore.
At last the bear could bear no more
Of that boar that bored him on the moor,
And so one morn he bored the boar –
That boar will bore the bear no more.

Suddenly swerving, seven small swans
Swam silently southward,
Seeing six swift sailboats
Sailing sedately seaward.

On mules we find two legs behind
And two we find before.
We stand behind before we find
What those behind be for.

Horse Power

On the day of the County Show, there was hustling and bustling on the farm. Mrs MacDonald had to feed the animals and collect the eggs by herself, because Old MacDonald was busy cleaning his tractor.

Every year, Old MacDonald gave rides on his tractor and trailer to the children. They loved it, but it was a lot of hard work for the farmer, with wheels to wash, and paint work to polish. Today, he also had ducks to shoo away when they began splashing about in the bubbles in his bucket!

But, at last, the tractor was spotlessly clean. Old MacDonald went into the farmhouse to put on his best boots.

"Here we go," said Doris the duck, as the farmer climbed into his tractor. "Cover your ears, little ones!"

But, when Old MacDonald turned the key, there was silence. The tractor simply would not start.

Old MacDonald tweaked the engine – and got his hands greasy. He stamped and stomped around – and got his best boots muddy. He muttered and moaned – and got rather red in the face. None of it did any good. The tractor didn't cough or splutter or show any sign of life.

"I hate to let the children down," groaned Old MacDonald. "But I can't pull the trailer if I don't have a tractor."

Now, Henry the cockerel is naughty and nosy, but sometimes he has good ideas. Henry jumped up on to Old George and Tilly's stable door and gave his loudest, "Cock-a-doodle-doo!"

Old MacDonald looked up in surprise, and then he gave a big smile.

"Goodness, gracious me!" he cried. "You're right, Henry – horse power! Now quick, jump out of the way. There's lots of work to be done!"

There were tails to untangle, coats to comb, and manes to thread with ribbons. There were harnesses to hitch and reins to clean and hang with gleaming brasses.

"It's just like the good old days," neighed Old George to Tilly.

There was no doubt who the stars of the County Show were that year. Children queued for ages, waiting to be pulled around by Old George and Tilly, who plodded proudly up and down with their coats shining and their heads held high.

At the end of the afternoon, Old MacDonald led the horses home and gave them a special supper of apples and oats.

"You know," he said with a sigh as he stroked their manes, "I miss the old days, too."

Old George and Tilly nodded their great heads, but it wasn't to show they agreed with him. They were asleep on their feet – they're not as young as they used to be, and it had been a very busy day!

A Spelling Lesson!

Wanda Witch went wandering through a very spooky wood. She loved to practise spooky spells, and the thought of doing anything good made her feel really ill.

She took great delight in turning a patch of beautiful bluebells into a pool of smelly, slimy goo. Then she gave a tree a creepy face that would frighten anyone who happened to be passing.

Creeping through the undergrowth, Wanda came upon a wizard, standing gazing into a pond. As quick as lightning, she waved her wand and the wizard fell straight into the water! Although the water wasn't very deep, it was very cold and full of horrible, slimy weeds.

The wizard leapt out in one huge jump, and was so angry with Wanda that he cast a spell as he landed next to her. His big red cloak wrapped itself around Wanda's body. Then it began to squeeze her really tight.

"Say sorry!" roared the wizard, "or you will stay like that!"

Wanda was shocked to have met someone who was even speedier and nastier than her! She apologised hastily to the wizard, and promised that from now on there would be no more nasty spells!

Witch's Brew

Winnie Witch was having a wonderful time! From her kitchen, deep inside a dark cave, came the sound of bubbling and singing as she stood stirring her huge cauldron. She was singing the spell for a magic monster as she threw the ingredients into the pot.

It had taken her days to collect the long list from her book of magic spells. Eye of lizard, toe of frog, tail of rat and bark of dog, sneeze of chicken, lick of weasel and smell of cat were all easy – but the cough of bat had been hard. Winnie had to chase a bat on her broomstick! It whizzed through the night sky so fast that Winnie thought she would fall off her broomstick. Eventually the bat must have choked on a fly. It coughed, spluttered, and slowed down. Winnie scooped up a cough and put it in her pocket before returning home for a rest!

The cauldron began to bubble furiously as Winnie stirred faster. Then… a monster's head began rising out of the pot.

"Ah!" sighed Winnie, "very pleased to meet you!"

"Mmm! Very pleased to *eat* you!" replied the monster!

Winnie went pale. Surely this wasn't right! She grabbed her wand and frantically shook it at the monster, whispering a spell. With a whoosh and a bang, the monster disappeared. Winnie won't be trying that spell again!

The Naughty Bears

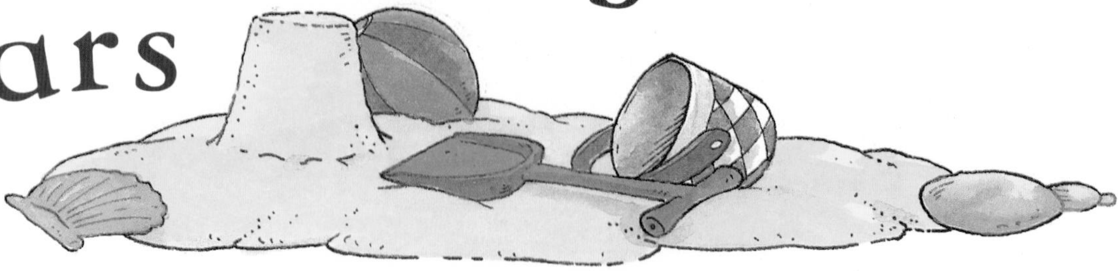

One sunny summer's day, Ben and Fraser's parents told them to pack their things, as they were going to the beach.

"Yippee!" said Ben. "Can we take our teddies?"

"As long as you keep an eye on them this time," said Daddy. "We don't want to spend all afternoon looking everywhere for them if you lose them again!"

Ben and Fraser took their teddies everywhere they went, but they were always losing them, and then there was a great hunt to find them. But the truth was, that when no one was looking, the naughty little teddies would run away in search of excitement and adventure.

Today was no different. The family arrived at the beach and unpacked their things. Daddy sat reading a newspaper and Mummy took out a book. Soon Ben and Fraser were busy building sandcastles. When the naughty teddies saw that no one was looking, they jumped up and ran away giggling, all along the beach.

"Let's go exploring," said Billy, who was the oldest bear. "I can see a cave over there." He pointed to a dark hole in the rocks close to the water.

"It looks a bit dark and scary," said Bella.

"Don't be silly," said Billy. "You're a bear, aren't you? I thought that bears liked dark caves!"

The little bears clambered over the rocks and into the cave. It was very deep, and very dark. Just then, Bella spotted something gleaming on the floor. She picked it up and showed it to Billy.

"Gold!" said Billy, in excitement, taking the little coin from Bella. "This must be a smugglers' cave! Maybe the smugglers are still here. Let's take a look!"

"No!" said Bella. "They could be dangerous. Let's go back." She turned and ran back outside, where she saw to her horror that while they had been exploring the tide had come in, and cut the rocks off from the beach.

"Billy!" she called. "Come quickly, we're stranded!"

Meanwhile, Ben and Fraser had finished making sandcastles and found that their teddy bears were missing.

"Oh, no," groaned Daddy. "Not again!"

The family hunted high and low along the beach, but there was no sign of the bears to be found. "Maybe they've been washed out to sea," said Fraser, his voice trembling at the thought.

Back at the cave the naughty teddies could see their owners looking for them. They jumped up and down and waved their paws. "It's no use," said Bella, "they can't see us. We're too small."

"Don't worry," said Billy, trying to sound braver than he felt.

Just then, two men appeared from the other side of the rocks. The teddies froze – these must be the smugglers! They trembled in fear as the men picked them up, clambered over the rocks, and tossed them into a little boat that had been hidden from view behind the rocks. The teddies clung together at the bottom of the boat as the men jumped in and began to row. Where were they taking them?

"Oh, Billy, I'm so frightened," whispered Bella. "Do you think they are going to hurt us?"

"No, Bella, I'm sure we'll be fine," answered Billy. But inside he didn't feel so sure. He was really very worried that they would never get home or see Ben and Fraser again.

Bella started to cry in little muffled whimpers, and big tears rolled down her cheeks. "If we ever get back home, I'm never going to run away again," she sobbed.

"There, there," comforted Billy, patting her gently.

After a while, the boat stopped and the men jumped out. They grabbed the bears and held them in the air high above their heads. One of the men called out in a loud voice, "Has anyone lost these bears?"

Everyone on the beach looked up, and Ben and Fraser raced over and grabbed their bears.

Daddy came running over to join them. He and the boys thanked the men for bringing the bears back. "We've been looking everywhere for them," said Ben and Fraser, grinning with relief.

"We found them up by that cave," said one of the men, pointing over to the cave. "You kids must have left them there."

"But the boys have been here building sandcastles all afternoon… " said Daddy, looking puzzled.

No one ever did find out how the naughty teddies got to the cave, or where the little coin in Billy's pocket came from. But from then on Daddy said they had to stay at home. The naughty teddies didn't really mind. They'd had enough adventures for the time being. And it gave them lots of time to play their favourite game – hide and seek!

No One Like You

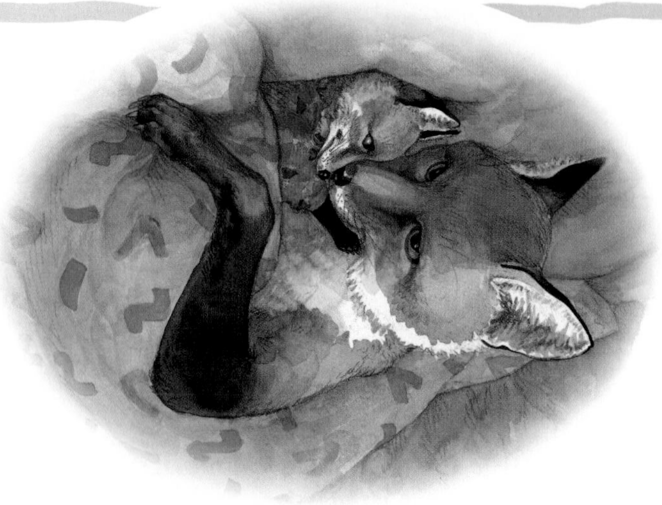

Ruff was hungry. A huge grumble rumbled round his tummy. He could hear Rufus clattering round in the kitchen. A delicious smell of freshly baked cakes sailed past his nose.

"Yummy," thought Ruff.

Ruff skipped into the kitchen – Rufus was washing up while the cakes cooled down.

"Would you like some help?" asked Ruff. "I could try one of those cakes for you."

"Oh, really!" said Rufus, smiling.

"No one makes cakes like you," said Ruff.

Ruff was bored. He twiddled his fingers, tapped his toes and twiddled his fingers again. He had no one to play with.

Later, Ruff tip-toed back into the living room – Rufus was reading.

"Would you like something better to read?" asked Ruff. "I could find you an exciting story."

"Oh, really!" said Rufus, smiling.

"No one tells a story like you," said Ruff.

Ruff was fed up. He was trying to make a model car. He fiddled and twiddled and fiddled, but he couldn't put it together.

Then he had an idea! Ruff galloped into the garden – Rufus was digging.

"Would you like something fun to do?" asked Ruff. "I could let you help me with my model car."

"Oh, really!" said Rufus, smiling.

"No one's as much fun as you," said Ruff.

It was bedtime! Rufus tucked Ruff into bed.

Ruff was feeling scared. He didn't like the shadows that flickered all round – it was very quiet. Then he had an idea! Ruff crept out of his bedroom and into Rufus' room.

Rufus was snoring loudly. It made Ruff giggle, which woke Rufus up.

"Would you like someone to cuddle?" asked Ruff. "I'm very good at cuddling."

"Oh, really!" said Rufus, smiling.

"No one cuddles like you," yawned Ruff, and he climbed into Rufus' bed.

"Oh, really!" said Rufus… "Well, no one loves you as much as I do, because there's no one like you."

Old Joe Brown

Old Joe Brown, he had a wife,
She was all of eight feet tall.
She slept with her head in the kitchen,
And her feet stuck out in the hall.

Poor Old Robinson Crusoe!

Poor old Robinson Crusoe!
Poor old Robinson Crusoe!
They made him a coat
Of an old nanny goat,

I wonder how they could do so!
With a ring a ting tang,
And a ring a ting tang,
Poor old Robinson Crusoe!

Old John Muddlecombe

Old John Muddlecombe lost his cap,
He couldn't find it anywhere, the poor old chap.
He walked down the High Street, and everybody said,
"Silly John Muddlecombe, you've got it on your head!"

Michael Finnegan

There was an old man called Michael Finnegan
He grew whiskers on his chinnegan
The wind came out and blew them in again
Poor old Michael Finnegan. Begin again...

Rub-a-dub Dub

Rub-a-dub dub,
Three men in a tub,
And who do you think they be?
The butcher, the baker,
The candle-stick maker,
Turn them out knaves all three.

Tommy Thumb

Tommy Thumb, Tommy Thumb,
Where are you?
Here I am, here I am,
How do you do?

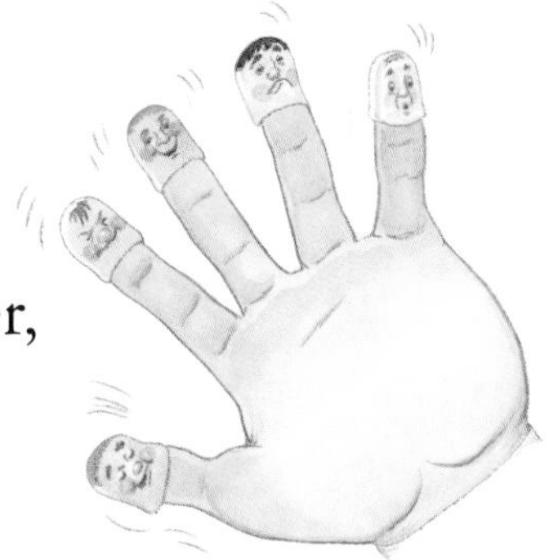

Peter Pointer, Peter Pointer,
Where are you?
Here I am, here I am,
How do you do?

Middle Man, Middle Man,
Where are you?
Here I am, here I am,
How do you do?

Ruby Ring, Ruby Ring,
Where are you?
Here I am, here I am,
How do you do?

Baby Small, Baby Small,
Where are you?
Here I am, here I am,
How do you do?

Fingers all, fingers all,
Where are you?
Here we are, here we are,
How do you do?

Solomon Grundy

Solomon Grundy,
Born on Monday,
Christened on Tuesday,
Married on Wednesday,
Sick on Thursday,
Worse on Friday,
Died on Saturday,
Buried on Sunday,
That was the end
Of Solomon Grundy.

Jack Sprat

Jack Sprat could eat no fat,
His wife could eat no lean,
And so between the two of them
They licked the platter clean.

Old Everest

Everest was one of the biggest horses in the world. He was also one of the strongest. When he was young, and already twice as big as other horses, he pulled the heavy cart filled with peas or potatoes, cabbages or corn, and everything grown on the farm. He took the vegetables from the farm down to the market, and he brought things from the market back to the farm. He pulled the huge machine that cut the wheat to make flour. He pulled the big plough that dug the soil, so the farmer could plant the seed that grew into wheat that made the flour... that Everest took to market. He did everything!

Everest was the best... but that was ages ago.

"So why don't you do everything now?" asked Puff the Pig.

"The farmer thinks I'm too old," said Everest, sadly. "He is trying to be kind. He thinks I need a rest."

Jacob the Lamb said, "I bet you are still stronger than anything, Everest! Nothing is as strong as you!" The huge horse lowered his head.

"Well... I am not as strong as I was, little one," smiled Everest. "Anyway, farmers don't use horses any more. They use a tractor instead!"

The big old horse had lots of time to think about when he was young and still worked on the farm. He spent most of the time now in his favourite meadow nibbling grass, and, when he grew bored with that, chasing rabbits or chickens, or biting large chunks out of the hedge.

But if Parsnip the Sheep, Waddle the Goose, or Scratchitt the Cat were in his field, he would tell them his stories. Sometimes he told the same stories again without realising, but no one minded.

But Everest still thought about the tractor. It wasn't the tractor's fault. He just wanted to work.

"Why did the farmer buy the tractor?" Puff wanted to know. Everest lowered his huge head and sighed.

"He liked the colour," said Everest.

Then one day the farmer said to Everest, "That tractor of mine! It won't start! I would ask you to help, Everest, but I suppose you are enjoying your rest." Everest shook his head from side to side.

"Even so," said the farmer, "I need to plough the field and the plough won't fit a horse, just the tractor! I don't know what to do."

Everest nudged the farmer gently over to the barn where the tractor was kept. His reins and harness were there too. The big horse picked up an old lead in his mouth and hooked it on the front of the tractor. Then, as easily as anything, he pulled out the tractor. Then he pulled the plough up behind the tractor.

"You mean you can pull both together?" said the farmer. Everest nodded his head up and down. The farmer was amazed! So the farmer hooked the plough to the tractor. Then he hooked the tractor to the horse. And Everest pulled the tractor and the tractor pulled the plough. Together they ploughed the field in the fastest time ever.

Everest was still the biggest and the strongest… and now the happiest horse in the whole world.

Puppy's Paw

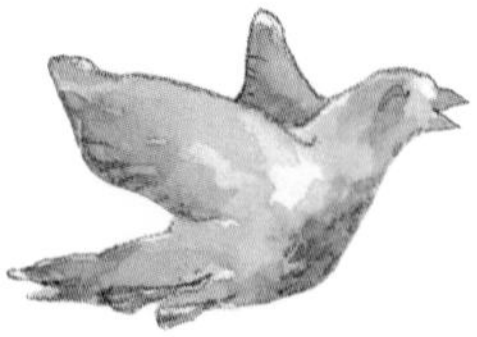

One sunny day, a small puppy sat in a grassy garden, watching Snowball and Snowdrop, his brother and sister, play. His coat was white with a few brown patches – and he had one brown paw. When he was born, his mummy said, "He looks like he's forgotten to put his other socks on! And that is how Socks got his name.

"Can I join in?" barked Socks.

"No, you can't!" Snowball yapped back.

"He looks like he's been having a mud bath, with those brown splodges," sneered Snowdrop. "Go and wash yourself properly, Socks."

"Maybe we should wash him," laughed Snowball. And the two puppies chased Socks towards the bird bath. Socks ran off as fast as he could and hid inside the shed – why didn't they like him? Was it because he didn't look like them? A big tear fell from his eye and trickled down his nose. Then, the two bouncy puppies appeared.

"Socks, where are you?" barked Snowdrop. Socks peeped out from behind the shed.

"We're going to the wood for a walk, Socks," called Snowball. "Bye-bye!"

Socks couldn't help himself. He ran out on to the lawn. "Please can I come?" he begged.

"You're much too young to come with us," said Snowdrop. "And you know Mummy says that you're too young to go out without her."

"I'm not too young," whined Socks. "I've been out loads of times."

"Well, you can't walk with us," said Snowball. "You must walk behind us."

"Okay," yapped Socks, eagerly. So, the two pups scampered through the garden gate, with Socks following. Snowball and Snowdrop ran down the lane towards the wood – Socks trotted behind!

In a clearing, there were two paths to choose from. Snowball's nose began to twitch. He could smell something wonderful. "This way!" he yelped and the two older pups rushed off.

"Don't those two ever stop to look where they're going?" wondered Socks, as he lifted his brown paw and followed. Round a bend, the puppies found a huge clump of beautiful, pink flowers. Socks pushed his soft, black nose into them. "Atishoo!" he sneezed, as yellow pollen flew into the air.

Snowdrop was busy chasing a butterfly. It fluttered away down another path and Snowdrop followed. "Come on, Socks!" barked Snowball. "Keep up!" and he set off after his sister.

"We'll get lost if we're not careful," thought Socks.

The butterfly led the puppies deeper and deeper into the wood. Suddenly, it flew high into the air and disappeared. Snowdrop and Snowball stopped and looked around. There were trees everywhere and they all looked the same!

"How are we going to find our way home now?" wailed Snowball.

"Listen," woofed Snowdrop. "There's someone through those trees. Let's see if they know the way home."

"I know the way… " began Socks. But Snowball and Snowdrop weren't listening. They had already dashed off along the path.

"It's easy," thought Socks to himself and set off after the others.

Tap-tap! Tap-tap! A woodpecker was trying to find some insects in a tree. "Can you help us find our way home?" asked Snowball and Snowdrop. But the woodpecker flew off!

"What are we going to do now?" whined Snowdrop. "I want my mummy!"

"Help!" they howled. "Help!"

"But I know the way home!" said Socks.

Snowdrop and Snowball turned to their brother and stared. "What did you say?" they asked.

"I said I know the way home," said Socks, again.

"How?" asked Snowball.

"It's easy," said Socks. "Every time we chose a path, we took the one on the side of my brown paw. To get home, we just turn round and take the path on the side of my white paw. Follow me and I'll show you."

So, back through the woods they went, with Socks in front. Each time they had to choose, Socks held up his brown paw, turned his head and took the other path. Back they scampered through the wood, past the pink flowers, down the lane, through the gate and into the garden, where their mummy was waiting for them.

"Where have you been?" she woofed, crossly. "I've been so worried."

"We got lost," said Snowball and Snowdrop. "It was all our fault."

"Socks was so clever," woofed Snowball. "We're so lucky to have him as a brother."

"I wish I had a brown paw like him," said Snowdrop. "Do you want to play ball, Socks?"

"Oh, yes please!" he woofed, flicking the ball across the lawn to his brother and sister. Sometimes it was good to be different!

Fishes Swim

Fishes swim in water clear,
Birds fly up into the air,
Serpents creep along the ground,
Boys and girls run round and round.

Cut Thistles

Cut thistles in May,
They'll grow in a day;
Cut them in June,
That is too soon;
Cut them in July,
Then they will die.

Little Robin and Pussycat

Little Robin Redbreast jumped
upon a wall,
Pussy cat jumped after him,
and almost got a fall!
Little Robin chirped and sang,
and what did pussy say?
Pussy cat said, "Mew" and
Robin jumped away.

Little Robin Redbreast sat upon a tree,
Up went pussy cat, and down
went he!
Down came pussy, and away Robin ran;
Says little Robin Redbreast,
"Catch me if you can!"

Feathers

Cackle, cackle, Mother Goose,
Have you any feathers loose?
Truly have I, pretty fellow,
Half enough to fill a pillow.
Here are quills, take one or two,
And down to make a bed for you.

You Shall be Queen

Lilies are white,
Rosemary's green,
When I am king,
You shall be queen.

Jemmy Dawson

Brave news is come to town,
Brave news is carried;
Brave news is come to town,
Jemmy Dawson's married.

First he got a porridge-pot,
Then he bought a ladle;
Then he got a wife and child,
And then he bought a cradle.

My Little Cow

I had a little cow,
Hey diddle, ho diddle!
I had a little cow,
and I drove it to the stall;
hey diddle, ho diddle!
and there's my song all.

The Coachman

Up at Piccadilly oh!
The coachman takes his stand,
And when he meets a pretty girl,
He takes her by the hand;
Whip away for ever oh!
Drive away so clever oh!
All the way to Bristol oh!
He drives her four-in-hand.

Jerry Hall

Jerry Hall,
He is so small,
A rat could eat him,
Hat and all.

Susie and the Mermaid

Today was Susie's birthday. Mum and Dad had given her a pretty sea-blue dress and shoes to match. Susie tried on the dress and shoes. They shimmered just like a mermaid's tail. Susie had always wanted to be a mermaid. She loved to sit on Mermaid Rock gazing out to sea dreaming of what it would be like to be a mermaid.

"I'll make a birthday wish," thought Susie, and closed her eyes. "I wish I could be a mermaid." When she opened her eyes, she was no longer wearing her birthday dress – she had a mermaid's tail! Susie couldn't believe her luck, her birthday wish had come true.

Then Susie heard someone crying. She looked around and saw someone sitting on the other side of Mermaid Rock wearing a blue dress just like her new birthday dress! "Why are you crying?" Susie asked the little girl.

"Because I've lost my tail," she replied. "You see, I'm a mermaid. But without my tail I can't go home!" Susie realised what had happened, her birthday wish must have made her swap places with the mermaid. Susie told the mermaid about her birthday wish.

"How can I change us back again?" asked Susie.

"If you can collect my tears from the sea, then you could wish again," said the mermaid.

Susie slipped into the sea. The water didn't feel a bit cold now that she was a mermaid. With her strong new

tail she swam quickly to the bottom of the sea.

Susie asked the sea creatures to help her search for the tears. Crabs and fish, lobsters and winkles peered into holes and lifted up stones, but it was no use. They couldn't find any tears. Susie didn't know what to do!

Then she heard, "One-two-three, one-two-three..." and from an underwater cave danced a large octopus wearing a long string of pearls! Its eight long arms whirled around as it danced and twirled.

"Hello, little mermaid!" said the octopus. "Can you help me?" asked Susie. "I'm looking for mermaid tears. But I don't know where to start."

"Ah! Well these pearls are just what you are looking for!" said the octopus. "That's what happens to mermaid tears you know – they turn into pearls! You can have them if you help me take them off!" laughed the octopus. "Oh, thank you so much!" cried Susie untangling the pearls.

"Farewell, little mermaid!" laughed the octopus as it danced away, singing, "One-two-three, one-two-three..."

Susie swam back to Mermaid Rock as quickly as she could with the pearls. Susie closed her eyes and wished again. Instantly, she was wearing her blue dress and the mermaid had her tail back.

"Thank you, Susie," said the mermaid. "I hope I'll see you again."

Susie waved goodbye as the mermaid slipped into the sea and swam away. Susie hurried home for her birthday tea. She glanced down at her new blue dress to make sure it was still clean. Down the front of the dress were sewn lots of tiny tear-shaped pearls!

The Birthday Party

Rosy was walking down the stairs, when the post popped through the letter box and flopped on to the mat. One envelope had a picture of a rabbit and Rosy's name written in big writing on it. She picked it up and rushed into the kitchen. "Look, Mum!" cried Rosy, "a letter for me. Who do you think it's from?"

"I don't know," replied Mum. "Let's open it and find out."

Inside the envelope was an invitation to a party from Rosy's friend, Laura. "Wow! A party!" cried Rosy. "I can't wait!" she said and, with a little bit of help, answered "yes" to the invitation. But then, Rosy began to worry. "What am I going to buy Laura as a present for her birthday?" she asked.

Mum had an idea. "Let's go into town tomorrow and look for something special." So, the next day, Rosy and Mum went to the toy shop. "What does Laura like best?" asked Mum.

"Rabbits," said Rosy. "Laura loves them."

"Come with me," smiled Mum. "I've seen just the thing."

Mum took Rosy to a corner of the toy shop, where they found lots of fluffy toys. And there sat a cute little rabbit, with bright blue trousers and a tiny orange carrot. "Do you think Laura would like that rabbit?" asked Mum.

"She would love him," said Rosy. So, they bought the rabbit and some wrapping paper and went back home.

At home, Rosy wrapped the rabbit in the pretty paper. Then, she drew a card with a big rabbit on the front and wrote her name in red crayon inside it. "Mum," asked Rosy, "what will I do at the party?"

"Well, there will be lots of games to play," said Mum.

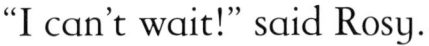

"I can't wait!" said Rosy.

At last, the afternoon of the party arrived. Rosy put on her pretty party dress. Mum gave her Laura's card and present. "Mum," asked Rosy, "what if I don't like the food?"

"Don't worry," said Mum. "At parties, there are always lots of tasty things to eat – I promise."

"I can't wait!" cried Rosy and skipped out of the door.

When Rosy arrived at the party, Laura opened the front door. There were lots of

children standing behind her, but Rosy couldn't see anyone else that she knew. "Hello, Rosy," said Laura, giving her a big hug. Rosy gave Laura her birthday present. As Laura pulled off the paper, a huge smile spread across her face. "Oh, Rosy!" she cried. "He's perfect!"

Everyone wanted to hold the rabbit. Rosy felt better already. "Time for some games!" called Laura's mum. Rosy stood by the door and watched.

"I don't know how to play," she whispered.

"Just do what I do," said Laura and held her friend's hands. Rosy was soon having a wonderful time. Party games were great fun.

Just then, Laura's mum said, "It's time for the birthday tea."

Rosy couldn't wait to see what there was to eat. She was feeling really hungry! "Wow!" gasped Rosy, when she saw the party food. All of her favourite things were there – sausages, pizza, cakes and strawberry jelly! There were balloons, paper plates and cups, which all had rabbits on them.

Rosy sat next to Laura. "Wait till you see my cake," laughed her friend. At that moment, Laura's mum walked into the room. She was carrying a birthday cake – in the shape of a big rabbit! Laura blew out the candles and everyone sang "Happy birthday!" as loudly as they could.

After tea, everyone played Pass the Parcel. Rosy really liked this game. It was very exciting, waiting for the music to stop and then watching, while someone tore the paper off the parcel. "I can't wait for my turn," thought Rosy. Suddenly, the music did stop, just as Rosy held the parcel. And this time, there was only one piece of paper left. She ripped it off – inside was a jigsaw puzzle.

It wasn't long before mums and dads came to take their children home. "Thanks for my rabbit," said Laura, to Rosy.

"And thanks for a great party," said Rosy. Then, Laura gave everyone a balloon and a badge – with a rabbit on it. On the way home, Mum asked Rosy if she'd had a good time.

"Oh, yes!" said Rosy. "The games were fun, Laura's other friends were great and the food was really yummy! Mum," asked Rosy, "how long is it until my birthday?"

"About four weeks," said Mum. "Why?"

"Please can I have a party?" replied Rosy.

"I've got lots of friends to invite and I know just which games I want to play. And I'd really like a big dinosaur cake."

"I can't wait!" laughed Mum.

The Naughty Kitten

Ginger was a naughty little kitten. He didn't always mean to be naughty, but somehow things just turned out that way.

"You really should be more careful," warned Mummy. But Ginger was too busy getting into trouble to listen.

One day, Ginger was in a particularly playful mood. First, he tried to play tag with his smallest sister – and chased her right up an old apple tree. It took Daddy all morning to get her down.

Then, Ginger dropped cream all over the dog's tail. The dog whirled round and round as he tried to lick it off. He got so dizzy that he fell right over. That really made Ginger laugh until his sides hurt.

After that, Ginger thought it would be fun to play hide-and-seek with the mice – and frightened them so much that they refused to come out of their hole for the rest of the day.

Then, Ginger crept up behind the rabbit and shouted, "HI!" The poor rabbit was so surprised that he fell head-first into his breakfast. Ginger thought he looked ever so funny covered in lettuce leaves and carrots.

For his next trick, Ginger knocked over a wheelbarrow full of apples while he was trying to fly like a bird. He really couldn't help laughing when the apples knocked his little brother flying into the air.

And when one of the apples splashed into the garden pond, Ginger decided to go apple bobbing. How he laughed as the goldfish bumped into each other in their hurry to get out of his way.

Ginger laughed so much that, WHO-OO-AH! he began to lose his balance. He stopped laughing as he tried to stop himself falling into the pond. But, SPLASH! It was no good – he fell right in.

"Help! I can't swim," wailed Ginger, splashing wildly around. But he needn't have worried, the water only reached up to his knees.

"Yuck!" he moaned, squirting out a mouthful of water.

"Ha, ha, ha!" laughed the other kittens, who had come to see what the noise was about. And the dog and the rabbit soon joined in.

"You really should be more careful," said Mummy, trying not to smile.

"It's not funny," said Ginger. He gave the other animals a hard glare as Daddy pulled him out of the pond. But then he caught sight of his reflection in the water. He did look very funny. Soon he was laughing as loudly as the others.

After that, Ginger tried hard not to be quite so naughty. And do you know what? He even succeeded... some of the time!

Abou Ben Adhem

Abou Ben Adhem (may his tribe increase!)
Awoke one night from a deep dream of peace,
And saw, within the moonlight in his room,
Making it rich, and like a lily in bloom,
An angel writing in a book of gold:–
Exceeding peace had made Ben Adhem bold,

And to the presence in the room he said,
"What writest thou?" – The vision raided its head,
And with a look made of all sweet accord,
Answered, "The names of those who love the Lord."

"And is mine one?" said Abou. "Nay, not so,"
Replied the angel. Abou spoke more low,
But cheerily still; and said, "I pray thee then,
Write me as one that loves his fellow-men."

The angel wrote, and vanished.
The next night
It came again with a great
wakening light,

And showed the names whom
love of God had blessed,
And lo! Ben Adhem's name
led all the rest.

The Bells

Hear the sledges with the bells –
Silver bells!
What a world of merriment
their melody foretells!
How they tinkle, tinkle, tinkle,
In the icy air of night!
While the stars that oversprinkle
All the heavens, seem to twinkle
With a crystalline delight;
Keeping time, time, time,
In a sort of Runic rhyme,
To the tintinnabulation that so musically wells
From the bells, bells, bells, bells, bells, bells, bells –
From the jingling and the tinkling of the bells.

Edgar Allan Poe

Kubla Khan

In Xanadu did Kubla Khan
  A stately pleasure-dome decree;
Where Alph, the sacred river, ran
  Through caverns measureless to man
Down to a sunless sea.

So twice five miles of fertile ground
  With walls and towers were girdled round;
And here were gardens bright with sinuous rills
  Where blossomed many an incense-bearing tree;
And here were forests ancient as the hills,
  Enfolding sunny spots of greenery.

Where Lies the Land

Where lies the land to which the ship would go?
  Far, far ahead, is all her seamen know.
And where the land she travels from? Away,
  Far, far behind, is all that they can say.
On sunny noons upon the deck's smooth face,
  Linked arm in arm, how pleasant here to pace;
Or, o'er the stern reclining, watch below
  The foaming wake far widening as we go.
On stormy nights when wild north-westers rave,
  How proud a thing to fight with wind and wave!
The dripping sailor on the reeling mast
  Exults to bear, and scorns to wish it past.

The Castle in the Clouds

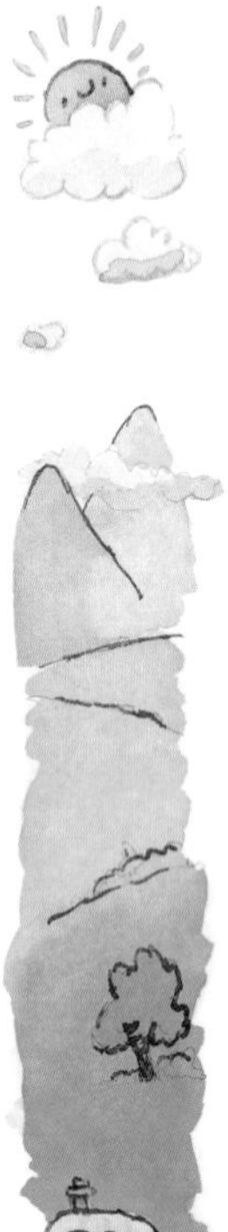

There was once a family that lived in a little house, in a village at the bottom of a mountain. At the top of the mountain was a great, grey castle made of granite. The castle was always shrouded in clouds, so it was known as the castle in the clouds. From the village you could only just see the outline of its high walls and turrets. No one in the village ever went near the castle, for it looked such a gloomy and forbidding place.

Now in this family there were seven children. One by one they went out into the world to seek their fortune, and at last it was the youngest child's turn. His name was Sam. His only possession was a pet cat named Jess, and she was an excellent rat-catcher. Sam was most upset at the thought of leaving Jess behind when he went off to find work, but then he had an idea.

"I'll offer Jess's services at the castle in the clouds. They're bound to need a good ratter, and I'm sure I can find work there, too," he thought.

His parents were dismayed to discover that Sam wanted to find work at the castle, but they could not change his mind. So Sam set off for the castle with Jess at his side. It grew cold and misty as the road wound up the mountainside through thick pine forests. Rounding a bend they suddenly found themselves up against a massive, grey stone wall. They followed the curve of the wall until they came to the castle door.

Sam went up to the door and banged on it. The sound echoed spookily. "Who goes there?" said a voice.

Looking up, Sam saw that a window high in the wall had been opened and a face was eyeing him suspiciously.

"I... I... I wondered if you'd be interested in employing my cat as a rat-catcher," began Sam.

The window slammed shut, but a moment later the castle door opened. Stepping inside, Sam and Jess found themselves face-to-face with an old man. "Rat-catcher, did you say?" said the old man raising one eyebrow. "Very well, but she'd better do a good job or my master will punish us all!"

Sam sent Jess off to prove her worth. Meanwhile Sam asked the old man, who was the castle guard, if there was any work for him, too.

"You can help out in the kitchens, but it's hard work!" the guard said.

Sam was soon working very hard in the kitchens. He spent all day peeling vegetables, cleaning pans and scrubbing the floor.

By midnight he was exhausted. He was about to find a patch of straw to make his bed, when he noticed Jess wasn't around. He set off in search of her down dark passages, up winding staircases, but there was no sign of her. By now he was hopelessly lost but he suddenly saw Jess's green eyes shining like lanterns at the top of a rickety spiral staircase. "Here, Jess!" called Sam softly. But Jess stayed just where she was.

Jess was sitting outside a door and seemed to be listening to something on the other side. Sam put his ear to the door. He could hear the sound of sobbing. He knocked gently at the door. "Who is it?" said a girl's voice.

"I'm Sam, the kitchen boy. Can I come in?" said Sam.

"If only you could," sobbed the voice. "I'm Princess Rose. When my father died my uncle locked me in here so that he could steal the castle. Now I fear I shall never escape!"

Sam pushed and pushed at the door, but to no avail. "Don't worry," he said, "I'll get you out of here."

Sam knew exactly what to do. He had seen a pair of keys hanging on a nail in the rafters high above the guard's head. He had wondered why anyone should put keys out of the reach of any human hand. Now he thought he knew – but first he had to get the keys himself!

When Sam and Jess finally made their way back, they found the guard was fast asleep in his chair right underneath the keys! Jess leaped up on to the shelf behind his head, then she climbed until she reached the rafters. She took the keys in her mouth and carried them down. But, as she jumped from the shelf again, she knocked over a jug and sent it crashing to the floor. The guard woke with a start. "Who goes there?" he growled. He just caught sight of the tip of Jess's tail as she made a dash for the door.

"You go a different way," hissed Sam, running up the stairs to Rose's door, while the old man disappeared off after Jess. Sam put one of the keys in the lock. It fitted! He turned the key and opened the door. There stood the loveliest girl he had ever seen. The princess ran towards him, as he cried, "Quick! There's not a moment to lose." He grabbed her hand and led her out of the tower.

"Give me the keys," she said. She led him down to the castle cellars. At last they came to a tiny door. The princess put the second key in the lock and opened it. Inside was a cupboard, and inside that was a golden casket filled with jewels. "My own casket – stolen by my uncle," cried Rose.

Grabbing the casket the pair ran to the stables and saddled a horse. Suddenly Jess appeared with the guard chasing him. With a mighty leap Jess landed on the back of the horse. "Off we go!" cried Sam.

And that was the last that any of them saw of the castle in the clouds. Sam married the princess and they all lived happily ever after.

Sports Day

The sun peeped over the higgledy-piggledy, messy alley. It was much too early to be awake – or was it? Lenny the kitten slowly opened his eyes and grinned – it was 'time-to-get-up' time.

"Get up, Sleepyhead!" he yelled to his twin sister, Lulu. "It's a great day for running and jumping." And he started to run round and round the dustbins.

"Okay, Lenny," yawned Lulu, still half asleep, "I'm coming."

"I'll race you to the end of the alley," cried Lenny.

"But you always win," moaned Lulu.

"That's because you're a big, podgy pussy," laughed Lenny.

Lulu giggled. "Cheeky kitty!" she cried. "Bet you can't catch me!" And she ran down the alley as fast as she could.

"That was fun!" cried Lenny, as he finally caught up with his sister. "What about some jumping now?"

"Great idea," purred Lulu.

So, huffing and puffing, the little kittens piled up some boxes and put a pole across the gap.

Lenny leapt over it first. "Whee!" he cried. "I bet I can jump higher than you!"

Suddenly, Lulu spotted a tatty old ball. "I bet I can throw it further than you!" she cried.

"No, you can't," cried Lenny. He picked up the ball and threw his best throw ever – but it hit Uncle Bertie right on the head!

Scampering down the alley as fast as they could go, the two kittens quickly hid behind a heap of old potato sacks before Uncle Bertie could spot them!

"Pooh!" said Lulu. "These sacks are really very smelly!"

Suddenly, Lenny had an idea...

Sticking his feet into one of the old potato sacks, he pulled it up to his tummy and began hopping and jumping around!

"Hey, what about a sack race?" he giggled.

Lenny hopped and skipped. Lulu wiggled and giggled.

"I'm winning!" squealed Lulu. "I'm winning!"

"No, you're not!" cried Lenny. He jumped his best jump ever – and knocked a huge pile of boxes over Cousin Archie!

"Uh-oh!" groaned Lenny. "Trouble time!"

Uncle Bertie and Cousin Archie were not happy. They stomped off to find Hattie, the kittens' mother.

"Those kittens of yours are so naughty," they complained. "You've got to do something about them!"

Hattie sighed. Then, spying two pairs of tiny ears peeping out from behind a watering can, she tip-toed over. "Time-to-come-out-time!" she boomed.

"What have you two been up to?" Hattie asked Lenny and Lulu.

"Running and jumping, Mummy," whined Lenny.

"We didn't mean to hurt anyone," whispered Lulu. But Hattie wasn't cross. She knew her kittens were only playing.

"I've got an idea," she said. "Why don't we have a sports day? We can all join in – there'll be plenty of running and jumping for everyone!"

Archie and Bertie didn't want to play – they wanted a cat nap!

"Okay," said Hattie. "We'll simply ask the dogs to join us instead."

So, later that day, Hattie explained her idea to the Alley Dogs, who all thought it sounded like great fun. And it wasn't long before Hattie had organised everyone and everything!

"We'll have lots of races," cried Lenny, excitedly, "running, skipping, leaping and jumping ones – perhaps a sack race!"

Suddenly, six pussy eyes peeped over the fence.

"Okay, everyone," cried Hattie. "Let's begin. Ready... steady... "

"Er, Hattie," asked Cousin Archie, popping out from behind the fence, "can I join in?"

"Us too?" cried Uncle Bertie and Auntie Lucy.

"Of course you can," laughed Hattie.

"Ready... steady... GO!"

Cousin Archie and Harvey raced up the alley and passed the winning line together. "Archie and Harvey are the winners!" cried Hattie. "Time for the sack race now!"

The dogs and cats all clambered into their sacks. But Lenny and Lulu began before Hattie could say "Go!"

"Hey!" cried Hattie. "Come back you two, that's cheating!" But it was too late. Everyone began leaping and jumping after the kittens.

"STOP!" shouted Hattie.

Lenny and Lulu stopped – but no one else did! They crashed into each other and fell in a big Alley Cat and Dog pickle!

Luckily, no one was hurt, but now they were all tired.

"Well, that was the best sports day ever!" said Harvey.

Hattie looked at the higgledy-piggledy mess.

"You're right," she laughed. "But tomorrow we're going to play another game. It's called tidy-up the alley!"

Suddenly, lots of barking and meowing filled the air. "Oh, no!" they groaned, and then they all laughed.

The Princess of Hearts

Princess Ruby was given her name because she was born with ruby red lips the shape of a tiny heart. When she grew up she was very beautiful, with coal black hair down to her waist, green eyes and skin as pale as milk. She was a charming and friendly girl, but she insisted that everything she owned was heart-shaped! Her bed was heart-shaped, her table and chair were heart-shaped, even the sandwiches her maid brought her at teatime were cut into the shape of hearts!

As soon as she was old enough, the king and queen wanted Princess Ruby to find a husband. "There is a prince in the next kingdom who is looking for a wife," they told her. "He is brave and handsome and rich. Everything a princess could wish for."

But the foolish princess declared: "I will only marry this prince if he can change the stars in the sky to hearts!"

When Prince Gallant came to visit Princess Ruby she liked his kindly eyes and his pleasant smile. They spent the afternoon walking in the palace gardens, and talking about everything under the sun. But Prince Gallant could not promise to change the stars. As she watched the prince ride away, Princess Ruby suddenly wished she had not been so foolish!

Prince Gallant, too, was unhappy as he rode home. Suddenly, he heard a screeching sound. In the forest clearing, a dragon was attacking a peacock.

The prince took out his sword and chased the dragon away. The peacock's beautiful tail feathers were lying around him.

"Thank you for saving me," said the peacock. The prince was astonished to hear the peacock talk. "I have magical powers," explained the peacock. "But I am now very weak. The dragon has pulled out some of my magic feathers!"

The Prince set to work gathering up all the peacock's feathers. As soon as the feathers had been returned, the peacock gave a loud cry and spread his tail wide. The peacock's tail glowed.

"Before I go, I will grant you a single wish," he told the prince. Prince Gallant wished that the stars in the sky would take on the shape of hearts!

Later that night Princess Ruby was in her bedchamber. She was beginning to regret that she had refused to marry Prince Gallant.

She looked out of the window at the full moon and fields beyond the palace. Then she glanced at the stars – and couldn't believe her eyes!

Every single one was in the shape of a silver heart!

At that moment she saw Prince Gallant riding over the hill. He stopped his horse beneath Princess Ruby's window.

The prince again asked Princess Ruby if she would marry him. And of course she happily agreed!

They were married on a lovely summer's day. And, when Princess Ruby made her wedding vows, she promised never to ask for anything foolish, ever again!

Oranges and Lemons

Oranges and lemons,
  Say the bells of St Clements.
I owe you five farthings,
  Say the bells of St Martins.
When will you pay me?
  Say the bells of Old Bailey.
When I grow rich,
  Say the bells of Shoreditch.

London Bridge is Falling Down

London bridge is falling down,
  Falling down, falling down,
London bridge is falling down,
  My fair lady.

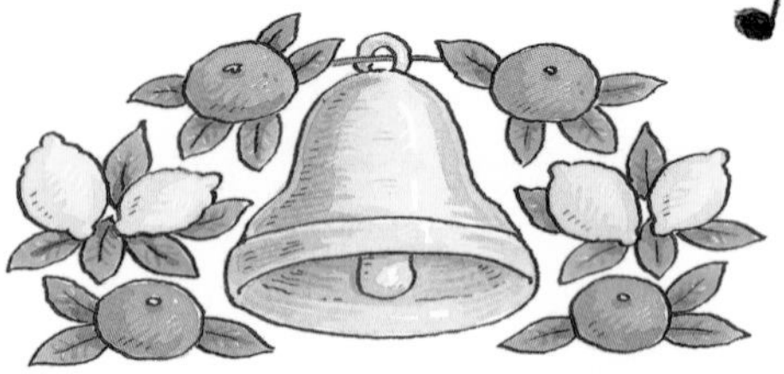

Frère Jacques

Frère Jacques, Frère Jacques,
  Dormez-vous, dormez-vous?
Sonnez les matines,
  Sonnez les matines,
Ding, dang, dong,
  Ding, dang, dong.

The Miller of Dee

There was a jolly miller
  Lived on the river Dee:
He worked and sang from morn till night,
  No lark so blithe as he;
And this the burden of his song
  For ever used to be –
I jump mejerrime jee!
  I care for nobody – no! not I,
Since nobody cares for me.

Ding Dong Bell

Ding, dong, bell,
  Pussy's in the well!
Who put her in?
  Little Tommy Green.
Who pulled her out?
  Little Johnny Stout.
What a naughty boy was that
  To try to drown poor pussy cat,
Who never did any harm,
  But killed the mice in his
  father's barn.

Little Cottage in the Wood

Little cottage in the wood,
  Little old man by the window stood,
Saw a rabbit running by,
  Knocking at the door.
"Help me! Help me! Help me!" he said,
  "Before the huntsman shoots me dead."
"Come little rabbit, come inside,
  Safe with me abide."

The Bells of London

Gay go up and gay go down,
  To ring the bells of London town.
Halfpence and farthings,
  Say the bells of St Martin's.
Pancakes and fritters,
  Say the bells of St Peter's.
Two sticks and an apple,
  Say the bells of Whitechapel.

Have You Seen the Muffin Man?

Have you seen the muffin man,
  the muffin man, the muffin man,
Have you seen the muffin man
  that lives in Drury Lane O?

Yes, I've seen the muffin man,
  the muffin man, the muffin man;
Yes, I've seen the muffin man who
  lives in Drury Lane O.

The Smart Bear and the Foolish Bear

It was the start of winter. The first snow had fallen, and the lake had begun to freeze. It was nearly time for all the bears to start their winter sleep. But there was one foolish bear who wasn't ready to sleep yet. "I'll just catch one more fish," he told himself, "to keep me going through winter." And, although he knew it was dangerous, he crept out onto the icy lake.

He lay down on his tummy, and broke a hole in the ice. He could see lots of fish swimming in the water below. He dipped his paw into the hole, and scooped out a fish in a flash! But the foolish little bear leapt up, shouting, "I caught one!" With a great crack, the ice gave way beneath him, and he fell into the freezing water!

Luckily a smart little bear cub heard his cries, and rushed to help. He found a fallen log and pushed it over the ice. The foolish bear grabbed it, and pulled himself to safety, still holding the fish.

"How can I thank you?" he asked.

"That fish would do nicely," said the smart little bear, and he strolled away to start his winter's sleep.

Rusty's Big Day

Long ago there lived a poor farmer called Fred, who had a horse called Rusty. Once Rusty had been a good, strong horse. He had willingly pulled the plough and taken his master into town to sell his vegetables. Now he was too old to work on the farm, but the farmer couldn't bear to think of getting rid of him because he was so sweet-natured. "It would be like turning away one of my own family," Fred used to say. Rusty spent his days grazing in the corner of the field. He was quite content, but he felt sad that he was no longer able to help the poor farmer earn his living.

One day, Fred decided to go to town to sell a few vegetables. He harnessed Beauty, the young mare, to the wagon and off they went.

Beauty shook her fine mane and tossed a glance at Rusty as if to say, "Look who's queen of the farmyard!"

While Fred was in the town, his eye was caught by a notice pinned to a tree. It said:

Horse Parade at 2 pm today
The winner will pull the king's carriage to the Grand Banquet tonight

"There's not a moment to lose, my girl!" said Fred. "We must get you ready for the parade." And he turned the wagon around. "Giddy-up, Beauty!" he called, and she trotted all the way back to the farm.

Fred set to work to make Beauty look more lovely than she had ever done before. He scrubbed her hoofs and brushed her coat until it shone. Then he plaited her mane and tied it with a bright red ribbon. Rusty watched from the field. "How fine she looks," he thought, wistfully. "She's sure to win." He felt a bit sad that he was too old to take part in the parade, so he found a patch of the sweetest grass to graze on, to console himself.

All at once, he heard Fred approach. "Come on, old boy," he said, "you can come, too. It'll be fun for you to watch the parade, won't it?"

Rusty was thrilled. It was a long time since the master had last taken him into town.

Soon the three of them set off back into town, with Fred riding on Beauty's back and Rusty walking by their side. When they reached the parade ground, there were already a lot of people and horses there. There were horses of every shape and size!

The parade began. The king and members of the royal court entered the parade ground and took their places. Then the king announced three contests. First there would be a race from one end of the parade ground to the other. Then there would be a contest of strength. Each horse would have to try to pull a heavy carriage. Lastly, there would be a trotting competition. Each horse would have to carry a rider around the parade ground.

Rusty tried his best, but he couldn't compete with the younger horses in the race and the contest of strength. All the other horses stared at him. "What's an old horse like you doing taking part in a contest like this?" one of them asked disdainfully. "You shouldn't have been allowed to compete at your age!" taunted another.

Then came the trotting competition. "I shall ride each horse in turn," declared the king. He climbed up on to the first horse, but it bolted and left the king hanging by the stirrups. The next horse threw the king right up in the air! The next horse was so nervous that his teeth chattered. Then it was Beauty's turn. She carried the king magnificently, until she stumbled at the end. At last it was Rusty's turn. Rusty carried the king quite slowly and

steadily, making sure he picked his feet up carefully, so that his royal highness would not be jolted. "Thank you for a most pleasant ride," said the king dismounting. There was a hush as the horses and their owners awaited the result of the contest. "I have decided," announced the king, "that Rusty is the winner. Not only did he give me a most comfortable ride, but he accepted his other defeats with dignity. Speed and strength are not everything, you know."

Rusty and Fred were overjoyed, and even Beauty offered her congratulations. "Although I probably would have won if I hadn't stumbled," she muttered.

So Rusty proudly pulled the king's carriage that evening, and he made such a good job of it that the king asked him if he would do it again the following year. Then the king asked Fred if his daughter could ride Beauty from time to time. He even gave Fred a bag of gold to pay for the horses' upkeep. So the three of them were happy as they never had been before as they returned home to the farm that night.

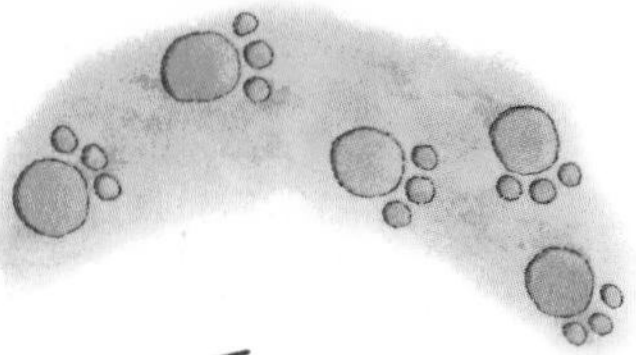

One Man Went To Mov

One man went to mow, went to mow a meadow,
One man and his dog, Spot,
Went to mow a meadow.

Two men went to mow, went to mow a meadow,
Two men, one man and his dog, Spot,
Went to mow a meadow.

Three men went to mow, went to mow a meadow,
Three men, two men, one man and his dog, Spo
Went to mow a meadow.

Four men went to mow, went to mow a meadow,
Four men, three men, two men, one man and hi
dog, Spot,
Went to mow a meadow.

Hey de Ho

Hey de, hey de ho,
The great big elephant
Is so slow.
Hey de, hey de ho,
The elephant is so slow.

He swings his tail
From side to side,
As he takes the children
For a ride.

Hey de, hey de ho,
The elephant is so slow.

Tom, He Was a Piper's Son

Tom, he was a piper's son,
He learnt to play when he was young,
And all the tune that he could play,
Was, "Over the hills and far away."

Over the hills and a great way off,
The wind shall blow my topknot off.

Little Miss Muffet

Little Miss Muffet
  Sat on a tuffet,
Eating her curds and whey;
  There came a big spider,
Who sat down beside her,
  And frightened Miss Muffet away.

Little Bo-Peep

Little Bo-peep has lost her sheep,
  And can't tell where to find them;
Leave them alone, and they'll come home,
  And bring their tails behind them.

Little Bo-peep fell fast asleep,
  And dreamt she heard them bleating;
But when she awoke, she found it a joke,
  For they were still a-fleeting.

Then up she took her little crook,
  Determined for to find them;
She found them indeed, but it made her heart bleed,
  For they'd left all their tails behind'em.

The Farmer's in his Den

The farmer's in his den,
  The farmer's in his den,
E I E I
  The farmer's in his den.

The farmer wants a wife,
  The farmer wants a wife,
E I E I
  The farmer wants a wife.

The wife wants a child,
  The wife wants a child,
E I E I
  The wife wants a child.

The child wants a nurse,
  The child wants a nurse,
E I E I
  The child wants a nurse.

The nurse wants a dog,
  The nurse wants a dog,
E I E I
  The nurse wants a dog.

We all pat the dog,
  We all pat the dog,
E I E I
  We all pat the dog.

Milly the Greedy Puppy

Milly the Labrador puppy just loved eating. She wasn't fussy about what she ate, and didn't really mind whom it belonged to.

"You'll get fat," warned Tom, the farm cat. But Milly was too busy chewing a tasty fishbone to take any notice.

One day, Milly was in a particularly greedy mood. Before breakfast she sneaked into the kitchen and ate Tom's biscuits. After a big breakfast of fresh sardines and milk, she took a short break before nibbling her way through the horse's oats. The horse didn't seem to mind.

Then Milly had a quick nap. She felt quite hungry when she awoke, so she ate all the tastiest titbits from the pigs' trough. But she made sure she left plenty of room for lunch.

After a light lunch, Milly couldn't help feeling just a bit hungry – so she wolfed down Farmer Jones's meat pie. He'd left it on the window ledge so he obviously didn't want it.

After that, Milly knocked over the dustbin and rifled through the kitchen waste. It was full of the yummiest leftovers.

There was just enough time for another nap before nipping into the milking shed for milking time. Milly always enjoyed lapping up the odd bucketful of fresh milk when Farmer Jones wasn't looking.

Dinner was Milly's favourite meal of the day. It was amazing how fast she could eat a huge bowl of meat and biscuits.

Before going to bed, Milly walked around the yard cleaning up the scraps the hens had left behind. Wasn't she a helpful puppy!

Just as Milly was chewing a particularly tasty bit of bread, she saw something black out of the corner of her eye. It was Tom the farm cat, out for his evening stroll. If there was one thing Milly liked doing best of all, it was eating Tom's dinner when he wasn't looking.

Milly raced across the yard, around the barn and through the cat flap.

"Woof! Woof!" yelped Milly. She was stuck half-way through the cat flap. Greedy Milly had eaten so much food that her tummy was too big to fit through.

"Ha! Ha!" laughed the farm animals, who thought it served Milly right for eating all their food.

"Oh, dear!" smiled Tom when he came back to see what all the noise was about. He caught hold of Milly's legs and tried pulling her out. Then he tried pushing her out. But it was no good – she was stuck.

All the farm animals joined in. They pulled and pulled, until, POP! Out flew Milly.

Poor Milly felt so silly that she never ate anyone else's food again – unless they offered, that is!

Gym Giraffe

Jeremy Giraffe loved going out with his dad to gather the juicy green leaves for their dinner.

"This is where the most delicious leaves are," said Dad, reaching w-a-a-a-y up to a very high branch. "Remember the tallest trees have the tastiest leaves, and the tiny top leaves are the tenderest!"

One morning, Jeremy decided it was time to gather leaves on his own. "The tallest trees have the tastiest leaves," he whispered to himself, "and the tiny top leaves are the tenderest."

Jeremy stopped at a very tall tree and looked up. There at the top were some tiny, tender, tasty-looking leaves. Str - e - e - e - e - etching his neck just as he had seen his dad do, Jeremy reached as high as he could. It wasn't very high! "Oh, no," he thought. "How will I reach the tiny, tasty top leaves if my neck won't stretch?"

So Jeremy went back home with his neck hanging down in despair.

"Why, Jeremy, what's wrong?" asked his mum. When Jeremy told her, she gave his neck a nuzzle. "Your neck's still growing," she assured him. "Eat your greens and get lots of sleep, and you'll soon be able to reach the tastiest, tenderest leaves on the tallest trees in the jungle!"

That afternoon, Jeremy went out to try again. Portia Parrot saw Jeremy struggling to reach the top of the tree. Trying to be helpful, she swooped down and plucked a few of the tenderest leaves for him.

When Portia gave Jeremy the leaves, his spots went pale with shame and embarrassment.

"I should be able to get those myself," he wailed. "Why won't my neck stretch?"

"Oh, Jeremy," said Portia, "your neck is just fine! Keep eating your greens and getting lots of sleep, and it will grow!"

"But I can't wait," Jeremy insisted. "Isn't there anything I can do to stretch my neck now?"

"Perhaps there is," said Portia, thoughtfully. "Follow me!"

Portia led Jeremy through the jungle to a clearing. Jeremy's eyes widened with wonder at what he saw. There was so much going on! Seymour Snake was wrapping himself round a fallen tree trunk. "Hello, Jeremy," he hissed. "Jussssst doing my sssssslithering exercisessssss!"

Emma, Ellen and Eric Elephant were hoisting logs. "Hi, Jeremy," they called. "This is our trunk-strengthening workout!"

In the river, Claudia Crocodile was breaking thick branches in half. "Just limbering up my jaw muscles," she snapped.

Leonard Lion was taking his cubs, Louis and Lisa, through their pouncing paces. "Welcome to the Jungle Gym!" he called.

A few minutes later, Grandpa Gorilla and Leonard Lion came to greet Jeremy.

"What can we do for you?" they asked.

"Can you help me stretch my neck?" asked Jeremy. "I want to be able to reach the tasty, tiny, tender leaves."

"You're still growing," said Leonard Lion. "You just have to eat your greens and get lots of sleep."

Jeremy's face fell, until Grandpa Gorilla said, "But we will help things along with some special neck-stretching exercises. Come with us!"

Grandpa got Jeremy started right away.

"S-t-r-e-t-c-h to the left! S-t-r-e-t-c-h to the right!" Grandpa Gorilla shouted. "Chin lifts next," said Leonard Lion.

Jeremy s-t-r-e-e-e-t-c-h-e-d his neck to reach the branch.

"Come on, you can do it!" Portia said, cheering him on. Grandpa Gorilla told Jeremy to lie down. Then he called Seymour Snake. "Start slithering!" he said.

"Aaaaakkkk!" gasped Jeremy, as Seymour wrapped himself round his neck. "Not so tight," said Grandpa.

"That's better!" said Jeremy, as Seymour slithered along, pu-u-u-l-l-ing his neck muscles. All the exercise made Jeremy hungry.

At supper, he had three BIG helpings of greens. He was tired, too, so he went to bed early and slept soundly.

Jeremy loved the Jungle Gym and couldn't wait to go back. After his workout each day, Jeremy ate a good supper.

"Exercising makes me soooo hungry..." he said, "...and soooo tired," he yawned, as he fell asleep.

The next time Jeremy and his dad went out leaf-gathering together, Jeremy spotted some sweet-looking leaves right at the top of a tall tree.

"I'm going to get those," he said.

"They're so high up!" said Dad.

Jeremy didn't hear him. He was too busy stretching… and stretching… and stretching… until he stretched right up to the very top branch!

"I've done it, Dad!" he cried happily. "The exercises worked!"

"I don't think it matters," said his mum. "What matters is that you have a fine, strong, long neck that any giraffe would be proud of!"

"And I am!" said Jeremy, taking another mouthful of tasty, tender leaves. He chewed the leaves extra thoroughly – because he knew they had a very long way to go!

The Fieldmouse

Where the acorn tumbles down,
  There the ash tree sheds its berry,
With your fur so soft and brown,
  With your eye so round and merry,
Scarcely moving the long grass,
  Fieldmouse, I can see you pass.

Little thing, in what dark den,
  Lie you all the winter sleeping?
Till warm weather comes again,
  Then once more I see you peeping
Round about the tall tree roots,
  Nibbling at their fallen fruits.

Fieldmouse, fieldmouse, do not go,
  Where the farmer stacks his treasure,
Find the nut that falls below,
  Eat the acorn at your pleasure,
But you must not steal the grain
  He has stacked with so much pain.

Make your hole where mosses spring,
  Underneath the tall oak's shadow,
Pretty, quiet, harmless thing,
  Play about the sunny meadow.
Keep away from corn and house,
  None will harm you, little mouse.

CECIL FRANCES ALEXANDER

The Camel's Complaint

Canary-birds feed on sugar and seed,
  Parrots have crackers to crunch;
And as for the poodles, they tell me the noodles
  Have chicken and cream for their lunch.
    But there's never a question
    About *my* digestion –
      Anything does for me.

Cats, you're aware, can repose in a chair,
  Chickens can roost upon rails;
Puppies are able to sleep in a stable,
  And oysters can slumber in pails.
    But no one supposes
    A poor camel dozes –
      Any place does for me.

The Tyger

Tyger! Tyger! burning bright
  In the forests of the night,
What immortal hand or eye
  Could frame thy fearful symmetry?

In what distant deeps or skies
  Burnt the fire of thine eyes?
On what wings dare he aspire?
  What the hand dare seize the fire?

And what shoulder, and what art,
  Could twist the sinews of thy heart?
And, when thy heart began to beat,
  What dread hand? and what dread feet?

What the hammer? what the chain?
  In what furnace was thy brain?
What the anvil, what dread grasp
  Dare its deadly terrors clasp?

When the stars threw down their spears,
  And water'd heaven with their tears,
Did he smile his work to see?
  Did he who made the Lamb make thee?

Tyger! Tyger! burning bright
  In the forests of the night,
What immortal hand or eye,
  Dare frame thy fearful symmetry?

WILLIAM BLAKE

Wynken, Blynken, and Nod

Wynken, Blynken,
  and Nod one night
Sailed off in a
  wooden shoe –
Sailed on a river
  of crystal light,
Into a sea of dew.

"Where are you going,
  and what do you wish?"
The old moon asked
  the three.
"We have come to fish
  for the herring fish
That live in this beautiful sea.

Jimbo Comes Home

Jimbo the circus elephant was snoring away in his cage one night when he heard a strange noise. At first he thought it was part of his dream. In his dream he was walking across a hot, dusty plain while in the distance there was the sound of thunder.

All at once Jimbo was wide awake. He realised that he was in his cage after all and that what he thought was the sound of thunder was the noise of his cage on the move. Now this worried him, because the circus never moved at night. He rose to his feet and looked around. He could see men pulling on the tow bar at the front of the cage. These were strangers – it certainly wasn't Carlos his trainer! Jimbo started to bellow, "Help! Stop thief!" But it was too late. His cage was already rumbling out of the circus ground and down the road.

Eventually, the cage passed through a gate marked "Zipper's Circus" and Jimbo knew what had happened. He had been stolen by the Zipper family, his own circus family's greatest rivals! Jimbo was furious. How had the

thieves got away with it? Surely someone at Ronaldo's Circus must have heard them stealing him? But Jimbo waited in vain to be rescued.

The next morning, the thieves opened up Jimbo's cage and tried to coax him out, but he stayed put. In the end, after much struggling, they managed to pull him out. Once he was out of his cage, he took the biggest drink of water he could from a bucket and soaked his new keeper! He refused to cooperate, kicked over his food, and when he appeared in the circus that night he made sure he got all the tricks wrong.

"Don't worry," said Mr Zipper to Jimbo's new trainer, "he'll just take a little while to settle down. Soon he'll forget that he was once part of Ronaldo's Circus." But Jimbo didn't forget for, as you know, an elephant never forgets.

One night, a mouse passed by his cage. "Hello," called Jimbo mournfully, for by now he was feeling very lonely, and no one had cleaned out his cage for days.

"Hello!" said the mouse. "You don't look very happy. What's the matter?" Jimbo explained how he had been stolen and wanted to escape back to his own circus. The mouse listened and then said, "I'll try to help."

So saying, he scampered off and soon he was back with a bunch of keys. Jimbo was astonished. "Easy!" said the mouse. "The keeper was asleep, so I helped myself."

Jimbo took the keys in his trunk and unlocked the door to the cage. He was free! "Thank you!" he called to the mouse, who was already scurrying away.

Jimbo's first thought was to get back to his own circus as fast as possible. However, he wanted to teach those thieves a lesson. He could hear them snoring in their caravan. He tiptoed up, as quietly as an elephant can tiptoe, and slid into the horse's harness at the front.

"Hey, what do you think you're doing?" neighed one of the horses, but Jimbo was already hauling the robbers' caravan out of the gate and down the road.

So gently did he pull the caravan that the thieves never once woke up. Eventually they reached Ronaldo's Circus. Mr Ronaldo was dumbstruck to see Jimbo pulling a caravan just like a horse! Mr Ronaldo walked over to the caravan and was astonished to see the robbers still fast asleep. He raced to the telephone and called the police, and it wasn't until they

heard the police siren that the robbers woke up. By then it was too late. As they emerged from the caravan scratching and shaking their heads they were arrested on the spot and taken off to jail. "There are a few questions we would like to ask Mr Zipper regarding the theft of some other circus animals, too," said one of the police officers.

Mr Ronaldo, and Jimbo's keeper Carlos, were both delighted to see Jimbo back home again. And Jimbo was just as delighted to be back home. Then Mr Ronaldo and Carlos started whispering to each other and began walking away looking secretive. "We'll be back soon, we promise," they said to Jimbo. When they returned, they were pushing Jimbo's old cage. It had been freshly painted, there was clean, sweet-smelling straw inside, but best of all there was no lock on the door! "Now you can come and go as you please," said Carlos.

And Jimbo trumpeted long and loud with his trunk held high, which Carlos knew was his way of saying, "THANK YOU!"

The Dotty Professor

Professor Von Bean was very excited. He had finished building his machine and it was ready to use. It was the most complicated contraption he had ever built and he was very proud of it.

The professor called his assistant to come to watch him start the machine. The wheels were green and brown, and there were levers on either side. The side panels were striped red and white, and there was a big chimney on the top for the smoke to escape. There was a cupboard on the side which, the professor explained, was to hang a wet coat. There was a shelf on the back for a box of plants.

While Professor Von Bean was getting more and more excited, his assistant looked very worried and puzzled.

"But what does it *do?*" he asked, timidly.

The professor scratched his head and thought.

"Oh dear, oh dear!" he sighed. "What a fool I have been! Why I didn't think of that? It does absolutely nothing useful at all!"

My Funny Family

I think that there is definitely something very strange about my family, in fact they are all very funny!

My auntie May has got a brain like a sieve, she forgets where things live. She puts a chop in the teapot and carrots in the mugs!

My uncle Fred has ears like cauliflowers, he can hear an ant whistling from a mile away, butterflies beating their wings and woodlice snoring!

My cousin Bob has eyes like a hawk, he can see from London to New York and unknown planets orbiting in space!

My brother Tom has spiders and bugs up his sleeve, which he loves to wave under my nose so that I scream.

My dog Jasper will eat anything, but especially loves fish and chips, cakes and buttered toast.

Luckily I am not so strange, I just like to dance all day!

Rapunzel

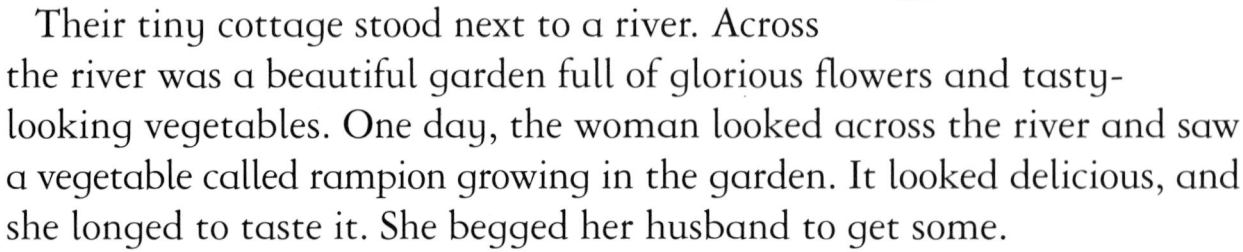

Once upon a time there lived a couple who, after many years, found they were expecting a baby.

Their tiny cottage stood next to a river. Across the river was a beautiful garden full of glorious flowers and tasty-looking vegetables. One day, the woman looked across the river and saw a vegetable called rampion growing in the garden. It looked delicious, and she longed to taste it. She begged her husband to get some.

The garden belonged to an evil witch, and he refused. But his wife would eat nothing else, and grew thin and pale. At last he agreed.

That night, the man crossed the river, entered the witch's garden and picked handfuls of rampion. Suddenly, the evil witch appeared. "How dare you steal from me!" she roared.

"F-Forgive me," the man stammered. "My wife is expecting a baby and longed for some of this vegetable. If she doesn't have it, I'm afraid she will die."

"Very well," said the witch, "take all you want. But you must give me something in return. When your baby is born, I must have it."

Terrified, the man agreed and fled.

The wife was overjoyed and made a salad with the rampion. She ate it hungrily.

After that, the man went to the witch's garden every day. He brought home baskets full of rampion for his wife, and she grew strong and healthy. A few months later she gave birth to a beautiful baby girl.

The man had forgotten all about his promise to the witch, but when the baby was just a day old, she burst in and took her away. The baby's parents were heartbroken and never saw her or the witch again.

The witch called the baby Rapunzel. She took her to a cottage deep in a forest, and took good care of her.

On Rapunzel's twelfth birthday, the witch imprisoned her in a forbidding high tower, with no doors and just one small window at the very top.

Every day the witch came and stood at the bottom of the tower, and called:

"Rapunzel, Rapunzel!
Let down your long hair!"

Rapunzel would let down her long, golden hair, and the witch would begin to climb up.

Rapunzel spent many lonely years in her tower. To pass the time, she often sat by the window and sang.

One day, a prince rode through the forest. Enchanted by the sound of Rapunzel's sweet voice, the young prince followed it until he came to the doorless tower.

Just then the witch arrived. The prince quickly hid as she called:

"Rapunzel, Rapunzel!
Let down your long hair!"

The witch began to climb the hair, and the prince knew that this was the way he would be able to meet the owner of the beautiful voice.

After the witch had gone, the prince stood beneath the tower and called in a voice like the witch's:

"Rapunzel, Rapunzel!
Let down your long hair!"

When Rapunzel's golden hair came tumbling down, he climbed up to the window.

Rapunzel was frightened when she saw the prince. But he was gentle and kind, and she quickly lost her fear.

The prince came to see Rapunzel often, and they soon fell in love. He asked her to marry him – but how would Rapunzel leave the tower?

Rapunzel had an idea. "Each time you visit," she told the prince, "bring me a ball of strong silk. I will plait it into a long, long ladder. When it is finished I will climb down and run away to marry you."

The prince did as Rapunzel asked, and soon the ladder was ready.

But, on the very day she was to run away, something terrible happened. When the witch climbed through the window, Rapunzel absent-mindedly asked, "Why do you pull so hard at my hair? The prince is not so rough." Suddenly, Rapunzel realised what she had said.

The witch flew into a raging fury. "You ungrateful little wretch!" she screamed. "I have protected you from the world, and you have betrayed me. Now you must be punished!"

"I'm sorry," Rapunzel sobbed, as she fell to her knees. "I didn't mean to make you cross."

The witch grabbed a pair of scissors and – snip-snap-snip-snap – cut off Rapunzel's long golden hair. Then, using the ladder to climb down, the witch carried Rapunzel off to a faraway land, where she left her to wander all alone without any food, water or anything to keep her warm.

That evening, when the prince called, the witch let down Rapunzel's hair. The prince climbed up quickly, and couldn't believe his eyes!

"The bird has flown, my pretty!" the witch cackled evilly. "You will never see Rapunzel again!"

Overcome with grief, the sad

prince threw himself from the tower. His fall was broken by some brambles, but they also scratched and blinded him.

The prince stumbled away and wandered the land for a year, living on berries and rain water.

Then one day the prince heard a beautiful sound – the sweet voice of Rapunzel! He called her name and she ran into his arms, weeping tears of joy. The tears fell onto the prince's wounded eyes and suddenly he could see again.

The prince took his Rapunzel home to his castle, where they were married and lived happily ever after.

The Football Fairy

Georgina loved to play football. But there was just one problem. "I'm fed up with these silly wings," she said, wiggling her shoulders. "They just get in the way."

"Flying is brilliant, and anyway football is a game for elves, not fairies!" said Sparkle.

"In that case, I don't want to be a fairy!" said Georgina, and stamped off. "She'll change her mind," said the wise fairy, "just wait and see."

But Georgina wouldn't change her mind. She pulled on her football boots and went to play with the elves.

The football game was very rough. The ball bounced around the field and, quite often, off the field! Sometimes it went up into the trees. Two birds who were trying to build their nest got very fed up.

Georgina flew up to get it. "Perhaps my wings can be useful after all," she thought. She looked round quickly, hoping no one had seen her.

But Barry, the elf, had and he couldn't wait to tell the fairies. "Ah," nodded the wise fairy. "I knew she would use her wings sooner or later."

The next time Georgina played football, the game was rougher than ever. One elf kicked the ball so hard it flew into the tree and hit the birds' nest. This time there was an egg in it!

The egg began to topple, but none of the elves noticed; they were far too busy arguing with the referee.

Georgina flew up and, just in time, caught the egg before it hit the ground. Then she flew up to the nest.

"Thank you," said the mummy bird, tucking the egg back under her. "But please, be more careful when you play football!"

Next time she played football, Georgina checked the tree first. The mummy bird was away. "Good!" she thought. "She can't complain this time." But, thanks to a naughty elf, the football knocked into the birds' nest. A small bundle of feathers tumbled out. It was a baby bird!

Georgina spotted it and, quick as lightening, she flew up to catch him. Gently, she held him in her arms and flew back to the nest. When he was safely inside she sprinkled him with fairy dust to keep him from further harm. Just then the mummy bird came back.

"I shall tell everyone about your kindness," she said, as her baby snuggled under her feathers. "And, as you're such a good fairy, will you be baby Beak's godmother?"

"Oh, thank you! I'd be delighted!" said Georgina.

When they heard the news, the other fairies were very proud of her.

"Perhaps it's not so bad being a fairy after all," grinned Georgina, happily.

This is the Way the Ladies Ride

This is the way the ladies ride:
  Tri, tre, tre, tree,
  Tri, tre, tre, tree!
This is the way the ladies ride:
  Tri, tre, tre, tre, tri-tre-tre-tree!

This is the way the gentlemen ride:
  Gallop-a-trot,
  Gallop-a-trot!
This is the way the gentlemen ride:
  Gallop-a-gallop-a-trot!

This is the way the farmers ride:
  Hobbledy-hoy,
  Hobbledy-hoy!
This is the way the farmers ride:
  Hobbledy hobbledy-hoy!

This is the way the butcher boy rides,
  Tripperty-trot,
  Tripperty-trot.
Till he falls in a ditch
  With a flipperty,
  Flipperty, flop, flop, FLOP!

One Moisty Morning

One misty moisty morning,
  When cloudy was the weather,
There I met an old man
  Clothed all in leather;

Clothed all in leather,
  With cap under his chin –
How do you do, and how do you do,
  And how do you do again!

The Lion and the Unicorn

The lion and the unicorn
  Were fighting for the crown:
The lion beat the unicorn
  All round the town.
Some gave them white bread,
  Some gave them brown:
Some gave them plum-cake
  And drummed them out of town.

Old MacDonald

Old Macdonald had a farm,
E...I...E...I...O
And on that farm he had
some cows,
E...I...E...I...O
With a moo-moo here,
And a moo-moo there,
Here a moo, there a moo,
Everywhere a moo-moo,
Old Macdonald had a farm,
E...I...E...I...O

Old Macdonald had a farm,
E...I...E...I...O
And on that farm he had
some ducks,
E...I...E...I...O
With a quack-quack here,
And a quack-quack there,
Here a quack, there a quack,
Everywhere a quack-quack,
Old Macdonald had a farm,
E...I...E...I...O.

For Want of a Nail

For want of a nail, the shoe was lost;
For want of the shoe, the horse was lost;
For want of the horse, the rider was lost;
For want of the rider, the battle was lost;
For want of the battle, the kingdom was lost;
And all for the want of a horseshoe nail.

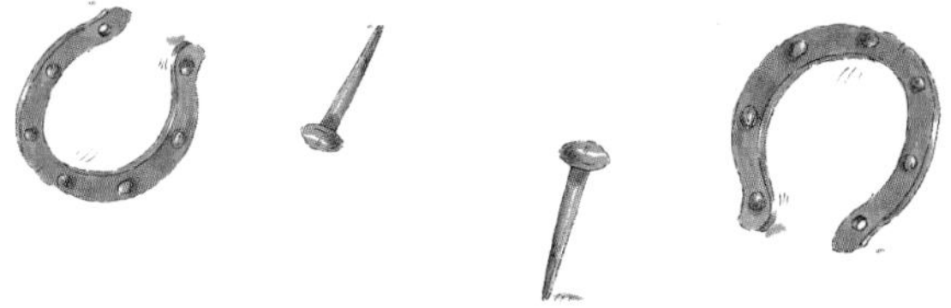

A Farmyard Song

I had a cat and the cat pleased me,
I fed my cat by yonder tree;
Cat goes fiddle-i-fee.

I had a hen and the hen pleased me,
I fed my hen by yonder tree;
Hen goes chimmy-chuck, chimmy-chuck,
Cat goes fiddle-i-fee.

I had a duck and the duck pleased me,
I fed my duck by yonder tree;
Duck goes quack, quack,
Hen goes chimmy-chuck, chimmy-chuck,
Cat goes fiddle-i-fee.

Bone Crazy

Alfie sat in his basket chewing on a large bone. Mmm! It tasted good. When he had chewed it for long enough, he took it down to the bottom of the garden, to bury it in his favourite spot, beneath the old oak tree. He didn't see next door's dog, Ferdy, watching him through a hole in the fence.

The next day, when Alfie went to dig up his bone, it was gone! He dug all around, but it was nowhere to be found. Just then, he spied a trail of muddy paw prints leading to the fence, and he realised what had happened. Alfie was too big to fit through the fence and get his bone back, so he thought of a plan, instead! Next day he buried another bone. This time, he knew Ferdy was watching him.

Later he hid and watched as Ferdy crept into the garden and started to dig up the bone. Just then, Ferdy yelped in pain. The bone had bitten his nose! He flew across the garden and through the fence leaving the bone behind.

Alfie's friend Mole crept out from where the bone was buried. How the two friends laughed at their trick! And from then on, Ferdy always kept safely to his side of the fence!

Little Tim and his Brother Sam

Little Tim was a very lucky boy. He had a lovely home, with the nicest parents you could hope for. He had a big garden, with a swing and a football net in it. And growing in the garden were lots of trees that you could climb and have adventures in. Little Tim even had a nice school, which he enjoyed going to every day and where he had lots of friends. In fact, almost everything in Tim's life was nice. Everything that is apart from one thing – Tim's brother Sam.

Sam was a very naughty boy. Worse still, whenever he got into mischief – which he did almost all of the time – he managed to make it look as though someone else was to blame. And that someone was usually poor Tim!

Once Sam thought that he would put salt in the sugar bowl instead of sugar. That afternoon, Sam and Tim's parents had some friends round for tea. All the guests put salt in their cups of tea, of course, thinking it was sugar. Well, being very polite they didn't like to complain,

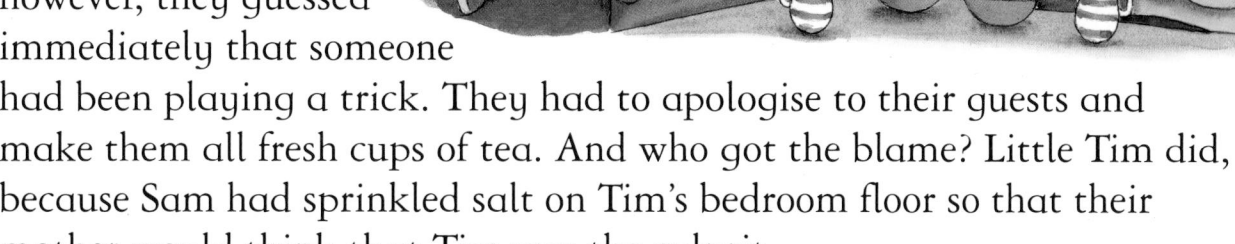

even though their cups of tea tasted *very* strange! When Sam and Tim's parents tasted their tea, however, they guessed immediately that someone had been playing a trick. They had to apologise to their guests and make them all fresh cups of tea. And who got the blame? Little Tim did, because Sam had sprinkled salt on Tim's bedroom floor so that their mother would think that Tim was the culprit.

Then there was the time when Sam and Tim's Aunt Jessica came to stay. She was a very nice lady, but she hated anything creepy-crawly, and as far as she was concerned that included frogs. So what did Sam do? Why, he went down to the garden pond and got a big, green frog to put in Aunt Jessica's handbag. When Aunt Jessica opened her handbag to get her glasses out, there staring out of the bag at her were two froggy eyes.

"Croak!" said the frog.

"Eeek!" yelled Aunt Jessica and almost jumped out of her skin.

"I told Tim not to do it," said Sam.

Tim opened his mouth and was just about to protest his innocence when his mother said, "Tim, go to your room immediately and don't come out until you are told."

Poor Tim went to his room and had to stay there until after supper. Sam thought it was very funny.

The next day, Sam decided that he would play another prank and blame it on Tim. He went to the garden shed and, one by one, took out all the garden tools. When he thought no one was watching, he hid them all in Tim's bedroom cupboard. In went the spade, the fork, the watering can, the trowel – in fact, everything except the lawnmower. And the only reason that the lawnmower didn't go in was because it was too heavy to carry!

But this time, Sam's little prank was about to come unstuck, for Aunt Jessica had seen him creeping up the stairs to Tim's bedroom with the garden tools. She guessed immediately what Sam was up to, and who was likely to get the blame. When Sam wasn't about, she spoke to Tim. The two of them whispered to each other for a few seconds and then smiled triumphantly.

Later that day, Sam and Tim's father went to the garden shed to fetch the tools to do some gardening. Imagine his surprise when all he saw were some old flower pots and the lawnmower. He searched high and low for the garden tools. He looked behind the compost heap, under the garden steps, behind the sandpit and in the garage. But they weren't anywhere to be seen.

Then he started searching in the house. He looked in all the kitchen cupboards, and was just looking under the stairs when something at the top of the stairs caught his eye. The handle from the garden spade was sticking out of the door to Sam's bedroom. Looking rather puzzled, he went

upstairs and walked into Sam's bedroom. There, nestling neatly in the cupboard, were the rest of the tools.

"Sam, come up here immediately," called his father.

Sam, not realising anything was amiss, came sauntering upstairs. Suddenly he saw all the garden tools that he had so carefully hidden in Tim's cupboard now sitting in *his* cupboard. He was speechless.

"Right," said his father, "before you go out to play, you can take all the tools back down to the garden shed. Then you can cut the grass. Then you can dig over the flower beds, and then you can do the weeding."

Well, it took Sam hours to do all the gardening. Tim and Aunt Jessica watched from the window and clutched their sides with laughter. Sam never did find out how all the garden tools found their way into his bedroom, but I think you've guessed, haven't you?

Hearts, Like Doors

Hearts, like doors, will open with ease
To very, very, little keys,
And don't forget that two of these
Are "I thank you" and "If you please".

Mother Shuttle

Old Mother Shuttle
Lived in a coal-scuttle
Along with her dog and her cat;
What they ate I can't tell,
But 'tis known very well
That not one of the party was fat.

Little Husband

I had a little husband,
No bigger than my thumb;
I put him in a pint pot
And there I bade him drum.
I gave him some garters
To garter up his hose,
And a little silk handkerchief
To wipe his pretty nose.

Rumpty-iddity

Rummpty-iddity, row, row, row,
If I had a good supper,
I could eat it now.

Willy Boy

Willy boy, Willy boy,
Where are you going?
I will go with you,
If that I may.
I'm going to the meadow
To see them a-mowing,
I am going to help them
Turn the new hay.

Two Little Dogs

Two little dogs
Sat by the fire
Over a fender of coal-dust;
Said one little dog
To the other little dog,
If you don't talk, why, I must.

The Robins

A robin and a robin's son
Once went to town to buy a bun.
They couldn't decide on a plum or plain,
And so they went back home again.

The Merchants of London

Hey diddle dinkety, poppety, pet,
The merchants of London they wear scarlet;
Silk in the collar and gold in the hem,
So merrily march the merchant men.

The Dame of Dundee

There was an old woman,
Who lived in Dundee,
And in her back garden
There was a plum tree;
The plums they grew rotten
Before they grew ripe,
And she sold them
Three farthings a pint.

Christmas Eve

On Christmas Eve I turned the spit,
I burnt my fingers, I feel it yet;
The little cock sparrow flew over the table,
The pot began to play with the ladle.

Gingerbread Men

Smiling girls, rosy boys,
Come and buy my little toys;
Monkeys made of gingerbread,
And sugar horses painted red.

First

First in a carriage,
Second in a gig,
Third on a donkey,
And fourth on a pig.

The Wedding

Pussicat, wussicat, with a white foot,
When is your wedding and I'll come to it.
The beer's to brew, and the bread's to bake,
Pussicat, wussicat, don't be too late.

A Good Example

Tilly and Old George were kind old horses, but they didn't understand the young animals who tore around the farmyard.

"Look at that piglet," Tilly grumbled one day. "He's leaving muddy trotter-prints all over the yard."

"And those noisy chicks and ducklings are not behaving very well either," neighed Old George, nodding his head in agreement. "They should know better than to cheep and quack during our afternoon nap."

"Things were very different in the old days," sighed Tilly. "Youngsters were well brought up then. When we were foals, we were tidy and very, very quiet."

Unfortunately, Tilly and Old George didn't keep their feelings to themselves…

The next morning, Tilly told Percy the pig how to discipline his piglets.

Old George gave Jenny and Henrietta the hens some advice and tips on bringing up chicks. And both the horses had a word with Doris the duck about the correct time and place for ducklings to quack.

By lunch time, there wasn't a single animal on the farmyard who wasn't feeling cross with Tilly and Old George.

"I'd like to see them look after even one little one," said Doris.

Strangely enough, it was that afternoon that Old MacDonald brought a new foal to the farm for Tilly and Old George to care for. Percy, Jenny, Henrietta and Doris looked forward to having some fun!

But the animals were disappointed. The new foal, whose name was Frances, was remarkably good. She never spilled her oats, or splashed the water in her trough. She wasn't noisy, or nosy, or naughty.

Worse still, Tilly and Old George looked terribly pleased with themselves.

"You see," Old George told Percy, "it's a matter of setting a good example. If a young animal sees her parents are quiet and sensible, she naturally copies them."

And Old George made a grand, sweeping gesture with his hoof, and his shoe, which had been a little loose lately, flew right off!

The shoe shot across the farmyard. Clang! It knocked over a bucket of pig food. Clonk! It bounced off the bucket and whizzed straight through a window and into the farmhouse. Crash!

Mrs MacDonald stormed out into the yard. She was holding an apple pie with a large horseshoe sticking in it!

"Who has done this," she cried, "and made so much noise and mess?"

Old George tried to look unconcerned and calm, but the eyes of every other animal in the farmyard were upon him. And anyway, who else had shoes that big?

These days, Tilly and Old George are not quite so quick to criticise their friends. And the story of George's flying footwear still brings a smile to everyone's face – all except for Mrs MacDonald, of course!

The Mermaid in the Pool

John and Julia were on holiday at the seaside. Their mum and dad had found an amazing house with a big swimming pool. But, best of all, their bedroom overlooked the beach. It was perfect!

The first night there was a storm. The wind howled and waves crashed over the beach, right up to the house. The children sat on the bed watching the storm outside.

In the morning, the garden furniture had blown over, there was seaweed all over the lawn and there was a mermaid swimming up and down the swimming pool! John and Julia rushed outside but, when the mermaid saw them coming, she huddled in a corner of the pool. "I'm sorry I swam into your blue pool," said the frightened mermaid.

"It's okay!" said Julia gently. "We didn't mean to frighten you. We just wanted to meet you. We've never seen a mermaid before."

"My name is Marina," said the mermaid. "I was playing in the sea with my friend Blue the dolphin, when the storm began. A huge wave washed me in, and now I'm stranded, and Blue is missing!"

"We'll help you look for Blue," said Julia at once. "We might be able to see your friend from our bedroom window."

When their mum and dad were safely out of the way, John and Julia found a wheelbarrow and wheeled Marina into the house. "I've only had sky over my head," said Marina. "The house won't fall down will it?"

"Of course not," smiled John. They showed Marina all sorts of things she had never seen before. She thought the moving pictures on the television were weird. She thought Julia's teddy bear was wonderful, and that beds were the silliest things she had ever seen! But, although they looked out of the window, there was no sign of Blue the dolphin in the sea.

"I have to go home soon!" Marina said sadly. "I can't stay out of the water for long, and I must find Blue. If only I hadn't lost my shell horn in the storm I could call him."

"We'll take you down to the sea," said John. "And help you look for your shell," said Julia.

They lifted Marina back into the wheelbarrow and pushed her down to the beach. They spent the rest of the day searching for Marina's shell along the seashore. Suddenly, Julia spotted a large shell half buried in the sand. John found a stick and dug it out.

"It's my shell!" cried Marina. They washed off the sand and Marina blew into it. The most beautiful sound drifted out across the waves and, straight away, there was an answering call! Far out to sea, they saw a streak of blue-grey leaping high over the waves, swimming towards them. It was Blue the dolphin!

Marina gave a cry of joy and swam to meet him. She flung her arms round his neck and hugged him. Then she called out to the watching children. "Thank you both for helping me."

"See you next year!" called John and Julia.

And they watched as Marina and Blue swam swiftly and smoothly together, back out to sea.

Dance, Little Baby

Dance, little baby, dance up high,
Never mind, baby, mother is by;
Crow and caper, caper and crow;
There, little baby, there you go;

Up to the ceiling, down to the ground,
Backwards and forwards, round and round;
Dance, little baby, and mother will sing,
With the merry coral, ding, ding, ding!

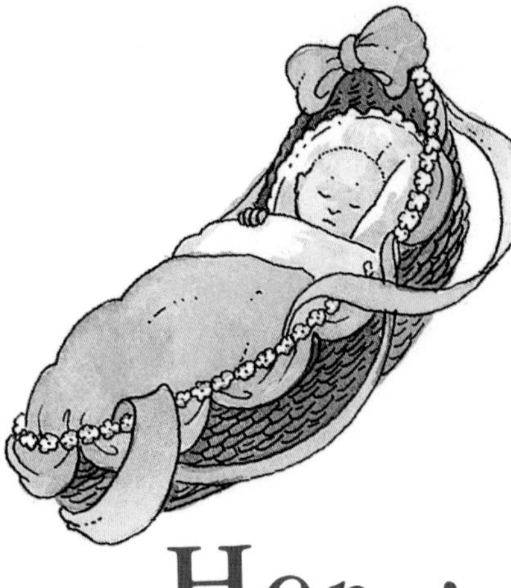

How Many Days Has My Baby to Play?

How many days has my baby to play?
Saturday, Sunday, Monday;
Tuesday, Wednesday, Thursday, Friday,
Saturday, Sunday, Monday.

Hush-a-bye, Baby

Hush-a-bye, baby, on the tree top,
When the wind blows the cradle will rock;
When the bough breaks the cradle will fall,
Down will come baby, cradle and all.

Here's a Ball for Baby

Here's a ball for baby,
Big and fat and round.

Here is baby's hammer,
See how it can pound.

Here are baby's soldiers,
Standing in a row.

Here is baby's music,
Clapping, clapping so.

Here is baby's trumpet,
Tootle-tootle-oo!

Here's the way the baby
Plays at peek-a-boo.

Here's a big umbrella,
To keep the baby dry.

Here is baby's cradle,
Rock-a-baby-bye.

Rock-a-bye, Baby

Rock-a-bye, baby, thy cradle is green;
Father's a nobleman, Mother's a queen,
And Betty's a lady, and wears a gold ring,
And Johnny's a drummer, and drums for the King.

Hush-a-bye, Don't You Cry

Hush-a-bye, don't you cry,
Go to sleepy little baby.
When you wake
You shall have
All the pretty little horses.
Blacks and bays,
Dapples and greys,
Coach and six white horses.
Hush-a-bye, don't you cry,
Go to sleepy little baby.
When you wake
You shall have cake
And all the pretty little horses.

Baby, Baby Bunting

Baby, baby bunting,
Father's gone a-hunting,
To fetch a little rabbit-skin
To wrap his baby bunting in.

The Baby in the Cradle

The baby in the cradle
Goes rock-a-rock-a-rock.
The clock on the dresser
Goes tick-a-tick-a-tock.

The rain on the window
Goes tap-a-tap-a-tap,
But here comes the sun,
So we clap-a-clap-a-clap!

Patch on Patrol

Early one morning, Farmer Sam was driving his tractor, when he saw something moving at the side of the road. He stopped the tractor and jumped down to take a look. "Well, well," said Sam. "What are you doing here?"

A small puppy tried to wag his tail. He was shivering and crying. Sam gently picked up the puppy, brushed away the dirt and leaves and tucked him inside his warm jacket. "I'd better get you to Haven Farm Animal Hospital," he said.

At the animal hospital, the Haven family took the puppy from Farmer Sam, promising to look after him. "What a scruffy mess!" said Dad. "I'm sure a bath and some good food will make him feel much better." So, Sally and Joe decided to call the puppy Scruff. After a bath, they put him in a basket by the fire. "Scruff's so friendly!" said Sally. "I'm sure he must have a family, somewhere. They'll be missing him so much."

"Let's make a poster," said Joe. "We can put it up in the village, when we go shopping with Mum."

Later that day, Joe and Sally pinned their poster on the village

notice board. Mum followed with Scruff on a lead. Scruff was so excited that he ran round and round, getting Mum in such a tangle! "Scruff's going to be so good at rounding up people!" said Joe, laughing.

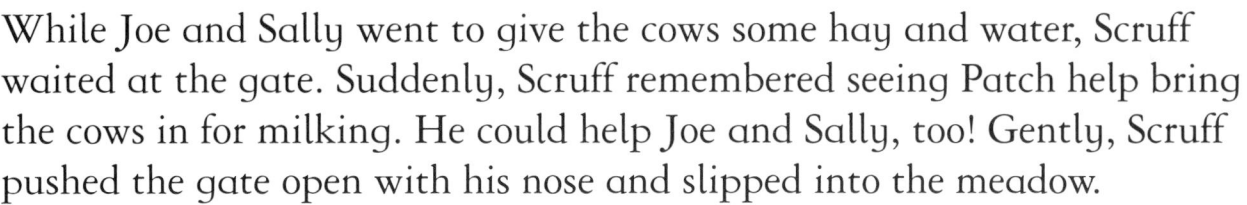

Back at the farm, Sally and Joe took Scruff with them so that he would get used to all the other animals. While Joe and Sally went to give the cows some hay and water, Scruff waited at the gate. Suddenly, Scruff remembered seeing Patch help bring the cows in for milking. He could help Joe and Sally, too! Gently, Scruff pushed the gate open with his nose and slipped into the meadow.

Scruff barked and ran round the meadow, the same way he had seen Patch round up the sheep! The cows ran in every direction, until Marigold, the oldest cow, led them all out of the field towards the milking shed. "No, Scruff, no!" wailed Joe and Sally. "It's not milking time yet!" But Scruff, pleased to have helped, just wagged his tail, which, like the rest of him, was covered in mud, grass and cow dung!

Luckily, Patch heard the cows coming up the lane and knew just what to do. He stopped Marigold before she reached the milking shed and barked at her to go back to the meadow. Mooing loudly, Marigold turned around and all the other cows followed her back. "Good dog, Patch!" said Sally. "As for you, Scruff, you'll have to have a bath. You pong!"

Scruff lay in the warm sun with Patch, while everybody had lunch.

Then he left Patch snoozing and trotted off to explore the farm. Patch opened one eye and sighed. He would have to follow Scruff to make sure he didn't get into any more trouble!

Scruff decided to look in the stables. There, he spotted Tabby the cat, asleep on top of the hay. Scruff wanted to say hello, so he leapt on to the hay, barking with excitement. Tabby woke with a fright and was so alarmed that she ran away into Old Major's stall. Chasing after her, Scruff came right up against Old Major's huge back feet. Thump! The grumpy horse knocked Scruff out of the way. The puppy was bowled over and over, until he landed behind some hay bales. Just then, Patch arrived. He gently nudged Scruff and knew that he had to get help so he ran back to the farmhouse to find Joe and Sally.

"Hey, Patch," said Joe, as Patch appeared in the kitchen doorway, barking,"what's the matter?"

"Where's Scruff, Patch?" asked Sally, looking around for the puppy. Patch just barked all the more.

"Mum!" said Joe. "Something's wrong!" Joe, Sally and Mum followed Patch to the stables, where Scruff was lying in the hay.

"Look! Poor Scruff's hurt!" cried Sally. Mum knelt beside Scruff and gently examined him.

"He's hurt his leg," she said. "He must have gone too near Old Major. We'll take him to the surgery." Joe and Sally carefully placed the puppy into Mum's apron and took him to Dad. Dad had a good look at Scruff, while Sally, Joe and Patch watched.

"How is he?" asked Joe.

"Well, his leg is broken, I'm afraid," said Dad. "It should mend quite quickly, but he won't be able to run around for a while."

"I expect Patch and the other animals will be pleased about that!" laughed Sally.

A few days later, Dad had good news for them all. "Scruff's owners have just called!" he told them. "They saw your poster and they're coming to collect him." Joe and Sally didn't want to lose Scruff, but they knew that the puppy should be back with his family.

"I hope they are nice," whispered Sally to Joe. She needn't have worried! That afternoon, a little boy and his mum came to Haven Farm.

"Thanks for looking after my puppy," the boy said, happily. And, even though Scruff's leg wasn't quite better, it didn't stop him running to his owner! "Look after yourself, Scruff," said Joe and Sally. Scruff barked and held up his paw to say goodbye. He would come back soon to visit his new friends at Haven Farm.

Who Can Save the Chicks?

One morning on Windy Farm, three naughty chicks escaped from their hen house and waddled into the farmyard. "Yippeeeeee!" they cheeped, noisily. "I know that Mummy said we weren't allowed outside the hen house by ourselves," cheeped Chalky Chick, "but there's nothing to do inside! Let's go to the river and play."

"That's a great idea!" cried the other chicks. What fun the chicks had, down by the river. But, as the chicks had fun, they didn't realised that danger was nearby!

Wicked Fox was hiding behind the tree. "Lunch!" he murmured. "I'm going to get them!" Luckily, up in the tree, Owl had woken and spotting Fox he flew off to the farm, for help. But everyone was out searching for the missing chicks. Only Pig was left.

"Quickly," cried Owl to Pig. "Fox is going to eat the chicks!" Pig got up and ran after Owl, as fast as he could. Once Pig got moving, there was no stopping him! And, as he staggered to the river, he crashed into that nasty fox, tossing him into the water with a big, loud SPLASH!

"Everyone was worried about you," said Pig to the little chicks, sternly.

"We're sorry!" cheeped the chicks. "We won't do it again – but getting wet was fun!" And Pig and the chicks dripped all the way back home!

It's Not Fair!

"I want to swim with the ducklings," said Kitten to Mother Cat, as they walked past the pond.

"You can't," Mother Cat told her. "Your fur isn't waterproof."

"I want to roll in the mud with the piglets," said Kitten, when they walked past the pigsty.

"You can't," Mother Cat told her. "Your long fur will get knotted and matted with mud."

"I want to fly with the baby birds," said Kitten to Mother Cat, as she tried to climb where baby birds were learning to fly.

"You can't," Mother Cat told her. "You have fur, not feathers and you haven't got wings. Kittens aren't meant to fly."

"It's not fair!" shouted Kitten. "Kittens don't have any fun!"

Later, Kitten curled up on a rug by the kitchen fire, with a saucer of milk.

"I want to sleep by the fire," said Duckling, standing at the door.

"And I want to lie on a rug," said Piglet, trottting past the door.

"And I want to drink a saucer of milk, said a Baby Bird as he flew past.

"It's not fair!" shouted Duckling, Piglet and Baby Bird as Mother Cat shooed them away.

"Oh yes, it is!" mewed Kitten, smiling!

Tough Ted Loses his Growl

The alarm clock started to ring and Katie jumped out of bed, bursting with energy. Tough Ted opened one sleepy eye (which was all he could do, as the other one had fallen off years ago) and stretched out his paws.

"Another morning," he yawned. "I don't suppose it will be a good one."

Tough Ted was a very old bear. He had belonged to Katie's mum when she was young. He had been a smart teddy then, and happy, but now he was in a sorry state and was always grumpy. He was the oldest of the toys and had been through some tough times. The others loved him, but they were fed up with his constant moaning and groaning.

"When is this bed going to be made? I can't get comfortable with all these covers thrown back!" he complained. "And they should pull that blind down, the sun's shining straight into my eye," he grumbled. "Talking of which, it's about time they gave me a new one," he moaned. He carried on growling all morning.

"If he doesn't stop complaining soon I'm going to stuff my hat in his mouth," whispered Soldier to Clown, as they sat nearby on the shelf.

"Not if I put my juggling balls in there first!" said Clown. All the toys giggled.

"It's about time we taught him a lesson," said Rag Doll.

"But what can we do to stop him moaning?" said Soldier.

"What about sticking a plaster over his mouth while he's asleep?" twittered Owl, who was always wise.

"That's a brilliant idea, Owl!" said Rag Doll, and everyone agreed.

So that night, Rag Doll fetched a plaster from the bathroom cabinet, and stuck it firmly over Tough Ted's mouth while he was asleep. All the toys were delighted – peace and quiet at last!

The next morning the alarm clock went off and Katie went into the bathroom. Tough Ted opened his eye and was just about to moan that the alarm was still ringing, when he realised he could not open his mouth! He pulled and stretched and twisted his face as hard as he could, but he could not get his mouth to open. Then he noticed that all the toys were

watching him. When he looked and saw the plaster in the mirror he was furious! He ripped it off and turned to face the other toys angrily.

"Who did this?" he bellowed. "When I find out who it was, there'll be trouble, growwwll! Have you no respect for an old bear?" He went on and on and on. He grew red in the face, and looked terribly cross. All the toys became quite scared.

Then, as he was growling at the top of his voice, a funny thing happened. His voice began to crack. He tried to clear his throat, but it was no use. No matter how hard he tried, he could not make a sound. He had lost his voice completely!

"Well it serves you right!" said Rag Doll. "All you do is moan, moan, moan, and we're tired of listening to you. We put the plaster on your mouth to teach you a lesson. But now you've moaned so much that you've made yourself lose your voice completely."

With that, a big tear rolled down Tough Ted's cheek. He was not so tough after all. He hadn't realised that he moaned so much, and he felt very sorry.

Rag Doll did not like seeing Tough Ted so sad. All the toys felt a bit guilty for what they had done.

"I'll go and get some honey from the kitchen," said Rag Doll. "It will soothe your throat. But you must promise not to start moaning again."

After Rag Doll had given Tough Ted a spoonful of honey, he whispered, "I'm sorry. I promise I'll try not to moan any more. I didn't realise I'd become such a grumpy old bear."

With that, all the toys gave Tough Ted a hug and Rag Doll gave him some more honey.

Since then Tough Ted has tried really hard not to moan. But, whenever he does, he thinks about the plaster and quickly stops himself before anyone hears! And the rest of the toys do their best to look after him and keep him happy.

Where's Wanda?

Sally was worried. Wanda, her cat, was getting fat. She was behaving very strangely, too. She wouldn't go in her basket. "She must be ill," Sally told her mummy. "Her tummy's all swollen, and she hasn't slept in her basket for days."

"Don't worry," said Mummy, giving Sally a hug. "If she's not better in the morning, we'll take her to the vet."

"Sssh!" whispered Sally. "You know how much Wanda hates the V-E-T." But it was too late, Wanda had already gone.

Sally and her mummy couldn't find Wanda anywhere. She didn't even come running when they left out a saucer of milk. Wanda was still missing the following morning.

"She must have heard us talking about the vet," said Sally, as they searched around the house. "Perhaps she's hiding in the garden," she said.

They looked in the flowerbed, under the hedge, and up the tree. But all they found there were the birds. "Sometimes she sunbathes in the vegetable patch," said Sally. But the only animal there was a fluffy rabbit.

"Wanda!" called Mummy, looking in the shed. Wanda often liked sleeping in there. Today all they found there were mice.

"Maybe she's been locked in the garage," said Sally.

They looked around the car. They looked in the car. They even looked under it. But all they found there were spiders.

Wanda was nowhere around the house or garden, so Mummy took Sally to look in the park. "Here, Wanda!" called Sally. But all they found there were dogs. Wanda hated dogs, so she wouldn't be there.

On the way home, Sally even sat on Mummy's shoulders so that she could look on top of people's garages and sheds. "She must have run away," cried Sally. "We're never going to find her."

But Mummy had an idea. She helped Sally to draw some pictures of Wanda. Then they wrote MISSING and their telephone number on the pictures. They posted the leaflets through all the letterboxes in the street.

In the afternoon Mrs Jones from next door popped her head over the hedge. "Come and see what I've found in my laundry basket," smiled Mrs Jones. Sally and her mummy rushed next door at once. When Sally saw what Mrs Jones had in her laundry basket she couldn't believe her eyes.

There, sitting amongst the washing, was Wanda. She looked very slim and very proud. And beside her lay five tiny kittens. They were so young that their eyes were still closed. Wanda hadn't been ill after all. She'd been expecting kittens!

Mrs Jones said that they could keep the basket until Wanda had finished with it. So Mummy carried the new family home as Sally skipped beside her.

Sally was so excited. She just couldn't wait to tell people how they'd gone searching for one cat and found six!

The Owl and the Pussy-cat

The Owl and the Pussy-cat went to sea
In a beautiful pea-green boat,
They took some honey, and plenty of money,
Wrapped up in a five-pound note.

The Owl looked up to the stars above,
And sang to a small guitar,
"O lovely Pussy! O Pussy, my love,
What a beautiful Pussy you are,
You are, you are!
What a beautiful Pussy you are!"

I Saw Three Ships

I saw three ships come sailing by,
Come sailing by, come sailing by;
I saw three ships come sailing by,
On New Year's Day in the morning.

And what do you think was in them then,
Was in them then, was in them then?
And what do you think was in them then,
On New Year's Day in the morning?

Three pretty girls were in them then,
Were in them then, were in them then;
Three pretty girls were in them then,
On New Year's Day in the morning.

And one could whistle, and one could sing,
And one could play on the violin –
Such joy there was at my wedding,
On New Year's Day in the morning.

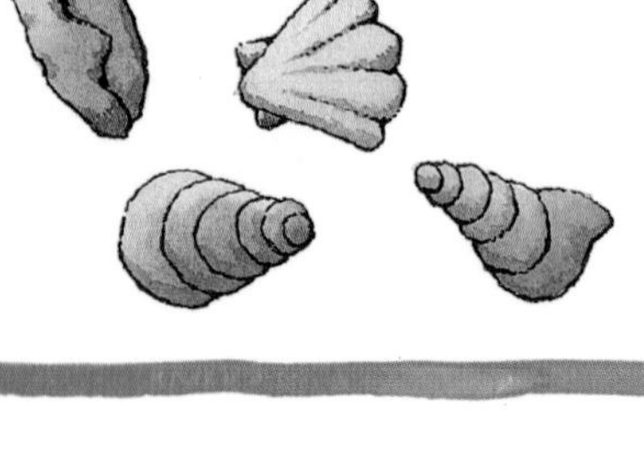

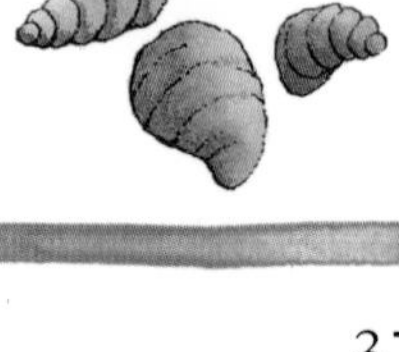

Bobbie Shaftoe's Gone to Sea

Bobbie Shaftoe's gone to sea,
Silver buckles at his knee;
When he comes back
He'll marry me,
Bonny Bobbie Shaftoe!

If All the Seas Were One Sea

If all the seas were one sea,
  What a great sea that would be!
And if all the trees were one tree,
  What a great tree that would be!
And if all the axes were one axe,
  What a great axe that would be!
And if all the men were one man,
  What a great man he would be!
And if the great man took the great axe,
  And cut down the great tree,
And let it fall into the great sea,
  What a splish splash that would be!

I Saw a Ship a-Sailing

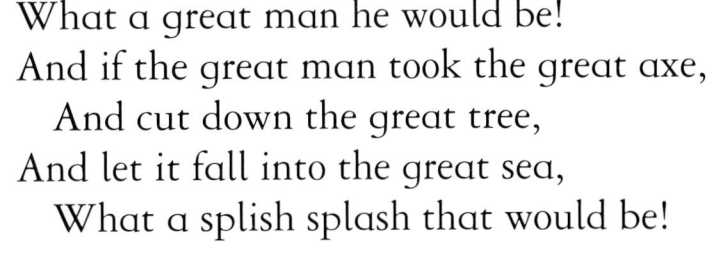

I saw a ship a-sailing,
  A-sailing on the sea;
And, oh! it was all laden
  With pretty things for thee!

There were comfits in the cabin,
  And apples in the hold
The sails were made of silk,
  And the masts were made of gold.

The four-and-twenty sailors
  That stood between the decks,
Were four-and-twenty white mice
  With chains about their necks.

The captain was a duck,
  With a packet on his back;
And when the ship began to move,
  The captain said, "Quack! quack!"

Dance to Your Daddy

Dance to your daddy,
  My little babby;
Dance to your daddy,
  My little lamb.

You shall have a fishy,
  In a little dishy;
You shall have a fishy
  When the boat comes in.

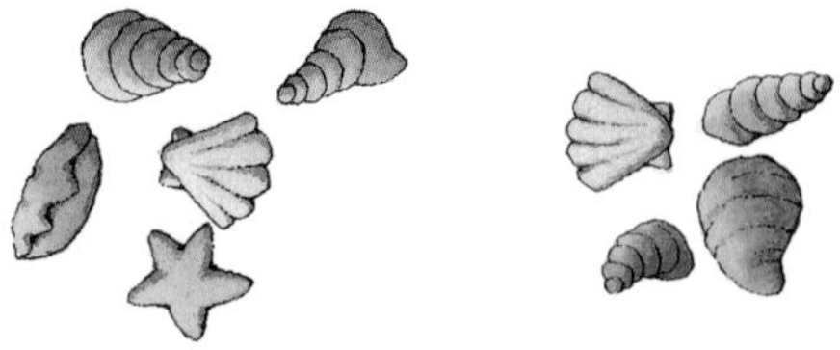

The Disappearing Trick

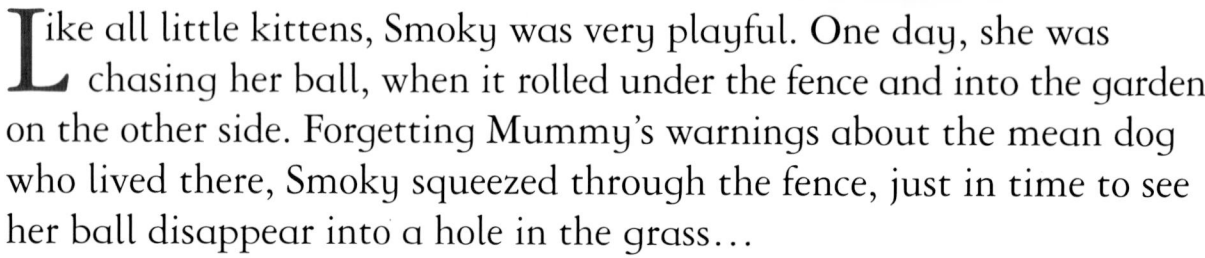

Like all little kittens, Smoky was very playful. One day, she was chasing her ball, when it rolled under the fence and into the garden on the other side. Forgetting Mummy's warnings about the mean dog who lived there, Smoky squeezed through the fence, just in time to see her ball disappear into a hole in the grass...

Smoky looked down into the hole, but it was very deep and there was no sign of the ball. Just then, she heard a low growl, and turned to see an angry dog snarling at her.

In a flash, she scrambled into the hole, with the dog's sharp teeth snapping at her heels. She squeezed down a long tunnel and into a little room at the bottom.

"Hello!" said Rabbit, handing Smoky the ball. "You must be looking for this!"

Smoky was amazed to find she was in Rabbit's burrow. She told him about the angry dog. "Don't worry," said Rabbit, "we'll trick him!"

He dug a new tunnel and in no time they were back in Smoky's garden.

"Over here!" Rabbit called through the fence to the poor dog still guarding the hole! How the two friends laughed to see the puzzled look on his face.

The Chocolate Soldier

In the window of Mrs Brown's sweet shop there stood a chocolate soldier. He had chocolate ears and eyebrows and a curly chocolate moustache of which he was particularly proud. But best of all he loved his shiny foil uniform with its braid on the shoulders and cuffs, and smart red stripes down each leg. All day long the chocolate soldier stood to attention on a shelf in the window, staring straight ahead into the street. Standing next to him on the shelf were more chocolate soldiers, some lollipops, some sugar mice and a twist of liquorice bootlaces.

It was summer time and the sun shone through the window of the sweet shop. At first the chocolate soldier felt pleasantly warm; then he started to feel uncomfortably hot. Next he began to feel most peculiar indeed. His chocolate moustache was wilting and his arms were dripping. Soon he was completely melted and, before he knew it, he had slipped out through a hole in his silver foil shoe and was pouring off the shelf and out into the street.

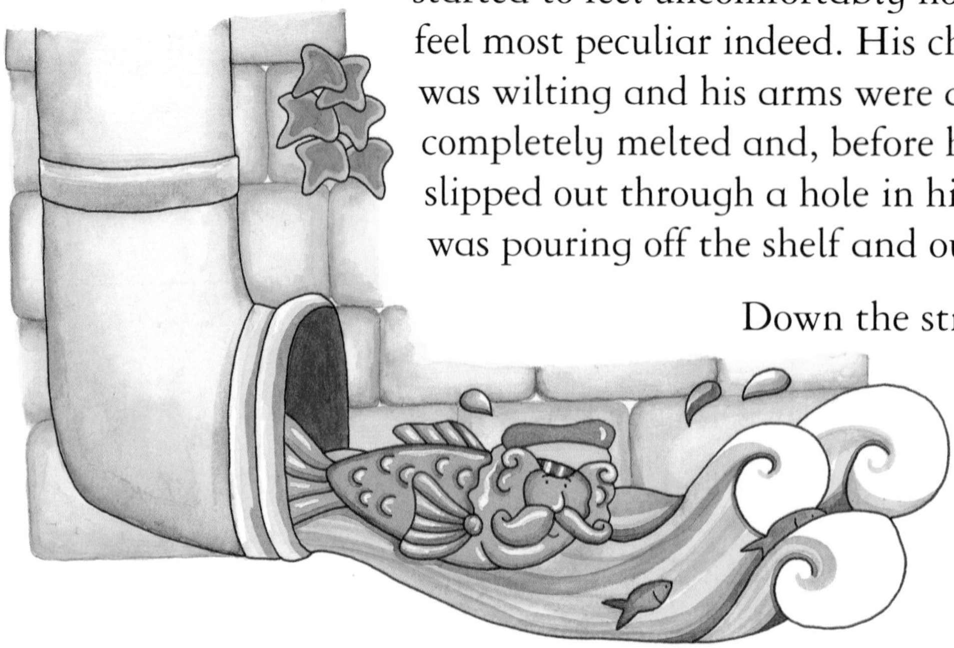

Down the street he poured.

"Stop! Help me!" he shouted, but nobody could hear his cries.

Now he could hear the sound of gushing water and, to his horror, he could see he was heading for a stream at the bottom of the street.

"Help me! I can't swim! I'm going to drown!" the chocolate soldier cried as he plunged into the cold, running water. But now something very strange was happening – he found he could swim quite easily. He looked round and saw that he had a chocolate tail covered in scales. Then he looked at his arms, but there was a pair of fins instead. The cold water had hardened him into the shape of a chocolate fish!

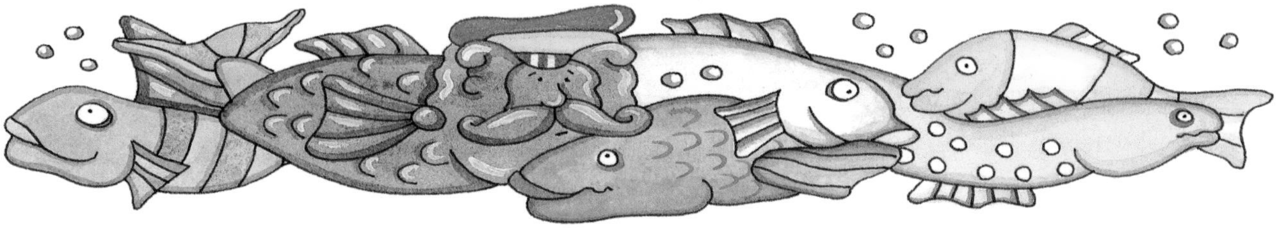

The water carried the chocolate soldier until the stream broadened out and became a river. He realised that he would soon be carried out to sea.

"Whatever shall I do?" wondered the chocolate soldier. "I'm sure to get eaten by a bigger fish or maybe even a shark!" He tried to turn around and swim against the river's flow but it was no good. The current swept him away down river again.

Soon he could see the waves on the shore. He smelt the sea air and tasted the salt in the water. Now he found himself bobbing up and down on the sea. He could see a boat not far away and then all of a sudden he felt a net closing around him. He struggled to get out, but the net only tightened and soon he felt himself being hauled out of the water and landed with a "thwack!" on the deck among a pile of fish. The smell was awful, and the chocolate soldier was quite relieved when he felt the boat being rowed towards the shore.

"I'll hop over the side as soon as we land and run away," he thought, quite forgetting that he had no legs but only a fish's tail.

But there was no chance of escape. As soon as the boat reached the shore, he and all the other fish were flung into buckets and lifted into a van. The van stopped outside a shop and a man carried the buckets inside, where it smelt of fried fish, chips and vinegar. The chocolate soldier found himself being lifted up with a lot of other fish in a huge metal basket. He looked down and saw a terrible sight below. They were heading for a vat of boiling oil! At that very moment he felt very peculiar once again. His scales melted, his tail drooped and he felt himself slide through the holes in the basket and into the pocket of a man's overalls.

The chocolate soldier lay in the corner of the pocket while the man worked in the shop. Then the man went home, with the chocolate soldier bouncing up and down in the overall pocket as the man walked along. Soon they arrived at the man's house. He reached into his pocket.

"Look what I've found," he said to his small son. "A coin. Here, you can have it – but don't spend it all at once!" he said, chuckling to himself. The chocolate soldier felt himself being passed from one hand to another.

"So now I've become a chocolate coin," he thought. "And I'm going to be eaten!" But to his surprise he was slipped into the boy's pocket.

The chocolate soldier felt himself bouncing up and down as the boy ran up the street and into a shop. The chocolate soldier peeped out and to his astonishment saw that he was back in Mrs Brown's sweet shop. The boy believed he was a real coin and was going to try and spend him!

The chocolate soldier called out to his soldier friends in the window,

"Pssst! It's me! Help me!" One of the soldiers looked down, but all he could see was a chocolate coin sticking out of the boy's pocket. Then he recognised the voice.

"I'm a chocolate soldier too, but I've been turned into a coin. Help!" cried the chocolate soldier.

"Just leave it to me," replied the soldier on the shelf. "Don't worry, we'll have you out of there in a jiffy!"

The word was passed along and one of the sugar mice chewed off a length of liquorice bootlace. Then the soldier lowered the lace into the boy's pocket, where it stuck to the chocolate coin. Carefully the soldiers hauled the coin up on to the shelf. The chocolate soldier was delighted to find his foil uniform was still there on the shelf, just where it had been before. All the effort of getting on to the shelf had made him quite warm, and he found he could slip quite easily back through the hole in the shoe and into his uniform again.

"I'd like a chocolate soldier," said the boy to Mrs Brown. But when he reached in his pocket the coin had gone.

"Never mind," said kind Mrs Brown. "You can have one anyway." She reached into the window and took down a soldier from the end of the row and gave it to the boy. And as for our chocolate soldier? In the cool of the night he turned back into a smart-looking soldier again.

There Was a Man, and His Name was Dob

There was a man, and his name was Dob,
And he had a wife, and her name was Mob
And he had a dog, and he called it Cob,
And she had a cat, called Chitterabob.
Cob, says Dob,
Chitterabob, says Mob,
Cob was Dob's dog,
Chitterabob Mob's cat.

Me, Myself, and I

Me, myself, and I –
We went to the kitchen and ate a pie.
Then my mother she came in
And chased us out with a rolling pin.

Swan Swam Over the Sea

Swan swam over the sea –
Swim, swan, swim,
Swan swam back again,
Well swum swan.

Hey, Dorolot, Dorolot!

Hey, dorolot, dorolot!
Hey, dorolay, dorolay!
Hey, my bonny boat, bonny boat,
Hey, drag away, drag away!

My Grandmother Sent Me

My grandmother sent me a new-fashioned three cornered cambric country cut handkerchief. Not an old-fashioned three cornered cambric country cut handkerchief, but a new-fashioned three cornered cambric country cut handkerchief.

Adam and Eve and Pinchme

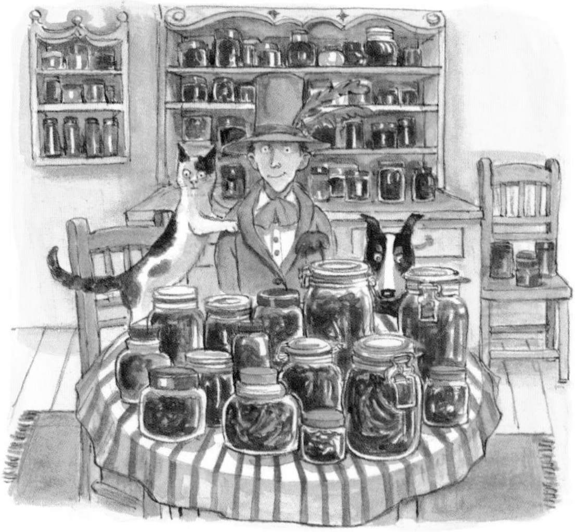

Adam and Eve and Pinchme
Went down to the river to bathe.
Adam and Eve were drowned –
Who do you think was saved?

Peter Piper

Peter Piper picked a peck of pickled pepper;
A peck of pickled pepper Peter Piper picked;
If Peter Piper picked a peck of pickled pepper,
Where's the peck of pickled pepper Peter Piper picked?

Robert Rowley

Robert Rowley rolled a round roll round,
A round roll Robert Rowley rolled round;
Where rolled the round roll Robert Rowley rolled round?

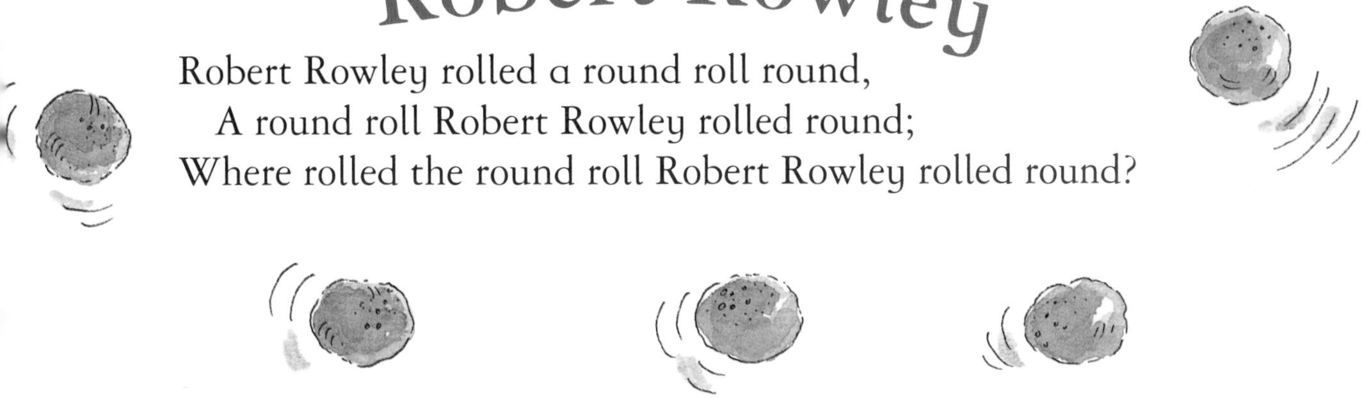

Desmond Grows Up

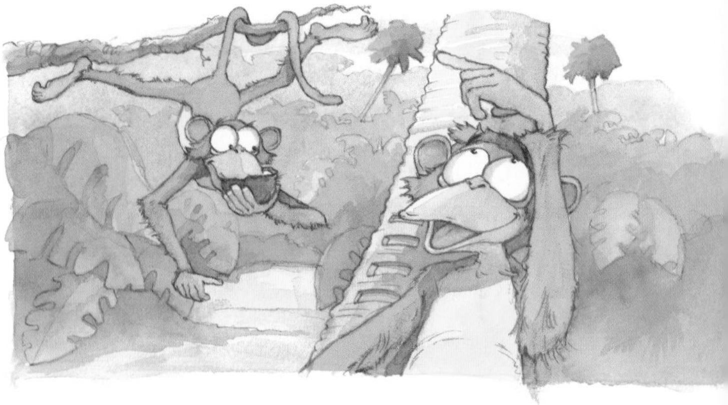

Desmond was the smallest monkey in the group. He couldn't wait to grow up. "Will you measure me?" he asked his friend Rodney. "I only measured you last Monday, and now it's Friday," said Rodney. "You won't have grown in four days!"

Rodney took him to the tallest tree in the jungle and made him stand with his back against it. Then he made a mark on the trunk at the top of Desmond's head. It was in the same place as the last mark.

"See," he said, "you are still the same size."

"Botheration!" said Desmond.

Later he spoke to his friend Bubbles. "Watch the top of my head," he said to her.

"Whatever for, Dethmond?" said Bubbles. She always called him Dethmond.

"Just watch," said Desmond. So Bubbles watched the top of his head.

"Well?" asked Desmond. "Well what?" replied Bubbles.

"Am I growing? Can you see me growing?" asked Desmond.

"No, of course not!" she said. "I knew it!" said Desmond. "I knew it! I'm never going to grow."

"Dethmond," said Bubbles, "you will grow! Honestly you will."

But Desmond was not so sure. "What can I do to get taller?" he asked Rodney. "Wait!" said Rodney. So Desmond stood next to Rodney... and waited. And waited. "You won't grow that fast!" laughed Rodney. "It will be ages before you grow up."

But Desmond didn't have ages. He wanted to collect coconuts... NOW! He tried to stretch. He asked all his friends to pull on his arms and legs and to squeeze him so that he would get thinner and taller. He hung from the branches of trees by his toes. Nothing worked!

Every day he watched as the other monkeys climbed the tall palm trees to pick coconuts and drop them to the ground.

One day, there was a competition to see who could collect the most coconuts. Rodney was the favourite to win. He climbed to the top and wriggled through the palm leaves, and then... oh dear... he got stuck!

"Help!" he called." I can't move." One of the other big monkeys went up to help, but he was too big to get through the leaves.

"Let me try," begged Desmond.

"OK," they said grudgingly. Desmond raced up the trunk. At the top he was small enough to reach his friend and help him to get free. Then he picked six or seven coconuts and dropped them to the ground.

When they climbed down the other monkeys crowded round to pat Desmond on the back.

"Wow!" said Bubbles. "No one has ever climbed a tree that fast before."

"Maybe you are all too big!" said Desmond happily. "I'm not in such a hurry to grow up after all!"

After that he didn't worry so much about being small, especially after he managed to collect more coconuts than anyone else, and won the competition!

Town Mouse and Country Mouse

Once there was a roly-poly, wiggly-whiskered mouse, who lived in a snug little nest under an oak tree. Country Mouse loved his home. He had plenty of acorns, nuts and berries to eat and a warm and cosy straw bed to sleep in. Squirrel and Robin, who lived in the oak tree, were the best neighbours he could ever wish for.

One day, Country Mouse had a surprise. His cousin, Town Mouse, came to visit from the Big City. Town Mouse was sleek and slender, with a smooth, shiny coat. His whiskers were smart and elegant. Country Mouse felt a little ordinary beside him. But he didn't mind. All he wanted to do was make Town Mouse feel welcome. "Are you hungry, Cousin?" he said. "Come and have some supper!"

But Town Mouse didn't like the acorns and blackberries that Country Mouse gave him to eat. They were tough and sour. And Town Mouse thought his cousin's friends were boring. The straw bed that he slept in that night was so rough and scratchy that he didn't sleep a wink!

Next day, Town Mouse said, "Come to the Big City with me, Cousin. It's so much more exciting than the country! I live in a grand house, eat delicious food and have exciting adventures. Come with me and see what you've been missing!" It sounded so wonderful, Country Mouse couldn't resist it. Saying goodbye to his friends, the cousins set off for the city.

When they arrived in the Big City, Country Mouse was frightened. It was so noisy – horns blared and wheels clattered all around them. Huge lorries roared and rumbled down the street and the smelly, smoky air made them choke and cough. And there were dogs *everywhere*!

At last, they arrived safely at Town Mouse's house. It was very grand, just as Town Mouse had said. But it was *so* big! Country Mouse was afraid that he would get lost!

"Don't worry," said Town Mouse to Country Mouse. "You'll soon learn your way around the house. For now, just stay close to me. I'm starving – let's go and have a snack." Country Mouse was hungry, too, so he followed his cousin to the kitchen.

Country Mouse had never seen so much delicious food – there were plates full of fruit, nuts, cheese and cakes.

He and his cousin ate and ate and ate! But Country Mouse wasn't used to this sort of rich food. Before he knew it, his tummy was aching.

Suddenly, a huge woman came into the room. "Eek! Mice!" she screamed. She grabbed a big broom and began to swat the mice, who scampered off as fast as they could.

As the two mice scurried across the floor, Country Mouse thought things couldn't possibly get worse. But how wrong he was! A big cat suddenly sprang out from behind a chair! With a loud "MEEOOWW," he pounced on the two little mice. Country Mouse had never been so frightened. He darted and dashed as fast as his aching tummy would let him. The two mice jumped through a mousehole and were safe at last in Town Mouse's house.

"Phew! I think we've done enough for one day," said Town

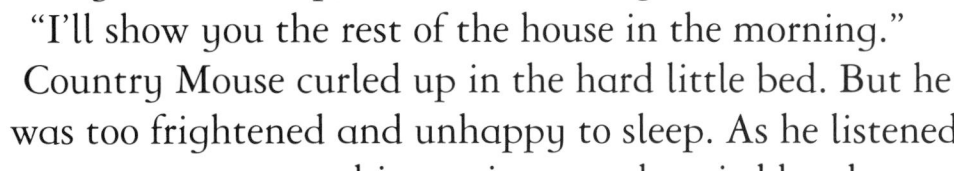

Mouse, when they had caught their breath. "Let's get some sleep," he said, with a yawn. "I'll show you the rest of the house in the morning."

Country Mouse curled up in the hard little bed. But he was too frightened and unhappy to sleep. As he listened to his cousin snore, he tried hard not to cry.

Next morning, Town Mouse was ready for more adventures, but Country Mouse had had more than enough. "Thank you for inviting me," he told his cousin, "but I have seen all I want to see of the Big City. It is too big and noisy and dirty – and too full of danger for me. I want to go back to my quiet, peaceful home in the country."

So, Country Mouse went back to his snug, cosy home under the oak tree. He had never been so happy to see his friends – and they wanted to hear all about his adventures. Country Mouse was pleased to tell them everything that had happened in the Big City – but he *never, ever* went back there again!

Cock Crow

The cock's on the wood pile
Blowing his horn,
The bull's in the barn
A-threshing the corn,
The maids in the meadow
Are making the hay,
The ducks in the river
Are swimming away.

The Old Woman's Three Cows

There was an old woman had three cows,
Rosy and Colin and Dun.
Rosy and Colin were sold at the fair,
And Dun broke her heart in a fit of despair,
So there was an end of her three cows,
Rosy and Colin and Dun

An Apple a Day

An apple a day
Sends the doctor away.
Apple in the morning
Doctor's warning,
Roast apple at night.
Starves the doctor outright.
Eat an apple going to bed,
Knock the doctor on the head.
Three each day, seven days a week,
Ruddy apple, ruddy cheek.

Sing, Sing

Sing, sing,
What shall I sing?
The cat's run away
With the pudding string!
Do, do,
What shall I do?
The cat's run away
With the pudding too!

Sulky Sue

Here's Sulky Sue
What shall we do?
Turn her face to the wall
'Til she comes to.

To the Snail

Snail, snail, put out
your horns,
And I will give you bread
and barley corns.

Little Poll Parrot

Little Poll Parrot
  Sat in his garret
Eating toast and tea;
  A little brown mouse
Jumped into the house,
  And stole it all away.

I Had a Little Horse

I had a little horse,
  His name was Dappled Grey,
His head was made of gingerbread,
  His tail was made of hay.
He could amble, he could trot,
  He could carry the mustard pot,
He could amble, he could trot,
  Through the old town of Windsor

One for the Mouse

One for the Mouse
  One for the house,
One for the crow,
  One to rot,
One to grow.

The Legacy

My father died a month ago
  And left me all his riches;
A feather bed, a wooden leg,
  And a pair of leather breeches;
A coffee pot without a spout,
  And a cup without a handle,
A tobacco pipe without a lid,
  And half a farthing candle.

Roses are Red

Roses are red,
  Violets are blue,
Sugar is sweet
  And so are you.

Such a Pickle!

Old MacDonald has quite a few pigs on his farm. He has two that are favourites – Percy, and the eldest one, Jonathan Jakes Jermington Jollop.

Jonathan Jakes Jermington Jollop is the pig's birth name, but now he is called something much less grand! This is the story of how he got his new name.

When Jonathan Jakes Jermington Jollop was a piglet, he somehow got the idea that he was much better than all the other animals that lived on the farm. It was partly because he had such a long name, and partly because Old MacDonald liked to come and chat to him.

"I don't know what's the matter with that young pig," clucked Henrietta the hen. "I said hello to him this morning, and he didn't say a word. He just put his nose in the air and trotted off."

"He did the very same to me," neighed Old George the horse.

Soon there wasn't an animal left on the farm who had a good word to say about Jonathan Jakes Jermington Jollop – and the piglet only had himself to blame!

So, when Jonathan Jakes Jermington Jollop saw Henry the cockerel standing on the henhouse roof, and he decided to climb on to the roof of his sty, that is why no one tried to stop him.

Now, pigs are not well-known for their climbing skills, but this didn't stop Jonathan Jakes Jermington Jollop! He scrabbled and scrambled, puffed and panted, and eventually the young pig found himself perched rather uncomfortably on the top of his sty.

He soon realised that he had a very big problem. Getting up had not been easy, but he could see that getting down was going to be practically impossible – and he discovered that he was scared of heights!

Before long, there was a crowd around the pigsty. There was mooing and baaing, neighing and clucking, as they looked at the panicking pig on the roof.

"How did that silly piglet get into such a pickle?" Annabel the cow mooed.

"What a ridiculous place for a piglet to sit," clucked Henrietta the hen. "That's a place for hens not piglets!"

"Hey, Pickle Piglet!" quacked Doris the duck. "What are you doing up there, and how are you going to get down?" she asked.

"I've been really silly," said Jonathan Jakes Jermington Jollop, looking very upset. "Please help me!"

With a laugh, Old George picked him up by his tail and plonked him on the floor.

Jonathan Jakes Jermington Jollop looked very relieved to have all four trotters on firm ground again, and he smiled happily at the other farm animals as they crowded round him.

Jonathan Jakes Jermington Jollop never put on airs and graces again, and no one let him forget his climbing adventure. From that day on, Jonathan Jakes Jermington Jollop was forever known as Pickles the pig!

At the Monster Café

Down at the Monster Café there are sights you just would not believe! Monsters love their food, their portions are huge and the colours are scary. As for the ingredients, it might be better not to know, as you will see!

A monster stew is a grisly mixture of turnip tops and vile black drops, and monsters have spaghetti hoops with liquorice loops! They eat brown rats' tails, slugs and snails, and add lots of little flies for decoration.

As for the favourite monster drink – it is lime green, mauve and pink, and made with peas and dead gnat's knees. They say that this goes particularly well with the favourite monster sweets. These are made of dragons' feet, with sugared claws and chocolate paws – sounds really gruesome doesn't it?

Monster snacks start to bubble when you take off the wrapper. They are made from tar and bits of car, which sounds more like torture than a treat! Fortunately most monsters have very large, sharp teeth so they can munch away merrily on their snacks without breaking them.

The most frightening part of the monster menu is the price list – it is very expensive to eat at the Monster Café. But to a monster it is a real treat. Will you be saving up for a visit?

Cooking up a Storm

Wizards love to cook. They have a huge cauldron for mixing their magic potions, which means they also have all they need to create huge and wonderful stews for their wizard friends.

There is a difference between what you or I might think of as a stew, and what a stew might be to a wizard. For instance, we can go to a local shop to buy our ingredients whereas a wizard might go down to his local pond! The favourite wizard stew is called Storm and, when you know what goes in it, you will understand why!

First the wizard has to put a handful of cat's whiskers into a cauldron of boiling dirty pond water. Then he adds the tails from three young pups, a big ladle of eyeballs and two cups of froggy slime. This is stirred slowly for seventeen minutes before adding giant fireworks, a bunch of old tin cans, a pair of cymbals and a big bass drum. Then the windows start to shake and the sky darkens – here comes the storm that goes with the stew! As it rains cats and dogs, and a shower of nasty frogs, the stew is ready. The wizard has cooked up a storm!

Barking Night

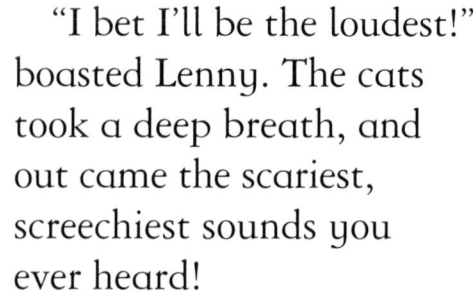

It was the middle of the night. Harvey and his gang were fast asleep in the higgledy-piggledy, messy alley, dreaming of yummy bones and chasing dustmen! The only sounds were the gentle rumblings of Ruffle's tummy and Bonnie's snores!

Everyone and everything was fast asleep – or were they? Six naughty Alley Cats peeped over the fence. They spied the snoozing dogs and, grinning and sniggering, they scribbled and scrabbled up the fence.

"I've got an idea!" whispered Archie. "Listen... "

Wibbling and wobbling, the Alley Cats stood in a line along the top of the fence...

"Those dippy dogs are in for a fright!" giggled Archie.

"I bet I'll be the loudest!" boasted Lenny. The cats took a deep breath, and out came the scariest, screechiest sounds you ever heard!

The terrible noise woke Harvey with a start and made him fall off his mattress, straight on to Mac!

"What's that noise?" yelped Mac. "Is it the bagpipe ghost?"

"G-Ghost?" cried Puddles, rushing up to Harvey. "Help!"

The noise made Patchy and Ruffles jump. They fell in a big heap on top of Ruffles' bed! "Save us!" they cried.

Harvey spotted the culprits. "Oh, it's just those pesky pussies," he groaned, "up to mischief as usual. Don't worry, everyone, let's just ignore them and go back to sleep."

But those naughty cats weren't finished yet!

"Look!" cried Lenny. "One of them is still asleep. We must try harder."

They were right – Bonnie was still snoring in her dustbin!

"Louder! Louder!" screeched Archie to the others. But could they wake Bonnie? Oh no! She just kept on snoring and snoring and snoring!

"Someone should teach those cats a lesson," growled Mac. "When I was a pup I'd..."

"Not now, Mac!" shouted the others.

Harvey smiled, he had an idea. The gang huddled together and listened as Harvey told them his idea.

"And me! And me!" cried Puddles, squeezing herself in.

The cats thought they were so clever. They laughed and then they wailed even louder than before!

Then suddenly, Lenny slipped and grabbed Lulu, who grabbed Hattie, who grabbed Bertie, who grabbed Lucy, who grabbed Archie – and they all tumbled headfirst into the pile of boxes and bins!

"Bravo!" woofed the dogs. "More! More!" The cats squealed and wailed and ran away. They'd had enough of playing tricks for one day!

"Now to get our own back," chuckled Harvey. The gang sneaked along the alley as quiet as little mice.

"Ready?" whispered Harvey. "Steady – GO!"

"WOOF! WOOF!"

The ground shook and the cats jumped high into the air.

"Ha-ha!" roared the dogs. "Scaredy-cats! Scaredy-cats! We've got our own back! I think that's enough frights for one night!" said Harvey.

"You're right," agreed Archie, sheepishly. "Let's go back to bed. No more tricks tonight."

Just then Bonnie woke up. "Is it 'time-to-get-up' time?" she asked, rubbing her eyes.

"No!" said Patchy, "it's 'time-for-bed' time!" and they all laughed and laughed.

"Oh, goody!" yawned Bonnie. "Bedtime! The best time of the day!"

"Oh, Bonnie," smiled Harvey. "What a sleepyhead you are!"

But Bonnie didn't care. With another enormous yawn and a stretch, she turned away and wandered back to her dustbin – she was *soooo* tired!

At last the cats and dogs of the higgledy-piggledy, messy alley snuggled down to sleep, dreaming of yummy bones and chasing dustbin men – and bowls of scrummy fish! The only sounds were the rumblings of Ruffles' tummy and Bonnie's snores.

Everyone and everything was fast asleep – or were they?

"TOOWHIT TOOWHOOOOOOo!"

On My

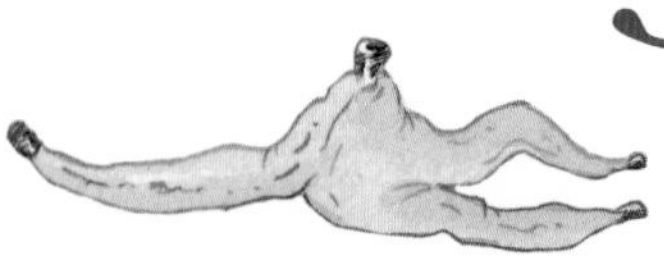

Own

Deep in the jungle, where only wild things go, Mungo's mum was teaching him what a young monkey needs to know. "Some things just aren't safe to try alone," she said.

"Why not?"said Mungo. "I'm big enough to do things – on my own!"

"Now Mungo," said Mum, "listen carefully, please. We're going to go through these trees. Stay close to me, and hold my hand. Did you hear what I said? Do you understand?"

"It's okay, Mum. I won't slip or fall. I can swing across there with no trouble at all," said Mungo. "I'm big enough to do it – on my own!"

And off he swung! "Hissss," hissed Snake, in a snake wail. "That pesky Mungo pulled my tail!" And did Mungo hear poor old Snake groan? No!

Mungo just laughed. "I told you I could do it on my own."

"Now, we're going to cross the river using these stones," said Mum. "But, Mungo, I'd rather you didn't do this alone."

"But Mum," said Mungo, and he ran on without stopping, "I'm really good at jumping and hopping. I'm big enough to do it – on my own!"

And off he sprang! "That Mungo trampled on my nose!" said Croc. "Next time, I'll nibble off his toes!" And did Mungo hear poor old Croc groan? No!

Mungo just smiled. "I told you I could do it on my own."

"Mungo," said Mum, with a serious look on her face, "the jungle can be a dangerous place. There are all sorts of corners for creatures to hide, so, from here on, make sure that you stay by my side."

"Oh, Mum," said Mungo, "I don't need to wait for you. I can easily find my own way through. I'm big enough to do it – on my own!"

Mungo thwacked Lion's nose as he sped past. "Ouch!" That Mungo's so careless!" Lion said. Did Mungo hear poor old Lion groan? No! Mungo just grinned. "I told you I could do it – on my own."

"I think I've had quite enough for one day," Mum said. "So off you go, little monkey! Now it really is time for bed!" It was Mungo's turn to let out a groan.

"I don't want to go to bed – on my own!"

"Don't worry," said Mum. "Come on, kiss me goodnight, and I promise I'll hold you and cuddle you tight."

Lion roared "Is that Mungo still awake?"

"Yes!" snapped Crocodile.

"Let's help him go to sleep," hissed Snake.

And into the velvety, starry sky drifted the sounds of a jungle lullaby.

Here is the Church

Here is the church,
  Here is the steeple,
Open the doors,
  And here are the people.
Here is the parson, going upstairs,
  And here he is a-saying his prayers.

Matthew, Mark, Luke, and John

Matthew, Mark, Luke, and John
  Bless the bed that I lie on.
Before I lay me down to sleep,
  I pray the Lord my soul to keep.

Four corners to my bed,
  Four angels there are spread;
Two at the foot, two at the head:
  Four to carry me when I'm dead.

I go by sea, I go by land:
  The Lord made me with His right hand.
Should any danger come to me,
  Sweet Jesus Christ deliver me.

He's the branch and I'm the flower,
  Pray God send me a happy hour;
And should I die before I wake,
  I pray the Lord my soul to take.

For Every Evil Under the Sun

For every evil under the sun,
  There is a remedy, or there is none.
If there be one, try and find it;
  If there be none, never mind it.

I See the Moon

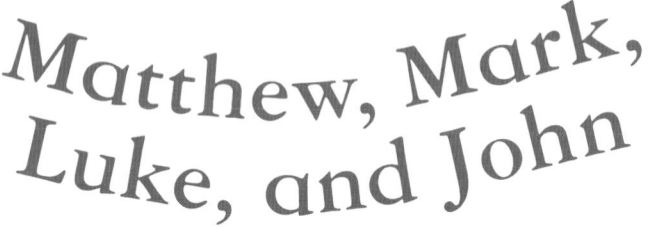

I see the moon,
  And the moon sees me;
God bless the moon,
  And God bless me.

The Key of the Kingdom

This is the key of the kingdom:
In that kingdom is a city,
In that city is a town,
In that town there is a street,
In that street there winds a lane,
In that lane there is a yard,
In that yard there is a house,
In that house there waits a room,
In that room there is a bed,
On that bed there is a basket,
A basket of flowers.

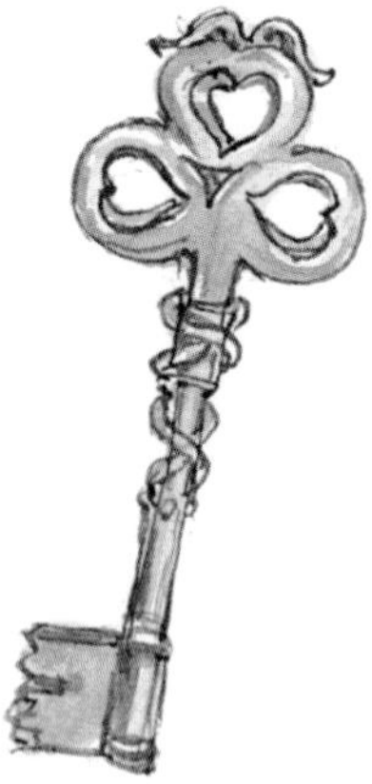

Flowers in the basket,
Basket on the bed,
Bed in the chamber,
Chamber in the house,
House in the weedy yard,
Yard in the winding lane,
Lane in the broad street,
Street in the high town,
Town in the city,
City in the kingdom:
This is the key of the kingdom.
Of the kingdom this is the key.

Star Light, Star Bright

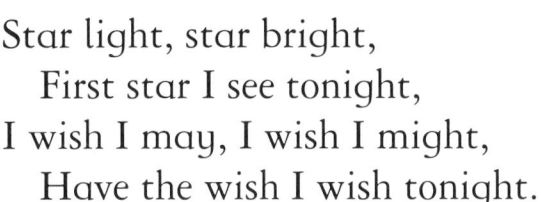

Star light, star bright,
First star I see tonight,
I wish I may, I wish I might,
Have the wish I wish tonight.

How Many Miles to Babylon?

How many miles to Babylon? –
Threescore and ten.
Can I get there by candlelight? –
Aye, and back again!

Twinkle, Twinkle, Little Star

Twinkle, twinkle, little star,
How I wonder what you are!
Up above the moon so high,
Like a diamond in the sky.

Sparky the Baby Dragon

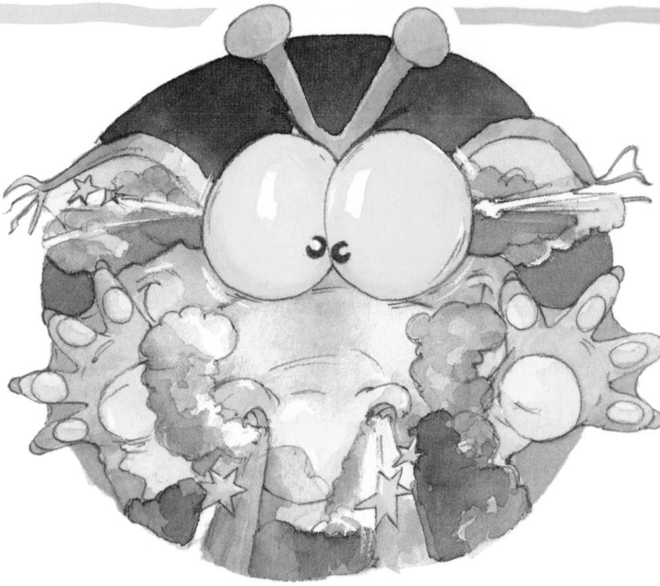

Sparky was a young dragon who lived in a cave far, far away. Now, as you know, dragons can breathe flames out of their noses! But you may not know that baby dragons have to learn how to do it. "Watch me," said Mum to Sparky. She puffed out a long flame and lit a candle.

"Now watch me," said Dad, and he breathed over some logs in the fireplace and made a fire. Sparky watched very carefully.

"Now watch me," he said, and he puffed until he was purple in the face. Two or three little sparks came out of his nose and ears!

"Bravo!" said Dad. "It's coming on!" said Mum. Sparky felt very proud.

One day Mum and Dad had to go out. "Stay indoors," they told Sparky. "Don't go out, and don't let anybody in. The wicked witch hates little dragons and turns them into teapots, just for fun!"

"Oh!" said Sparky. But he didn't mind staying in. He had some new toy knight figures to play with. He had just started when he heard a bell outside. "Ting-a-ling," it went, "ting-a-ling." And then a voice said, "Ice cream! Ice cream! Come and get your ice cream!"

Sparky peeped out. Outside was a brightly painted ice-cream cart and sitting behind the wheel was an old woman with a big grin. Then the woman laughed! It was a loud, cackling laugh and when Sparky heard it, he knew it was the witch. He slammed the door and locked it.

"Phew!" thought Sparky. "That was close." The afternoon passed peacefully. Then, the doorbell rang. "Who is it?" Sparky called out.

"It's Uncle Jack," said a voice, "I've come to take you fishing." Sparky liked Uncle Jack, and he liked fishing!

"Is it really you?" he asked. "Of course it is," laughed Uncle Jack. But, as soon as Sparky heard the loud, cackling laugh, he knew it was the witch.

"Go away!" he shouted. Then he heard someone crying. He peered through the door and saw a baby dragon on the doorstep!

"I've lost my mummy!" sobbed the dragon. "You'd better come in," said Sparky. He opened the door and the baby dragon rushed in. Then...

"Got you!" snapped the baby dragon – and turned into the witch! Sparky gasped. The witch raised her wand and shouted the magic words "Ta-ra-ra-boom-de-ay" and started to spin very fast.

Sparky puffed as hard as he could. Then he had a big surprise! The witch was surrounded by a puff of smoke. Then, as the smoke cleared, he saw that she had turned into a teapot!

Just then Mum and Dad came back. "Have you had any trouble while we've been away?" asked Mum, kissing him.

"Not much!" said Sparky. "But, next time you go out, can I come with you?"

"Of course you can!" said Mum. "Now why don't I make some tea in this nice new teapot!"

The Haughty Princess

There was once a king who had a very beautiful daughter and many dukes, earls, princes and even kings came to ask for her hand in marriage. But the princess was proud and haughty and would have none of them. She would find fault with each suitor, and send him off with a rude remark.

She said to a plump suitor, "I shall not marry you, Beer Belly." To a pale faced suitor she said, "I shall not marry you, Death-Mask." And to a third suitor who was tall and thin she said, "I shall not marry you, Ramrod." A prince with a red complexion was told,

"I shall not marry you, Beetroot." And so it went on, until every unmarried duke, earl, prince, and even king, had been rejected, and her father thought she would never find a man she liked.

Then a prince arrived who was so handsome and polite, that she found it hard to find a fault with him. But the princess's pride won, and she looked at the curling hairs under his chin and said, a little reluctantly, "I shall not marry you, Whiskers."

The poor king finally lost his temper, "I'm sick of your rudeness. I shall give you to the first beggar who calls at our door for alms, and good riddance to you!"

It wasn't long before a poor beggar knocked at the door, asking for food and clothes. His own clothes were in tatters, his hair dirty, and his beard long and straggling. Sure enough, the king kept his word and he married his daughter to the bearded beggar. The princess cried and and tried to run away, but there was nothing for it.

The beggar led his bride into a wood. He told her that the wood and the land around belonged to the king she had called Whiskers. The princess was even sadder that she had rejected the handsome king, and hung her head in shame when she saw the poor, tumble-down shack where the beggar lived. The place was dirty and untidy, and there was not even a fire burning in the grate. The princess put on a plain dress, helped her husband make the fire, clean the place and prepare a meal.

The beggar gathered some twigs of willow, and after their meal, the two sat together making baskets. But the twigs bruised the princess's fingers, and she cried out with the pain. The beggar was not a cruel man, so he gave her some cloth and thread, and set her to sewing. But although the princess tried hard, the needle made her fingers bleed, and again tears came to her eyes. So the beggar bought a basket of cheap earthenware pots and sent her to market to sell them.

The princess did well at market on the first day, and made a profit. But the next morning, a drunken huntsman rode through the market place, and his mount kicked its way through all the princess's pots. She went home in tears.

The beggar persuaded the cook at the palace of King Whiskers to give his wife a job as a kitchen maid. The princess worked hard, and the cook gave her food to take home. The princess liked the cook, and got on quite well in the kitchen, but she was still sorry she had rejected King Whiskers.

A while later, the palace suddenly got busier, King Whiskers was getting married. "Who is going to marry the king?" asked the princess. But no one knew who the bride was going to be. The princess and the cook decided to go and see what was going on in the great hall. They opened the door quietly and peeped in.

King Whiskers was in the room. He strode over when he saw them. "Spying on the king? You must pay for your nosiness by dancing a jig with me."

The king took her hand, led her into the room, and all the musicians began to play.

But as they whirled around, food began to fly out of her pockets, and everyone in the room roared with laughter. The princess began to run to the door, but the king caught her and took her to one side.

"Do you not realise who I am?" he asked her, smiling kindly. "I am King Whiskers, and your husband the beggar, and the drunken huntsman who broke your pots in the market place. Your father knew who I was, and we arranged all this to rid you of your pride."

The princess was so confused she did not know what to say. All sorts of emotions welled up inside her, but the strongest of all these feelings was love for her husband, King Whiskers.

The palace maids helped her to put on a fine dress fit for a queen. She went back to her husband, and none of the guests realised that the new queen was the poor kitchen maid who had danced a jig with the king.

Hannah Bantry

Hannah Bantry,
In the pantry,
Gnawing on a mutton bone;
How she gnawed it,
How she clawed it,
When she found herself alone.

Go to Bed

Go to bed late,
Stay very small;
Go to bed early
Grow very tall.

Sippity, Sippity, Sup

Sippity sup, sippity sup,
Bread and milk from a china cup.
Bread and milk from a bright silver spoon
Made of a piece of the bright silver moon.
Sippity sup, sippity sup,
Sippity, sippity sup.

Little Blue Ben

Little Blue Ben, who lives in the glen,
Keeps a blue cat and one blue hen,
Which lays of blue eggs a score and ten;
Where shall I find the little Blue Ben?

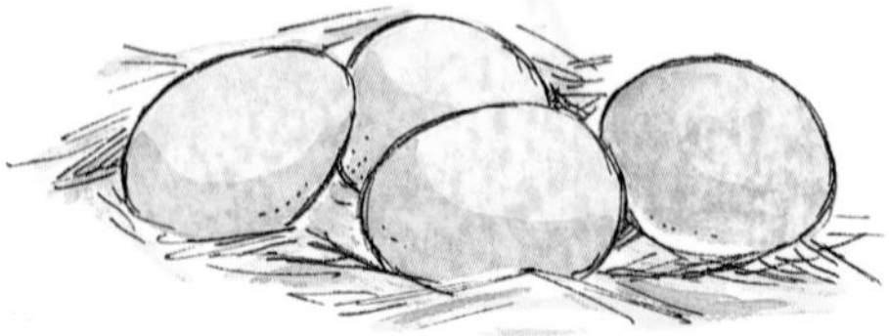

Eeper Weeper

Eeper, Weeper, Chimney sweeper,
Married a wife and could not keep her
Married another,
Did not love her,
Up the chimney he did shove her!

Where Am I?

X, Y, and tumbledown Z,
The cat's in the cupboard
And can't see me!

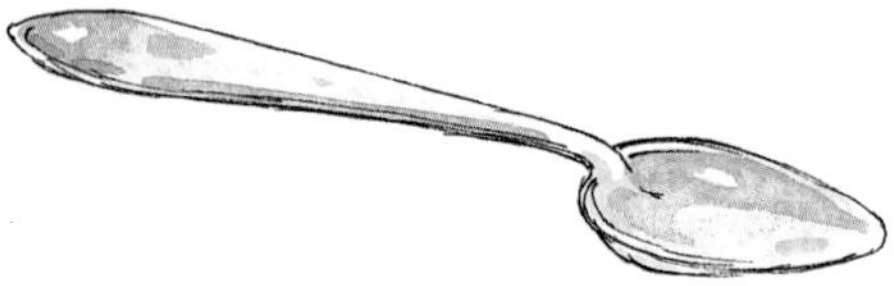

Dame Trot

Dame Trot and her cat
Sat down for a chat;
The dame sat on this side
And puss sat on that.

"Puss," says the dame,
"Can you catch a rat,
Or a mouse in the dark?"
"Purr," says the cat.

I Do Not Like Thee

I do not like thee, Doctor Fell,
The reason why, I cannot tell;
But this I know, and know full well,
I do not like thee, Doctor Fell.

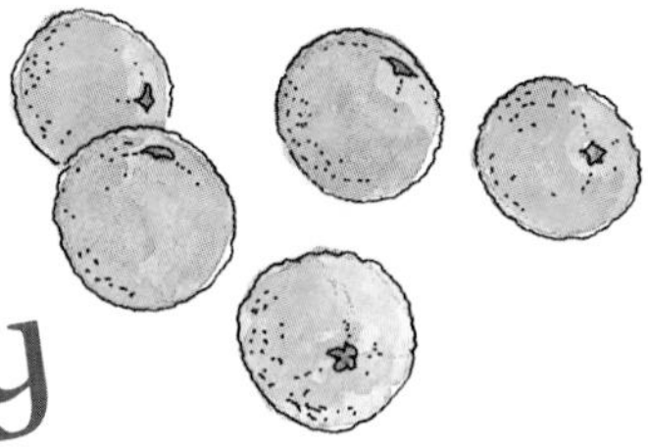

My Mummy's Maid

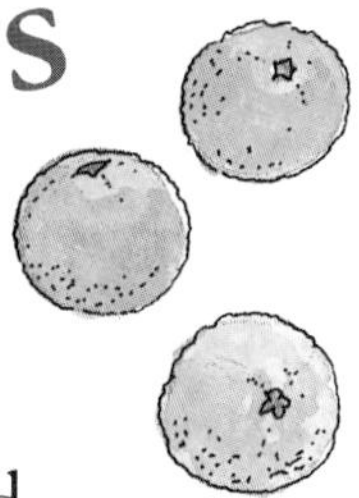

Dingty diddlety,
My mummy's maid,
She stole oranges,
I am afraid;
Some in her pocket,
Some in her sleeve,
She stole oranges,
I do believe.

Charlie Wag

Charlie Wag,
Charlie Wag,
Ate the pudding
And left the bag.

Sunshine

A sunshiny shower
Won't last half an hour.

Old Bandy Legs

As I was going to sell my eggs,
I met a man with bandy legs;
Bandy legs and crooked toes,
I tripped up his heels and
he fell on his nose.

One, Two

One, two, whatever you do,
Start it well and carry it through.
Try, try, never say die,
Things will come right,
You know, by and by.

One Little Indian

One little, two little, three little Indians
Four little, five little, six little Indians
Seven little, eight little, nine little Indians
Ten little Indian boys.

Ten little, nine little, eight little Indians
Seven little, six little, five little Indians
Four little, three little, two little Indians
One little Indian boy.

The Fluff Monsters

This is the story of the Fluff monsters. Everyone has seen fluff under the bed. That's because the Fluff monsters live under beds.

The Fluff monsters only come out when it's dark. They think it's scary just being out during the day. Who knows what might be out in the daylight? Once, Fluff-boy was having a quiet meal eating fluff and custard, when suddenly the magic-sucking thing appeared. It made a terrible noise as it came closer and closer. Then a tube with a brush on the end sucked up all the fluff after he'd spent ages collecting it!

But Fluff-boy had only ever lived under his bed. He wanted to know what it was like under other beds. "Only naughty Fluff monsters go out in daylight," said Fluff-mummy, "and the Little Girl will get you!"

Fluff-boy's eyes opened wide. "Who's the Little Girl?" he asked.

"The Little Girl is a monster who lives in the bed!" said Fluff-mummy. "She is really clean and pretty! She will take you away and wash you and put you in a room with sun shining through the windows! She will open the doors and fill the room with fresh air from outside!"

"That's horrible! I don't believe you," said Fluff-boy.

"You'll have to be good," said Fluff-mummy, "or you'll find out!"

Well, I'm not scared of the Little Girl!" said Fluff-boy.

Fluff-boy wanted to know what it was like under other beds. One day, while everyone was asleep, Fluff-boy slipped away. Outside, bright sunlight filled the room. He wandered into the next room and found another bed to slide under. There were spiders and daddy-long-legs, cobwebs and lots and lots of fluff! It was perfect! So Fluff-boy ate some fluff (though he did miss his mum's home-made custard) and settled into his new home.

But Fluff-boy couldn't sleep, he was thinking about the Little Girl. Plucking up courage, he carefully climbed up the bed covers. Suddenly, the Little Girl woke and sat up. Fluff-boy was so surprised he jumped with fright. "Aaargh!" shrieked Fluff-boy.

"Aaargh!" screamed the Little Girl. They scrambled to each end of the bed and stared at each other.

"You gave me a fright!" said Fluff-boy.

"Me frighten you?" said the Little Girl. "You frightened me!"

"Did I?" said Fluff-boy. "Why?" laughed Fluff-boy. "I'm Fluff-boy. I've just moved in under this bed. Do you live in this bed too?"

"No, silly," said the Little Girl. "I just sleep here at night. I thought scary Bogeymen lived under the bed. But you're not scary at all!"

"How about this then?" asked Fluff-boy. He stuck his thumbs in his ears, wiggled his fingers and poked out his tongue. The girl laughed.

"That's not at all scary!" she said. "This is scary," and she pulled out the corners of her mouth with her fingers and crossed her eyes. And that was how Fluff-boy and the Little Girl discovered that there is nothing scary under the bed or in it!

The Dog with No Voice

There once lived a prince whose words were pure poetry. He amused the court with his witty, rhyming verse, yet his kind and thoughtful words made him popular with all. It was said he could even charm the birds from the trees.

One day, he was walking in the forest when he came upon an old lady with a huge bundle on her back. "Let me help," said the prince. He took the load and walked along beside the woman. They chatted away and before long they had reached the old lady's door.

Now the old lady – who was really a witch – had been listening intently to the prince's words. "What a fine voice he has!" she thought to herself. "I would like my own son to speak like that. Then maybe he could find himself a wealthy wife and we'd be rich for ever more!"

"You must be thirsty," she said to the prince. "Let me give you something to quench your thirst to repay you for your kindness." The prince gratefully accepted, and was given a delicious drink which he drained to the last drop. He was about to thank the witch when he began to feel very peculiar. He found he

was getting smaller and smaller. He looked down at his feet and saw two hairy paws. Then he turned round and saw to his horror that he had grown a shaggy tail! He tried to shout at the witch but all that came out of his mouth was a loud bark!

The witch hugged herself for joy. "My spell worked!" she cackled. "Come here my son!" she called.

There appeared at the door a rough-looking young man. "What's going on, my dearest mother?" he said in a voice that sounded familiar to the prince. Then he looked down and exclaimed, "Where did you find this poor little dog?"

Now the prince understood what had happened. "The old lady has turned me into a humble hound and given my voice to her son. Whatever am I to do?" he thought miserably. "I can't return to the palace. They'll never let a stray dog in." He turned with his tail between his legs and trotted off forlornly into the forest.

The witch and her son were delighted with his new voice. She made him scrub himself clean from top to toe and dressed him in the prince's clothes. "Now go," she said, "and don't return until you've found a rich girl to marry!"

The young man set off, eager to try out his new voice. Soon he was feeling very pleased with himself as he talked to passers-by.

The witch's son travelled far and wide until at last he came to a castle where he spied a fair princess sitting on her balcony. He called to her and straight away she arose and looked down into the garden, enraptured by the sound of his beautiful voice. She was enchanted by his fine words and guessed they must belong to a prince. Soon the princess and the witch's son were chatting away merrily, and to his delight when he asked her to marry him she readily agreed. "For one with so beautiful a voice," she thought to herself, "must indeed be a fine young man."

Meanwhile, the poor dog-prince wandered in the forest, surviving as best he could by foraging for roots and fruits in the undergrowth. Feeling truly miserable, he stopped to drink from a stream. As he dipped his long dog's tongue in the cool water, he caught sight of someone sitting on a bridge. It was a pixie, fishing with a tiny net.

"Cheer up!" said the little fellow, "I saw everything that happened and I know how we can get your voice back. Follow me!" And with that he was off, dancing away through the forest with the dog-prince trotting along behind. They seemed to go on forever, and the pads of his paws were quite sore, by the time they reached the castle. He could see the witch's son in the garden calling to the princess on the balcony. The dog-prince's eyes filled with tears, for she was quite the loveliest girl he had ever seen and he wished he could marry her himself.

"We will be married today," the witch's son said in the prince's voice. "I will await you by the church, my fairest one." Seizing his fishing net, the pixie leaped in the air. As the words "my fairest one" floated up to the balcony, he caught them in the net and gave them back to the dog-prince.

As soon as he swallowed the words, the dog-prince could speak again. "Thank you, little pixie," he cried, "but what can I do? I am a dog with a prince's voice. The princess will never marry me."

"If you want to break the witch's spell, you must go to the church – fast!" said the pixie, and then he disappeared!

Straight away, the dog-prince ran to the church door where the princess was looking confused, for standing beside her was the witch's son – with not a word in his head. "I don't understand," she cried. "I thought I was to marry a silver-tongued young man, but now I find he is a dumb ragamuffin!"

"I can explain," exclaimed the dog-prince.

The princess spun around. "Who can explain?" she asked, for all she could see was a dog in front of her. "What a handsome dog!" she cried, bending down and kissing him on the nose. To her astonishment, the dog's hairy paws and shaggy tail immediately disappeared and there stood the prince. "But you're… but he…" she stammered looking from the prince to the witch's son.

Well, the prince explained everything that had happened, and after that he and the princess were married with great rejoicing. And the witch's son? The prince taught him to speak again – with a beautiful voice – and he married the princess's younger sister.

Easter Bunnies

It was Easter and the naughty bunnies had hidden eggs for the animals to find. How they chuckled when they saw the farm cat shaking water from her fur. She had been searching by the pond and had fallen in! The bunnies giggled as they watched the hens shooing the pig away from the henhouse. "They're not in here!" the hens clucked.

Eventually, when the animals had searched high and low, Daisy the cow said, "It's no use, we can't find them! We give up!"

"Here's a clue," said the bunnies. "Where do you find eggs?"

"In a nest," answered Mrs Goose.

"And what do you make a nest with?" asked the bunnies.

"Straw!" said the horse.

"They must be in the haystack!" cried all the animals at once.

They rushed to the field and there, hidden in the haystack, was a pile of lovely Easter eggs.

What a feast they had!

The Mad Gardener's Song

He thought he saw an Elephant,
That practised on a fife:
He looked again, and found it was
A letter from his wife.
"At length I realize," he said,
"The bitterness of Life!"

He thought he saw a Buffalo
Upon the chimney-piece:
He looked again, and found it was
His Sister's Husband's Niece.
"Unless you leave this house," he said,
"I'll send for the Police!"

He thought he saw a Banker's Clerk
Descending from the bus:
He looked again, and found it was
A Hippopotamus:
"If this should stay to dine," he said,
"There won't be much for us!"

All Things Bright and Beautiful

All things bright and beautiful,
All creatures great and small,
All things wise and wonderful,
The Lord God made them all.

Each little flower that opens,
Each little bird that sings,
He made their glowing colours,
He made their tiny wings.

The purple-headed mountain,
The river running by,
The sunset, and the morning,
That brightens up the sky.

The cold wind in the winter,
The pleasant summer sun,
The ripe fruits in the garden,
He made them every one.

He gave us eyes to see them,
And lips that we might tell,
How great is God Almighty,
Who has made all things well.

Thaw

Over the land freckled with snow half-thawed
The speculating rooks at their nests cawed
And saw from elm-tops, delicate as flower of grass,
What we below could not see, winter pass.

Donkey Riding

Were you ever in Quebec,
Stowing timbers on a deck,
Where there's a king in his golden crown
Riding on a donkey?

Hey ho, and away we go,
Donkey riding, donkey riding,
Hey ho, and away we go,
Riding on a donkey.

Were you ever in Cardiff Bay,
Where the folks all shout, Hooray!
Here comes John with his three
months' pay,
Riding on a donkey?

Hey ho, and away we go,
Donkey riding, donkey riding,
Hey ho, and away we go,
Riding on a donkey.

Were you ever off Cape Horn,
Where it's always fine and warm?
See the lion and the unicorn
Riding on a donkey.

Hey ho, and away we go,
Donkey riding, donkey riding,
Hey ho, and away we go,
Riding on a donkey.

Autumn Fires

In the other gardens
And all up the vale,
From the autumn bonfires
See the smoke trail!

Pleasant summer over
And all the summer flowers,
The red fire blazes,
The grey smoke towers.

Sing a song of seasons!
Something bright in all!
Flowers in the summer,
Fires in the fall!

ROBERT LOUIS STEVENSON

Happy Thought

The world is so full
of a number of things,
I'm sure we should all be
as happy as kings.

The Hare and the Tortoise

Hare was the most boastful animal in the whole forest. On this fine, sunny morning, he was trotting down the forest path singing, "I'm handsome and clever and the fastest hare ever! There's no one as splendid as me!"

Mole, Mouse and Squirrel watched him from the fallen log. "Hare is so annoying," said Mole. "Someone should find a way to stop him boasting all the time!"

"I'll get him to stop!" said Squirrel and he jumped on to the path right in front of Hare. "I'm as handsome as you are, Hare," he said. "Look at my big bushy tail."

"It's not as handsome as my fluffy white tail and my long silky ears!" boasted Hare.

"Well, I'm as clever as you are!" said Mouse, hurrying out to join them. "I can dig holes under trees and store enough nuts and seeds to last all winter!"

"That's nothing!" said Hare. "In winter, I can change my coat to white, so that I can hide in the snow!"

"Now, is there anyone who thinks they can run as *fast* as me?" said Hare to the animals, who had gathered round. "Who wants a race?" No one said anything! All the animals knew that Hare was *very fast* and no one thought they could beat him. "Ha!" exclaimed Hare. "That proves it! I'm the handsomest, the cleverest *and* the fastest."

"Excuse me," said a small voice.

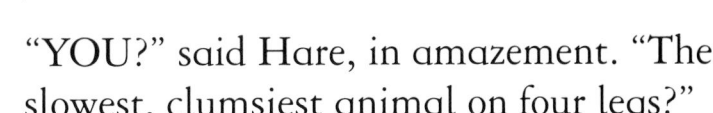

"Yes?" said Hare, turning around.

"I will race you," said Tortoise.

"YOU?" said Hare, in amazement. "The slowest, clumsiest animal on four legs?"

"Yes," said Tortoise, quietly. "I will race you." The other animals gasped and Hare roared with laughter.

"Will you race me to the willow tree?" Hare asked Tortoise.

"Yes," said Tortoise.

"Will you race past the willow tree, to the stream?" asked Hare.

"Yes, I will," said Tortoise.

"Will you race past the willow tree, past the stream and all the way to the old oak tree?" asked Hare.

"Of course I will," said Tortoise.

"Fine," said Hare. "We'll start at nine o'clock in the morning! We'll meet here, at the big oak tree."

"All right," said Tortoise. The other animals ran off to tell their friends the news.

The next morning, everyone had turned out to watch the big race. Some were at the starting line and others were going to the finish, to see who would get there first.

Magpie called, "Ready, steady, GO!" And Tortoise and Hare were off! Hare shot past Tortoise and, when there was no one to show off for, he slowed down just a bit. He reached the willow tree and looked behind him – Tortoise was not in sight!

"It will take him ages just to catch me," Hare thought. "I don't need to hurry. I may as well stop and rest." He sat down under the willow tree and closed his eyes. In minutes, he was fast asleep.

Meanwhile, Tortoise just plodded on. He didn't try to go faster than he could, but he didn't stop, either. He just kept going, on and on and on. The sun climbed higher in the sky and Tortoise felt hot. But he still kept going. His stubby legs were beginning to ache, but he knew he mustn't stop. Hare kept snoring under the willow tree.

Some time later, Tortoise reached Hare. First of all, Tortoise thought he should wake Hare up. Then he changed his mind. "Hare is very clever," he told himself. "He must have a reason for sleeping. He would only be cross if I woke him!" So, Tortoise left Hare sleeping and went on his way, walking slowly towards the finish line.

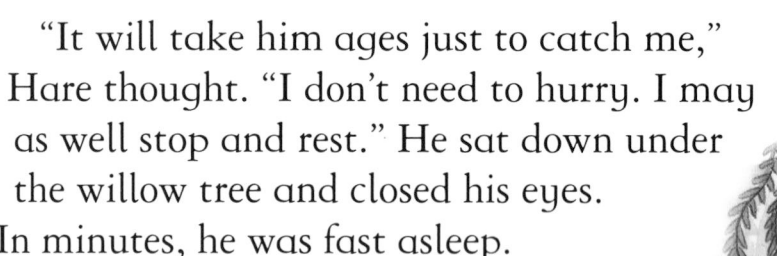

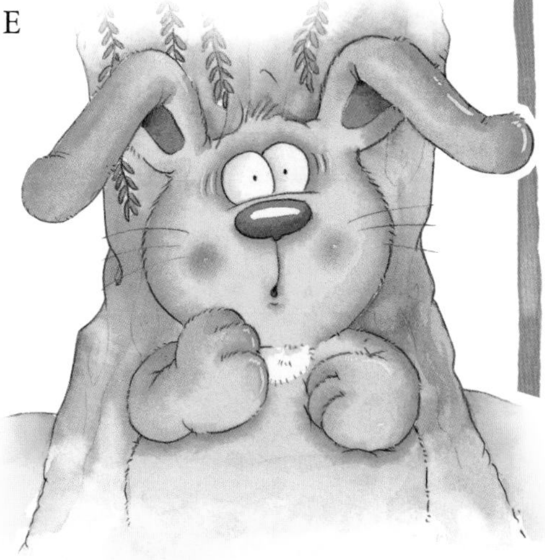

Later that afternoon, as the sun began to sink and the air grew chilly, Hare awoke with a start. "The race!" he thought. "I have to finish the race!" He looked around to see if Tortoise was nearby. There was no sign of him. "Hah!" said Hare. "He still hasn't caught up with me. No need to hurry, then."

And he trotted towards the clearing, with a big grin on his face. When he neared the finish, Hare could hear cheers and clapping. "They must be able to see me coming," he thought. But, as he got closer, he saw the real reason for all the noise and his heart sank. There was Tortoise, crossing the line. Tortoise had won! The animals were cheering wildly. As Hare crept up to the finishing line, the cheers turned to laughter. His ears turned bright red and drooped with embarrassment. Hare moped off and everyone gathered round to congratulate Tortoise, who looked shy, but very proud. He had proved that slow but steady always wins the race.

Somehow the animals knew that they wouldn't have to listen to Hare's loud, annoying boasting any more!

Little Red Riding Hood

Once upon a time there was a little girl who lived with her mother at the edge of a deep, dark forest. Everyone called the girl "Little Red Riding Hood", because she always wore a bright red cloak with a bright red hood.

One sunny morning her mother said, "Granny isn't feeling very well. Please will you take this basket of goodies to her, to make her feel better?"

"I will," replied Little Red Riding Hood.

"Remember," said her mother, "stay on the path, and don't stop to talk to any strangers on the way."

Little Red Riding Hood hopped and skipped along the path to Granny's house. She had only gone a short way into the deep, dark forest, when a sly, nasty wolf with big shiny teeth and long sharp claws jumped out onto the path, right in front of her.

"Hello, my pretty one," said the wolf. "Where are you going on this fine morning?"

"Good morning," said Little Red Riding Hood politely. "I'm going to see my granny, who isn't feeling very well. She lives all the way on the other side of the forest. But please excuse me, I am not allowed to talk to strangers."

"Of course, little girl," sneered the crafty wolf. "You must be in a hurry. But why not take a moment to pick a big bunch of these lovely wild flowers to cheer up your granny?"

"Thank you, Mr Wolf, that sounds like a very good idea," said Little Red Riding Hood, putting her basket down on the ground. "I'm sure that Granny would love them."

So, while Little Red Riding Hood picked a bunch of sweet-smelling flowers, the wicked wolf raced ahead through the deep, dark forest and soon arrived at Granny's pretty cottage.

The wolf lifted the knocker and banged hard at the door.

Sweet old Granny sat up in bed. "Who is it?" she called.

"It's me, Little Red Riding Hood," replied the wolf in a voice which sounded just like Little Red Riding Hood's.

"Hello, my dear," called Granny. "The door is not locked – lift up the latch and come in."

So the wolf opened the door

and, as quick as a flash, he gobbled up Granny. Then, he put on her nightie and nightcap, and crawled under the bedclothes to lie in wait for Little Red Riding Hood.

A short time later, Little Red Riding Hood arrived at the cottage and knocked on Granny's door.

"Who is it?" called the wolf, in a high voice sounding just like Granny.

"It's me, Granny," came the reply, "Little Red Riding Hood."

"Hello, my dear," called the wolf. "The door is not locked – lift up the latch and come in."

So Little Red Riding Hood lifted the latch, opened the door and went into Granny's cottage.

Little Red Riding Hood couldn't believe her eyes. "Oh, Granny," she said, "it is so nice to see you, but what big ears you have!"

"All the better to hear you with," said the wolf. "Come closer, my dear."

Little Red Riding Hood took a step closer to the bed.

"Oh, Granny," she said, "what big eyes you have!"

"All the better to see you with," said the wolf. "Come closer, my dear."

So Little Red Riding Hood took another step closer. Now she was right beside Granny's bed.

"Oh, Granny!" she cried. "What big teeth you have!"

"All the better to eat you with, my dear!" snarled the wolf, and he jumped up and swallowed Little Red Riding Hood in one BIG gulp!

Now it just so happened that a woodcutter was passing Granny's cottage that sunny morning. He was going to work on the other side of the forest. He knew that Granny had not been feeling very well, so he decided to look in on her.

What a surprise he had when he saw the hairy wolf fast asleep in Granny's bed!

When he saw the wolf's big, fat tummy, he knew just what had happened.

Quick as a flash, he took out his shiny, sharp, axe and sliced the wolf open! Out popped Granny and Little Red Riding Hood, surprised and shaken, but safe and well.

The woodcutter dragged the wolf outside and threw him down a deep, dark well so he would never trouble anyone ever again. Then the woodcutter,

Granny and Little Red Riding Hood sat down to tea and ate all of the yummy goodies from Little Red Riding Hood's basket.

After tea, Little Red Riding Hood waved goodbye to her Granny and the woodcutter and ran all the way home to her mother, without straying once from the path or talking to any strangers. What an eventful day!

The Perfect Place

One sunny day, Old MacDonald looked at his farm – everything looked perfect.

But in the farmyard, the happy scene was about to change. Percy the pig noticed it first. As he lay dozing after a splendid dinner of apple cores and potato peelings, he heard a scritch-scratching in the corner of his sty. For a while, he took no notice. He was far too full to move.

But the scritch-scratching went on... and on... and on... and on... until, finally, Percy dragged himself up and went to see what on earth it was.

To his surprise, he saw that a family of mice had made their home in his sty!

Meanwhile, in another corner of the busy farmyard, Old George the horse felt something tickling the back of his neck.

"Something's tickling my neck, dear," he said to Tilly, who swung her great head round and peered closely at him. Then she gave a neigh of surprise!

"Why, George! There's a baby mouse asleep in your mane!"

Down by the duck pond, Doris the duck swam over to her nest. It was time to settle down in the shade for a little snooze. But she let out an angry quack when she reached the bank. Inside her nest, three little mice were playing leapfrog – or leapmouse, I suppose!

By the end of the day, every single animal on the farm had found a mouse and they were not happy! Henrietta the hen called an emergency meeting. No one stayed away.

"Something has to be done!" said Maria the sheep.

"Baa! Moo! Cluck! Quack! Woof! Neigh! Oink!"

All the animals agreed with her. They all turned their heads and looked at Milly and Lazy, the cats.

"We think this is your job," said Bruce the sheepdog. "Cats eat mice, don't they?"

Lazy and Milly looked at each other. "Well *we* don't!" they said.

It soon became clear that the cats were too fond of mice

to dream of having them for supper! None of the animals could believe their ears!

"We're doomed," groaned Percy.

Suddenly a little voice could be heard. "I'm Maisie Mouse," it squeaked. "We don't want to cause trouble, but my family has nowhere to live!"

Bruce the sheepdog had an idea. "Come with me," he said. "I know the perfect place for you. But you must be very quiet."

Silently, he led the mice over to the farmhouse, up the stairs and into the attic.

Old MacDonald and his wife work so hard on their farm, they always sleep soundly. And that is just as well, now that a family of mice has moved in upstairs!

Bumble Bee Helps Out

Bumble Bee was the busiest bee in the hive. Her job was collecting flower pollen, which the other bees used to make honey. Bumble Bee had lots of friends, but she was usually far too busy to stop and chat. "Maybe tomorrow," she would cry, as she flew around from one flower to the next.

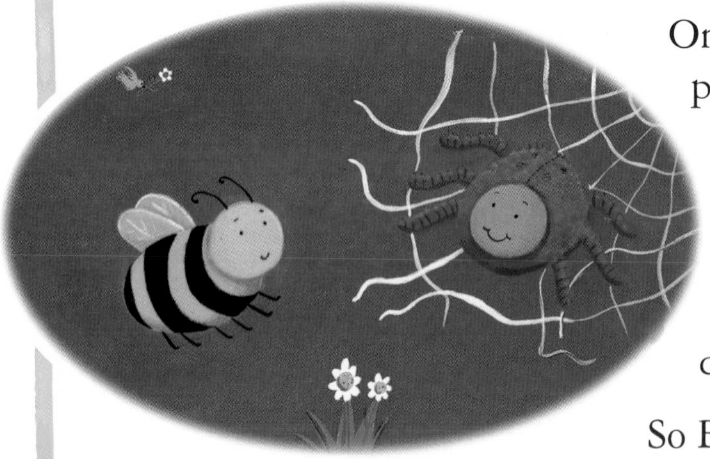

One day, Bumble Bee collected too much pollen. "I can't carry it all," she thought, "I'll ask Sammy Spider for help!"

But Sammy Spider was busy mending his web. "I'm glad you flew past!" he said. "Would you help me and hold these threads?"

So Bumble Bee helped Sammy, and they worked at the web together.

Next Bumble Bee went to find her friend Anita Ant, who was struggling with her brothers to carry a really heavy pea-pod.

"We're very glad to see you!" they cried. "Can you help us carry this pea-pod home?"

Poor Bumble Bee thought, "I need some help to carry the pollen, but perhaps this won't take very long."

So she helped the ants carry their pea-pod home.

"Now who can I find to help me?" thought Bumble Bee. Just then, she heard Lizzie Ladybird sobbing.

"I've lost my baby sister," said Lizzie. "I can't find her anywhere – will you help me look?" Bumble Bee helped Lizzie Ladybird search the woods until they found Lizzie's baby sister, lying fast asleep on a bright red leaf.

"No wonder I couldn't find you!" cried Lizzie.

At the end of the day, Bumble Bee stood looking at her pile of pollen, wondering what to do. Suddenly all of her friends arrived at once, led by Belinda Butterfly with her beautiful wings. Everyone helped her carry the pollen back to the hive.

"Oh thank you!" cried Bumble Bee.

"You helped us and now it's our turn to help you," they all replied. "That's what friends are for!"

The Grand Old Duke of York

The grand old Duke of York,
He had ten thousand men;
He marched them up to the top of the hill,
And he marched them down again!

And when they were up they were up,
And when they were down they were down;
And when they were only halfway up,
They were neither up nor down.

What is the Rhyme for Porringer?

What is the rhyme for porringer?
The King he had a daughter fair,
And gave the Prince of Orange her.

Grey Goose and Gander

Grey goose and gander,
Waft your wings together,
And carry the good king's daughter
Over the one strand river.

Old King Cole

Old King Cole
Was a merry old soul,
And a merry old soul was he;
He called for his pipe,
And he called for his bowl,
And he called for his fiddlers three.
Every fiddler had a fine fiddle,
And a very fine fiddle had he;
Twee tweedle dee, tweedle dee, went the fiddlers,
Very merry men are we;
Oh there's none so rare
As can compare
With King Cole and his fiddlers three.

Ten Little Men

Ten little men standing straight,
Ten little men open the gate,
Ten little men all in a ring,

Ten little men bow to the king,
Ten little men dance all day,
Ten little men hide away.

There Was a King and He Had Three Daughters

There was a king,
And he had three daughters,
And they all lived,
In a basin of water;
The basin bended,
My story's ended.
If the basin had been stronger,
My story would be longer.

When Famed King Arthur Ruled This Land

When famed King Arthur ruled this land
He was a goodly king:
He took three pecks of barley meal
To make a bag pudding.

A rare pudding the king did make,
And stuffed it well with plums;
And in it put such lumps of fat,
As big as my two thumbs.

The king and queen did eat thereof,
And noblemen beside,
And what they could not eat that night
The queen next morning fried.

The Queen of Hearts

The Queen of Hearts, she made some tarts,
All on a summer's day;
The Knave of Hearts, he stole the tarts,
And took them clean away.

The King of Hearts called for the tarts,
And beat the Knave full sore;
The Knave of Hearts brought back the tarts,
And vowed he'd steal no more.

Jade and the Jewels

Jade was the prettiest mermaid in the lagoon! Her jet black hair reached right down to the tip of her swishy, fishy tail. Her eyes were as green as emeralds, and her skin was as white as the whitest pearl. But Jade was so big-headed and vain that the other mermaids didn't like her!

"That Jade thinks too much of herself!" the other mermaids would say. "One of these days she'll come unstuck!"

But one creature was fond of Jade. Gentle the giant turtle followed her wherever she went. But Jade didn't notice Gentle. She lived in her own world, spending all her time combing her hair and looking in the mirror.

One day Jade overheard the mermaids talking about a pirate ship that had sunk to the bottom of the ocean. On board was a treasure chest filled with precious jewels. "But no one dares take the jewels," whispered the mermaids, "because the pirate ship is cursed!"

"I'm going to find that pirate ship," Jade told Gentle, "and the treasure chest! Just imagine how beautiful I will look wearing all those jewels!" And Jade set off right away.

"Wait for me," called Gentle, paddling after her. "It's too dangerous to go alone!" Jade swam to a deep part of the ocean she had never been to before. She dived through shoals of colourful fish, past the coral reef and deep, deep down to the very bottom of the ocean. Finally, they found the shipwreck.

"Be careful, Jade," said Gentle. "Remember there is a curse on this pirate wreck."

"Nonsense," Jade told him. "I've come to get the jewels and I won't go home without them!" Jade saw the treasure chest through a porthole. Jade swam inside and reached out to touch the chest. The lid sprang open and brilliant jewels spilled over the sides. The colours were dazzling.

Jade lifted out a necklace and put it round her neck. There was a little gold and silver mirror in the chest. She held it up to admire her reflection. The necklace was beautiful! Jade looked lovelier than ever.

Suddenly, there was a loud crack, and the mirror shattered. The necklace turned to stone – it was the ship's curse! Jade tried to swim, but the necklace was so heavy she couldn't move.

"Help!" Jade cried out. "Help! Help!" Gentle the giant turtle heard her and swam to the porthole. "Help me, Gentle," she cried. "Please help me!"

Gentle's powerful flippers broke the necklace and freed Jade. As Jade and Gentle swam away from the wreck, Gentle said, "You don't need fancy jewels, Jade. You're pretty without them."

Once she was safely home, Jade told the other mermaids about the pirate ship curse.

"I've certainly learned my lesson," said Jade. "I'll never be vain again."

Red Sky

Red sky at night,
Shepherd's delight;
Red sky in the morning,
Shepherd's warning.

Rain

Rain before seven,
Fine by eleven.

Washing Up

When I was a little boy
I washed my mummy's dishes;
I put my finger in one eye,
And pulled out golden fishes.

What's the News

What's the news of the day,
Good neighbour, I pray?
They say the balloon
Is gone up to the moon.

My Hobby Horse

I had a little hobby horse, it was well shod,
It carried me to London, niddety nod,
And when we got to London we heard a great shout,
Down fell my hobby horse and I cried out:
"Up again, hobby horse, if thou be a beast,
When we get to our town we will have a feast,
And if there be but a little, why thou shall have some,
And dance to the bag-pipes and beating of the drum.

A Man in the Wilderness

A man in the wilderness asked me,
"How many strawberries grow in the sea".
I answered him, as I thought good,
"As many red herrings as swim in the wood."

Robin Hood

Robin Hood
Has gone to the wood;
He'll come back again
If we are good.

Cobbler Cobbler

Cobbler, cobbler, mend my shoe,
Get it done by half past two;
Stitch it up, and stitch it down,
Then I'll give you half a crown.

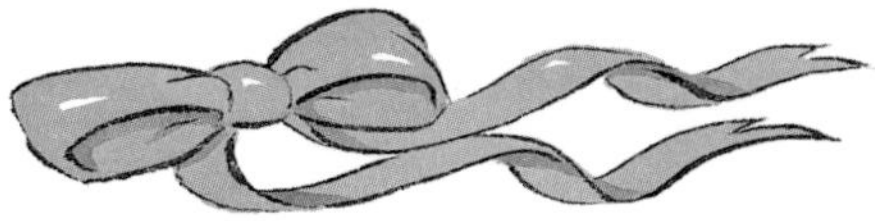

And That's All

There was an old man,
And he had a calf,
And that's half;
He took him out of the stall,
And put him on the wall,
And that's all.

The Little Rusty, Dusty Miller

O the little rusty, dusty miller,
Dusty was his coat,
Dusty was his colour,
Dusty was the kiss
I got from the miller.
If I had my pockets
Full of gold and silver,
I would give it all
To my dusty miller.

There was a Little Boy

There was a little boy and a little girl.
Lived in an alley;
Says the little boy to the little girl,
"Shall I, oh, shall I?"

Says the little girl to the little boy,
"What shall we do?"
Says the little boy to the little girl,
"I will kiss you."

Warning

The robin and the redbreast,
The robin and the wren:
If you takes from their nest
You'll never thrive again.

Mr East's Feast

Mr East gave a feast;
Mr North laid the cloth;
Mr West did his best;
Mr South burnt his mouth
With eating a cold potato.

Little Chick Lost

"Stay close, Little Chick!" said Mummy, as they set out to visit Mrs Duck, who lived on the pond. Little Chick tried to keep up with Mummy, but there were so many interesting things to look at that he soon got lost in the long grass.

He was busy amongst the toadstools watching a shiny beetle climb slowly up a stem of grass, when a dark shadow fell over him. He looked up to see a huge mouth coming silently towards him! It was a fox, and he looked rather hungry!

"Help!" cried Little Chick, looking around for somewhere to hide.

Just then, Spot, the farm dog, appeared and with a great woof he chased the fox away. He was good at protecting the farm animals.

Mummy arrived flapping her wings. "I told you to stay close," she said, tucking Little Chick safely under her wing.

And from then on, that is just where Little Chick stayed!

The Squeaky Van

Honk! Honk! went the horn on the old blue van. It was market day, and Dad was getting impatient. "Hurry up, you two," he called. "I want to get to the market early."

Dad reversed the old blue van out of the shed, and Rosie and Danny piled into the front. They all waved goodbye to Mum. Conker chased the van out of the farmyard barking loudly. Honk! Honk! Dad hooted at Joe as they passed him on the tractor.

"This van must be a hundred years old," muttered Danny, as they jolted over the bumpy road. "When are we going to get a new one?"

"I don't want a new one," protested Rosie. "Mum says this van has been at home since I was a baby."

"No, it's been at Faraway Farm since Grandad was a baby," laughed Dad. "And it still runs perfectly." But, as they were going down a long hill, Dad looked puzzled.

"Can you hear a funny sort of squeaking?" he asked.

"I think I can hear something," said Rosie. "But it's not very loud." Dad stopped in a lay-by and got out. He lifted the bonnet and poked around in the engine.

"I can't hear anything now," he said, scratching his head. "But we'll call into Tom's garage. Perhaps he can see if anything is wrong."

Soon they arrived at Tom's garage. "Morning, Tom," said Dad. "We've got a little problem with the van."

"We've got a squeak," added Rosie.

"I'll take a look," Tom gave her a big wink. "Maybe there's a mouse in the engine!" Tom peered at the engine. He checked the oil, fiddled with the fan belt, and poured water into the radiator. Then he started the engine again.

"I can't hear anything wrong," he announced. "The van's old but it should go on for a while yet."

They thanked Tom and drove into town. Everywhere was crowded because it was market day. Dad parked the van and they all got out. "Ooh, look!" Rosie pointed excitedly. "There's a roundabout. Can we have a ride?"

"Maybe later," replied Dad. "I must buy some tools and other bits and pieces first."

"And I want to go to the pet stall and buy a new collar for Conker," added Danny.

When they had bought everything they needed, Rosie had two rides on the roundabout. "That was great," she smiled.

"Now, let's get an ice cream," said Danny. Dad bought ice creams and loaded the van while Danny and Rosie ate them. Then they all jumped into the van and set off for home.

"There's that squeak again," said Rosie. "It's getting louder."

"I'll ask Joe to look underneath when we get home," said Dad, frowning.

"I don't think it's coming from the engine," said Danny.

"No, it's coming from the back," cried Rosie.

Before long they turned into the yard of Faraway Farm. Dad stopped the engine and they all went round to the back to unload.

"Shhh!" whispered Danny. "I can hear something."

He lifted up the floor of the van. There, sitting in the middle of the spare tyre was a fat brown hen with four tiny yellow chicks chirping at the tops of their voices. "Well, would you believe it?" said Dad, laughing. "That crafty old hen must have got inside and made a nest when the van was parked in the barn."

"Let me see," said Rosie, pushing between them.

"That explains it," smiled Dad. "To start with there was just one chick chirping and then as the others hatched out, the squeaking got louder."

"What about the nest?" asked Danny. "There are still three eggs left."

"We'll just leave them," smiled Dad. "I don't mind the hen using the tyre for a nest."

Just then Mum came out. "We've brought you back a surprise from market," laughed Danny.

"Some new babies!" said Rosie.

Peter, Peter, Pumpkin Eater

Peter, Peter, pumpkin eater,
Had a wife and couldn't keep her;
He put her in a pumpkin shell
And there he kept her very well.

Peter, Peter, pumpkin eater,
Had another and didn't love her;
Peter learned to read and spell,
And then he loved her very well.

Simple Simon

Simple Simon met a pieman
Going to the fair;
Said Simple Simon to the pieman,
"Let me taste your ware."

Said the pieman to Simple Simon,
"Show me first your penny";
Said Simple Simon to the pieman,
"Indeed I have not any."

There was a Little Boy

There was a little boy went into a barn,
And lay down on some hay;
An owl came out and flew about,
And the little boy ran away.

Johnny Shall Have a New Bonnet

Johnny shall have a new bonnet,
And Johnny shall go to the fair,
And Johnny shall have a blue ribbon
To tie up his bonny brown hair.

Tommy Snooks and Bessy Brooks

As Tommy Snooks and Bessy Brooks
Were walking out one Sunday.
Says Tommy Snooks to Bessy Brooks,
"Tomorrow will be Monday."

Wee Willie Winkie

Wee Willie Winkie runs through the town,
Up-stairs and down-stairs in his nightgown,
Peeping through the keyhole, crying through the lock,
"Are the children in their beds, it's past eight o'clock?"

When Jacky's a Very Good Boy

When Jacky's a very good boy,
He shall have cakes and a custard;
But when he does nothing but cry,
He shall have nothing but mustard.

Little Tommy Tucker

Little Tommy Tucker
Sings for his supper:
What shall we give him?
Brown bread and butter.
How shall he cut it
Without a knife?
How can he marry
Without a wife?

Bobby's Best Birthday Present

It was the morning of Bobby's birthday and he was very excited. When he came down to breakfast, there on the table was a big pile of presents. Bobby opened them one by one. There was a beautiful book with pictures of wild animals, a toy racing car and a baseball cap. Bobby was very pleased with his presents, but where was the present from his parents? "Close your eyes and hold out your hands!" said his mother. When he opened his eyes there was a large rectangular parcel in his hands. Bobby tore off the wrapping and inside was a box. And inside the box was a wonderful, shiny, electric train set.

For a moment, Bobby looked at the train set lying in the box. It was so lovely he could hardly bear to touch it. There was an engine and six carriages all lying neatly on their sides. Bobby carefully lifted the engine out of the box. Then he set up the track and soon he had the train whizzing round his bedroom floor. Freddie the cat came in and watched the train going round. Round and round he watched it go, then one time when the train came past Freddie

swiped at it with his paw and derailed it. The engine and the six carriages came tumbling off the track and landed in a heap on the floor. "Look what you've done!" wailed Bobby as he picked up the train and reassembled it. The carriages were undamaged, but the engine had hit the side of his bed and was really badly dented.

Bobby was very upset. "My brand new train is ruined!" he cried.

"Don't worry, Bobby," said his mother. "We can't take it back to the shop now, but we can take it to the toymender in the morning. I'm sure he'll make a good job of mending the engine and it'll look as good as new again." Bobby played with his racing car, he wore his new baseball cap and he read his new book, but really all he wanted to do was to play with his train set. He went to bed that night with the engine on the floor near his bed.

In the morning when Bobby woke up, the first thing he did was to look at the poor broken engine of his train set. He picked it up, expecting to see the buckled metal, but the engine was perfect. He couldn't believe his eyes! He ran to his parents. "Look, look!" he cried. They were as amazed as he was. The engine worked perfectly and Bobby played happily with his train set all day – but he made sure Freddie kept out of his room!

That night Bobby couldn't sleep. He lay in bed tossing and turning. Then he heard a noise. It was the sound of his train set rushing round the track. He peered into the darkness and, yes, he could definitely make out the shape of the train as it sped by. How had the train started? It couldn't start all by itself! Had Freddie crept into his room and flicked the switch? As his eyes gradually became accustomed to the dark Bobby

could make out shapes in the carriages. Who were the mysterious passengers? He slid out of bed and on to the floor beside the train set. Now he could see that the passengers were little folk wearing strange pointed hats and leafy costumes. "Elves!" thought Bobby.

At that moment one of the elves spotted Bobby. "Hello there!" he called as the train rushed past again. "We saw that your train set was broken. We so much wanted a ride that we fixed it. I hope you don't mind!" Bobby was too astounded to say anything at all. "Come with us for a ride," called the elf as his carriage approached again.

As the train passed him the elf leaned out of the carriage and grabbed Bobby by the hand. Bobby felt himself shrinking as he flew through the air, and the next instant he was sitting beside the elf in the carriage of his very own train set!

"Here we go – hold tight!" called the elf as the train left the track and went out through the window into the night sky.

"Now, where would you like to go? What would you like to see?" asked the elf.

"Toyland!" replied Bobby without hesitation. Sure enough, the train headed towards a track which curved up a mountain made of pink and white sugar.

Beside the track were toys going about their daily business. Bobby saw a ragdoll getting into a shiny tin car, then a wooden sailor puppet wound up the car with a large key and off went the doll. He saw three teddy bears setting off for school with their satchels on their backs.

The train stopped and Bobby and the elves got out. "Now for some fun!" said one of the elves. They had come to a halt by a toy fairground. Bobby found that this was like no other fairground he had ever been to before. For in Toyland, all the rides are real. The horses on the carousel were real horses. The Dodgem cars were real cars. And, when he got in the rocket for the rocket ride, it took him all the way to the moon and back!

Eventually one of the elves said they had to go before daylight came.

Bobby climbed wearily back into the train and soon he was fast asleep. When he woke up it was morning, and he was back in his bed. The train set lay quite still on its tracks. But in one of the carriages was a scrap of paper and on the paper, in tiny spidery writing, were the words:
We hope you enjoyed your trip to Toyland
– the elves.

Take the Ghost Train

Hidden in the depths of the countryside, miles from any villages or farms, there is a very old, very run-down railway station. But this is no ordinary railway station, the atmosphere is chilly, even on the warmest of nights…

Standing silently at the station is an old steam train that looks ready to leave. The carriages are full, there is a fireman, a guard and a driver. But when the guard blows his whistle the sound is an eerie shriek that will send shivers down your spine. As the wail of the whistle fills the air, the figures in the carriages begin to wave and shout from the windows – there is something very strange about them!

Their shapes become clearer in the glow from the station lights. They are witches, ghosts, goblins and ghouls, all waiting endlessly for the ghost train to pull out of the station silently and chug slowly up the phantom line.

This is one train ride you won't want to take!

Ode to Ghosts

You may not know this, but the life of a castle ghost is very sad. He spends his days haunting cold, lonely rooms and corridors, and on birthdays and at Christmas time the postman never arrives with cards and parcels for him.

All day long the ghost floats from one room to another. He howls and clanks his chains, but most people blame the noise on the wind outside or the ancient drains. Occasionally he might appear when everyone is sitting eating their supper in the hope of a snack and a chat, but everyone screams and runs away. Naturally this doesn't make him feel any better.

What is even worse, the poor ghost has to wander around all night while everyone else is tucked up in bed! He would really like a warm bed to sleep in – but as soon as anyone wakes up they scream and shout so loudly that the ghost feels embarrassed and slips away.

So, the next time you see a ghost wafting along a castle corridor, don't run away in fright. Stay a while and have a chat, you'll find him most polite!

Birthday Surprise

In the higgledy-piggledy, messy alley, the sun was just beginning to shine. It was very early. Even the birds hadn't begun to chirp and cheep yet. Everyone and everything was fast asleep. Or were they?

Slowly, a sleepy head peeped out of a dustbin. It was Uncle Bertie.

First he opened one eye... then the other...and gave a great big grin!

"It's here, at last!" he chuckled to himself.

"Happy Birthday to me! Happy Birthday to me!" he sang, at the top of his voice. He looked around, but no one had heard. Everyone was still snoozing and snoring! Didn't they know it was his birthday?

"Time-to-get-up time!" he shouted, as he banged on a dustbin lid – CLANG! CLANG! CLANG! Lenny and Lulu, the two kittens, fell out of their basket in fright. Cousin Archie tumbled off his branch, right on top of poor Hattie!

"Uncle Bertie!" snapped Hattie, the kittens' mother, "why are you bashing that dustbin lid?"

"Sorry!" said Uncle Bertie. "Er... it's just that it's my... er... well, it's time-to-get-up time!"

"Oh, Bertie!" sighed Hattie. Now she was awake, she decided to get up and get her kittens ready. How they wriggled and wiggled–they hated wash time!

Cousin Archie scritched and scratched his claws on an old mat. Auntie Lucy just rolled over and went back to sleep! Poor Uncle Bertie! How sad he looked. Wasn't anyone going to wish him a happy birthday?

"Do you know what day it is today, Hattie?" he asked.

"Yes, Bertie," she replied.

"Is it a special day?" Bertie asked, hopefully.

"No, it's just a normal Tuesday," replied Hattie. "Now run along, I've got breakfast to make."

Then Bertie spotted the twins chasing a butterfly.

"Hey, you two!" he called. "Bet you don't know what day it is today."

"Of course we do," said Lulu. "It's Saturday!"

"It's not, Loony Lulu!" said Lenny and pushed his sister into a puddle!

"Oh, Lenny!" cried Lulu. "I'm telling Mummy!"

"No, twins," said Uncle Bertie, "it's my… "

But the naughty kittens were already halfway down the alley.

Suddenly, Archie jumped out from behind a box.

"Hello, Cousin Archie," said Bertie. "Bet you don't know what today is!"

"Bet I do," said Archie, with a grin.

"What is it then?" asked Bertie.

"I'm not telling!" giggled Archie and scampered off down the alley. "It's for me to know and you to find out!"

"But I do know!" cried Bertie. "It's my *birthday*!"

But Archie had already disappeared down the alley.

"I know who will remember!" said Bertie. "Harvey, the Alley Dog will – he knows everything!" And he rushed up the alley to find him.

"Hello, guys," called Bertie to the dogs. "Guess what today is."

"Snack day?" rumbled Ruffles, the Old English Sheepdog.

"Christmas day?" woofed Puddles, the puppy.

"No!" meowed Bertie, crossly. "Doesn't anyone know? It's… "

"Chasing Bertie day!" barked Harvey and started to chase him.

Bertie ran down the alley as fast as he could and jumped over the fence into the orchard.

"I don't care anyway!" he sulked. "Who wants a rotten old birthday?"

Poor Bertie didn't see the five pairs of cats' eyes peeping over the fence. And he didn't hear five pussies, planning and giggling!

"This is the worst birthday ever!" wailed Bertie.

"Tee-hee," whispered Cousin Archie. "It looks as though our plan is going to work!"

"I need to find the Alley Dogs," purred Hattie and clambered down from the fence.

Luckily, Harvey was already there!

"Is everything ready?" she asked. Harvey smiled and nodded his head.

Back in the orchard, Uncle Bertie was fed up. He decided to go home and have a sleep. He squeezed through a tiny gap in the fence and settled down under a tree.

"SURPRISE!" yelled the Alley Cats and Dogs. The alley was decorated with bright, colourful streamers. There was even a cake in the shape of a fish! Bertie was so happy!

"You remembered!" said Bertie.

"Oh, Bertie," said Hattie, "how could we forget?" She gave him a hug.

"Thanks, gang!" grinned Bertie. "This is the best birthday ever!"

In the Darkness

In the darkness of Ben's bedroom, something was moving. It wasn't Ben. He was fast asleep. But Ben's teddy bear was wide awake. As Ben slept, his bear slipped from the bed, crept across the floor, and out through the bedroom door.

On the landing, Ben's bear climbed on to the banister, and slid downstairs with a whoosh! Then he rode Ben's trike down the hall and into the kitchen where he clambered through the cat flap and out into the cold, dark night.

In his bedroom, Ben was still fast asleep.

In the garden, Ben's teddy bear headed for the sand-pit. He piled the sand high and patted it with his paws. He stuck a twig in the top, threaded with a leaf to look like a flag.

Then he ran across to the swing and climbed on to the seat. He began to swing to and fro, faster and faster, higher and higher, as he tried to reach the twinkling stars.

In his bedroom, Ben dreamt of all the things that he and Bear had done that day.

In the garden, Ben's bear clambered up the steps to the top of the slide. He slithered down and landed with a scrunch in the pile of leaves at the bottom.

Suddenly, he spotted two bright yellow eyes peering at him from the flower bed. The cat! Time to go! He quickly scrabbled through the cat flap, back into the safety of the kitchen.

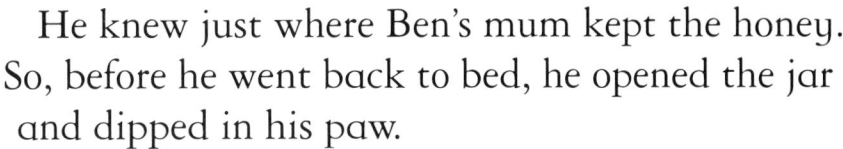

He knew just where Ben's mum kept the honey. So, before he went back to bed, he opened the jar and dipped in his paw.

In his bedroom, Ben turned over in his sleep, and yawned. Light was creeping through the curtains. He reached out for his bear.

"That's funny," thought Ben. "I can feel sand on the sheet." He opened his eyes, sleepily. "Strange," he thought. "What's that leaf doing, stuck behind Bear's ear?" He wondered whether he should ask Bear, but his bear was fast asleep, and Ben didn't want to wake him.

Ben was feeling hungry, he needed a honey sandwich. He slipped from the bed and turned the sticky handle of his bedroom door. He didn't notice the sticky bear print on the door handle!

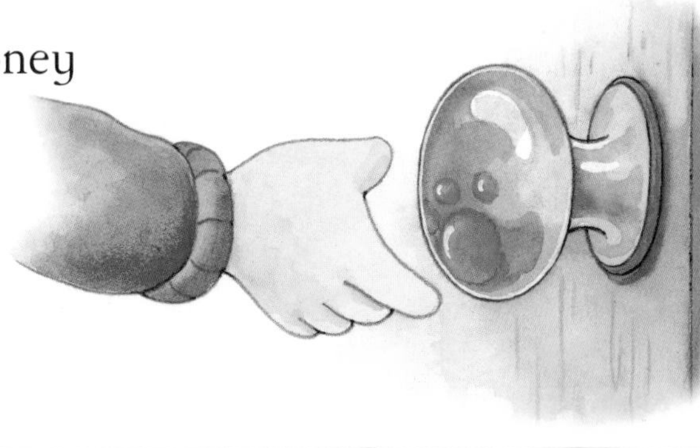

Sweet and Low

Sweet and low, sweet and low,
  Wind of the western sea,
Low, low, breathe and blow,
  Wind of the western sea!
Over the rolling waters go,
  Come from the dying moon,
    and blow,
Blow him again to me;
  While my little one, while my
    pretty one, sleeps.

Sleep and rest, sleep and rest,
  Father will come to thee soon;
Rest, rest, on mother's breast,
  Father will come to thee soon;
Father will come to his babe
    in the nest,
  Silver sails all out of the west
Under the silver moon:
  Sleep, my little one, sleep,
    my pretty one, sleep.

Bed in Summer

In winter I get up at night
  And dress by yellow candle-light.
In summer, quite the other way,
  I have to go to bed by day.

I have to go to bed and see
  The birds still hopping on the tree,
Or hear the grown-up people's feet
  Still going past me in the street.

And does it not seem hard to you,
  When all the sky is clear and blue,
And I should like so much to play,
  To have to go to bed by day?

The Moon

The moon has a face like the clock in the hall;
  She shines on thieves on the garden wall,
On streets and fields and harbour quays,
  And birdies asleep in the forks of the trees.

The squalling cat and the squeaking mouse,
  The howling dog by the door of the house,
The bat that lies in bed at noon,
  All love to be out by the light of the moon.

But all of the things that belong to the day
  Cuddle to sleep to be out of her way;
And flowers and children close their eyes
  Till up in the morning the sun shall arise.

The Sugar-Plum Tree

Have you ever heard of the Sugar-Plum Tree?
'Tis a marvel of great renown!
It blooms on the shore of the Lollipop sea
In the garden of Shut-Eye Town:
The fruit that it bears is so wondrously sweet
(As those who have tasted it say)
That good little children have only to eat
Of that fruit to be happy next day.

Evening

The day is past, the sun is set,
And the white stars are in the sky;
While the long grass with dew is wet,
And through the air the bats now fly.

The lambs have now lain down to sleep,
The birds have long since sought
their nests;
The air is still, and dark, and deep
On the hill side the old wood rests.

Yet of the dark I have no fear,
But feel as safe as when 'tis light;
For I know God is with me there,
And He will guard me through the night.

Night

The sun descending in the west,
The evening star does shine;
The birds are silent in
their nest,
And I must seek for mine.
The moon, like a flower,
In heaven's high bower,
With silent delight
Sits and smiles on the night.

Farewell, green fields and
happy groves,
Where flocks have took delight;
Where lambs have nibbled,
silent moves
The feet of angels bright;
Unseen they pour blessing,
And joy without ceasing,
On each bud and blossom,
And each sleeping bosom.

Hooray for Pepper!

Pepper was a very noisy puppy. He wasn't a bad puppy. He was just so happy that he barked all day long.

"Woof! Woof!" he barked at the cat, and she hissed and ran away.

"Woof! Woof!" he barked at the birds, and they flew up into the tree.

"Woof! Woof!" he barked at the tree, and it waved its branches angrily.

"Woof! Woof!" he barked at the postman, down the garden path

"Quiet, Pepper!" shouted Jimmy, Pepper's little boy. But Pepper just barked back cheerfully.

One day, Pepper had been barking so much that everyone was trying very hard to ignore him.

"Be quiet, Pepper," said Jimmy, as he lay down on the lawn. "I'm going to read my book and I can't concentrate if you keep barking."

Pepper tried his very best not to bark. He tried not to watch the butterflies and bees flitting about the garden. He tried to ignore the bright yellow ball lying on the path. And he tried extra hard not to bark at the birds flying high up in the sky. But, everywhere he looked, there were things to bark at, so he decided to stare at the blades of grass on the lawn instead.

As he stared at the grass, Pepper was sure that it began to move.

And as he carried on staring, Pepper was sure he could hear a strange slithering sound. He was just about to bark when he remembered Jimmy's words. He carried on staring. Now he could hear a hissing sound. Pepper stared more closely at the grass.

Pepper suddenly started to bark wildly.

"Woof! Woof!" he barked at the grass.

"Sshhh!" groaned Jimmy, as he turned the page of his book.

But Pepper didn't stop. He had spotted something long and slippery slithering across the lawn – something with a long tongue that hissed – and it was heading straight for Jimmy.

"Woof! Woof! WOOF!" barked Pepper.

"Quiet, Pepper!" called Jimmy's dad from the house.

But Pepper did not stop barking. Jimmy sat up, and looked around.

"Snake!" yelled Jimmy, pointing at the long slippery snake coming towards him.

Pepper carried on barking as Jimmy's dad raced across the lawn and scooped Jimmy up in his arms.

Later, after the man from the animal rescue centre had taken the snake away, Jimmy patted Pepper and gave him an extra special doggy treat.

"Hooray for Pepper!" laughed Jimmy. "Your barking really saved the day." That night, Pepper was even allowed to sleep on Jimmy's bed.

And, from that day on, Pepper decided that it was best if he kept his bark for special occasions!

Trunk Trouble

Emma, Ellen and Eric Elephant had spent nearly all day at the river, splashing and sploshing in the cool, clear water and giving each other excellent elephant showers. But now it was nearly dinner time, and their rumbling tummies told them it was time to head for home.

First the little elephants had to dry themselves off. They made their way out to the clearing, and carefully dusted themselves with fine earth and sand. WHOOSH! WHOOSH! PUFFLE! went Ellen and Emma with their trunks. Both sisters had long, graceful trunks, and they were very proud of them. WHOOSH! PUFFLE! WHOOSH PUFF! went Eric, when his sisters' backs were turned. COUGH! COUGH! AH-CHOO! went Emma and Ellen."Hey! Cut it out!" they shouted.

Eric giggled – he loved annoying his sisters. "I'll race you home!" Eric called. "Last one back is an elephant egg!" as he loped off to the jungle.

Ellen and Emma ran after him. "We'll get there first! We'll beat you!" they cried, going as quickly as they could. Ellen and Emma were running so fast and trying so hard to catch up that they forgot to look where they were going. All at once, Emma's feet got caught in a vine, and she lost her balance.

"Oh-oh-OOOOHHHH!" she cried as she slipped and staggered.

"Grab my trunk!" Ellen cried, reaching out. But Emma grabbed her sister's trunk so hard that she pulled Ellen down with her and their trunks got twisted together in a great big tangle.

"Help!" they cried. "Eric! Help!" Their brother came bounding back.

"Don't worry!" he called. "I'll save you!" Eric reached out with his trunk to try to help his sisters up. But the vine leaves were very slippery, and, as he grabbed his sisters' trunks, he slipped and lost his balance, too. Now Eric's trunk was all tangled up with Emma's and Ellen's! The three elephants sat there in a sad, tangled heap. They could barely move.

"What are we going to do?" wailed Emma.

"Don't worry, someone will come and help us," Ellen said, hopefully.

"This is all your fault!" Eric grumbled. "If it wasn't for you two, I'd be home now, eating my dinner!"

A moment later, Seymour Snake came slithering by. "Isss thisss an interesting new game? " he hissed, looking at the heap of elephants.

"No!" sobbed Emma. "We're all tangled together and we can't get up. Can you help us, Seymour?"

"Well I'll ccccertainly do my besssssst," said Seymour. "Let's see if I can untwissst you." He wriggled in amongst the tangle of trunks to see what he could do.

But everything was so muddled and jumbled together that Seymour couldn't even find his way out! "GRACIOUSSS ME!" he exclaimed. "I SSSEEM TO BE SSSSTUCK!"

"Great!" said Eric. "Now we have a snake to worry about, too!"

"I ssssuggest you sssstart thinking about a ssssolution to all thissss," Seymour hissed. "I'm not too tangled up to give you a nasssty nip!"

Just then Mickey and Maxine Monkey swung through the branches.

"HEY, YOU GUYS!" they shouted. They weren't very far away – Mickey and Maxine always shouted. "WHAT'S GOING ON?"

"We're stuck!" cried Ellen. "Please untangle us so we can go home!"

"Well, we can try pulling you apart," said Maxine, scurrying down. "Mickey, you take a tail, and I'll take some ears."

Mickey grabbed hold of Eric's tail and Maxine gripped Ellen's ears. Then they both pulled and pulled and p-u-l-l-e-d.

"OUCH-OUCH-OOUUCCHH!" bellowed Ellen. "I'm being ssssqueezzzed breathlesssss!" hissed Seymour in alarm.

Mickey and Maxine gave up. Pulling clearly wasn't going to work.

Suddenly there was a flapping up above as Portia Parrot and her daughter Penelope flew above with something in their beaks. As everyone looked up, they let it go and a large cloud of dry, dusty, earth drifted downwards.

"Cough-cough-ca-choooo!" spluttered Mickey and Maxine.

"Cough-cough-ca-choooo!" thundered the elephants. At first, they didn't know what had happened. Then they realised – they had sneezed themselves apart!

"Thank you," cried the elephants and Seymour.

"Happy to help!" said Portia.

"Everyone's invited to our house for dinner!" said Eric.

"Hooray!" cried the others.

With their trunks held high, the elephants led the way – walking calmly and very, very carefully!

There Was an Old Woman Went Up In a Basket

There was an old woman went up in a basket,
  Seventy times as high as the moon;
What she did there I could not but ask it,
  For in her hand she carried a broom.
"Old woman, old woman, old woman," said I,
  "Whither Oh whither oh whither so high?"
"To sweep the cobwebs from the sky,
  And I shall be back again by and by."

There Was an Old Woman Who Lived in a Shoe

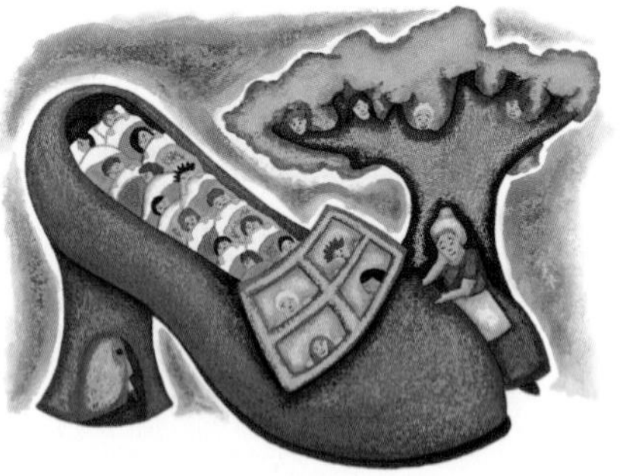

There was an old woman who lived in a shoe,
  She had so many children she didn't know what to do
She gave them some broth without any bread;
  And whipped them all soundly and put them to bed.

There Was an Old Woman Had Three Sons

There was an old woman had three sons,
  Jerry, and James, and John:
Jerry was hung, James was drowned,
  John was lost and never was found,
And there was an end of the three sons,
  Jerry, and James, and John!

Old Mother Goose

Old Mother Goose, when
  She wanted to wander,
Would ride through the air
  On a very fine gander.

There Was an Old Woman, and What Do You Think?

There was an old woman, and what do you think?
She lived upon nothing but victuals and drink:
Victuals and drink were the chief of her diet;
This tiresome old woman could never be quiet.

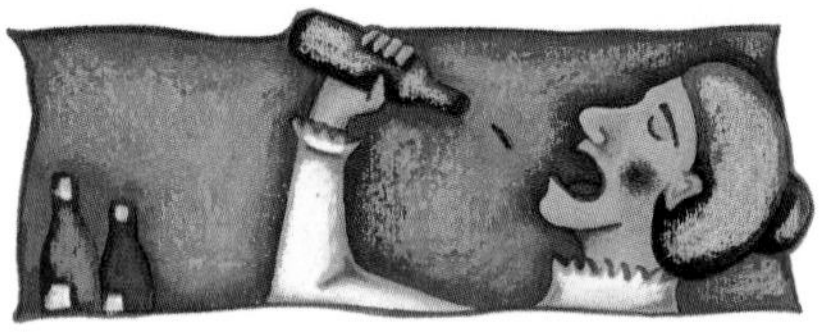

There Was an Old Woman Called Nothing-at-all

There was an old woman called Nothing-at-all,
Who rejoiced in a dwelling exceedingly small;
A man stretched his mouth to its utmost extent,
And down at one gulp house and old woman went.

Old Mother Hubbard

Old Mother Hubbard
Went to the cupboard
To get her poor dog a bone;
But when she came there
The cupboard was bare,
And so the poor dog had none.

She went to the fishmonger's
To buy him some fish,
And when she came back
He was licking the dish.

She went to the hatter's
To buy him a hat,
But when she came back
He was feeding the cat.

There Was an Old Woman Lived Under a Hill

There was an old woman
Lived under a hill,
And if she's not gone
She lives there still.

The Ugly Duckling

Once upon a time, there was a mother duck who laid a clutch of six beautiful little eggs. One day, she looked into her nest in amazement. For there were her six small eggs but lying next to them was another egg that was much, much bigger than the others. "That's odd," she thought, and went back to sitting on the nest.

Soon, one by one, the smaller eggs hatched, and out came six pretty yellow ducklings. Yet the bigger egg still had not hatched.

The mother duck sat on the large egg for another day and another night until eventually the egg cracked, and out tumbled a seventh duckling.

But this one was very different. He was big, with scruffy grey feathers and large brown feet.

"You do look different from my other chicks," exclaimed the mother duck, "but never mind. I'm sure you've got a heart of gold." And she cuddled him to her with all the other ducklings. Sure enough, he was very sweet-natured and happily played alongside the other ducklings.

One day, the mother duck led her ducklings down to the river to learn to swim. One by one they jumped into the water and splashed about. But when the big grey duckling leaped into the water he swam beautifully. He could swim faster and further than any of his brothers or sisters. The other ducklings were jealous and began to resent him.

"You're a big ugly duckling," they hissed at him. "You don't belong here." And when their mother wasn't looking they chased him right away.

The ugly duckling felt very sad as he waddled away across the fields. "I know I'm not fluffy and golden like my brothers and sisters," he said to himself. "I may have scruffy grey feathers and big brown feet, but I'm just as good as they are – and I'm better at swimming!" He sat down under a bush and started to cry. Just then he heard the sound of a dog. Only a short way from where he was hiding, a dog rushed past him, sniffing the ground. The ugly duckling did not dare to move. He stayed under the bush until it was dark and only then did he feel it was safe to come out.

He set off, not knowing which way he was going until eventually, through the darkness, he saw a light shining. The light came from a cosy-looking cottage. The ugly duckling looked inside cautiously. He could see a fire burning in the hearth and sitting by the fire was an old woman with a hen and a cat.

"Come in, little duckling," said the old woman. "You are welcome to stay here."

The ugly duckling was glad to warm himself by the fire. When the old lady had gone to bed, the hen and the cat cornered the duckling.

"Can you lay eggs?" enquired the hen.

"No," replied the duckling.

"Can you catch mice?" demanded the cat.

"No," replied the miserable duckling.

"Well, you're no use then, are you?" they sneered.

The next day, the old woman scolded the duckling: "You've been here a whole day and not one egg! You're no use, are you?"

So the ugly duckling waddled off out of the cottage. "I know when I'm not wanted," he said to himself mournfully.

He wandered along for a very long time until at last he reached a lake where he could live without anyone to bother him. He lived on the lake for many months. Gradually the days got shorter and the nights longer. The wind blew the leaves off the trees. Winter came and the weather turned bitterly cold. The lake froze over and the ugly duckling shivered under the reeds at the lake's edge. He was desperately cold, hungry and lonely, but he had nowhere else to go.

At last spring came, the weather got warmer and the ice on the lake melted. The ugly duckling felt the sun on his feathers. "I think I'll go for a swim," he thought. He swam right out into the middle of the lake, where the water was as clear as a mirror. He looked down at his reflection in the water and stared and stared. Staring back at him was a beautiful white bird with a long, elegant neck. "I'm no longer an ugly duckling," he said to himself, "but what am I?"

At that moment three big white birds just like himself flew towards him and landed on the lake. They swam right up to him and one of them said, "You are the handsomest swan that we have ever seen. Would you care to join us?"

"So that's what I am – I'm a swan," thought the bird that had been an ugly duckling. "I would love to join you," he said to the other swans. "Am I really a swan?" he asked, not quite believing it could be true.

"Of course you are!" replied the others. "You're just like us!"

The three older swans became his best friends and the ugly duckling, that was now a beautiful swan, swam across the lake with them and there they lived together. He knew that he was one of them and that he would never be lonely again.

Danny Duckling in Trouble

"Stay still so I can count!" quacked Mummy Duck crossly, as the little ducklings splashed about. "Just as I thought, Danny's missing again. We'd better go and look for him!" It was the third time that week Danny Duckling had got lost. He liked to swim at the end of the line and often got left behind. But this time he was in trouble...

Earlier that day, Danny had been following along through the reeds when his foot caught in something beneath the water.

"Bother!" he quacked as he tried to pull it free. He ducked into the water and saw that his foot was tangled in an old fishing net held fast in the mud. "Help!" he cried to the others, but they were already too far away to hear. The more Danny struggled, the tighter the net gripped his foot. "Help!" he quacked, flapping his fluffy little wings.

Luckily, Freya Frog heard his cries and dived under the water to try and free him, but it was no use. "I'll go and get help," she said, swimming off.

"Hurry!" Danny called after her. The tide was coming in and the river was rising fast!

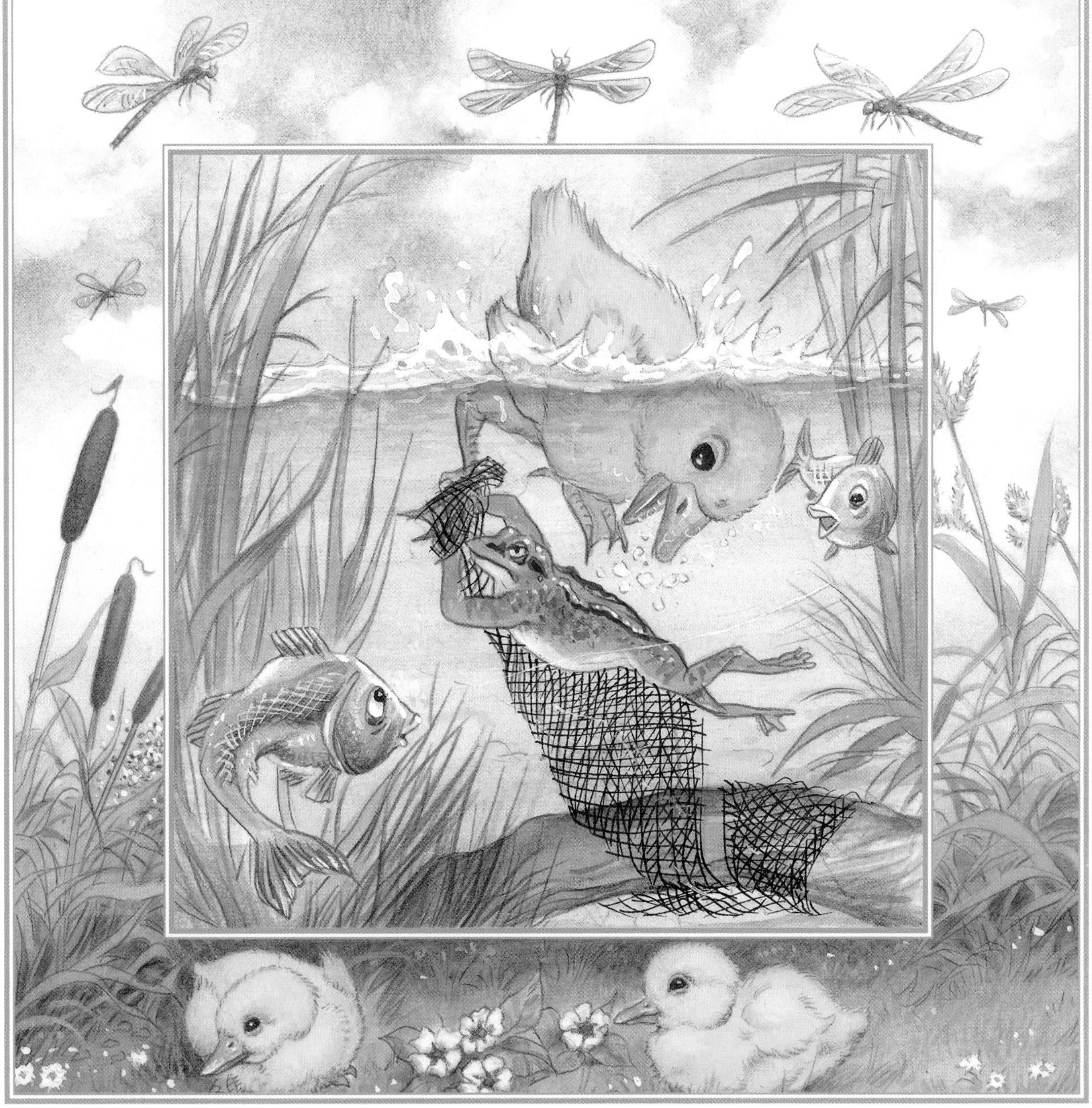

By the time Freya returned with Wally Water Rat, the water was covering Danny's back. "I'm going to be pulled under!" cried Danny. "Don't worry," said Wally. "We'll save you!" In no time at all, Wally's sharp teeth nibbled through the net, and Danny bobbed back to the surface just as his Mummy appeared.

"Thank goodness you're safe," said Mummy. "But from now on swim at the front of the line." And that is just what Danny did.

The World

Great, wide, beautiful, wonderful World,
With the wonderful water round you curled,
And the wonderful grass upon your breast –
World, you are beautifully dressed.

The wonderful air is over me,
And the wonderful wind is shaking the tree,
It walks on the water, and whirls the mills,
And talks to itself on the tops of the hills.

Ah, you are so great, and I am so small,
I tremble to think of you, World, at all;
And yet, when I said my prayers today,
A whisper inside me seemed to say,
"You are more than the Earth,
though you are such a dot:
You can love and think,
and the Earth cannot."

Spring

Sound the Flute!
Now it's mute.
Birds delight
Day and Night;
Nightingale
In the dale,
Lark in Sky,
Merrily,
Merrily, Merrily, to
welcome in the Year.

Little Boy,
Full of joy;
Little Girl,
Sweet and small;
Cock does crow,
So do you;
Merry voice,
Infant noise,
Merrily, Merrily, to
welcome in the Year.

William Blake

Snow

In the gloom of whiteness,
In the great silence of snow,
A child was sighing
And bitterly saying: "Oh,
They have killed a white bird up there on her nest,
The down is fluttering from her breast!"
And still it fell through that dusky brightness
On the child crying for the bird of the snow.

Answer to a Child's Question

Do you ask what the birds say? The sparrow, the dove,
The linnet and thrush say, "I love and I love!"
In the winter they're silent, the wind is so strong;
What it says I don't know, but it sings a loud song.
But green leaves, and blossoms, and sunny warm weather,
And singing and loving—all come back together.
But the lark is so brimful of gladness and love,
The green fields below him, the blue sky above,
That he sings, and he sings, and for ever sings he,
"I love my Love, and my Love loves me."

To Daffodils

Fair daffodils, we weep to see
You haste away so soon;
As yet the early-rising Sun
Has not attain'd his noon.
Stay, stay
Until the hasting day
Has run
But to the even song;
And, having pray'd together, we
Will go with you along.

Windy Nights

Whenever the moon and stars are set,
Whenever the wind is high,
All night long in the dark and wet,
A man goes riding by.
Late in the night when the fires are out,
Why does he gallop and gallop about?

Whenever the trees are crying aloud,
And ships are tossed at sea,
By, on the highway, low and loud,
By at the gallop goes he.
But at the gallop he goes, and then
By he comes back at the gallop again.

Robert Louis Stevenson

Nibbling Neighbours

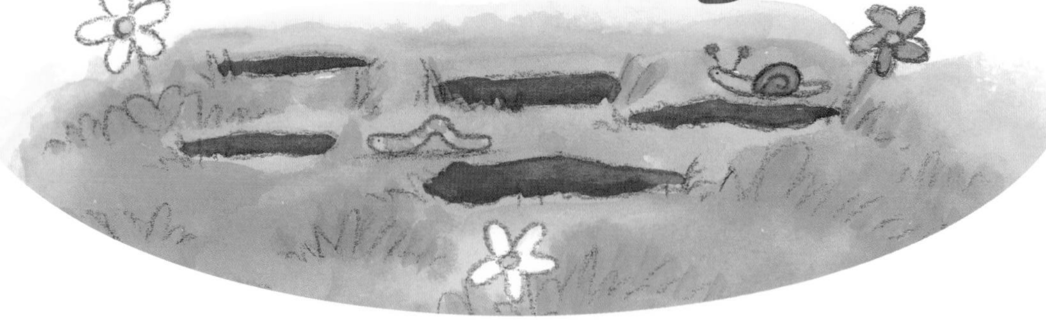

One sunny morning in the meadow, Annabel was happily munching away when she was surprised to discover a hole where there should be grass. "My dears," she mooed, "there's a hole in our field!"

There was no doubt about it. Someone had dug a round, deep hole in the ground.

"We must be careful not to fall into it," said Poppy, anxiously.

But the next morning, where there had been one hole before, now there were five! "If this goes on," said Poppy, "we'll have nowhere to stand at all!"

"And nothing to eat," added Emily, sounding alarmed.

By the end of the week,

there were over a hundred holes all over the meadow.

"You've got some nibbling neighbours," said Old MacDonald. "It looks like a family of rabbits has come to stay."

The cows shuddered. "Those hopping things with long ears?" asked Heather. "I can't look my best with them around!"

"And they have very, very large families," warned Emily. "Not just one baby at a time, like cows do."

"It's odd we've never seen one," said Poppy thoughtfully. "Maybe they do their digging in the dark. I'm going to keep watch tonight."

That night, as the full moon rose over the meadow, Poppy pretended to go to sleep.

Although she was expecting it, she was shocked when two bright little eyes and a twitchy nose popped up right in front of her.

"Aaaaaghh!" cried Poppy.

"Aaaaaghh!" cried the rabbit, and disappeared down its hole as fast as it had come.

"You should have followed it!"

cried Annabel, who had been woken by the sudden noises.

"Down a rabbit hole?" gasped Emily. "Don't be silly, Annabel. She's far too big!"

"Then we're doomed," said Heather, gloomily. "Those rabbits will take over without us even seeing them do it."

The next morning, the cows awoke to an amazing sight. Hundreds of rabbits were sitting all around them.

"Excuse me!" said the largest one. "We have come to ask for your help."

"Help?" echoed Annabel. "We're the ones who need help!"

The rabbit explained that his family lived in fear. "Your hooves are so big, you could stamp on us without noticing."

Just then, Poppy had one of her excellent ideas. "You would be much safer," she said, "if you lived under the hedgerow."

And they did. All day in the meadow, there's munching, mooing and mumbling. All night in the hedgerow, there's nibbling, digging and wiggling. And everyone is happy.

Clumsy Fred

Clumsy Fred was a very cross giant! Whatever he did became a disaster. He bumped into castles and turned homes into rubble. He sent garden sheds flying as he strode across the town, and he trod on lamp posts, demolishing them.

Everyone ran whenever Clumsy Fred was approaching. They could hear him coming for miles as he crashed and banged his way across the countryside and through the town.

People became more and more concerned, what was the matter with Fred? He used not to be so clumsy, and in fact for a one-eyed giant he was a very friendly chap. There was definitely something wrong, but no one was sure how to help.

Then a monster expert came to the rescue. He went to see Fred, who was feeling very sad. "Why am I so clumsy?" he asked. "I don't like upsetting everyone, but I just can't help it!"

The expert did a lot of tests, and found the solution. "I know what is wrong!" he said. "The problem is your eye!"

So Fred put on a monocle and suddenly he could see. He wasn't clumsy any more, and Fred was as happy as can be!

Oscar the Octopus

Oscar the Octopus was a keen footballer, he loved rushing about the field. With his many feet he was a real menace to the other team. Today was a big match, and he was playing at number eleven.

Oscar began to get ready, he stretched out a tentacle and put on the first boot, then he put on the second. As Oscar put on boot three the crowds had begun to gather beside the sea to watch the match. He could hear them singing their song about Oscar, the latest goal-scoring sensation. As Oscar put on boot four he was feeling on top form. On went boot five as the crowd swayed and cheered loudly. The harder Oscar tried to hurry, the longer it seemed to take!

Boot number six went on, and Oscar stood on his head and practised some tricks, then boot seven – he was almost ready. Now it was the last one – boot eight. Oscar was getting nervous and the laces were so fiddly that it took him ages.

At last he was ready and on to the pitch he went, ready for his debut in front of the crowd. But the referee said, "Sorry Oscar! You're too late. The game is over, the whistle has blown. Nobody scored and the crowd has gone home!"

Water Hunt

In the higgledy-piggledy, messy alley it was a very hot day. Harvey and his gang were melting!

"I need a slurpy, slippy ice lolly," sighed Ruffles.

"I need a cool pool to roll in," squeaked Puddles.

Those hot dogs just didn't know what to do!

"It's even too hot to sleep," complained Bonnie. "I'm the hottest dog in the whole world!"

"I bet I'm hotter than you!" snorted Ruffles.

"Oh no, you're not," replied Patchy. "I am!"

"I haven't been this hot," said Mac, "since I was in the desert when… "

"Not now, Mac!" the other dogs all yelled together.

"Stop!" cried Harvey. "It's much too hot to argue! Listen, I know what we'll do… "

"Let's play a game. Let's have a water hunt."

"Can I hunt, too?" yelped Puddles, hopping from one hot paw to the other.

"Do we have to move, Harvey?" groaned Patchy. "I don't think I can."

"Come on," said Harvey. "Where can we find some water?"

"I'm too hot to think," wailed Bonnie.

"We're too hot to do anything," said Patchy.

"Except eat yummy ice cold ice cream," replied Ruffles, with a grin.

"I know," cried Mac suddenly. "Let's go to the seaside! We could play in the sand and splish and splash in the water."

"Good thinking, Mac," smiled Harvey. "But it's too far for us to go on a day like today. Can you think of something else?"

"I've got a *really* good idea – diggin'!" grinned Ruffles.

"Digging?" cried the others. "Dig for water in this heat?"

"No," said Ruffles excitedly. "Dig for bones. The dirt will be really damp and cool and we could roll around in it and… "

"No way, Ruffles," said Harvey firmly. "Today is not a digging day."

"Let's all go to the park," suggested Patchy. "We could jump in and out of the paddling pool and play in the fountain."

Poor Puddles looked as though she were going to burst into tears.

"But I can't walk that far, Harvey," she whispered. "I've only got little legs!"

"Don't worry, Puddles," said Harvey. "We wouldn't go without you."

"Oh, there *must* be some water somewhere!" Patchy puffed and panted.

"If I don't find water soon, I'm going to melt into a big, hairy puddle!" groaned Ruffles.

"Haven't you got *any* ideas at all, Harvey?" asked Mac.

But even Harvey was too hot to think, and Bonnie had given up and had gone to sleep in her dustbin!

Those poor hot dogs– what on earth could they do?

Meanwhile, the sizzling Alley Cats were searching, too. But they weren't on a water hunt. Oh no! They were on a mouse hunt– Archie had lost his favourite toy mouse!

"I WANT IT BACK!" wailed Archie, looking under a box.

"Well, it's not in here!" called Bertie from the top of a flower pot.

"Phew!" groaned Hattie. "It's way too hot for hunting, Archie. Why don't we have a cat nap instead?"

"Cat nap time!" said Lucy. "Great idea."

So the Alley Cats snuggled down for an afternoon nap – or did they?

Lenny and Lulu – the two little kittens – weren't quite ready for a nap just yet!

"Naps are for babies," whispered Lenny to his sister. "Come on, Lulu, follow me."

"Yippee!" giggled Lulu, "an adventure."

The kittens clambered and climbed over the pots and pans and headed towards a hole in the fence.

"Hey, Lulu!" cried Lenny. "I bet we find Archie's mouse through here."

So, carefully and quietly, the kittens squeezed themselves through the tiny gap...

Suddenly, a strange, stripey monster jumped out in front of them!

"AAAAAGH!" screamed Lulu. "What is it?"

Swooping and swaying through the spikey grass, the monster wiggled and wiggled towards them. Then it lifted up its head and gave a loud, angry "HISSSSS!"

"Oh no! It's a snake!" yelled Lenny. "Let's scarper."

Running as fast as they could, the kittens bounded towards a tree trunk and scampered up into its branches!

"We'll be safe up here," gasped Lenny.

But Lenny was wrong!

The sinister snake hissed louder and louder and slithered up the tree after them.

Lenny and Lulu quivered and quaked.

"HELP!" they wailed.

As the snake swayed about in front of the kittens, the poor little pussies began to cry.

With one, last enormous "HISSSSSSS!", the swinging snake leapt towards them – and got stuck in a branch!

Suddenly a great big spurt of water gushed from the snake's mouth, shot over the fence and into the alley below – SPLOOOSH!

Those silly scallywags. It wasn't a snake at all. It was a hosepipe and the cool refreshing water woke up Harvey and the gang – they couldn't believe their eyes!

"It's rainy and sunny at the same time," laughed Harvey.

He looked up and saw Lenny and Lulu peeping shyly over the fence.

"You clever cats," he called up to them.

"Three cheers for Lenny and Lulu!" cried the Alley Dogs. "HIP! HIP! HOORAY!"

And so, two cool cats had made five hot dogs very happy!

The Enchanted Garden

The castle Princess Sylvie grew up in was beautiful, but it had no garden. So she loved to walk through the meadows just to look at the flowers. Princess Sylvie loved flowers! One day Princess Sylvie found an overgrown path. She asked a woman where the path led.

"To the garden of the enchantress!" said the woman.

"What is an enchantress?" Princess Sylvie asked.

"Someone who uses magic! So be warned… don't pick the flowers or who knows what terrible things might happen!"

Princess Sylvie followed the path until she came to a small cottage with the prettiest garden she had ever seen! It was filled with flowers of every colour and perfume!

After that, Princess Sylvie went every day. Winter came and snow lay thick, yet the garden stayed the same. Princess Sylvie forgot all about the enchantress. One wintry day, she picked a rose from the garden and took it back to the castle. As she put it in water, Princess Sylvie suddenly remembered the warning! She'd picked a flower from the enchanted garden and who knew what terrible things might happen?

But days passed and nothing happened. The rose stayed as fresh as the day it was picked. Then months passed and still

nothing happened. Forgetting her fears, Princess Sylvie went back to the enchanted garden.

When she saw the garden, Princess Sylvie wanted to cry! The grass was brown. The flowers had withered and died! Then she heard someone weeping. Inside the cottage the enchantress was sitting by the fire, crying. She was old and bent. Princess Sylvie was afraid, but she felt sorry for her.

"What happened to your lovely garden?" Princess Sylvie asked.

"Someone picked a rose from my magic garden!" said the enchantress. "The picked flower will live forever, but the rest must die! When the rose was picked, my magic was lost! And now, I too will wither and die!"

"What can I do?" said Princess Sylvie, heartbroken.

"Only a princess can bring my magic back," she replied. "She must bring me six sacks of stinging nettles! No princess would do that!"

Princess Sylvie ran to the meadow. She gathered up six sacks of nettles, not caring that they stung her. She took them back to the enchantress.

The enchantress said, "But the nettles must be picked by a princess."

"I *am* a princess," said Princess Sylvie.

Without delay, the enchantress made a magic potion with the nettles and drank it. Instantly, the garden became enchanted again! Princess Sylvie gasped! Gone was the bent old lady and in her place was a beautiful young woman.

"My beautiful garden is restored," smiled the enchantress, "and so am I!"

And so the enchantress and the princess became great friends and shared the enchanted garden.

Hark the Robbers

Hark at the robbers going through,
Through, through, through;
through, through, through;
Hark at the robbers going through,
My fair lady.

What have the robbers done to you,
You, you, you; you, you, you?
What have the robbers done to you,
My fair lady?

Stole my gold watch and chain,
Chain, chain, chain; chain,
chain, chain;
Stole my gold watch and chain,
My fair lady.

How many pounds will set us free,
Free, free, free; free, free, free?
How many pounds will set us free,
My fair lady?

A hundred pounds will set you free,
Free, free, free; free, free, free;
A hundred pounds will set you free,
My fair lady.

Handy Spandy, Jack-a-dandy

Handy Spandy, Jack-a-dandy
Loved plum-cake and sugar-candy;
He bought some at a grocer's shop,
And out he came, hop, hop, hop.

There Was a Crooked Man

There was a crooked man, and he went a crooked mile,
He found a crooked sixpence against a crooked stile;
He bought a crooked cat, which caught a crooked mouse,
And they all lived together in a little crooked house.

My Father he Died

My father he died, but I can't tell you how,
He left me six horses to drive in my plough:
With my wing wang waddle oh,
Jack sing saddle oh,
Blowsey boys bubble oh,
Under the broom.

I sold my six horses and I bought me a cow,
I'd fain have made a fortune
but did not know how:
With my wing wang waddle oh,
Jack sing saddle oh,
Blowsey boys bubble oh,
Under the broom.

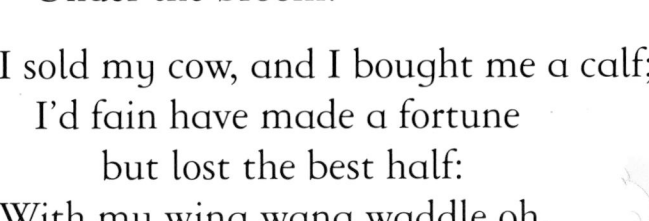

I sold my cow, and I bought me a calf;
I'd fain have made a fortune
but lost the best half:
With my wing wang waddle oh,
Jack sing saddle oh,
Blowsey boys bubble oh,
Under the broom.

Three Wise Men of Gotham

Three wise men of Gotham
Went to sea in a bowl:
And if the bowl had been stronger,
My song would have been longer.

I Hear Thunder

I hear thunder,
I hear thunder,
Oh! don't you?
Oh! don't you?

Pitter, patter raindrops,
Pitter, patter raindrops,
I'm wet through,
I'm wet through.

I see blue skies,
I see blue skies,
Way up high,
Way up high.

Hurry up the sunshine,
Hurry up the sunshine,
I'll soon dry,
I'll soon dry.

If You Hold My Hand

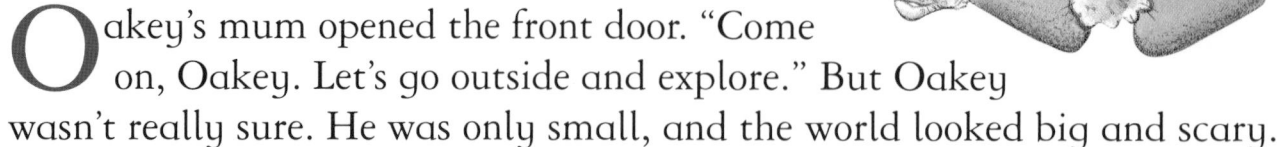

Oakey's mum opened the front door. "Come on, Oakey. Let's go outside and explore." But Oakey wasn't really sure. He was only small, and the world looked big and scary.

"Only if you promise to hold my hand," said Oakey.

So Oakey's mum led him down the long lane. Oakey wished he was back at home again!

"This looks like a great place to play. Shall we take a look? What do you say?" asked Oakey's mum.

"Only if you hold my hand," said Oakey. And Oakey did it!

"Look at me! I can do it!" he cried.

"This slide looks fun. Would you like to try?" asked Oakey's mum.

Oakey looked at the ladder. It stretched right up to the sky.

"I'm only small," said Oakey. "I don't know if I can climb that high – unless you hold my hand." And Oakey did it!

"Wheee! Did you see me?" he cried.

"We'll take a short cut through the wood," said Oakey's mum.

"I'm not sure if we should," said Oakey. "It looks dark in there. Well, I suppose we could – will you hold my hand?" And Oakey did it!

"Boo! I scared you!" he cried.

Deep in the wood, Oakey found a stream, shaded by beautiful tall trees.

"Stepping stones, look!" said Oakey's mum. "Do you think you could jump across these?"

"Maybe," said Oakey. "I just need you to hold my hand, please." And Oakey did it!

One... two... three... four... "Your turn now, Mum," cried Oakey, holding out his hand.

Beyond the wood, Oakey and his mum ran up the hill, and all the way down to the sea. "Come on, Oakey," called his mum. "Would you like to paddle in the sea with me?"

But the sea looked big, and he was only small. Suddenly, Oakey knew that didn't matter at all. He turned to his mum and smiled...

"I can do anything if you hold my hand," he said.

A Windy Day

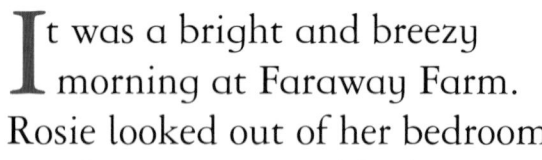

It was a bright and breezy morning at Faraway Farm. Rosie looked out of her bedroom window. "Come and look, Mum," she called. "The clouds are like big fluffy sheep running across blue grass."

"Mmm, it looks like a good day for hanging out the washing," said Mum. "It will soon dry in a breeze like this."

Rosie and Danny helped Mum sort out all the washing. There were sheets and towels, shirts and socks, Danny's muddy football jersey, Rosie's best party dress... Dad's stripy jumper and the yellow spotty rug that Conker the dog slept on. "Billy Rabbit needs a bath," said Rosie. "His ears are dirty and he's spilt cocoa all down his jacket."

"It was you that spilt cocoa down his jacket," laughed Danny.

"I only asked him if he wanted a little sip," replied Rosie.

Mum put on the radio and sang along with the music. Rosie put in

the washing powder and Danny turned the knobs. Conker got under everyone's feet and Stan the cat kept trying to sleep in the washing basket. The last thing to go in was Billy Rabbit.

The washing was soon done. Mum carried the basket full of heavy wet clothes. Rosie carried Billy. He was now beautifully clean but dripping wet. "We'll hang Billy on the line, too," said Mum. "He'll be dry in no time!"

When they went outside, the wind was blowing hard. Joe, the farm worker, was trying to mend the gate and hold on to his hat at the same time! "Ooh, look at the cloud sheep," cried Rosie. "They are really running fast now!"

"I should peg that washing on tight if I were you," shouted Joe. "The wind is getting stronger and stronger. Mick can't get his milk

lorry through because there's a fallen tree across the road." The sheets billowed like the sails of a ship, the socks bounced up and down and Dad's stripy jumper looked like it had somebody inside it. Danny spread his arms wide and ran around the yard pretending to be an aeroplane.

"Whee! I love windy days!" he cried.

"Billy Rabbit is dancing on the line," exclaimed Rosie.

"Come on. Inside, you two," ordered Mum.

The wind got stronger and stronger. It rattled the windows and made whistling noises under the door. "Look, here comes, Jack!" cried Rosie. "Oops! The wind has blown off his hat!"

"Oh dear," said Mum. "I think we had better check the washing."

Whooooosh! The wind nearly knocked them over when they went outside. "Help! I'm being blown awaaaay!" shouted Rosie.

"So are all Jack's letters. Look. They are all over the lane," said Danny.

"Mum!" gasped Danny. "Where's the washing gone? Where's my football jersey?"

"Where's my Billy?" wailed Rosie. There were sheets in the hedges, socks in the duck pond and letters all over the lane. Dad's stripy jumper was halfway up the apple tree.

"Here's my football jersey," shouted Danny. "It's muddier than when I played in it."

Conker found his spotty rug and sat down on it to stop it blowing in with the chickens. "Well, that's about the lot," said Mum. "Quick, let's take it inside before the wind gets it again."

"It looks like Jack found all his letters," said Danny.

"But where's my Billy?" sobbed Rosie.

"Come and look at this," called Joe. "The little piglets have found a new friend." Right in the middle of the pig pen sat Billy Rabbit. The piglets were squealing with excitement and twirling their curly tails.

"Oh there you are, you blow-away rabbit!" smiled Rosie.

"I know the piglets are very friendly but now you've got mud all over your jacket. You are a silly Billy. I'll have to give you a bath all over again."

Little Hare

Round about there
Sat a little hare,
The bow-wows came and chased him
Right up there!

Charlie Warley

Charley Warley had a cow,
Black and white about the brow;
Open the gate and let her through,
Charley Warley's old cow.

John Smith

Is John Smith within?
Yes, that he is.
Can he set a shoe?
Aye, marry, two;
Here a nail and there a nail,
Tick, tack, too.

Tickly, Tickly

Tickly, tickly, on your knee,
If you laugh, you don't love me.

Billy and Me

One, two, three,
I love coffee,
And Billy loves tea,
How good you be,
One two three,
I love coffee,
And Billy loves tea.

To the Magpie

Magpie, magpie, flutter and flee,
Turn up your tail and good luck
come to me.

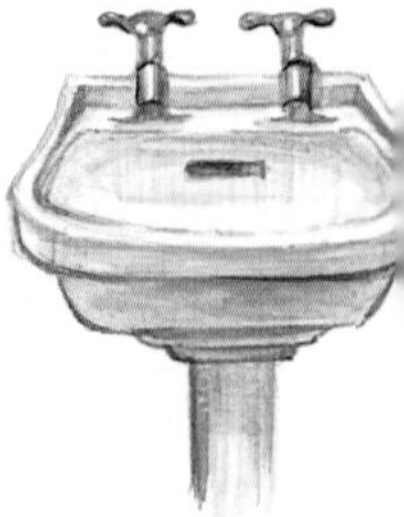

Mrs Mason's Basin

Mrs Mason bought a basin,
Mrs Tyson said "What a nice one,"
"What did it cost?" asked Mrs frost,
"Half a crown," said Mrs Brown,
"Did it indeed," said Mrs Reed,
"It did for certain," said Mrs Burton.
Then Mrs Nix, up to her tricks,
Threw the basin on the bricks.

Ten o'Clock Scholar

A diller, a dollar,
A ten o'clock scholar,
What makes you come so soon?
You used to come at ten o'clock,
But now you come at noon.

Round About

Round about the rose bush,
Three steps,
Four steps,
All the little boys and girls
Are sitting
On the doorsteps.

Daddy

Bring Daddy home
With a fiddle and a drum,
A pocket full of spices,
An apple and a plum.

Old Pudding-Pie Woman

There was an old woman
Sold pudding and pies;
She went to the mill
And dust blew in her eyes.
Hot puddings, and cold puddings,
And nice pies to sell;
Wherever she goes, if you have a good nose,
You may follow her by the smell.

Little Nag

I had a little nag
That trotted up and down;
I bridled him, and saddled him,
And trotted out of town.

The Giant

Fee, fi, fo, fum,
I smell the blood of
an Englishman:
Be he alive or be he dead,
I'll grind his bones
to make my bread

Clever Boogie

Boogie was a very clever pig. Most pigs aren't clever. They can't do sums. They can't tie their own shoelaces. Every single day they are given pig food to eat, and they say, "Oink! Oink! Pig food! My favourite!" They don't remember it's always the same.

But Boogie remembered every horrible meal he'd ever had, and was really fed up with pig food. It tasted like minced rubbish! Boogie lived in his own pen. In the field outside the pigpen lived a sheep, a horse and a cow. There were trees in the field too, but none near Boogie.

One day, acorns started falling from the biggest tree. The tree was a long way from Boogie, but just a few acorns bounced over and into his pen. An apple from another tree rolled until it rolled into Boogie's pen.

Now, usually the only thing inside a pigpen is a pig. Pigs eat everything else! They eat the grass, the roots, worms, stinging nettles, everything! All that is left is a pig in mud! Pigs think anything else in a pen must be food. So Boogie ate the acorns.

Acorns are really horrible to eat, but Boogie thought they were delicious! Then he ate the apple. He had never eaten anything so good in his life! He wanted all the acorns and apples! They were all around him, but he could not reach them. Suddenly, he had an idea.

Next to Boogie's pigpen was an old animal shed that had fallen to bits. Bricks and wood were spread about and wavy metal roof panels lay nearby. Boogie said to the cow, "Will you move that metal roof for me? I'll give you some of my food if you do."

"I have all this grass to eat!" said the cow.

"But that's just plain grass," said Boogie. "This is delicious lumps of pig food!"

"Oh, all right!" said the cow. She pushed the roof under the apple tree.

Boogie gave the cow some of his pig food. She chewed for ages before she realised pig food did not have any actual taste in it. She spat it out.

"Pwah! Tastes like minced rubbish!" she said, and trotted off.

Boogie said to the horse, "Will you move that barrel for me? I'll give you some of my food if you do."

"I have all this grass to eat!" said the horse.

"But yours is green grass," said Boogie. "This is rich brown pig food in lumps!" So the horse moved the barrel where Boogie wanted it and was given the rest of the pig food.

"Yuck!" said the horse, when he tried it. "Do you really eat this rubbish?" And he galloped off too.

Boogie looked at the sheep. The sheep said, "I know – you want me to move something! I'll do it, but please don't give me any pig food!"

The sheep moved the drainpipe to where Boogie wanted it.

When the next apple fell, it rolled down the iron roof into the drainpipe and flew into Boogie's pen! An acorn bounced off the barrel, and soon there were apples and acorns falling everywhere and bouncing into Boogie's pen.

Boogie dashed around, catching apples and acorns before they could even touch the ground!

And he never had to eat pig food again!

The Lost Lion

Once there was a lion cub called Lenny. He was a very tiny lion cub, but he was sure that he was the bravest lion in the whole of Africa. When his mother taught her cubs how to stalk prey, Lenny would stalk his mother and pounce on her. When she showed them how to wash their faces, Lenny licked his sister's face so that she growled at him. When the mother lioness led her cubs down to the watering hole to drink, he jumped into the water and created a huge splash that soaked everyone.

The other lionesses were not amused. "You'd better watch that son of yours," they said to Lenny's mother, "or he'll get into really big trouble."

One day the mother lioness led her cubs on their first big hunt. "Stay close to me," she said, "or you could get hurt."

She crawled off through the undergrowth with her cubs following on behind, one after the other. Lenny was at the back. The grass tickled his tummy and he wanted to laugh, but he was trying hard to be obedient. So he crawled along, making sure he kept the bobbing tail of the cub in front in his sight.

On and on they crawled until Lenny was beginning to feel quite weary.

"But a brave lion cub doesn't give up," he thought to himself. And on he plodded.

At last the grass gave way to a clearing. Lenny looked up, and to his dismay he saw that the tail he had been following was attached, not to one of his brothers or sisters, but to a baby elephant!

Somewhere along the trail he had started following the wrong tail and now he was hopelessly lost. He wanted to cry out for his mother but then he remembered that he was the bravest lion in all of Africa. So what do you think he did? He went straight up to the mother elephant and growled his fiercest growl at her. "That'll frighten her!" thought Lenny. "She won't dare growl back!" And, of course, she didn't growl back. Instead she lifted her trunk and trumpeted so loudly at Lenny that he was blown off his feet and through the air and landed against the hard trunk of a tree.

Lenny got up and found that his knees were knocking.

"Oh my," he thought, "that elephant has a very loud growl. But I'm still definitely the bravest lion in all of Africa." He set off across the plain. It was getting hot in the midday sun and soon Lenny began to feel sleepy. "I'll just take a nap in that tree," he thought, and started climbing up into the branches.

To his surprise, he found that the tree was already occupied by a large leopard. "I'll show him who's boss," thought Lenny, baring his tiny claws. The leopard raised his head to look at Lenny, and then bared his own huge, razor-sharp claws. He took a swipe at Lenny with his paw. Without even touching Lenny, the wind from the leopard's great paw swept Lenny out of the tree and he landed with a bump on the ground.

When Lenny got up he found that his legs were trembling. "Oh my," he thought, "that leopard had big claws. But I'm still definitely the bravest lion in Africa." He set off again across the plain. After a while he began to feel quite hungry. "I wonder what I can find to eat," he thought. Just then he saw a spotted shape lying low in the grass. "That looks like a tasty meal," thought Lenny as he pounced on the spotted shape. But the spotted shape was a cheetah! Quick as a flash, the cheetah sprang away and, as he did so, his tail caught Lenny a blow that sent him spinning round and round in circles.

When Lenny stopped spinning, he got up and found his whole body was shaking. "Oh my," he thought, "that cheetah is a fast runner." Then he added in rather a small voice, "But I'm still the bravest lion in Africa."

He set off again across the plain. By now it was getting dark and Lenny was wishing he was at home with his mother and brothers and sisters. "I wonder if they've noticed I've gone," he thought sadly as a tear rolled down his furry cheek. He felt cold and tired and hungry as he crawled into the undergrowth to sleep.

Some time later Lenny was woken by a noise that was louder than anything he'd ever heard before – louder even than the elephant's trumpeting. It filled the night air and made the leaves on the trees shake. The noise was getting louder and louder and the animal that was making it was getting nearer and nearer. Lenny peeped out from his hiding place and saw a huge golden creature with big yellow eyes that shone in the dark like lamps. It had a great crown of shaggy golden fur all around its head and its red jaws were open wide revealing a set of very large white fangs. How it roared! Lenny was terrified and about to turn tail and run, when the animal stopped roaring and spoke to him. "Come here, Lenny," said the animal gently. "It's me, your father, and I'm going to take you home. Climb up on my back, little one."

So Lenny climbed up on his father's back and was carried all the way home. And when they got there his father told his mother and his brothers and sisters that Lenny had been a very brave lion after all.

Scrub Your Dirty Face

Scrub your dirty face,
Scrub your dirty face,
With a rub-a-dub-dub,
And a rub-a-dub-dub,
Scrub your dirty face.

It's Raining, It's Pouring

It's raining, it's pouring,
The old man is snoring;
He went to bed and bumped his head
And couldn't get up in the morning.

One Finger, One Thumb

One finger, one thumb, keep moving,
One finger, one thumb, keep moving,
One finger, one thumb, keep moving,
We'll all be merry and bright.

One finger, one thumb, one arm, keep moving,
One finger, one thumb, one arm, keep moving,
One finger, one thumb, one arm, keep moving,
We'll all be merry and bright.

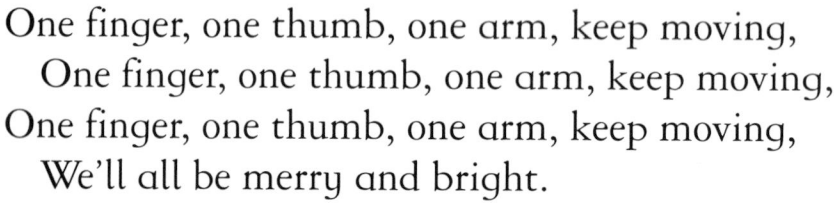

One finger, one thumb, one arm, one leg, keep moving,
One finger, one thumb, one arm, one leg, keep moving,
One finger, one thumb, one arm, one leg, keep moving,
We'll all be merry and bright.

One finger, one thumb, one arm, one leg,
one nod of the head, keep moving,
One finger, one thumb, one arm, one leg,
one nod of the head, keep moving,
One finger, one thumb, one arm, one leg,
one nod of the head, keep moving,
We'll all be merry and bright.

Rain, Rain, Go Away

Rain, rain,
Go away,
Come again
Another day.

Blow, Wind, Blow!

Blow, wind, blow! and go, mill, go!
  That the miller may grind his corn;
That the baker may take it,
  And into rolls make it,
And send us some hot in the morn.

Sneeze on Monday

Sneeze on Monday, sneeze for danger;
  Sneeze on Tuesday, kiss a stranger;
Sneeze on Wednesday, get a letter;
  Sneeze on Thursday, something better;
Sneeze on Friday, sneeze for sorrow;
  Sneeze on Saturday, see your sweetheart tomorrow.

Clap Your Hands

Clap your hands, clap your hands,
  Clap them just like me.
Touch your shoulders, touch your shoulders,
  Touch them just like me.
Tap your knees, tap your knees,
  Tap them just like me.
Shake your head, shake your head,
  Shake it just like me.
Clap your hands, clap your hands,
  Then let them quiet be.

Jackanory

I'll tell you a story
  Of Jackanory,
And now my story's begun;
  I'll tell you another
Of Jack his brother,
  And now my story's done.

Leap Frog

"Whee! Look at me! Look at me!" yelled Springy, the frog, as he went leaping through the air, jumping from one lily pad to the other with a great splash. "I'm the bounciest frog in the whole wide world! Whee!"

"Tut, tut!" quacked Mother Duck. "That young frog is a nuisance. He never looks where he's going, and he doesn't mind who he splashes."

"Quite dreadful," agreed Downy, the swan. "And he makes so much noise. Sometimes it's hard to hear yourself think!"

But Springy wasn't listening. He was far too busy jumping across the lily pads as high as he could.

"Come on!" he called to the little ducklings. "Come over here, we'll have a diving contest!"

"He's a bad influence on our youngsters," Mother Duck went on. "If only something could be done about him."

"I suppose it's just high spirits," said Downy. "He'll grow out of it."

But Springy didn't grow out of it – he grew worse. He would wake everyone up at the crack of dawn, singing loudly at the top of his croaky voice.

"Here comes the day, it's time to play, hip hooray, hip hooray!" And he would leap from place to place, waking up the ducks and swans in their nests, calling down Rabbit's burrow, and shouting into Water Rat's hole in the bank. Of course, Springy just thought that he was being friendly. He didn't realise that everyone was getting fed up with him.

"I'm all for a bit of fun," said Water Rat. "But young Springy always takes things too far."

Then, one day, Springy appeared almost bursting with excitement.

"Listen everyone," he called. "There's going to be a jumping competition on the other side of the pond. All the other frogs from miles around are coming. But I'm sure to win, because I'm the bounciest frog in the whole wide world!"

The day of the contest dawned, and everyone gathered at the far side of the pond to watch the competition. Springy had never seen so many frogs in one place before. But, to Springy's amazement, *all* the frogs could jump high, and far. They sprang gracefully across the lily pads, cheered on by the crowd.

Springy was going to have to jump higher and further than ever if he wanted to win. At last it was his turn. "Good luck!" cried the ducklings.

Springy took his place on the starting pad, then, gathering all his strength, he leapt up high and flew through the air, further and further, past the finish line, and on, until – GULP! He landed right in crafty Pike's waiting open mouth! As usual, Springy had not been looking where he was going!

The naughty pike swallowed Springy in one gulp, then dived down

and hid in the middle of the pond. Everyone looked around in dismay – Springy was gone.

Well, there was no doubt about it. Springy had jumped the highest, and the furthest.

"I declare Springy the winner," Warty, the toad, who had organised the contest, said glumly.

After that, things were much quieter for the other folk who lived around the pond. But, instead of enjoying the peace, they found that they rather missed Springy.

"He was a cheery little frog," said Downy.

But, deep in the pond, Pike was feeling sorry for himself. He thought he'd been very clever catching that frog, but he'd had terrible indigestion ever since. You see, Springy was still busy jumping away inside him! Pike rose up to the top of the water, and gulped at the air. And, as he did so, out jumped Springy!

Everyone was delighted to see him, and cheered as they gave him the medal for winning the jumping contest.

"This is wonderful," said Springy. "But I have learned my lesson – from now on I'll look before I leap!" and he hopped away quietly to play with the ducklings.

Thank You Kitty

"Come here, Kitty," calls Cat one day. "I've got a surprise for you." Kitty bounces over. "You can have lots of fun with this ball of wool," says Cat. Soon Kitty is laughing and leaping around.

"Watch me, Mum! I can pat the ball into the air."she shouts.

Just then Kitty hears someone calling her. "Kitty," calls Mother Bird. "Please can I have some of your wool for my nest?"

Kitty looks at Cat. "I won't have anything to play with," she says sadly. "It won't be as much fun."

Cat smiles, "It's much more fun to share things, Kitty," she says.

Kitty and Cat watch as Mother Bird tucks the wool into her nest. "The baby birds like the wool don't they, Mum?" laughs Kitty. "I like sharing," says Kitty. "Who else can I share my wool with, Mum?" asks Kitty.

"Why don't you ask the rabbits if they could use some?" says Cat.

"We're having a hopping race," says Little Rabbit. "A piece of wool is just what we need to make a finishing line. Thank you, Kitty."

Just then Cat calls Kitty over. "I have another surprise for you," she says. "It's a bell from Mother Bird," says Cat. "To thank you for sharing your wool."

"What a lovely present," says Kitty. "Would you like to play with it too, Mum?"

You Can Do It, Kitty

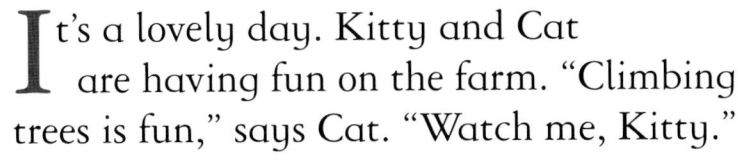

It's a lovely day. Kitty and Cat are having fun on the farm. "Climbing trees is fun," says Cat. "Watch me, Kitty."

Cat leaps up the tree. "Where are you, Mum?" calls Kitty.

"Climb up, Kitty," calls Cat. "You'll love it up here."

Kitty runs to the tree. But then she starts to cry. "I can't," she sobs. "It's too high."

Cat gives Kitty a snuggle. "Don't be upset," she says. "You can do anything you want to do. You'll soon be at the top of the tree. See that little calf over there, Kitty? He is trying to walk."

"But he cannot even stand up," says Kitty.

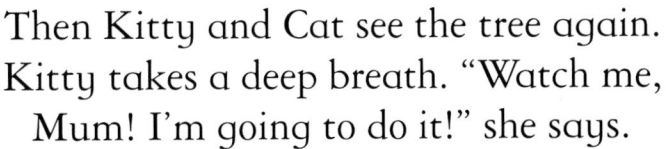

"Keep watching," says Cat. "Now he can run and jump."

Then Kitty and Cat see the tree again. Kitty takes a deep breath. "Watch me, Mum! I'm going to do it!" she says.

Kitty runs to the tree and... jumps! "You've done it, Kitty!" shouts Cat.

Kitty hugs Cat. "It's brilliant up here, Mum," she says. "I can see the whole farm."

Snow White

Long, long ago, in a faraway land, there once lived a king and queen who had a beautiful baby girl. Her lips were as red as cherries, her hair as black as coal and her skin as white as snow – her name was Snow White.

Sadly, the queen died and years later the king married again. The new queen was very beautiful, but also evil, cruel and vain. She had a magic mirror, and every day she looked into it and asked, "Mirror, mirror on the wall, who is the fairest one of all?"

And every day, the mirror replied, "You, O Queen, are the fairest!"

Time passed, and every year Snow White grew more beautiful by the hour. The queen became increasingly jealous of her stepdaughter.

One day, the magic mirror gave the queen a different answer to her question. "Snow White is the fairest one of all!" it replied.

The queen was furious and at once invented an evil plan. She ordered her huntsman to take Snow White deep into the forest and kill her.

But the huntsman couldn't bear to harm Snow White. "Run away!" he told her. "Run away and never come back, or the queen will kill us both!" Snow White fled.

As Snow White rushed through the trees she came upon a tiny cottage. She knocked at the door and then went in – the house was empty. There she found a tiny table with seven tiny chairs. Upstairs there were seven little beds. Exhausted, she lay down across them and fell asleep.

Many hours later, Snow White woke to see seven little faces peering at her. The dwarfs, who worked in a diamond mine, had returned home and wanted to know who the pretty young girl was.

Snow White told them her story and why she had to run away. They all sat round and listened to her tale.

When she had finished, the eldest dwarf said, "If you will look after our house for us, we will keep you safe. But please don't let anyone into the cottage while we are at work."

The next morning, when the wicked queen asked the mirror her usual question, she was horrified when it answered, "The fairest is Snow White, gentle and good. She lives in a cottage, deep in the wood!"

The queen turned scarlet with rage; she had been tricked. She magically disguised herself as an old pedlar and set off into the wood to seek out Snow White and kill the girl herself.

That afternoon, Snow White heard a tap-tapping at the window.

She looked out and saw an old woman with a basket full of bright ribbons and laces.

"Pretty things for sale," cackled the old woman.

Snow White remembered the dwarfs' warning. But the ribbons and laces were so lovely, and the old woman seemed so harmless, that she let her in.

"Try this new lace in your dress, my dear," said the old woman. Snow White was thrilled and let the woman thread the laces. But the old woman pulled them so tight that Snow White fainted.

Certain that at last she had killed her stepdaughter, the queen raced through the forest, back to her castle, laughing evilly.

That evening, the dwarfs returned home. They were shocked to discover Snow White lying on the floor – lifeless. They loosened the laces on her dress so she could breathe and made her promise once again not to let in any strangers when they were at work.

The next day, when the mirror told the queen that Snow White was still alive, she was livid and vowed to kill her once and for all. She disguised herself and went back to the cottage.

This time the old woman took with her a basket of lovely red apples. She had poisoned the biggest, reddest one of all. She knocked on the door and called out, "Juicy red apples for sale."

The apples looked so delicious that Snow White just had to buy one. She opened the door and let the old woman in. "My, what pretty, rosy cheeks you have, deary," said the woman, "the very colour of my apples. Here, take a bite and see how good they are." She handed Snow White the biggest one…

Snow White took a large bite and fell to the floor – dead. The old woman fled into the forest, happy at last.

This time, the dwarfs could not bring Snow White back to life. Overcome with grief, they placed her gently in a glass coffin and carried it to a quiet clearing in the forest. And there they sat, keeping watch over their beloved Snow White.

One day, a handsome young prince came riding through the forest and saw the beautiful young girl in the glass coffin. He fell in love with her at once and begged the dwarfs to let him take her back to his castle.

At first the dwarfs refused, but when they saw how much the prince loved their Snow White, they agreed.

As the prince lifted the coffin to carry it away, he stumbled, and the piece of poisoned apple fell from Snow White's mouth, where it had been lodged all this time. Snow White's eyes fluttered open, and she looked up and saw the handsome young man.

"Where am I?" she asked him in a bewildered voice. "And who are you?"

"I am your prince," he said. "And you are safe with me now. Please will you marry me and come to live in my castle?" He leant forward and kissed her cheek.

"Oh, yes, sweet prince," cried Snow White. "Of course I will."

The next day, the magic mirror told the wicked queen of Snow White's good fortune. She flew into a rage and disappeared in a flash of lightning.

Snow White married her prince, and went to live in his castle. The seven dwarfs visited them often, and Snow White and her prince lived happily ever after.

The Pig and the Jewels

Daisy was as pretty as a picture, and very kind too. Daisy looked after all the animals on the farm where she lived. She loved them all dearly, and the animals all loved her, too. But Daisy dreamt of being more than a farmer's daughter, she day-dreamed about being a princess.

One day she found a sick pig at the edge of the forest. She took him to the farm and nursed him back to health. The pig became her favourite animal, and he followed her wherever she went.

She told him all her secrets, and he listened carefully, his little eyes fixed on hers. It was as if he understood everything she said. She even told him the most important secret of all.

"Dear little pig," she whispered in his ear, " I wish, I wish I could be a princess!" That night the pig went away. When he returned the next morning, he had a tiara made of precious jewels on his head.

"Darling pig," cried Daisy, "is that for me?" The pig grunted. Daisy put the tiara on her head. It fitted her perfectly.

The next night the pig went away and in the morning he returned with a beautiful necklace. Daisy put it on.

"How do I look?" she asked him. But of course the pig just grunted.

After that the pig went away every night for six nights and returned with something different. First a dress of white silk, followed by a crimson cloak and soft leather shoes. Then jewelled bracelets, and long lengths of satin ribbon for her hair. And, finally, a ring made of gold and rubies.

Daisy put on all the gifts the pig had brought her and stood in front of her mirror. "At last," she whispered, "I look just like a real princess."

The next day the pig disappeared again. Daisy didn't worry because she knew he always returned. But days went by and then weeks, and the pig did not return. Daisy missed him more than she could say.

Daisy spent the evenings sitting by the fire in her white silk dress and crimson cloak. Her heart was sad and heavy when she thought about her dear, lost pig. "I would be happy just to remain a farmer's daughter if only he would return to me," she cried, watching the logs blaze in the hearth. Suddenly there was a noise at the door. Opening it, she saw the pig!

With a cry of joy she bent to kiss him and, as she did, he turned into a handsome prince! Daisy gasped with amazement.

"Sweet Daisy," said the prince taking her hand. "If it wasn't for you I would still be alone and friendless, wandering in the forest."

He explained how a wicked witch had cast a spell to turn him into a pig. "Your kiss broke the spell," said the prince. "Daisy, will you marry me?" It was a dream come true. At long last, Daisy really was going to become Princess Daisy!

Child's Song in Spring

The silver birch is a dainty lady,
She wears a satin gown;
The elm tree makes the old
churchyard shady,
She will not live in town.

The English oak is a sturdy fellow,
He gets his green coat late;
The willow is smart in a suit
of yellow,
While brown the beech trees wait.

Such a gay green gown
God gives the larches –
As green as He is good!
The hazels hold up their arms
for arches
When Spring rides through
the wood.

The chestnut's proud and the
lilac's pretty,
The poplar's gentle
and tall,
But the plane tree's
kind to the poor
dull city –
I love him best of all!

E. NESBIT

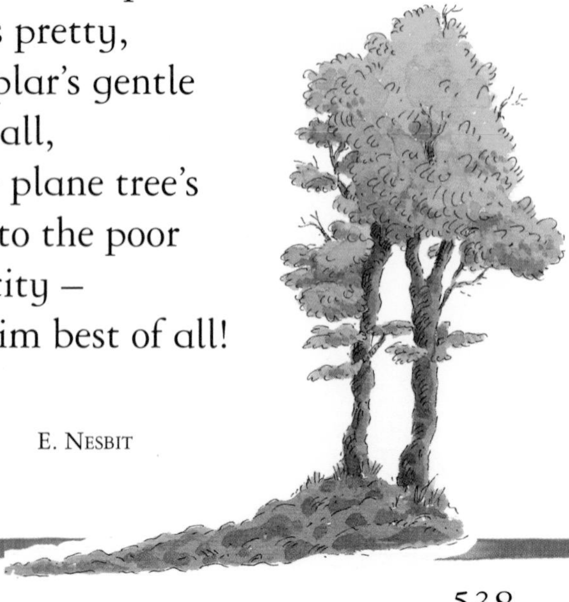

Weathers

This is the weather the cuckoo likes,
And so do I;
When showers betumble the
chestnut spikes,
And nestlings fly;
And the little brown nightingale
bills his best,
And they sit outside at
"The Travellers' Rest",
And maids come forth
spring-muslin drest,
And citizens dream of the
south and west,
And so do I.

Pippa's Song

The year's at the spring,
And day's at the morn;
Morning's at seven;
The hill-side's dew-pearl'd;
The lark's on the wing;
The snail's on the thorn;
God's in His heaven –
All's right with the world!

The Months of the Year

January brings the snow;
  Makes the toes and fingers glow.
February brings the rain,
  Thaws the frozen ponds again.
March brings breezes loud and shrill,
  Stirs the dancing daffodil.
April brings the primrose sweet,
  Scatters daisies at our feet.

May brings flocks of pretty lambs,
  Skipping by their fleecy dams.
June brings tulips, lilies, roses;
  Fills the children's hands with posies.
Hot July brings cooling showers,
  Strawberries and gilly-flowers.
August brings the sheaves of corn,
  Then the Harvest home is borne.

Warm September brings the fruit,
  Sportsmen then begin to shoot.
Fresh October brings the pheasant;
  Then to gather nuts is pleasant.
Dull November brings the blast,
  Then the leaves are falling fast.
Chill December brings the sleet,
  Blazing fire and Christmas treat.

Winter

When icicles hang by the wall,
  And Dick the shepherd blows
    his nail,
And Tom bears logs into the hall,
  And milk comes frozen home
    in pail;
When blood is nipp'd and ways
  be foul,
Then nightly sings the staring owl,
  To-whit! to-who!
    A merry note,
While greasy Joan doth keel the pot.

When all aloud the wind doth blow,
  And coughing drowns the
    parson's saw;
And birds sit brooding in the snow,
  And Marian's nose looks red
    and raw;
When roasted crabs hiss in the bowl,
Then nightly sings the staring owl,
  To-whit! to-who!
    A merry note,
While greasy Joan doth keel the pot.

WILLIAM SHAKESPEARE

The Disappearing Eggs

Mrs Hen had been sitting on her nest for a long time, and she was tired and uncomfortable. "I wish these eggs would hurry up and hatch!" she said to herself, crossly. But all she could do was sit and wait, so she closed her eyes and soon fell fast asleep.

She dreamt she was sitting on her nest when all of a sudden it started to wobble and shake. She was tipped this way, and that, being poked and prodded as the eggs moved beneath her – someone was stealing her eggs! A deep voice was saying, "What lovely big eggs!" It must be Mr Fox! She had to save her eggs!

Mrs Hen woke with a start, and looked down at her nest in alarm. Sure enough, her eggs had disappeared – but in their place were six fluffy chicks, all prodding her with their sharp little beaks.

"What lovely big chicks!" said a deep voice nearby. It was Old Ned, the donkey.

"Yes!" said Mrs Hen with relief. "They were certainly worth the wait!"

Tabby Cat and the Cockerel

Haven Farm is not only a hospital. There are also lots of animals, who live on the farm all the time. One of these is Tabby the cat. She came to Haven Farm as a stray kitten, a long time ago. Sally and Joe fell in love with her straight away and Tabby soon became part of the family. Tabby likes nothing better than to curl up in a sunny, quiet corner of the barn. But there is one thing that spoils Tabby's peace and quiet – Charlie the cockerel.

"Poor Tabby," said Sally one day, as she stroked the cat's head. "She just doesn't like Charlie."

"Well, he is noisy and bossy," said Joe. Charlie was strutting along the gate, watching Tabby out of the corner of his eye.

"Cock-a-doodle-doo!" he crowed, loudly. Suddenly, Tabby jumped out of Sally's arms and ran towards the cockerel.

"No, Tabby, no!" shouted Sally. But, as Tabby leapt up at the cheeky cockerel, Charlie just fluttered into the safety of the hen house, clucking and squawking. This was a game that Tabby and Charlie had played many times before.

"Missed him again!" laughed Joe. Tabby just looked cross and walked off to the barn for some peace and quiet.

A few days later, Tabby wasn't really in the mood for Charlie's antics. Her ear was hurting and, every time Charlie crowed, it made her feel worse. So, she curled up in her favourite spot and tried to go to sleep. "Cock-a-doodle-doo!" cried Charlie, suddenly. Tabby screeched and fled across the farmyard. Charlie thought how clever he had been to scare Tabby and crowed loudly again.

"Hey, look at Tabby!" cried Joe. Sally looked up to see Tabby running across the yard, as fast as she could go. "Something's frightened her," said Joe.

Then, they saw Charlie, looking very pleased with himself. They knew that he had been up to his old tricks again! "Come on, Joe," said Sally. "We must find Tabby." They walked towards the cow shed, where they had last seen her.

"Look!" said Joe. "There she goes." As they watched, Tabby ran straight up the side of the cow shed and jumped on to the roof.

"Oh, no!" said Sally. "We'll never get her now."At last, Tabby stopped running. That silly cockerel had really frightened her. Tabby looked around. The ground looked a long way down! She took a few, careful steps, but suddenly she felt very

dizzy and started to fall. Tabby landed with a bump! She had slipped off the roof and was now stuck between the cow shed and a wall!

"Miaooow!" she cried. Joe and Sally ran off to get Dad. They needed his help to rescue Tabby.

"Dad, come quick!" they shouted. "Tabby is in real trouble. She's just fallen off the roof!" Joe brought a cat carrier and Dad carried a special pole with a loop on the end of it.

Sally looked worried. "That won't hurt her, will it, Dad?" she asked.

"No, she just won't like it very much," said Dad, "but it's the safest way to catch her and pull her free." Dad squeezed his arm into the gap behind the cow shed. "I think I need to go on a diet," he joked. "You two had better make sure I don't get stuck as well!"

"Don't worry, Dad," said Joe. "We would rescue you." After a few tries, Dad slipped the loop over Tabby's head and gently pulled her towards him. She was crying and wriggling, as Dad put her into the cat basket.

"Right!" said Dad. "Let's take her to the surgery." Tabby sat on the examination table, while Dad gently checked her all over.

"Luckily, no bones broken," he said. Joe and Sally sighed with relief. Then, he used a special instrument to look in Tabby's ears. "But, she has got a nasty ear infection," he said. "That would have made her dizzy. I'll give her some pills to make her better and we'll keep her indoors for a little while."

"No more Charlie-chasing for you," said Sally, giving Tabby a big cuddle later that day.

"Not yet, anyway," Tabby thought to herself. She settled down in a comfy armchair, pleased with all the fuss, and was soon fast asleep. She didn't see Charlie peeking in the window, to see if she was all right. Happy that Tabby was going to be fine, Charlie strutted back to the hen house and very quietly crowed... "Cock-a-doodle-doo!"

Being quiet wouldn't be too hard. Well, until Tabby was back to her good old self!

A Bear for Everyone

There are tall bears and small bears,
Bears of every size;
Bears in waistcoats, bears in jumpers,
Bears in smart bow ties.

There are bears with fur that's long,
Bears with fur that's short;
Fur that's curly, fur that's straight
And fur of every sort.

There are bears in every brown shade
That you have ever seen;
There are bears in rainbow colours,
Yellow, red and green.

One thing that makes teddy bears
Such enormous fun,
Is if you look hard, you will find
A bear for everyone.

Fred's Ted

If there has been some trouble,
It's no use blaming Fred.
It's never Fred who's done it.
It's always his old Ted.

It's Ted who gets up early,
And wakes up Mum and Dad,
And then seems to be surprised
When both of them get mad.

It's old Ted who quite often
Leaves Fred's room in a mess;
And though he says he's tidied,
You'd never really guess.

It's Ted who's put his paw prints
On newly painted walls,
Then claims that he has never
Been near the walls at all.

It's Fred who really tries hard
To make old Ted be good,
But old Ted never,
ever does
What good
teddies should!

You Can Take a Bear Anywhere

Did you know that
you can take a bear
absolutely anywhere?

On a bus, or in a train;
To the beach in the sun;
For a walk in the rain.

n a bag with you
to school;
Or wrapped in a towel
To the swimming pool.

In a pocket of your coat,
To the park to help you
To sail your boat.

Best of all, to bed at night,
Under the blankets,
Snuggled up tight.

I always take my
teddy bear,
Absolutely anywhere.

Acrobatic Bear

I am an acrobatic bear.
I can stand on my head.
I somersault and touch my toes,
By bouncing on the bed.

I can do a row of cartwheels,
Along the garden wall,
And balance on the clothes line,
With no trouble at all.

I can swing, hanging upside down,
From the old climbing frame,
And score at least a dozen goals,
In any football game.

It's true I have a willing friend,
Who gives a helping hand,
But these things are tricky for a bear,
As I'm sure you'll understand.

The Chicklings

Duck and Hen both laid some eggs. They were very proud mothers. They would sit with silly smiles on their faces, fondly waiting for their eggs to hatch.

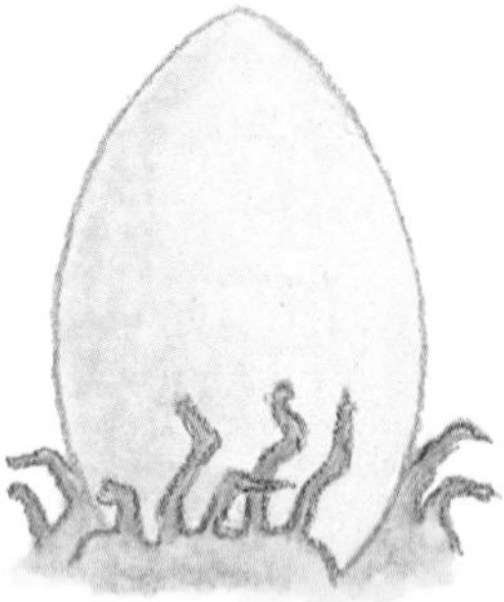

"Duck," said Hen, "let us put the eggs side by side, and see whose eggs are the most beautiful."

"If you like," said Duck, "but I already know mine are."

"Ha!" said Hen. "Wait until you have seen mine!"

Duck carried her eggs carefully, one by one, to a spot where there was soft hay on the ground. Hen carried her eggs over to the same spot and gently put them beside Duck's. Duck picked up the first egg from her side.

"Look at this one! This egg is so smooth!" she said. They both looked at how smooth the egg was. Hen picked up an egg too.

"This one is smooth as well… and it is so round! Look at the lovely shape of this egg." They both looked at the shape of the egg. They put back those two eggs and picked up two others.

Duck said, "This one is smooth and shapely, and has beautiful freckles."

By the time the last one was picked up and put back, the eggs were all mixed up together!

Hen said, "I am fatter than you, so my eggs must be the largest ones."

So Duck picked out the smallest eggs and put them back in her nest. Hen picked out the largest eggs and took them back to hers. Then they sat on them until the eggs hatched and out popped fluffy ducklings and chicks.

One day, Duck and Hen met with their babies.

"Now!" said Duck proudly. "Aren't these the handsomest ducklings you ever saw?"

"They are quite handsome," replied Hen, "but don't you think these are the most beautiful chicks in the whole world?"

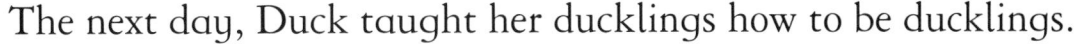

"They are quite beautiful," replied Duck.

The next day, Duck taught her ducklings how to be ducklings.

"Walk behind me, one behind the other!" she told them. "We are going to the pond for swimming lessons." But the ducklings just couldn't walk in single file. They ran circles around Duck. They ran over her and under her, until Duck became quite dizzy watching them. At the pond, the ducklings dipped their feet in the water, shook their heads and refused to go in!

Hen was teaching her chicks how to be chicks. She taught them to scratch and hop backwards to make the worms pop up out of the ground. But the chicks couldn't do it! They fell on their faces instead. They just followed her everywhere in a long line.

Duck and Hen knew by now that they had each taken the wrong eggs. The ducklings were chicks, and the chicks were ducklings.

"Never mind," said Hen. "Let's just call them Chicklings, and we will always be right."

And the duck chicklings played happily in the dog's bowl… and the chick chicklings played *on* the dog!

The Boy Who Wished Too Much

There once was a young boy named Billy. He was a lucky lad, for he had parents who loved him, plenty of friends and a room full of toys. Behind his house was a rubbish tip. Billy had been forbidden to go there by his mother, but he used to stare at it out of the window. It looked such an exciting place to explore.

One day, Billy was staring at the rubbish tip, when he saw something gold-coloured gleaming in the sunlight. There, on the top of the tip, sat a brass lamp. Now Billy knew the tale of Aladdin, and he wondered if this lamp could possibly be magic, too. When his mother wasn't looking he slipped out of the back door, scrambled up the tip and snatched the lamp from the top.

Billy ran to the garden shed. It was quite dark inside, but Billy could see the brass of the lamp glowing softly in his hands. When his eyes had grown accustomed to the dark,

he saw that the lamp was quite dirty. As he started to rub at the brass, there was a puff of smoke and the shed was filled with light. Billy closed his eyes tightly and, when he opened them again, he found to his astonishment that there was a man standing there, dressed in a costume richly embroidered with gold and jewels. "I am the genie of the lamp," he said. "Are you by any chance Aladdin?"

"N... n... no, I'm Billy," stammered Billy, staring in disbelief.

"How very confusing," said the genie frowning. "I was told that the boy with the lamp was named Aladdin. Oh well! Now I'm here, I may as well grant you your wishes. You can have three, by the way."

At first Billy was so astonished he couldn't speak. Then he began to think hard. What would be the very best thing to wish for? He had an idea. "My first wish," he said, "is that I can have as many wishes as I want."

The genie looked rather taken aback, but then he smiled and said, "A wish is a wish. So be it!"

Billy could hardly believe his ears. Was he really going to get all his wishes granted? He decided to start with a really big wish, just in case the genie changed his mind later. "I wish I could have a purse that never runs out of money," he said.

Hey presto! There in his hand was a purse with five coins in it. Without remembering to thank the genie, Billy ran out of the shed and down the road to the sweet shop. He bought a large

bag of sweets and took one of the coins out of his purse to pay for it. Then he peeped cautiously inside the purse, and sure enough there were still five coins. The magic had worked! Billy ran back to the garden shed to get his next wish, but the genie had vanished. "That's not fair!" cried Billy, stamping his foot. Then he remembered the lamp. He seized it and rubbed at it furiously. Sure enough, the genie reappeared.

"Don't forget to share those sweets with your friends," he said. "What is your wish, Billy?"

This time Billy, who was very fond of sweet things, said, "I wish I had a house made of chocolate!"

No sooner had he uttered the words than he found that he was standing outside a house made entirely of rich, creamy chocolate. Billy broke off the door knocker and nibbled at it. Yes, it really was made of delicious chocolate! Billy gorged himself until he felt sick. He lay down on the grass and closed his eyes. When he opened them again, the chocolate house had vanished and he was outside the garden shed once more. "It's not fair to take my chocolate house away. I want it back!" he complained, stamping his foot once again.

Billy went back into the shed. "This time I'll ask for something that lasts longer," he thought. He rubbed the lamp and there stood the genie again.

This time Billy wished for a magic carpet to take him to faraway lands. No sooner were the words out of his mouth than he could feel himself being lifted up and out of the shed on a lovely soft carpet. The carpet took Billy up, up and away over hills, mountains and seas to the ends of the Earth. He saw camels in the desert, polar bears at the North Pole and whales far

out at sea. At last, Billy began to feel homesick and he asked the magic carpet to take him home.

Billy was beginning to feel very powerful and important. He began to wish for more and more things. He wished that he did not have to go to school – and so he didn't! Billy began to get very fat and lazy. His parents despaired at how spoiled he had become. His friends no longer came to play because he had grown so boastful.

One morning, Billy woke up and burst into tears. "I'm so lonely and unhappy!" he wailed. He realised that there was only one thing to do. He ran down to the garden shed, picked up the lamp and rubbed it.

"You don't look very happy," said the genie, giving him a concerned glance. "What is your wish?"

"I wish everything was back to normal," Billy blurted out, "and I wish I could have no more wishes!"

"A wise choice!" said the genie. "So be it. Goodbye, Billy!" And with that the genie vanished. Billy stepped out of the shed, and from then on everything was normal again. His parents cared for him, he went to school and his friends came to play once more. But Billy had learned his lesson. He never boasted again and he always shared his sweets and all his toys.

Little Bunny and the Bully

Down in Cowslip Meadow lived lots and lots of bunnies. They were all friends and played together happily all day long – all except for one. Big Bunny was a bully! He didn't like the other bunnies having fun and was always teasing and scaring them! He'd hide behind bushes and jump out on them and pull the girls' ears and tweak their tails!

Big Bunny didn't have any friends or anyone to play with, because he was always so mean. But he didn't care!

"Who needs friends, anyway?" he said. "Not me!" And off he hopped, down to the stream. But one of the bunnies felt sorry for Big Bunny.

"Everyone should have a friend," thought Little Bunny, as he hopped after the rabbit. "Hey, Big Bunny," he called. "Would you like to share my carrot cake and be my friend?"

"No!" snarled the naughty bully. "I don't want to share. I want it all!"

And with one, big bunny bounce, he grabbed the yummy cake and knocked Little Bunny into the water – SPLOOSH! "I don't like sharing!" cried Big Bunny, hopping away. "And I don't want you to be my friend!"

Little Bunny shook himself dry and hopped back towards the meadow. "I'm going home," he muttered to himself. "Big Bunny is such a bully."

Suddenly, he heard a noise. It sounded like someone crying. "I wonder what that is?" thought Little Bunny. Following the noise, he hopped towards the edge of a steep bank and peeped over. There, at the very bottom, sat Big Bunny!

"Please help me, Little Bunny!" he called, weakly. "I've hurt my paw and I can't climb up!" Little Bunny bounced into action!

"Don't worry, I'll get some help!" he called to Big Bunny and raced off home, as fast as he could.

And even though Big Bunny had always been so mean to the other rabbits of Cowslip Meadow, when Little Bunny cried, "Big Bunny is hurt," they all rushed to help.

Little Bunny's daddy climbed down the bank and rescued the scared, injured rabbit.

"I'm sorry for being so nasty to you," cried Big Bunny, as he gave Little Bunny a big hug. "Thank you for saving me!"

"Well, that's what friends are for!" chuckled Little Bunny and everyone cheered!

Lazy Mary

Lazy Mary will you get up,
Will you get up, will you get up?
Lazy Mary will you get up,
Will you get up today?

Six o'clock and you're still sleeping,
Daylight's creeping o'er your windowsill.

Lazy Mary will you get up,
Will you get up, will you get up?
Lazy Mary will you get up,
Will you get up today?

Seven o'clock and you're still snoring,
Sunshine's pouring through your window pane.

Lazy Mary will you get up,
Will you get up, will you get up?
Lazy Mary will you get up,
Will you get up today?

Eight o'clock, you've missed your train,
Can you explain why you're still in your bed?

Little Betty Blue

Little Betty Blue
Lost a holiday shoe,
What can little Betty do?
Give her another
To match the other,
And then she may
swagger in two.

Anna Banana

Anna Banana
Played the piano;
The piano broke
And Anna choked.

See-saw, Margery Daw

See-saw, Margery Daw,
Johnny shall have a new master;
He shall have but a penny a day,
Because he can't work any faster.

Lucy Locket

Lucy Locket lost her pocket,
  Kitty Fisher found it.
Not a penny was there in it,
  Only ribbon round it.

Cinderella's umbrella's
  Full of holes all over.
Every time it starts to rain
  She has to run for cover.

Aladdin's lamp is getting damp,
  And is no longer gleaming.
It doesn't spark within the dark,
  But you can't stop it steaming.

Elsie Marley

Elsie Marley is grown so fine,
  She won't get up to serve the swine,
But lies in bed till eight or nine,
  And surely she does take her time.

Here Comes a Widow

Here comes a widow from Barbary-land,
  With all her children in her hand;
One can brew, and one can bake,
  And one can make a wedding-cake.
Pray take one, pray take two,
  Pray take one that pleases you.

Mary, Mary, Quite Contrary

Mary, Mary, quite contrary,
  How does your garden grow?
With silver bells, and cockle shells,
  And pretty maids all in a row.

The Wolf and the Seven Goats

There was once an old mother goat who had seven little goats. They all lived in a tiny house on the edge of a big, dark forest. One day, the mother goat had to go into the forest to collect food. Before she left, she called her seven little goats to her and said, "Now, children, promise me that while I am away you will lock the door and be on your guard against the wicked wolf. If you see him, don't let him in, because he would certainly eat you all up. You can recognize him by his gruff voice and his big black paws."

"Yes, mother," the little goats replied, "we promise to be very careful."

So the mother goat trotted cheerfully away into the forest, and the little goats locked the door.

Some time later, there was a knock at the door, and the little goats heard a voice calling, "Open the door, children, it is your mother. I have brought back a present for each of you."

But the little goats heard that the voice was gruff, and not the gentle voice of their mother, and so they called, "No, we will not let you in! You do not have a soft voice like our mother's, you have a gruff voice. You are the wolf!"

So the cunning wolf went to a shop and stole a jar of syrup and swallowed it to make his voice soft. Then back he went to the little house by the forest. "Open the door, children," he called in his new, soft voice. "It is your mother. I have brought back a present for each of you."

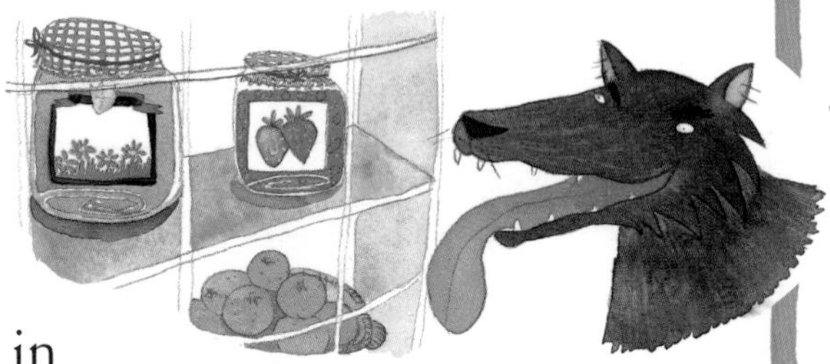

Now the little goats heard the soft voice, but in his eagerness to get into the house the wolf had put his big black paws on to the window ledge, and so the little goats cried out, "No, we will not let you in! Our mother has beautiful white feet, but you have black feet. You are the wolf!"

So the wolf ran back into the village and went to the baker's shop, where he stole some flour and covered his paws in it. The wolf ran back to the little house by the forest. "Children, children, open the door!" he called again. "It is your mother. I have brought back a present for each of you."

The little goats heard the soft voice but they could not see any paws, and they called out, "Let us see your paws so that we know you really are our mother." So the wolf lifted up his paws, which of course were all white from the flour plastered on them. The little goats thought that this time it really was their mother, and they unlocked the door.

The wolf rushed in. The little goats screamed and tried to hide. One jumped into a drawer; the second squeezed under the bed; the third buried itself in the bedclothes; the fourth leaped into a cupboard; the fifth went into the oven; the sixth hid under a basin; and the littlest one slipped inside the grandfather clock. But the wolf found them and gobbled them up – all except the youngest in his hiding place in the grandfather clock. When the wolf had finished his meal, he felt very full and very sleepy. He wandered out of the house into a nearby meadow, lay down on some dry leaves, and promptly fell asleep.

When the mother goat came home from the forest, imagine her horror as she saw the door open, the furniture strewn around the house and the little goats all gone. She started calling them by name, but nobody answered until she called out the name of the youngest little goat, who was still hiding in the grandfather clock. She quickly pulled him out, and then he told her what had happened to all his brothers and sisters.

She ran out of the house with the little goat trotting beside her and soon found the wolf sleeping in the meadow. She looked carefully at him and saw that there were six lumps in his fat stomach, and that they were all moving. "My little goats are still alive," she exclaimed with joy.

Quickly she sent the youngest goat back to her house for scissors, needle and thread. Then, while the wolf was still sleeping, she carefully cut a hole in the wolf's stomach. Soon a little goat popped out and then another and another, until all six were free and jumping for joy. They had not come to any harm, for in his greed the wolf had swallowed them all whole.

"Quick," cried the mother goat, "fetch me some rocks from the river so that I can fill up this wicked wolf's stomach." So the little goats each fetched a rock and the mother goat sewed them up inside the wolf's stomach.

When the wolf awoke, he was very thirsty. "What is the matter with me?" he thought. "I shouldn't have eaten all those goats at once. Now I've got indigestion." He set out to drink from the river. But his stomach was so heavy he could hardly walk and he staggered to the water's edge. As he bent over to drink, the weight of the stones pulled the wolf into the water, where he sank straight to the bottom and drowned. Then the mother goat and all her little goats – who had been watching from a hiding place – danced for joy. Never again would they be afraid of the wicked wolf!

Little Lost Lenny

One grey day, Lenny, the kitten, was happily chasing his twin sister, Lulu, around the higgledy-piggledy, messy alley. They were having great fun, leaping over boxes and jumping through tyres.

Hattie, their mummy, looked up at the big, dark clouds. "I think we had better tidy up before it rains," she said. "Come on, everyone, let's put everything away."

So Uncle Bertie and Cousin Archie moved the boxes.

Auntie Lucy helped Hattie tidy away the blankets. Even little Lulu helped by clearing away her toys – she didn't want the rain to make them squelchy and soggy!

Everyone was busy helping... or were they?

That little mischief-maker, Lenny, was planning something naughty! He hid behind Lulu's dustbin, then leapt out and snatched her teddy.

With a giggle, he ran off down the alley. Lulu gave a long wail. Teddy was her favourite toy.

"Mummy!" she yelled. "Lenny's got my teddy!"

Lenny stopped at the bottom of the alley and called to his sister.

"If you want Teddy," he said, "come and get him."

Lulu raced down the alley.

Lenny giggled and tossed the teddy high into the sky.

He went straight over his sister's head and disappeared behind a large fence!

Lulu stood and wailed until all the other cats came charging down the alley.

Lenny knew he was going to be in big trouble.

"Whatever's the matter?" cried Hattie. The little kitten sobbed and told her mummy what her naughty brother had done to her teddy.

Everyone looked at Lenny.

"Lenny, you really are a naughty pussy!" said his mother, crossly. "You know you're not supposed to come down to this part of the alley."

Bertie scooped up Lulu. "Don't worry," he said, kindly. "Archie and I will find Teddy for you later."

Lenny stood still, bit his lip and trembled.

"Why do you have to get into so much trouble?" asked Hattie. "And why can't you be more helpful like your sister?" And off she stomped, back towards her dustbin.

"Sorry, Mummy," whispered Lenny.

A big, fat tear trickled down his cheek.

"It's not fair," he thought. "I didn't mean to lose silly old Teddy!"

Lenny gave a sniff and wandered over to the gate. He peeped through the rusty iron bars. Mummy had said that they must never, ever go through this gate.

"But I don't know why," thought Lenny.

"I do know that Teddy's in there, though," he said, "and I must try and get him back."

So he squeezed himself through the bars...

Lenny found himself standing at the edge of a big building site. There were wooden planks and piles of bricks everywhere – Lenny thought it looked great fun.

"I don't know why Mummy told me to keep away from here," he laughed. "It's like having my very own adventure playground."

The naughty pussy soon forgot about feeling sad as he climbed ladders and walked across gangplanks, high above the ground.

"I'm Lucky Lenny the Pirate!" he laughed. Then he stopped and peered through the rain.

"And there's Teddy!" he cried.

As Lenny grabbed the bear, the plank tipped up.

The rain had made it very slippery and... down, down, down he fell

– all the way to the bottom of a mucky, muddy hole.

Luckily, cats always land on their feet, so he wasn't hurt, but he'd had a real fright!

Lenny's little claws tried to grip the sides of the hole, but the rain had loosened the soil. It sprinkled down all over his head!

Oh dear, now he really was stuck!

"Mummy! Mummy!" he meowed. "Help! I'm stuck!"

Meanwhile, back in the alley, the cats were sheltering from the rain. Suddenly, Hattie looked round.

"Where's Lenny?" she asked, but no one had seen him for ages.

Hattie ran out into the alley. "Lenny!" she cried through the pouring rain. "Lenny, where are you?"

She knew something was wrong.

"Go and get the dogs," she said to Archie. "Ask them to help us find my poor, little Lenny."

Archie quickly returned with Harvey and the gang.

"Don't worry, Hattie," said Harvey. "We'll soon find him."

All the dogs and cats ran out into the pouring rain, meowing and barking Lenny's name.

At the bottom of the alley, the Old English Sheepdog, Ruffles, sniffed.

"I can smell him!" he yelped. "He's very near!" He snuffled to the gate.

"Yes, he's in there!" cried Patchy, the dog with a patch over one eye, "I can hear him crying!"

The animals rushed through the gate and quickly found the muddy hole where Lenny was stuck.

"Don't worry!" called Harvey. "We'll soon get you out."

Uncle Bertie found a thick rope. "We can use this," he called.

Ruffles, Harvey and Bertie lowered the rope to Lenny. The tiny kitten clung on tight and was pulled to safety. Lenny gave Teddy back to Lulu. "I didn't mean to make you sad," he said.

"We were so worried!" said Hattie. "No kitty treats for you tonight."

"I'm really sorry, Mummy," sniffed Lenny.

Hattie smiled and gave her naughty, little kitten a big hug. "That's okay," she smiled. "At least you're safe now."

Then, all the Alley Cats went back to the alley for lots of cat-napping!

Misery the Grumpy Fairy

Misery didn't have any friends. It was her own fault, she was always grumbling. She grumbled at the fairy who baked the bread. She even grumbled at the fairy who collected her honey. Willow, her niece, couldn't understand her. "Why do you always find fault with everyone?" she asked.

"Because everybody is so useless," said her grumpy aunt. One day Misery told the fairy who baked the bread, "Your bread is too soft. I like crusty bread."

"If that's your attitude," said the baker fairy, "you can bake your own bread." "I shall!" said Misery.

The next day she was rude to the fairy who mended her shoes.

"No one speaks to me like that!" said the cobbler fairy. "From now on you can mend your own shoes." "I'll be glad to," said Misery grumpily.

Then she insulted the fairy who collected the honey from the honeybees. "How dare you?" said the fairy. "I'm not staying here to be insulted. You can collect your own honey." And she stormed off. Soon there was no one in the village who would do anything for Misery.

"How are you going to manage?" asked Willow.

"No problem," said Misery. "I shall do everything myself." And with that she set to work to bake some bread. Misery lit the fire to get the oven really hot, then she mixed and kneaded the dough until her arms ached, then she left it to rise. Then she put the loaf in the oven, and sat down for a well-earned rest. But, Misery fell asleep until a smell of burning woke her! All that was left of the loaf of bread were a few burnt cinders. What Misery didn't realise was that the baker fairy used a special baking spell – a spell that Misery didn't know!

Misery was still determined to carry on. She went to collect some honey from the bees. She watched them buzzing round the hive. Misery just waved her arms at them, shouting, "Out of my way, bees." They didn't like it one little bit! Their answer was to swarm around her and sting her nose and chin. You see, what Misery didn't know was that the honey fairy used the special honey-collecting spell.

Misery ran from the bees as fast as she could and, as she did, she lost her shoe! Oh dear! What a state she was in! Burnt bread, bee stings on her nose and chin, and only one shoe!

"You can't go on like this," said Willow, when she saw her. Misery did some serious thinking. "Tell all the fairies I've turned over a new leaf," she told Willow. "From now on I shan't be a grumpy fairy any more."

Willow was delighted! So were the other fairies. Misery didn't complain about anything for months after that, and Willow kept her fingers crossed that it would last!

Blow, Blow, thou Winter Wind

Blow, blow, thou Winter wind,
  Thou art not so unkind
As man's ingratitude;
  Thy tooth is not so keen,
Because thou art not seen,
  Although thy breath be rude.
Heigh ho! sing heigh ho! unto the green holly;
  Most friendship is feigning, most loving mere folly:
    Then heigh ho, the holly!
      This life is most jolly.

Freeze, freeze, thou bitter sky,
  Thou dost not bite so nigh
As benefits forgot;
  Though thou the waters warp,
Thy sting is not so sharp
  As friend remembered not.
Heigh ho! sing heigh ho! unto the green holly;
  Most friendship is feigning, most loving mere folly:
    Then heigh ho, the holly!
      This life is most jolly.

Whole Duty of Children

A child should always say what's true,
  And speak when he is spoken to,
And behave mannerly at table:
  At least as far as he is able.

Address to a Child during a Boisterous Winter Evening

What way does the Wind come? What way does he go?
He rides over the water, and over the snow,
Through wood, and through vale; and o'er rocky height,
Which the goat cannot climb, takes his sounding flight;
He tosses about in every bare tree,
As, if you look up, you plainly may see;
But how he will come, and whither he goes,
There's never a scholar in England knows.
He will suddenly stop in a cunning nook,
And rings a sharp 'larum; but, if you should look,
There's nothing to see but a cushion of snow
Round as a pillow, and whiter than milk,
And softer than if it were covered with silk.
Sometimes he'll hide in the cave of a rock,

Then whistle as shrill as the buzzard cock.
Yet seek him – and what shall you find in his place?
Nothing but silence and empty space;
Save, in a corner, a heap of dry leaves,
That he's left, for a bed,
to beggars or thieves!

A Baby-Sermon

The lightning and thunder
They go and they come;
But the stars and the stillness
Are always at home.

All at Sea

It was a lovely spring day when Dippy Duckling peeked out of her warm nest at the shimmering river. How cool and inviting the water looked. Soon she was swimming along happily, calling out to all the animals that lived on the riverbank as she went by. She didn't realise how fast or how far the current was carrying her as she swept along past forests and fields.

As Dippy floated on enjoying the warm sun on her back Sally Seagull flew by, squawking loudly. "I've never seen a bird like that on the river before," thought Dippy, in surprise. Then, just as she came round a great bend in the river, she saw the wide, shining ocean spread out in front of her! Dippy began to shake with terror – she was going to be swept out to sea! She started to paddle furiously against the tide, but it was no use.

The current was too strong. Just then, a friendly face popped up nearby. It was Ollie Otter. He was very surprised to find Dippy so far from home.

"Climb on my back," he said. Soon his strong legs were pulling them back up the river and safely home.

"Thank you, Ollie," said Dippy. "Without you, I'd be all at sea!"

A Friend for Barney

It was Saturday morning at Faraway Farm. Danny, Rosie and Conker the dog went down to the pond to feed some breadcrumbs to the ducks. "All the ducks are friends," said Rosie. "They never fight about who gets the biggest piece."

"Not like you," said Danny.

"That's because you always get the biggest piece," said Rosie.

When they went to see the chickens, Danny asked, "Are they friends too?"

"I think so," said Rosie, "but some of them are a bit pecky."

"What about the pigs? Sometimes Bessie can be a bit grumpy with her piglets," said Danny.

"Oh, that's just because she is their mum," said Rosie, "and they are very greedy sometimes so Bessie has to tell them off. She is very friendly really."

"Everybody at Faraway Farm has friends," agreed Danny. "Even the red tractor is friends with the old blue van."

"My best friend is Stan," said Rosie.

"Cats are boring," declared Danny. "They just sleep all the time. My best friend is Conker. He is the fastest dog in the world and he can catch sticks in the air. Watch this!"

"But Barney the scarecrow doesn't have a friend," said Rosie frowning. "He just stands on the hill all day with no one to talk to. Let's go and see him."

When they went back to the house, Rosie said to her mum. "Barney's lonely. I want him to have a friend."

"Then why don't you make him one?" asked Mum.

In the afternoon Mum took them to a jumble sale in town so they could get some clothes for a new scarecrow.

Danny found an old pair of sports shoes and a pair of motorbike gloves. Rosie found a nice pink party dress and a hat with a green ribbon. They asked Dad if he would help them to make a scarecrow. "Yes," said Dad. "All we need is a sack and some straw and a big pumpkin."

Danny stuffed the sack with straw and Dad helped Rosie to paint a face on the pumpkin. "She looks friendly already," smiled Rosie.

"But she'll still scare the birds," said Danny. Mum made some hair out of wool, then she found a necklace and a bright blue handbag.

"What a beauty," said Dad. "All she needs is a name."

"I want to call her Mary, like my favourite dolly," said Rosie.

"Scary Mary Crow," said Danny. "That's a great name." So, that's what they called her. They took Scary Mary up the hill.

"Hello, Barney," greeted Danny. "We've brought you a friend."

"Now you won't be lonely any more," added Rosie.

"I think Barney likes her," said Danny.

"He can see by looking at the boots she is wearing that she's very good at football."

"I think he likes her because she has a smiley face," said Rosie. Dad put some money in Barney's pocket and some more in Mary's handbag. "Now they can go to the beach and buy an ice cream," he said.

Rosie skipped all the way home to tell Stan the cat all about Scary Mary. "I'm very happy, Stan," she said, giving him a big hug. "Now everybody at Faraway Farm has got a friend."

A Farthing

I went into my grandmother's garden,
  And there I found a farthing.
I went into my next door neighbour's;
  There I bought
A pipkin and a popkin,
  A slipkin and a slopkin,
A nailboard, a sailboard,
  And all for a farthing.

Jack Sprat's Cat

Jack Sprat,
  Had a cat,
It had but one ear;
  It went to buy butter
When butter was dear.

Butterfly

I'm a little butterfly
  Born in a bower,
Christened in a teapot,
  Died in half an hour.

My Little Maid

Hey diddle dout,
  My candle's out,
My little maid's not at home;
  Saddle the hog,
And bridle the dog,
  And fetch my little maid home.

Home she came, trittity trot,
  She asked for the porridge she left in the pot;
Some she ate, and some she shod,
  And some she gave to the truckler's dog.

In Marble Halls

In marble walls as white as milk,
  Lined with skin as soft as silk;
Within a fountain crystal clear,
  A golden apple doth appear.
No doors there are to this stronghold –
  Yet thieves break in and steal the gold

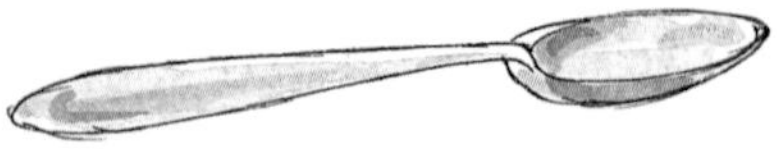

Ice cream

Ice cream, a penny a lump!
  The more you eat, the more you jump.

Liddle

Tiddle liddle lightum,
  Pitch and tar;
Tiddle liddle lightum,
  What's that for?

The Flying Pig

Dickery, dickery, dare,
The pig flew up in the air;
The man in brown
Soon brought him down,
Dickery, dickery, dare.

Four Stiff Standers

Four stiff standers,
Four dilly-danders,
Two lookers,
Two crookers,
And a wig-wag!

A Song

I'll sing you a song,
Nine verses long,
For a pin;
Three and three are six,
And three are nine;
You are a fool,
And the pin is mine.

When the Wind...

When the wind is in the East,
'tis neither good to man or beast.
When the wind is in the North,
the skilful fisher goes not forth.
When the wind is in the South,
it blows the bait in the fish's mouth.
When the wind is in the West,
then it is at its very best.

Roundabout

Round about, round about,
Maggoty pie;
My father loves good ale,
And so do I.

Kindness

If I had a donkey that would not go,
Would I beat him? Oh no, no.
I'd put him in the barn and give him some corn,
The best little donkey that ever was born.

Little Friend

In the greenhouse lives a wren,
Little friend of little men;
When they're good she tells them where
To find the apple, quince and pear.

Boink

Boink was a small round monster. His name was Boink, but it was also the sound he made when he moved around. You and I can walk and run, but Boink the monster bounced like a ball – BOINK! BOINK! BOINK! – until he got to where he was going. He looked like a space hopper toy and he was rubbery too, to help him bounce.

No one knew that Boink lived in an empty dog kennel at the end of Joe's garden. He couldn't even remember how he had got there. His only problem was having nothing to play with.

Joe didn't have anyone to play with but he had lots of toys. Boink watched him as he took all his cars out of a big green box and played with them. When Joe did this he made a strange sound.

"Brmmm! Brmmm!" he went, "Brmmm! Brmmm!"

Boink practised making the noise on his own at night. "Brmmm!" he said softly, and then louder, "Brmmm! Brmmm!" But it wasn't any fun without the cars. Boink wanted some toys of his own. So he decided to borrow some!

One night, when Joe was asleep, Boink bounced in through Joe's open window. In the bedroom there were toys everywhere. Boink took two cars out of the green box. Then he bounced back out of the window.

The first thing Joe noticed the next morning was that some of his cars were missing.

"Mum," he called, "have you seen my cars?" But Joe's mum hadn't seen them. The next day Joe whizzed around the garden with his aeroplanes going, "Neeaw! Neeaw!" Boink watched Joe playing, and that night he took two aeroplanes from Joe's bedroom!

Joe's Mum said he must have left them in the garden, but Joe knew he hadn't. Joe had to play with his train set instead.

That night Joe pretended to go to sleep. He couldn't believe his eyes when he saw a roly poly monster bounce in through the window and take his train set! As Boink bounced back out of the window Joe leapt out of bed and watched him disappear with the train set into the kennel.

After breakfast, Joe went to the dog kennel and peeped inside. There, fast asleep, was a roly poly monster. All around him were Joe's missing toys! Joe was so surprised, he gave a startled yelp and Boink woke up.

"Brmmm! Brmmm!" said Boink.

"What do you mean, Brmmm! Brmmm!?" said Joe.

"Neeaw! Neeaw!" said Boink.

"You can play with me if you like," said Joe, "but you must promise never to take my toys without asking."

"Chuff! Chuff!" said Boink.

"Let's play with the train set," said Joe.

"Toot! Toot!" said Boink.

And that's what they did. When Joe's mum looked out of the window, she was pleased to see that Joe had found his missing toys. And she was surprised to see a space hopper in the garden!

The Invisible Imp

One day, Sarah Jones was pegging out her washing. It was a lovely day and she was looking forward to visiting her friend Rose. "I'll just get this washing on the line while the sun's shining," she said to herself, "and then I'll be on my way."

After a while, she stopped and looked down into the basket. "That's very peculiar!" she thought. "I know I've already pegged out that green shirt and there it is back in the basket." She carried on pegging out the clothes. Now she shook her head in disbelief. For, although she had been working away for quite a while, the basket of washing was still full and there was almost nothing on the line! She began to get quite cross, for she was going to be late getting to Rose's house.

Try as she might, she just could not get that washing pegged out. In the end, she had to leave the basket of wet washing and run to Rose's house.

"I'm so sorry I'm late, Rose," she gasped, all out of breath from running. Sarah told Rose all about what had happened.

"Well," said Rose, "that's a strange coincidence. I was baking some cakes for us to have for tea. Every time I put them in the oven and turned away, they were out of the oven and on the table again! In the end I had to stand guard over them – which reminds me, they were just beginning to cook nicely when you knocked on the door."

The two women went into Rose's kitchen and there were the cakes, sitting on the table again, half-cooked. "Now they're all ruined!" cried Rose. "Whatever shall we do?"

At that moment, there was a noise in the street. Rose and Sarah looked out of the window to see Elmer, the postman, surrounded by a crowd of people all shouting and waving envelopes in the air. The two women ran out into the street. "What's going on?" they cried.

"Elmer's given us all the wrong post," said Rose's neighbour, Dora. "He's normally so reliable, but this morning he seems to have gone completely crazy. Now we've got to sort out all the mail for him."

"I don't know what's happened," wailed Elmer in anguish. "I'm sure I posted all the letters through the right doors."

"Well," said Sarah, "Rose and I have found strange things happening to us this morning." She told the crowd their stories. Everyone forgave Elmer when they realised it wasn't his fault, but they were still truly mystified as to what – or who – could have caused all these problems.

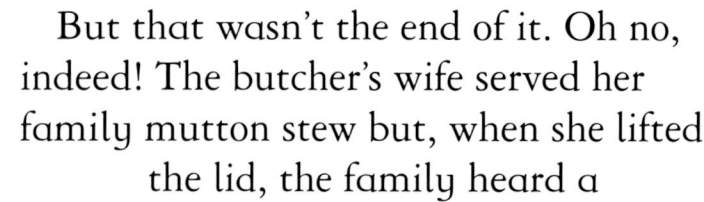

But that wasn't the end of it. Oh no, indeed! The butcher's wife served her family mutton stew but, when she lifted the lid, the family heard a bleating sound and a little lamb leaped out of the pot. The milkman delivered the milk as usual but, when people took their milk indoors, they found the bottles were full of lemonade. Old Mr Smith tried to pull his chair up to the table and found it was stuck hard to the floor. And, when Mrs Smith painted her bedroom blue, she came back and found it had changed to pink with purple spots.

Can you guess what had happened? Do you know who'd been up to all these tricks? It was an imp, of course! The wicked little fellow had become bored playing pranks on the fairies and goblins in fairyland. By now, they knew all his tricks and he was finding it harder and harder to catch them out. Then he had an idea. Why not play tricks in the human world where he would be invisible? So that's exactly what he did.

At first, he really only meant to play one or two tricks, but he had such fun that he couldn't resist carrying on.

Well, the invisible imp continued with his tricks. But of course, as you know, pride comes before a fall, and one day he just went too far. Sarah Jones had been invited to a party. It was to be a fancy dress party and on the invitation it said: *"Please wear red"*. Now Sarah fretted because she had no red clothes at all. Then she had an idea. She got out an old blue frock from the back of the cupboard. "I'll dye it red," she thought.

She mixed a big tub of red dye and was just about to put the dress into it, when along came the invisible imp. "Here's some fun!" he thought. "I'll turn the dye blue. Then she won't know why her dress hasn't changed colour. Won't that be funny!" And he started giggling to himself! He danced up and down on the edge of the tub, thinking up a really evil spell to turn the dye blue. But he laughed so much that he slipped and fell right into the bright red mixture. Fast as lightning out he scrambled and cast his spell.

Sure enough Sarah fished out the dress from the tub, and to her dismay saw that it was exactly the same colour as when she had put it into the dye. She was about to peer into the tub when something caught her eye. There, sitting on the table, chuckling and holding his sides with laughter, was a bright red imp. And there was a trail of tiny red footprints from the tub of dye to the table. The silly imp had no idea that he was no longer invisible and that he could be seen! In a flash Sarah realised what had happened. She chased the imp out of the house and down the street and, I'm glad to say, he wasn't able to play his mischievous tricks ever again.

The Three Jovial Welshmen

There were three jovial Welshmen,
  As I have heard them say,
And they would go a-hunting
  Upon St David's day.

All the day they hunted,
  And nothing could they find
But a ship a-sailing,
  A-sailing with the wind.

One said it was a ship;
  The other he said nay;
The third said it was a house,
  With the chimney blown away.

And all the night they hunted,
  And nothing could they find
But the moon a-gliding,
  A-gliding with the wind.

One, Two, Three, Four, Five

One, two, three, four, five,
  Once I caught a fish alive;
Six, seven, eight, nine, ten,
  Then I let him go again.
Why did you let him go?
  Because he bit my finger so.
Which finger did he bite?
  This little finger on the right.

Five Little Monkeys

Five little monkeys walked along the shore;
  One went a-sailing,
Then there were four.
  Four little monkeys climbed up a tree;
One of them tumbled down,
  Then there were three.
Three little monkeys found a pot of glue;
  One got stuck in it,
Then there were two.
  Two little monkeys found a currant bun;
One ran away with it,
  Then there was one.
One little monkey cried all afternoon,
  So they put him in an aeroplane
And sent him to the moon.

I Love Sixpence

I love sixpence, pretty little sixpence,
  I love sixpence better than my life;
I spent a penny of it, I spent another,
  And took fourpence home to my wife.

Oh, my little fourpence, pretty little fourpence,
  I love fourpence better than my life;
I spent a penny of it, I spent another,
  And I took twopence home to my wife.

Oh, my little twopence, my pretty little twopence,
  I love twopence better than my life;
I spent a penny of it, I spent another,
  And I took nothing home to my wife.

Oh, my little nothing, my pretty little nothing,
  What will nothing buy for my wife?
I have nothing, I spend nothing,
  I love nothing better than my wife.

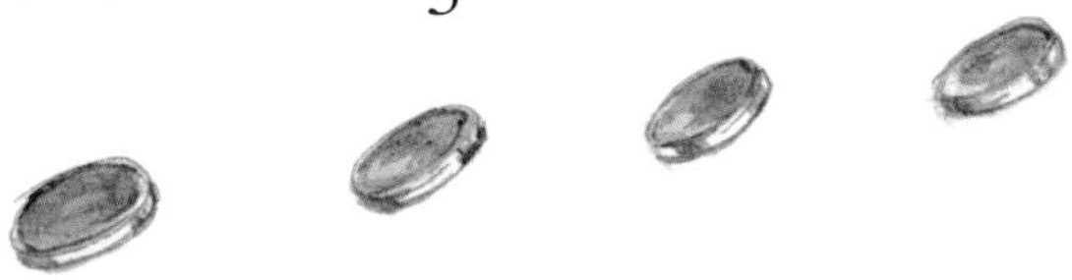

Three Young Rats

Three young rats with black felt hats,
  Three young ducks with white straw flats,
Three young dogs with curling tails,
  Three young cats with demi-veils,
Went out to walk with two young pigs
  In satin vests and sorrel wigs;
But suddenly it chanced to rain,
  And so they all went home again

One, Two, Buckle My Shoe

One, two,
  Buckle my shoe;
Three, four,
  Shut the door;
Five, six,
  Pick up sticks;
Seven, eight,
  Lay them straight;
Nine, ten,
  A good fat hen;

Eleven, twelve,
  Who will delve?
Thirteen, fourteen,
  Maids a-courting;
Fifteen, sixteen,
  Maids a-kissing;
Seventeen, eighteen,
  Maid a-waiting;
Nineteen, twenty,
  My stomach's empty.

Slow Down, Bruce

On Old MacDonald's farm, no one works harder than Bruce the sheepdog – except, of course, Old MacDonald! All day long, Bruce dashes around the farm, keeping an eye on everything that goes on.

It was Bruce who barked to warn the farmer when a branch of the old apple tree was just about to fall on his head!

It was Bruce who found the lambs about to escape through a hole in the hedge!

And it was Bruce who pulled one of Milly's kittens out of the duck pond.

Bruce is on the go from dawn to dusk – he really loves his job!

So, when Bruce stayed in his kennel one morning with his head on his paws, everyone began to worry.

"It's not like him at all," clucked Henrietta the hen.

"He can hardly open his eyes," purred Milly the cat.

"I've never known him have a day's illness in his life," said Old George the horse, "and I remember him as a pup."

Old MacDonald was more worried than any of them.

"Just stay there, old boy," he said gently. "I'll get someone to help you." And he hurried off to call the vet.

The vet arrived very quickly. She too was very fond of Bruce.

She carefully examined him, lifting his paws one by one, and checking every part of him thoroughly. Then she patted the old dog's head and said, "You're like your master. You need to stop dashing around so much and take better care of yourself. You'll be fine in a day or two, but just slow down, Bruce. Take it easy for once, please."

Bruce nodded his head gratefully and went back to sleep.

Now, Mrs MacDonald had been listening, and returned to the farmhouse with a thoughtful look on her face.

Bruce did as he was told, and by the end of the week he was as right as rain – it would soon be time to go back to work.

When he saw Old MacDonald rushing through the yard, hurrying to finish a job, Bruce dashed after him.

But Mrs MacDonald rushed out of the farmhouse and called to the farmer.

"Husband!" she cried. "Did you hear what the vet said about Bruce? You must set him a good example! Please be a little more thoughtful!"

So, Old MacDonald began to slow down, and so did Bruce. The sheepdog soon felt better for it – and so did

Old MacDonald. And Mrs MacDonald, who had been begging her husband to take it easy for years, felt very happy indeed.

Dino's

There's a prehistoric venue that is open all day and night. It's the place where dinosaurs meet to catch up on the news, and have a bite to eat. But a bite for a dinosaur is rather large!

Dino's Downtown Diner is full to bursting with large, noisy dinosaurs. The triceratops call in to try the Diplodocus dips, and pterodactyls leave the sky for Dino's famous chips. Raptors are enraptured by the tasty deep-fried Lizard. There's Stegosaurus Steak and Brontosaurus Brunch, a massive Mammoth milkshake and a three course Caveman's Lunch. The plates are huge and are laden with hot and tasty food.

A word of warning though, in case you were thinking of visiting Dino's Downtown Diner one night. They have an extra special dish which, if you join the queue, might not be your idea of fun. Why? Because it's YOU!

Monsters Everywhere

You can find monsters everywhere, if you know where to look! In the jungles and the valleys, in the cupboard under the stairs, in the bedroom and the kitchen – they are lurking everywhere.

In any lake, or pond or puddle, anywhere that fishes swim, you can be sure that lurking there is something rather grim. If you trek up the highest craggy mountain where the snow lies all year long, and listen to the silence you can hear the yeti's song. And if you gaze up into the sky at night, into the depths of the starry twilight, you might just glimpse a UFO. It could be from outer space, a traveller in time zooming towards earth to visit us. Hidden in the depths of the pyramids there are monsters galore, but beware! If you wake a sleeping mummy, it might come chasing after you!

But don't let this talk of monsters make you think it isn't safe to go out anywhere. A monster is part of our imagination. We can make them as horrible and revolting as we like! No one knows if they really exist, do they?

Big Top

It was a grey day in the higgledy-piggledy, messy alley. Harvey and his gang were fed up!

"I'm bored!" moaned Ruffles. "There's nothing to do!"

"What about a game of hide-and-seek?" asked Harvey.

"Boring! Boring!" called Puddles, hanging upside down on the fence.

"What we need is some fun!" yawned Bonnie. "I've got an idea… "

Soon Bonnie and Puddles were jumping on an old mattress. BOINGG! BOINGG! BOINGG! They bounced up and down, up and down.

"*This* is fun!" shrieked Puddles. "I bet I can bounce the highest."

"I'm the Amazing Bouncing Bonnie," giggled Bonnie. "Look!"

She bounced high into the air– and landed with a thud on a clump of grass! "Ooops-a-daisy," she said. "I think I missed!"

Then Mac clambered onto the clothesline.

"WHEEEE! Look at me! I'm the wibbly wobbly dog."

"Oh no!" gasped Patchy. "Here comes tumble-time,"

as Mac toppled over onto the mattress below. Mac sat up and rubbed his head, grinning.

Harvey laughed. His friends' tricks had given him an idea. "Let's put on a circus," he said.

The Alley Dogs all agreed and they scampered off to the playground in search of their big top!

"Okay, everyone," said Harvey, when they arrived. "First, we need to make a circus ring."

"Do you think these old tyres will make good seats?" asked Ruffles.

"They sure will," said Patchy. "And these old plastic bags can be the curtains!"

In no time at all, the big top was ready.

"Well done! We must let everyone know that the circus is in town!" said Harvey. "Come on, Ruffles, you've got the loudest voice."

So, Ruffles took a deep breath and boomed out loud, "Roll up! Roll up! Come to Harvey's Big Top. See the Greatest Show on Earth!"

Soon the air was filled with woofing and yapping as their pals queued up to see the circus!

The nervous gang huddled behind the curtain.

"Right," said Harvey. "Who's going first?"

Patchy peeped out. "Not me!" she whispered. "There are far too many dogs out there and I'm a bit shy."

"And I'm still practising!" cried Ruffles.

The others shook their heads; no one wanted to go first. They were all scaredy-cats!

Harvey crept behind the curtain. His friends were quivering and quaking. "Silly billies," he smiled. "There's nothing to be scared of. Watch me."

He quickly pulled on a cape and ran back into the ring.

"Let the show begin with Harvey the Brave!" he cried, and the audience gave a loud cheer.

"For my first trick," he announced, "the Tricky Tightrope!" He wibbled and wobbled across the top of the swing from one end to the other – and didn't fall off once.

"How does he do it?" gasped the audience, holding their breath in wonder. "Whatever next?"

Harvey climbed to the top of a huge pile of bricks.

"Eeek! What if he falls?" squeaked a little dog. "I can't bear to look."

But Harvey made it – *and* balanced on one paw!

The Alley Dogs peeped out from behind the curtain. Harvey was having such a good time that it didn't look in the least bit scary. So at last, Harvey's Amazing Daring Dogs rushed to join in the fun.

"Look at me," said Ruffles. "I can balance a ball on my tummy."

The audience laughed and cheered and clapped.

Patchy and Mac tumbled and turned on their bouncy mattress – what a pair of acrobats!

The show ended with the dangerous and daring Trolley Trick. Everyone held their breath. Bonnie and Ruffles stood on the bottom, Patchy and Mac climbed onto their shoulders and little Puddles balanced on the very tip-top. When they were ready, Harvey pushed the trolley round and round the ring.

"More! More!" roared the crowd, as the show came to an end.

"Well, Puddles," smiled Harvey, when they finally got back to their higgledy-piggledy, messy alley, "was that boring, boring, boring?"

"Oh no, Harvey," she said. "It wasn't boring, it was fun, fun, fun!"

The Tooth Fairy

Pansy was nearly five. She couldn't wait for her birthday because Mum had promised her a party in the garden with a birthday cake, balloons and a funny clown. There was only one problem! Pansy's two front teeth were loose. They wobbled whenever she bit into anything. How was she going to enjoy her party food?

"Mum," she asked, for the hundredth time, "will my wobbly teeth come out before my birthday party?"

"They'll come out when they're ready," said Mum, smiling.

That night Pansy woke suddenly. The curtains were open and her bed was covered in silvery moonlight. But that wasn't all! Sitting on Pansy's pillow was... can you guess? A fairy! She was tiny, with pale yellow wings, a wand and a sparkly dress. Pansy could not believe it. She stared at the fairy, and the fairy stared back at her.

The fairy spoke first. "Can you see me?" she asked. "Yes," said Pansy.

"That's funny," said the little fairy. "Usually I'm invisible!" "Are you the tooth fairy?" asked Pansy.

"Yes, I'm Bobo," said the fairy. "I need two tiny front teeth to replace the keys on my piano." Pansy showed Bobo her two front teeth. They were very wobbly. "I hope they come out before my birthday party," said Pansy.

"They'll come out when they are ready," said Bobo. "If they come out in time, I'll play my piano at your party!"

At teatime Bobo watched from behind a bowl of fruit, as Pansy ate all her cheese on toast, including the crusts. Still her teeth didn't come out!

"Try brushing your teeth," Bobo whispered to her before Pansy went to bed.

"Oh yes! That will do it!" said Pansy. And she brushed and brushed, but the wobbly teeth just stayed stubbornly in her mouth.

The day before Pansy's birthday her two front teeth came out! It didn't hurt one little bit. "Look!" she said to Mum, pulling a face, and showing a big gap where her teeth should be.

That night Pansy went to bed early. She put her teeth under the pillow.

Later Bobo came in, but Pansy was fast asleep. Bobo even whispered Pansy's name, but Pansy was fast asleep. Pansy didn't wake until the sun shone through her curtains the next morning. The first thing she did was look under the pillow. The two tiny teeth had gone! In their place were two coins.

Pansy's fifth birthday party was the best she'd ever had. All her friends came. There was jelly and ice cream, balloons and the funniest clown she'd ever seen.

Her friends sang Happy Birthday so loudly that Mum had to put her fingers in her ears. But only Pansy could hear the tiny fairy playing a piano and singing Happy Birthday in a silvery voice.

You Can Cuddle a Kitten

You can cuddle a kitten,
  And stroke a dog.
But it's hard to cuddle up
  to a frog.

A budgie can talk to you,
  Tell you its name.
A chat with a bat just isn't
  the same.

A stick
insect is easy,
  It stays in one place.
But spiders surprise you
  by tickling your face.

If you're choosing an animal,
  Make sure that you get
    Something that's
    certain to make
      a good pet!

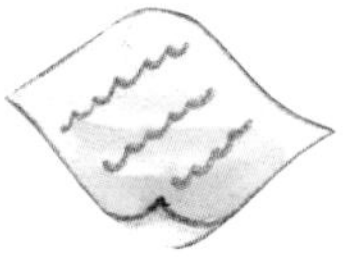

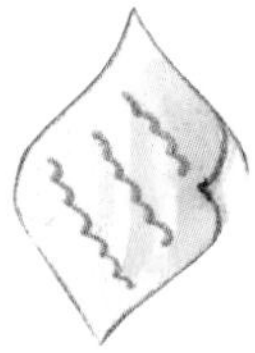

My Hamster

My hamster tears up paper
  'Cos that's what hamsters do.
He isn't being naughty
  But hamsters like to chew!

It causes lots of trouble
  And everyone gets mad.
"Who ate my daily paper
  And made this mess?" yells Dad.

My mum starts cooking dinner,
  Then shouts, "Just come and look!
Your hamster's chewed a hole
  Right through my cookery book!"

My brother's homework's missing.
  It's in my hamster's cage.
My hamster is quite happy.
  My brother's in a rage!

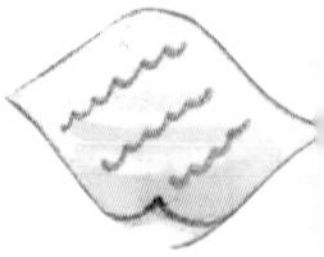

My hamster just chews paper
  To make himself a nest,
So why are they all shouting,
  "That hamster is a pest!"

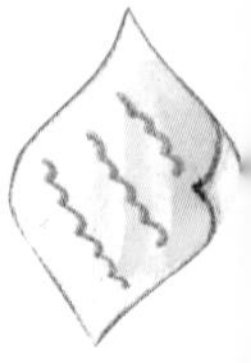

What Are We?

I buzz around the garden for
hours and hours,
Gathering pollen from sweet-
smelling flowers.

My front legs are short and
my back legs are strong.
You'll hear me call, "Ribbit"
as I hop along.

I hoot as I swoop, when I
fly round at night.
If mice see me coming, it
gives them a fright.

I slide and I slither, so
close to the ground.
Apart from a soft hiss,
I don't make a sound.

I have a long tail,
and such soft
silken fur.
If you stroke
me gently, you
might hear
me purr.

What are we?

Please Tell Me Why

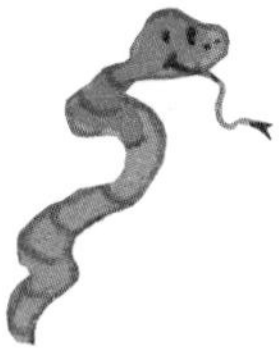

"Come on, tortoise!" says my mum,
When I'm too slow getting dressed.
Can't she see that I don't wear a shell
And that all I have on is my vest?

Dad calls me a mischievous monkey,
But I don't see how that can be.
I don't have a tail, I'm not covered in fur,
Though I'm quite good at climbing, you see.

Mum calls me "night owl", when I can't sleep,
Though I don't hoot and I don't have wings.
And I certainly do not have feathers,
And owls must have all of those things.

It's true that I slither into their bed.
'Cos I like to say "Hi!" when I wake.
But my skin isn't scaly, so please tell me why
Dad says, "Here comes that wriggly snake"?

Making a Splash!

One day, Mrs Hen and her chicks were walking near the pond, when Mrs Duck swam by, followed by a line of ducklings. The ducklings were playing games as they swam along. They chased each other around and ducked down under the water.

"Can we play in the water too?" the chicks asked Mrs Hen. "It looks like fun!"

"Oh, no, dears," said Mrs Hen. "Chicks and water don't mix! You haven't got the right feathers or feet!"

This made the chicks very miserable. "It's not fair!" they grumbled. "We wish we were ducklings!"

On the way home, a big black cloud appeared and it started to rain. Soon the chicks' fluffy feathers were wet through.

They scurried back to the henhouse as fast as they could and arrived wet, cold and shivering. They quickly snuggled under their mothers' wings and they were soon feeling better. Their feathers were dry and fluffy in no time at all.

"Imagine being wet all the time!" said the chicks. "Thank goodness we're not ducklings, after all!"

The Ant and the Grasshopper

Grasshopper was a lively, happy insect, who didn't have a care in the world. He spent the long summer days relaxing in the sunshine or bouncing and dancing through the grass. "Come and play!" he said to Bee one day.

"I'd love to," said Bee, "but I'm *much* too busy. If I don't gather this pollen, we bees won't be able to make honey. Then, when winter comes, we'll have nothing to eat."

"Well, work if you want to," said Grasshopper. "But *I'd* rather play!" And off he hopped. Then, Grasshopper saw Ladybird crawling along a leaf. "Come and play!" he called.

"Sorry, Grasshopper, not today," replied Ladybird. "I'm looking after the roses. They depend on us to guard them from greenfly!"

"Well, I think you're silly to spend this beautiful day working!" said Grasshopper, hopping away. Grasshopper went happily on his way, until he saw Ant, who was struggling to carry some grain on her back.

"Why are you working so hard?" asked Grasshopper. "It's such a sunny day! Come and play!"

"I have no time, Grasshopper," said Ant. "I have to take this grain back to my nest, so that my family and I have enough food when winter comes. Have you built your nest yet?"

"Nest?" laughed Grasshopper. "Who needs a nest when life in the great outdoors is so wonderful? And there's plenty of food – why should I worry?" And off he hopped.

At night, while the other insects slept, Grasshopper sang and danced under the moonlight. "Come and play!" he called to Spider, who was the only one awake.

"Sorry, Grasshopper," said Spider. "I have a web to spin. Can't stop now!"

"Suit yourself!" said Grasshopper, as he danced away. Day after day, Grasshopper played, while the other insects worked. And, night after night, he danced and sang while the others tried to sleep. The other insects were fed up.

"Stop that noise!" shouted Bee, one night. "You're keeping the whole hive awake!"

"Yes, be quiet!" said Ladybird.

As the summer went on, the long, sunny days began to get shorter and cooler. But lazy Grasshopper hardly noticed. He was still too busy enjoying himself. One day, Grasshopper saw Ant with her seven children. They were all carrying food back to their nest.

"My, look at all your helpers," said Grasshopper.

"Well, we're running out of time," puffed Ant. "What are you doing about building a nest and storing food for the winter?"

"Oh, I can't be bothered," said Grasshopper. "There's lots of food around now, so why worry?"

That night, there was a chill in the air and Grasshopper didn't feel like dancing. "Maybe you'd better start getting ready for winter," warned Spider. It was getting colder, but Grasshopper didn't want to think about that now.

"There's still *loads* of time for that!" said Grasshopper and he began to sing.

Soon the trees began to lose their leaves. Grasshopper was spending more time looking for food, but there wasn't much food to be found. One afternoon, Ant and her children scurried across his path, each carrying a fat, ripe seed. "Where did you find those?" asked Grasshopper, eagerly. "Are there any more?"

"There are plenty over there," said Ant, pointing. "When are you going to make a nest? Winter will be here soon!"

"I'm too hungry to think about that now," said Grasshopper, rushing towards the seeds and gobbling down as many as he could.

A few days later, it began to snow. Ladybird was in her nest, fast asleep. Bee was in her hive, sipping sweet honey with her friends and relations. Grasshopper was cold and all alone. He was hungry and there wasn't a crumb of food to be found anywhere!

"I know," said Grasshopper. "Ant will help me. She has plenty of food." So he set out to look for Ant's nest. At last, Grasshopper found Ant's cosy nest, safe and warm beneath a rock.

Ant came out to see him. "What do you want?" she asked.

"Please, Ant," said Grasshopper, "have you any food to spare?"

Ant looked at him. "All summer long, while my family and I worked hard to gather food and prepare our nest, what did you do?"

"I played and had fun, of course," said Grasshopper. "That's what summer is for!"

"Well, you were wrong, weren't you," said Ant. "If you play all summer, then you must go hungry all winter."

"Yes," said Grasshopper, sadly, as a tiny tear fell from the corner of his eye. "I have learned my lesson now. I just hope it isn't too late!"

Ant's heart softened. "Okay, come on in," she said. "And I'll find some food for you." Grasshopper gratefully crawled into the warm nest, where Ant and her family shared their food with him.

By the time Spring came around, Grasshopper was fat and fit and ready to start building a nest of his very own!

Humpty Dumpty

Humpty Dumpty sat on a wall,
  Humpty Dumpty had a great fall;
All the king's horses and all the king's men
  Couldn't put Humpty together again.

We're All in the Dumps

We're all in the dumps,
  For diamonds and trumps,
The kittens are gone to St Paul's,
  The babies are bit,
The moon's in a fit,
  And the houses are built without walls.

Daffy-Down-Dilly

Daffy-Down-Dilly
  Has come up to town
In a yellow petticoat
  And a green gown.

Tweedle-dum and Tweedle-dee

Tweedle-dum and Tweedle-dee
  Agreed to have a battle,
For Tweedle-dum said Tweedle-dee
  Had spoiled his nice new rattle.
Just then flew down a monstrous crow,
  As big as a tar-barrel,
Which frightened both the heroes so,
  They quite forgot their quarrel.

Cushy Cow Bonny

Cushy cow bonny, let down thy milk,
And I will give thee a gown of silk;
A gown of silk and a silver tee,
If thou wilt let down thy milk for me.

Hector Protector

Hector Protector was dressed all in green;
Hector Protector was sent to the Queen.
The Queen did not like him,
Nor more did the King;
So Hector Protector
Was sent back again.

Higglety, Pigglety, pop!

Higglety, Pigglety, pop!
The dog has eaten the mop;
The pig's in a hurry,
The cat's in a flurry,
Higglety, pigglety, pop!

There was a Piper

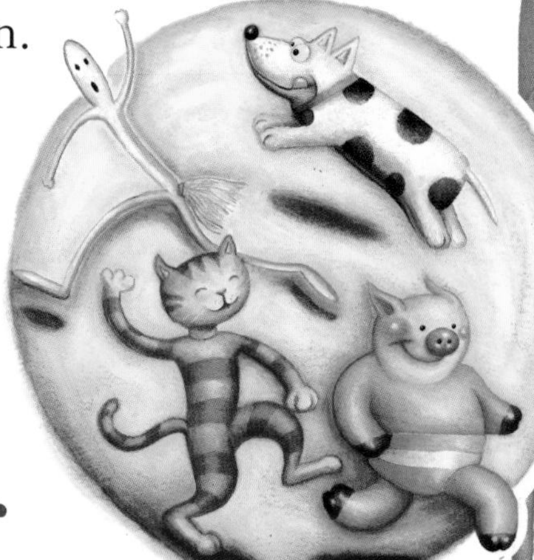

There was a piper, he'd a cow,
And he'd no hay to give her;
He took his pipes and played a tune:
"Consider, old cow, consider!"

The cow considered very well,
For she gave the piper a penny,
That he might play the tune again,
Of "Corn rigs are bonnie".

The Rainy Day

Rain! Rain! Rain! It had rained all day at Faraway Farm. It splashed on the windows, gurgled down the drainpipes, and made puddles all over the yard. Big muddy footprints were everywhere. Danny and Rosie's bored faces peered through the window, longing for it to stop.

Out in the pig sty, Bessie and her piglets wallowed in a giant mud bath. It was such fun! There were squeals of delight.

On the pond, the ducks bobbed along looking pleased with themselves. As long as the raindrops kept falling they were happy.

Cosy inside, Conker slept in his basket by the stove and Stan the cat sat on the window sill washing his paws. Rosie drummed her fingers on the window and pressed her forehead against the pane. She sang a little song to herself: "Rain, rain go away. Stop, I want to go and play."

Down by the bridge, the river was rising higher and higher. Eventually, it spilled over its banks and brown muddy water flowed across the road

and under the farm gate. The cows all gathered to shelter under an old tree.

Joe was busy fixing the tractor in the barn. He wore bright overalls and stomped round the yard in his big muddy boots. He caught sight of the postman riding his bike up to the farm and waved. The rain still pelted down. All of a sudden there came a shout from the road.

"Help, Joe! I'm stranded by the flood," called Jack, the postman. Joe frowned seeing the poor postman stranded.

"Don't worry, Jack," he shouted back. "We'll soon get you across."

Joe put down his tools and climbed up into the tractor cab. He started the engine and reversed out of the barn. The trailer was hooked on. The windscreen wipers swished to and fro. The water splashed down the sides of the cab.

Rosie and Danny emerged from the house in their waterproofs and ran down to the bridge with Conker. "Look," gasped Rosie. "The ducklings are swimming all over the garden. And Jack the postman's trapped by the flood!"

Joe rumbled up in the tractor. "Get on the trailer," he shouted to the children. "I'll reverse it through the flood." They splashed through the water and climbed on to the wall. Danny helped Rosie and Conker on to the trailer.

"Nice weather for ducks," puffed Jack, as he scrambled aboard. "Thanks, kids. Oh, no! There goes my cap!"

Conker barked wildly and jumped in after it. "Oh, come back, Conker," wailed Rosie. "You'll be swept away in the flood."

"No he won't, silly," said Danny. "He's a champion swimmer. Go fetch it, boy!" Conker grabbed the postman's cap in his mouth, and paddled back to the trailer. He dropped it and wagged his tail expectantly.

"Good old Conker!" shouted everyone. "Well done, boy!" Conker shook himself furiously, spraying them all with water.

Joe drove back to the yard and they all jumped off the trailer. Danny climbed up into the cab and Joe let him switch off the engine.

"Thank you, everyone," said Jack, picking up his cap. "Especially you, Conker. I'm very fond of this old cap."

"Come inside," called Mum. "You're all wet through."

"The letters are a bit damp this morning," said Jack. "So is my cap. But at least I've still got one, thanks to Conker."

"Put it by the kitchen stove to dry out," suggested Mum.

"Brave dog," said Danny, giving Conker a pat.

Jack stood by the stove, warming up and drinking a cup of coffee. "We'll help you with the rest of your round. You can sit on the back of the trailer and Rosie and Danny will help deliver the letters," Joe said kindly. So that's what they did.

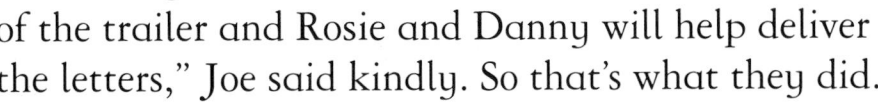

"That was fun," said Rosie, when she got home.

"I'm going to be a postman when I grow up," said Danny. "But I'm going to have a boat, not a bicycle. And I'm always going to take Conker with me in case I lose my cap."

Princess Rosebud

In a beautiful palace in a land far away, lived a little princess. The king and queen called her Princess Rosebud, because on her left ankle was a small pink mark in the shape of a rose.

On her third birthday, the Princess Rosebud was given a pretty white pony. She rode her pony with her nanny and her groom at her side. They went to the edge of the forest, then stopped for a rest. The pretty white pony was tied to a tree branch while the nanny and the groom talked together. The little princess wandered along a forest path collecting flowers and they didn't notice her disappear. Soon Princess Rosebud was lost. She called and called for her nanny. No one came and it began to get dark. The little princess was scared and began to cry.

Princess Rosebud walked on until she saw a light through the trees. There was a little house with a straw roof and tiny little windows and a small wooden door. Suddenly, the door opened. There stood a little old woman!

Now, the old woman was blind and couldn't see the little princess, but she could hear a small child crying. She took the little princess inside and sat her by a warm fire. Then she gave her thin slices of bread and honey, and a glass of milk.

"What is your name, child?" she asked.

"Rosebud," replied the princess. "I got lost in the forest."

"Well, you can stay with me until someone comes to find you, my dear," said the kind old woman.

Back at the palace, the king and queen were very upset that their only daughter was lost. They offered a reward of a hundred gold coins to anyone who could find her. But many years went by and no one found the little princess. The king and queen thought they would never see the princess again.

Meanwhile Rosebud was very happy living in the forest. She forgot that she had ever been a princess and had lived in a palace! She even forgot her white pony!

One day, when she was walking in the garden, a pony appeared. He was as white as milk, with a jewelled saddle and bridle. Rosebud loved him immediately! She climbed into the saddle, and the pony galloped off. He took her to the palace gate. Rosebud felt she had seen the palace before, but could not remember. The pony trotted through the gate as the king and queen were walking in the gardens. When they saw the little girl they thought she was the prettiest girl they had ever seen.

Just as Rosebud was mounting the pony to ride home, the queen saw, to her surprise, the pink rose on her left ankle!

"Sire!" she cried to the king. "It is our daughter, Princess Rosebud."

Rosebud realised where she was, and that the king and queen were her parents. She explained where she had been living and how the old woman had looked after her. The old woman was offered a reward for caring for the princess, but she said, "I only want to be near Rosebud for the rest of my days." So the old woman came to live in the palace with Princess Rosebud.

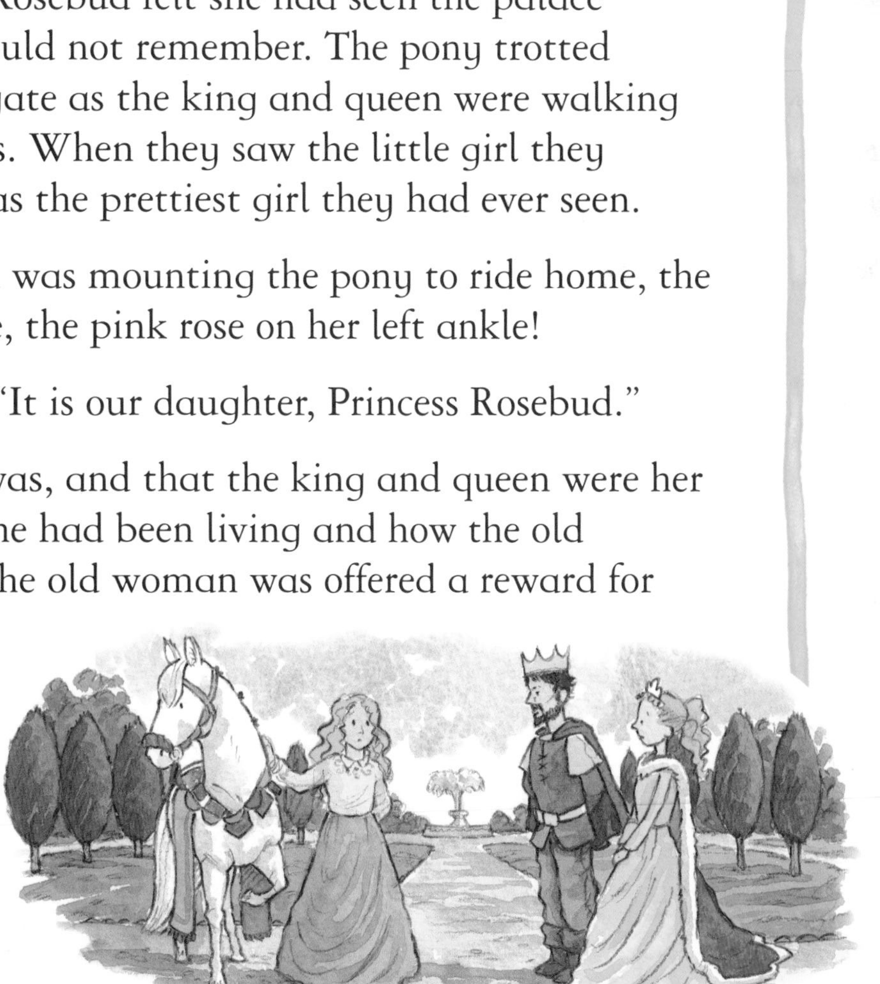

Against Quarrelling and Fighting

Let dogs delight to bark and bite,
For God hath made them so:
Let bears and lions growl and fight,
For 'tis their nature, too.

But, children, you should never let
Such angry passions rise:
Your little hands were never made
To tear each other's eyes.

Let love through all your actions run,
And all your words be mild:
Live like the blessed Virgin's Son,
That sweet and lovely child.

His soul was gentle as a lamb;
And as his nature grew,
He grew in favour both with man,
And God his Father, too.

Now, Lord of all, he reigns above,
And from his heavenly throne
He sees what children dwell in love,
And marks them for his own.

Little Things

Little drops of water,
Little grains of sand,
Make the mighty ocean
And the beauteous land.

And the little moments,
Humble though they be,
Make the mighty ages
Of eternity.

So our little errors
Lead the soul away,
From the paths of virtue
Into sin to stray.

Little deeds of kindness,
Little words of love,
Make our earth an Eden,
Like the heaven above.

Dreams

Here we are all, by day;
by night we are hurled
By dreams, each one into
a several world.

Simple Gifts

'Tis the gift to be simple,
'Tis the gift to be free,
'Tis the gift to come down
Where we ought to be,
And when we find ourselves
In the place just right,
'Twill be in the valley
Of love and delight.
When true simplicity
is gained
To bow and to bend
We sha'n't be ashamed,
To turn, turn will be our delight,
Till by turning, turning
We come round right.

Wagtail and Baby

A blaring bull went wading through,
The wagtail showed no shrinking.

A stallion splashed his way across,
The birdie nearly sinking;
He gave his plumes a twitch and toss,
And held his own unblinking.

Next saw the baby round the spot
A mongrel slowing slinking;
The wagtail gazed, but faltered not
In dip and sip and prinking.

A perfect gentleman then neared;
The wagtail, in a winking,
With terror rose and disappeared;
The baby fell a-thinking.

I Sell You the Key of the King's Garden

I sell you the key of the King's garden:
I sell you the string that ties the key of the King's garden:
I sell you the rat that gnawed the string that ties the key of the King's garden:
I sell you the cat that caught the rat that gnawed the
string that ties the key of the King's garden:
I sell you the dog that bit the cat that caught the rat that
gnawed the string that ties the key of the King's garden.

The Dragon who was Scared of Flying

Once upon a time, in a land far away, there lived a dragon named Dennis. He lived in a cave high up in the mountains. All his friends lived in caves nearby, and his own brothers and sisters lived right next door. Now you would think that Dennis would have been a very happy dragon, surrounded by his friends and family, wouldn't you? Well, I'm sorry to say that Dennis was, in fact, a very unhappy and lonely dragon.

The reason for this was that Dennis was scared of flying. Every day his friends would set off to have adventures, leaving poor Dennis behind on his own. Dennis would stare out of his cave at the departing dragons. How he wished he could join them!

After they had gone, he would stand on the ledge outside his cave, trying to build up the courage to fly. But, as soon as he looked over the edge, he felt all giddy and had to step back. Then he would crawl back into his cave defeated and spend the rest of the day counting the stalactites on the ceiling or rearranging his large collection of bat bones.

Every evening, the other dragons would return with amazing tales of what they had been up to that day. "I rescued a damsel in distress," one would say.

"I fought the wicked one-eyed giant and won," boasted another.

"I helped light the fire for a witch's cauldron," announced a third.

"What have you been up to?" Dennis's sister Doreen used to ask him.

"Oh... um... this and that," Dennis would reply mournfully, looking down at his scaly toes. Then Doreen would lead him out of the cave and try to teach him to fly. Dennis would take a running jump and flap his wings furiously but his feet would stay firmly on the ground. Then the other dragons would laugh so much that, in the end, he always gave up.

One day, Dennis could stand it no longer. The other dragons flew off as usual to find adventure but Dennis, instead of retreating into his cave, set off down the mountain side. It was very tiring having to walk. Dennis had never really been further than from his cave to the ledge and back, and soon he was puffing and panting. He was about to rest at the side of the path when his eye was caught by something colourful in the distance. Down in the valley he could make out some brightly coloured tents, and now he could hear the faint strains of music drifting up to him. "I'd better take a closer look," thought Dennis. "Maybe I can have an adventure, like the other dragons!" He got so excited at the thought of his very own adventure that he started to run.

At last Dennis reached the tents and found himself in a world more exotic than he could ever imagine. He was surrounded by creatures such as he had never seen before. There was a yellow creature that roared and another one with stripes and fierce teeth. There were also quite a few hairy creatures with long tails. Can you guess what all these creatures were? Of course, Dennis had never seen a lion or a tiger or a chimpanzee before. He thought they were very peculiar! The animals thought Dennis was very odd, too. They stood in a circle around him. "How strange," snarled the lion. "A slimy thing with wings!"

"Look at its funny, knobbly tail," giggled the chimpanzees.

Dennis began to feel unhappy and unwanted again, but at that moment he heard a friendly voice saying, "Hello, there! Welcome to Chippy's Circus. I'm Claude the clown. How do you do?"

Dennis turned round. Now he felt really confused, for standing behind him was a man with the unhappiest face Dennis had ever seen. He had great sad eyes and a mouth that was turned down so far that it seemed to touch his chin. Yet he spoke so cheerfully!

"I'm Dennis the dragon," said Dennis.

"A dragon, eh?" said Claude. "Well, we've never had a dragon in the circus before. Might be quite a crowd puller! Would you like to join the circus?" he asked.

"Oh, yes please," cried Dennis.

"Good!" said Claude. "I'm sure you're very talented," he added.

So Dennis joined the circus and was happy for the first time in his life. The other animals became friendly when they knew what he was. Claude taught Dennis to ride the unicycle and to do acrobatic tricks. He also learned how to dive into a bucket of water. He didn't mind that a bit because his slimy skin was quite waterproof!

Now, as you know, dragons are particularly good at breathing fire, so Dennis soon became the circus's champion fire-eater. Folk would come from far and near to see Dennis shooting flames high into the dark roof of the big top.

One evening, when Dennis had finished his fire-eating act, he sat eating an ice cream to cool his hot throat and watched Carlotta, the tight-rope walker. She was pirouetting high up on the rope as usual. Then all at once she lost her footing and Dennis saw to his horror that she was going to fall. He dropped his ice cream and, without thinking, flapped his wings furiously. As Carlotta fell, Dennis found himself flying up towards her. He caught her gently on his back and flew down to the ground with her clinging on tightly. The crowd roared and burst into applause. They obviously thought it was all part of the act.

"Thank you, Dennis," whispered Carlotta in Dennis's ear. "You saved my life."

Dennis was overjoyed. Not only had he saved Carlotta's life, he had also learned to fly. And he said with a grin, "I do declare that flying is actually rather fun."

The Spooks' Ball

It is midnight and the spooks are going to the Annual Ball in the old Haunted Hall. By the light of the moon they will dance to a band that will play terrible tunes all night.

A spooks' band has instruments the like of which you will never have seen! The drums are made from skulls of all different shapes and sizes, the piano is made from the teeth of a dinosaur, and the violin is played with a bow made from cats' whiskers. But the strangest sound comes from the skeletons when they take to the dance floor. They shake their bones in time to the band, making a rattling tune which makes them howl with glee! In amongst the shaking skeletons is a witch dancing with her cat, but her boots are so big that she can't keep up with everyone else! A ghost with his head tucked underneath his arm is slowly feeding himself crisps.

As the sun rises the spooks all fade away and the Ball is over for another year – or have you been dreaming?

The Haunted House

Have you ever been in a haunted house? No? Well, follow me and I will take you on a guided tour...

Step carefully through the rusty gates, but be quiet as a mouse, you don't want to upset the residents. Open the front door very slowly – otherwise it will creak and squeak, then everyone will know we are here. The hallway is full of ghosts wafting backwards and forwards, and look... some are walking through the doors when they are closed!

There are ghastly ghouls lurking on the stairs, and imps and sprites are having pillow fights. Look out – you will get covered in feathers!

Push open the kitchen door and a wizard is making slug and spider pies. I don't think we will stay to sample those when they are ready to come out of the oven!

Upstairs, skeletons are getting dressed and vampires are brushing their teeth. A suit of armour is about to get in the bath – we won't stay in case he goes rusty!

So, an ordinary day in a haunted house – would you like to move in?

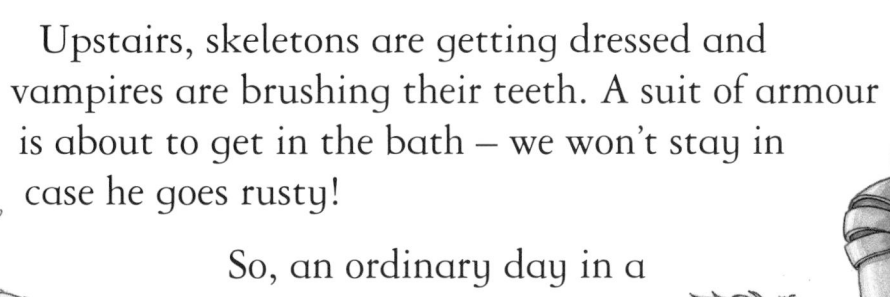

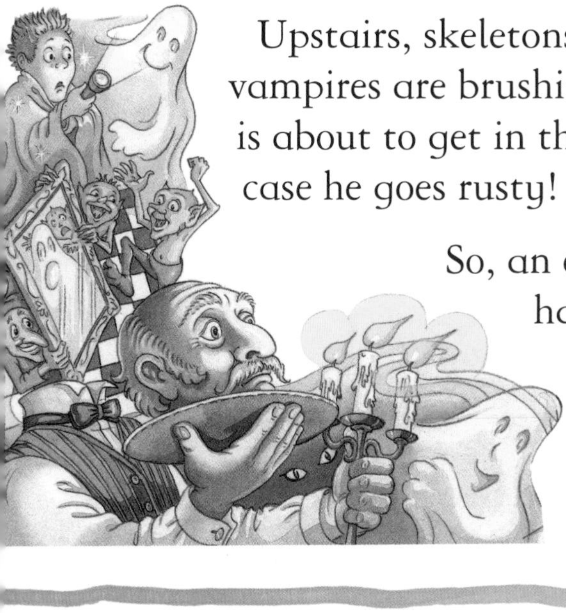

The Three Little Pigs

Once upon a time, there were three little pigs who lived with their mummy in a big stone house.

One day, Mummy Pig said, "Children, it's time for you to go out and find your fortune in the big wide world." So she packed a little bag of food and a drink for each of them, and sent them on their way.

"Goodbye!" she called, as the three little pigs set off on their adventure. "Good luck, my dears, and remember to watch out for the big, bad wolf!"

"We will, Mummy," called the little pigs as they waved goodbye.

After a while, the three little pigs stopped for a rest and decided that they should each build a house to live in. Just then, they saw a farmer coming along the road with a wagon full of golden straw.

"Please, sir," said the first little pig, "may I have some of your straw to build myself a house?"

"Yes, little pig," said the farmer, "of course you can."

So the first little pig built his house of straw. Soon it was finished. It looked very good indeed, and the first little pig was happy.

The other two little pigs set off on their journey together and, after a while, they met a man carrying a large bundle of sticks.

"Please, sir," said the second little pig, "may I have some of your sticks to build myself a house?"

"Yes, little pig," said the man, "of course you can."

So the second little pig built his house of sticks. Soon it was finished. It looked very good indeed, and the second little pig was happy.

The third little pig set off on his journey alone. He saw lots of people with wagons of straw and bundles of sticks, but he did not stop until he met a man with a cart filled to the brim with bricks.

"Please, sir," said the third little pig, "may I have some bricks to build myself a house?"

"Yes, little pig," said the man, "of course you can."

So the third little pig built his house of bricks. Soon it was finished. It looked very good indeed. It was strong and solid,

and the third little pig was very, very pleased.

That evening, the big, bad wolf was walking along the road. He was very hungry and looking for something good to eat. He saw the first little pig's house of straw and looked in through the window.

"Yum, yum," he said to himself, licking his lips. "This little pig would make a most tasty dinner."

So, in his friendliest voice, the wolf called through the window, "Little pig, little pig, please let me in!"

But the first little pig remembered his mummy's warning, so he replied, "No, no, I won't let you in, not by the hair on my chinny-chin-chin!"

This made the wolf really angry. "Very well!" he roared. "I'll huff and I'll puff, and I'll blow your house down!"

The poor little pig was very afraid, but he still would not let the wolf in. So the wolf huffed... and he puffed... and he BLEW the straw house down.

Then the big, bad wolf chased the little pig and gobbled him up!

But the wolf was still hungry! He walked down the road and soon came to the house made of sticks. He looked through the window and called to the second little pig, "Little pig, little pig, please let me in."

"No, no!" cried the second little pig. "I won't let you in, not by the hair on my chinny-chin-chin!"

"Very well," cried the wolf. "Then I'll huff and I'll puff, and I'll blow your house down!"

And that's just what the big, bad wolf did. He huffed… and he puffed… and he BLEW the stick house down! Then he gobbled up the second little pig.

But the big, bad wolf was still hungry. So he walked down the road and soon came to the house made of bricks. He looked through the window and called to the third little pig, "Little pig, little pig, please let me in."

"No, no!" cried the third little pig. "I won't let you in, not by the hair on my chinny-chin-chin!"

"Very well," roared the big, bad wolf. "I'll huff and I'll puff, and I'll blow your house down!"

So the wolf huffed and he puffed... he HUFFED and he PUFFED... and he HUFFED and he PUFFED some more, but he could not blow the brick house down!

By now the big, bad wolf was very, very angry. He scrambled up onto the roof and began to climb down through the chimney.

But the third little pig was a clever little pig, and he had put a big pot of boiling water to bubble on the fire.

When the wolf came down the chimney, he landed – ker-splosh! – right in the middle of the pot of boiling water! He burned his bottom so badly that he ran out of the house and down the road just as fast as his legs could carry him, howling so loudly with pain that he could be heard for miles.

The third little pig was very pleased with his house of bricks and lived in it for many years, happy and content. And nothing was ever heard of the big, bad wolf again.

Copycat Max

Max was a little tiger with a bad habit. He was a terrible copycat! He copied everyone and everything. When the parrot said, "Pretty Polly, Pretty Polly," Max repeated it. "Pretty Polly, Pretty Polly!" Then, when the parrot got cross and said, "Shut up, Max, shut up Max," he repeated that as well. It was very annoying.

One day, he set off to explore. "I shall copy everything I see," he said to himself. And that's when the trouble really started!

First, he met a stork standing on one leg.

"Why are you doing that?" asked Max.

"Because it's comfortable," said the stork.

"How long can you do it for?" asked Max.

"For ages!" said the stork. "Only birds can stand like this."

"Hmmm!" said Max, and lifted up one leg.

"Now lift up two more," said the stork. Max did, and fell in a heap on the ground. "Told you!" said the stork. Max picked himself up.

Exploring further, he met a brown chameleon sitting on a green leaf. The amazing thing about chameleons is that they can change colour when they want to. The chameleon saw Max and changed his colour to green, like the leaf! Max could no longer see him.

"Where have you gone?" asked Max, looking everywhere.

"I'm still here," said the chameleon. "Watch this," he added, and he jumped on to a red flower and turned... red!

"Watch this then," said Max, and he lay down on some grass. "Now I'm green," he said.

"You're not," said the chameleon. "Only chameleons can change colour."

"Hmmm!" said Max. He rolled over and over in some mud. "Look," he said, "now I'm brown." Then he rolled in some white feathers. The feathers stuck to the mud. "Look," he said, "now I'm all white!"

"It won't last," said the chameleon.

Max decided to set off for home. He passed the stork still standing on one leg. The stork didn't recognise him.

He arrived home late in the evening. His brothers and sisters were playing down by the river. They saw a white figure coming towards them.

"WOooo!" wailed Max, pretending to be a ghost. "I've come to get you!" The tiger cubs were so scared, they rushed into the river and started to swim to the other side.

"WOooo!" wailed Max and rushed in after them. Of course, as soon as Max got wet, the mud and feathers disappeared. When the others saw it was only Max they were really cross.

"You frightened us," they told him.

"It was only a joke," said Max.

They agreed to forgive him if he promised not to copy anything again.

"Oh, all right," said Max. And, for the moment, he meant it!

Betty Pringle

Betty Pringle had a little pig,
Not very little and not very big;
When he was alive he lived in clover;
But now he's dead, and that's all over.
So Billy Pringle,
he laid down and cried,
And Betty Pringle,
she laid down and died;
So there was an end of one,
two, and three:
Billy Pringle he,
Betty Pringle she,
And the piggy wiggy.

If Wishes were Horses

If wishes were horses,
Beggars would ride;
If turnips were watches,
I'd wear one by my side.

Jack be Nimble

Jack be nimble,
And Jack be quick:
And Jack jump over
The candlestick.

As I Walked by Myself

As I walked by myself,
And talked to myself,
Myself said unto me,
Look to thyself,
Take care of thyself,
For nobody cares for thee.

I answered myself,
And said to myself,
In the self-same repartee,
Look to thyself,
Or not look to thyself,
The self-same thing will be.

Yankee Doodle

Yankee Doodle went to town,
  Riding on a pony;
He stuck a feather in his hat,
  And called it macaroni.
Yankee Doodle fa, so, la,
  Yankee Doodle dandy,
Yankee Doodle fa, so, la,
  Buttermilk and brandy.

Yankee Doodle went to town
  To buy a pair of trousers,
He swore he could not see the town
  For so many houses.
Yankee Doodle fa, so, la,
  Yankee Doodle dandy,
Yankee Doodle fa, so, la,
  Buttermilk and brandy.

If All the World was Apple-pie

If all the world was apple-pie,
  And all the sea was ink,
And all the trees were bread and cheese,
  What should we have for drink?

Fire on the Mountain

Rats in the garden – catch'em Towser!
  Cows in the cornfield – run boys run!
Cat's in the cream pot – stop her now, sir!
  Fire on the mountain – run boys run!

The Man in the Wilderness

The man in the wilderness asked me,
  How many strawberries grew in the sea?
I answered him as I thought good,
  As many red herrings as grew in the wood.

Hide and Seek

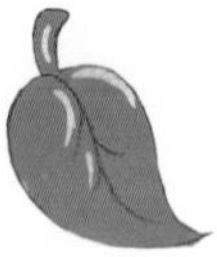

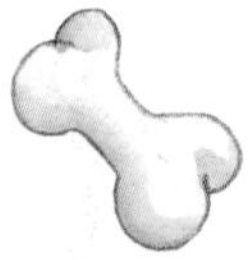

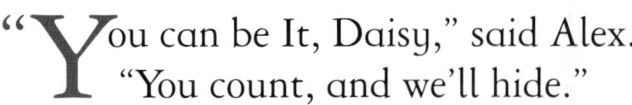

"You can be It, Daisy," said Alex. "You count, and we'll hide."

"Okay," said Daisy. "Poppy can help me to look for you." Poppy was Daisy's new puppy.

"Don't be silly," laughed Sam. "A puppy can't play hide and seek."

"She can because…" began Daisy. But the others weren't listening. They had all run off across the field to hide. "Never mind, Poppy," Daisy told her puppy. "You'll just have to sit here and be good."

Daisy turned round to face the tree. She closed her eyes and began to count. "…ninety eight, ninety nine, one hundred." That should have given everyone long enough to hide. Daisy looked round the field. There was no one to be seen. Poppy whined as Daisy ran off towards the hole in the hedge where they had made a den.

She found Sam almost straightaway. He was tucked down in a corner of the den. She took him back to the tree. Poppy whined at them. "Dogs can't play hide and seek," Sam told the puppy, and tickled her ear. "You can sit here with me."

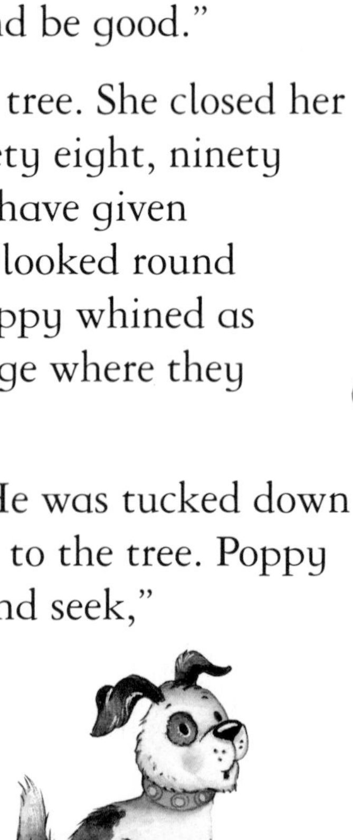

Then Daisy found Sarah and Michael just as easily. Emily was harder to find – she was lying very still in the long grass

at the end of the field. Her green t-shirt and trousers made her difficult to see. Daisy took her back to the tree, where the others were all waiting. Poppy whined each time she came back.

"Shhh!" said Daisy. "I won't be long now." But Daisy was wrong – she couldn't find Alex anywhere! Daisy had looked in all their favourite hiding places, but he wasn't in any of them. She didn't know what to do.

"We'll help you to find Alex," said Michael.

So the children searched every corner of the field and every bit of the hedge, but Alex couldn't be found anywhere. Then Poppy began to whine even more loudly.

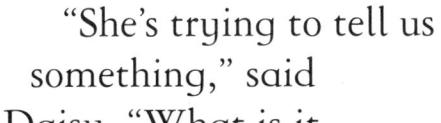

"She's trying to tell us something," said Daisy. "What is it, Poppy? Show me."

Poppy jumped up. She ran to the tree trunk, leapt up, and began barking. The children all looked up. And there was Alex, sitting on a branch above them, laughing!

"See!" he said. "Daisy was right – puppies can play hide and seek."

Going to Nursery

It was Monday morning. Jodie opened her eyes when she heard Mum coming up the stairs. "Time to get up!" Mum called, as she put her head round the door.

"Don't you want to go and see the nursery?"

"Yes, I do!" Jodie said. She wanted to find out more about the nursery that Mum had talked so much about. Jodie jumped out of bed and Mum helped her to get dressed.

"Mum?" said Jodie. "What's it like at nursery?"

"Do you like climbing frames?" Mum asked her.

"Yes, I do!" said Jodie.

"Then you'll like nursery," Mum said. "There are lots of exciting things, like climbing frames, to play on. Come on, let's hurry up and then you can see for yourself."

Dad was waiting for Jodie in the kitchen. "All ready to look at the nursery?" he said.

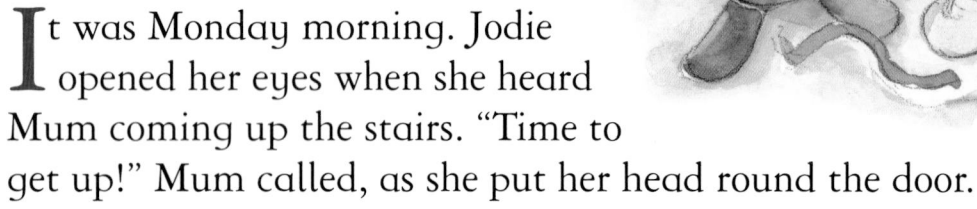

Jodie ate her cereal and her toast. "I'm ready!" she cried. "Let's go!" When they arrived at the nursery, a lady was waiting to meet them. "You must be Jodie," she said, smiling.

"I'm Mrs Clark. Would you like to see what we do here?" Jodie nodded.

Mrs Clark opened a door into a big room full of children having fun. Some of them were playing on a yellow climbing frame. Some of them were digging in the sand tray, with buckets and spades. "Mum," said Jodie, "you were right. There are lots of exciting things to do at nursery."

Soon, it was time to go, but Jodie had so many questions about nursery. "When do I start?" she asked, on the way home.

"Next week," said Mum.

While she was eating lunch, Jodie said, "How long will I stay there?"

"Just for the morning, to start with," replied Dad.

Watching television with Mum that afternoon, Jodie asked, "Can I take teddy with me to nursery?"

"Of course," smiled Mum. "I think he'll enjoy it."

Next morning, Jodie and Mum went to the park. As Jodie was climbing up the slide, she met a small boy, who was standing at the top.

The little boy's mum smiled at Jodie's mum. "He's starting at nursery next week," she said.

"So am I!" cried Jodie. "What's your name?" she asked the boy.

"Jack!" he said, whooshing down the slide. "Do you like nursery?"

"I think so," Jodie told him.

"I'll see you there," said Jack and he ran off, waving.

The week quickly passed and, at last, the day came for Jodie to start nursery. She was very excited and a little bit scared, all at the same time.

"Where am I going to put my coat?" she asked Mum, as they pushed open the door of the nursery.

"They'll have your very own place ready for you," said Mum.

"Hello again, Jodie," said Mrs Clark. "Can you see the hook for your coat? It's the one with the blue pig. Now, what would you like to do first?"

Jodie noticed a boy, who was working on a big puzzle of a fire engine. It was Jack.

"Hi, Jack," she said. "Can I help?" She picked up a piece of puzzle and fitted it into place.

"I think it's time for me to go," whispered Mum, giving Jodie a hug.

"Okay, Mum," Jodie smiled. "See you later," and she picked up another piece of puzzle.

"Jodie's really good at this, isn't she?" said Mrs Clark to Jack. Jack nodded – it was fun at nursery.

Then, Mrs Clark asked if they would like to help pass round the drinks and apple slices.

"Oh yes, please," said Jodie and Jack, together.

"Everyone, come and meet Jack and Jodie," said Mrs Clark. All the girls and boys came over to say "Hello". Then, Mrs Clark asked Jodie and Jack what they would like to do next. Jodie knew exactly what she wanted to do. She tugged Jack over to the dressing-up box.

"Look!" she said, pulling out two hats, "we could be firemen."

Jack pointed to a big red car, standing in the corner. "And that could be our fire engine," he said.

After Jodie and Jack had put out lots of pretend fires, they saw two girls, busy making things at a table. They ran over to join them. There were boxes and cardboard tubes and glue and paint everywhere.

"Let's make a fire engine," said Jodie.

Jodie started to glue two boxes together. She cut some card circles for wheels and Jack helped her stick them on. Then, they painted the whole thing bright red.

Just as they finished, Jodie's mum slipped in through the door. Jodie ran over to her.

"Come and see," she said, dragging Mum over to the modelling table. "We made a fire engine."

"It's lovely!" smiled Mum. "Shall we take it home with us? It's time for lunch now."

Jodie put on her coat and waved to Jack. "Did you have a good time?" asked Mum. "Do you want to come again?"

"Yes, I do!" cried Jodie. "Nursery is great fun."

Putting on a Nightgown

Little man in a coal pit
  Goes knock, knock, knock;
Up he comes, up he comes,
  Out at the top.

Ickle Ockle

Ickle, ockle, blue bockle,
  Fishes in the sea,
If you want a pretty maid,
  Please choose me.

Old Farmer Giles

Old Farmer Giles,
  He went seven miles
With his faithful dog Old Rover;
  And Old Farmer Giles,
When he came to the stiles,
  Took a run, and jumped clean over.

Little Fishes

Little fishes in a brook,
  Father caught them on a hook,
Mother fried them in a pan,
  Johnnie eats them like a man.

Jim Crow

Twist about, turn about,
  Jump Jim Crow;
Every time I wheel about
  I do just so.

Bob Robin

Little Bob Robin,
  Where do you live?
Up in yonder wood, sir,
  On a hazel twig.

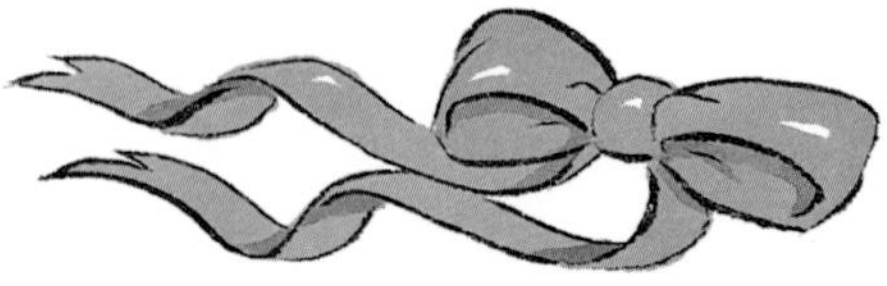

Fidget

As little Jenny Wren
Was sitting by the shed,
She waggled with her tail,
She nodded with her head;
She waggled with her tail,
She nodded with her head;
As Little Jenny Wren
Was sitting by the shed.

Praise

Robinets and Jenny Wrens
Are God Almighty's
cocks and hens.
The martins and the swallows
Are God Almighty's bows
and arrows.

In Lincoln Lane

I lost my mare in Lincoln Lane,
I'll never find her there again;
She lost a shoe,
And then lost two,
And threw her rider in the drain.

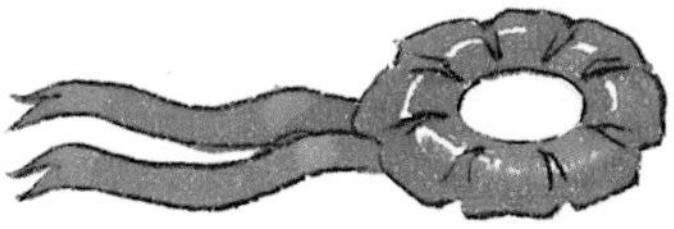

Red Stockings

Red stockings, blue stockings,
Shoes tied up with silver;
A red rosette upon my breast
And a gold ring on my finger.

The Dove Says

The dove says, Coo, coo,
What shall I do?
I can scarce maintain two.
Pooh, pooh, says the wren, I have ten,
And keep them all like gentlemen.
Curr dhoo, curr dhoo,
Love me, and I'll love you.

Charley Barley

Charley Barley, butter and eggs,
Sold his wife for three duck eggs.
When the ducks began to lay,
Charley Barley flew away.

The Smiley Crocodile

Open-wide was the friendliest crocodile for miles around. While all the grumpy crocodiles were snapping and snarling and being very cross, Open-wide grinned at everyone. He had a very, very big smile.

"You smile too much," the others told him. "Be fierce… like a real crocodile!"

"I'll try," said Open-wide, and he put on a scowly face. It lasted two seconds and then the smile came back again. "How was that?" he asked. "Hopeless!" the others said.

One day, some hippos came to the river. They were very large and there were a lot of them. They waded into the part of the river that the crocodiles liked the best. Open-wide liked watching them having fun. He liked it when they sank to the bottom and then came up very slowly making lots of ripples. He liked it when they had a contest to see who could make the biggest splash. He liked it when they blew fountains of water up into the air. The grumpy crocodiles didn't like it one little bit!

"We'll soon get rid of them," they said. Open-wide saw a baby hippo playing in the water. His name was Sausage.

"I bet you can't do this!" said Sausage to Open-wide, and he blew a million bubbles so that they floated in a cloud across the top of the water.

"I bet I can," said Open-wide. And he did… through his nose!

"What about this?" said Sausage, and he turned on his back and sank below the surface. Open-wide did the same, and then he swam very fast to the opposite bank of the river. They played like this all day... and every day after that! Open-wide had never had such a good time.

The grumpy crocodiles were very fed up. They got together to think of ways of getting rid of the hippos. First they tried being frightening by showing lots of teeth. The hippos just smiled... and showed even bigger teeth! Then the grumpy crocodiles tried being rude.

"Scram!" they shouted... and, when that didn't work, "Smelly old hippos!" The hippos thought it was a joke.

Next they charged the hippos while they were swimming. The hippos sank to the bottom of the river where it was too deep for the crocodiles.

The crocodiles didn't know what else to do. Open-wide had an idea! "Why don't I just smile at them and ask nicely if they will move?" he said.

"Pooh!" said the crocodiles. "Fat lot of good that will do!"

Open-wide didn't give up. "Please?" "Oh, go on then," said the grumpy crocodiles, "but it won't work, you'll see."

But it did! The hippos liked Open-wide; he had a big smile just like them. They listened politely when he explained that the crocodiles didn't really like fun. They would rather be on their own and grumpy.

"We'll move further down the river if you will still come and play with Sausage," they said. And that's what happened.

The crocodiles were amazed! They didn't say anything to Open-wide, but secretly they wondered if smiling was better than scowling after all!

The Sad Clown

Bongo the clown had a bit of a problem. Clowns were supposed to be happy, funny, jolly people, but Bongo was a very sad clown. Nothing at all seemed to make him laugh.

Whenever the circus came to town people from all around flocked to the big top hoping for an exciting day out. They thrilled to the daring performance of the high-wire act, as the acrobats leaped from one swinging trapeze to the next. They enjoyed the jugglers, who tossed bright, sparkling balls into the air while standing on one leg. And the crowd delighted in seeing the beautiful white horses parading around the circus ring with the bareback riders balancing on their backs. When the seals came on, there was always a big cheer from the crowd, for everyone loved them and could watch their clever antics for hours.

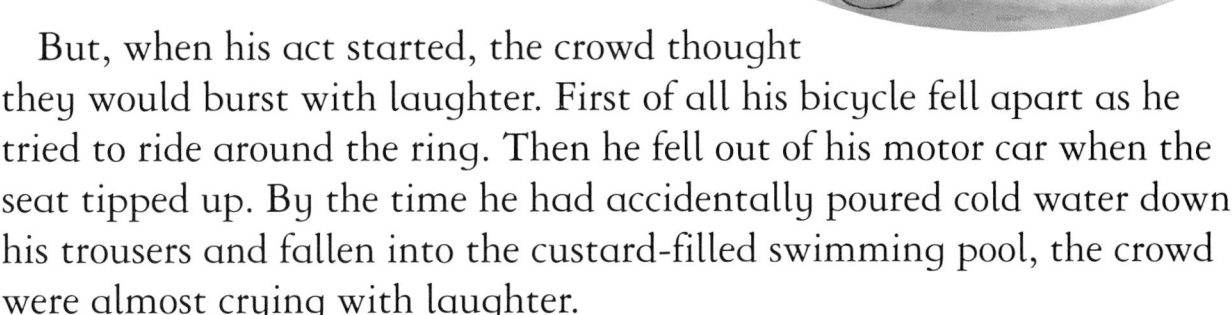

But the biggest favourite of the crowd, especially with all the children, was the clown. Everyone laughed to see him dressed in his big baggy trousers and with his funny walk. They laughed even more when they saw his big floppy hat with the revolving flower on it. Even his painted clown face made them laugh.

But, when his act started, the crowd thought they would burst with laughter. First of all his bicycle fell apart as he tried to ride around the ring. Then he fell out of his motor car when the seat tipped up. By the time he had accidentally poured cold water down his trousers and fallen into the custard-filled swimming pool, the crowd were almost crying with laughter.

But, beneath all the make up, Bongo the sad clown wasn't smiling at all. In fact, he saw nothing funny at all in bicycles that fell apart as you used them, or cars that tipped you out as you went along, or having cold water poured down your trousers, or even ending up face first in a swimming pool full of custard. He simply hadn't got a sense of humour.

All the other performers in the circus decided they would try to cheer up the sad clown.

"I know," said the high-wire trapeze acrobat, "let's paint an even funnier face on him. That'll make him laugh."

So that's what they did, but Bongo still didn't laugh and was still just as sad.

"Let us perform some of our tricks, just for him," said the seals.

So they sat on their stools and tossed their big coloured balls to each other, clapped their flippers together and made lots of honking sounds. But Bongo still didn't laugh. In fact, nothing that anyone tried made poor Bongo smile. He was still a very sad clown.

Then Percival the ringmaster spoke. "You know, I think I know what the problem is," he said. "There is nothing a clown likes better than playing tricks on other clowns. Perhaps, if we had a second clown, that would cheer up Bongo."

So right away they hired another clown, called Piffle.

The circus arrived in the next town and soon it was time for Bongo and Piffle's act. Piffle started riding around on his bike while Bongo pretended to wash the car by throwing a bucket of water over it. Instead of the water landing on the car, of course, it went all over Piffle, who just happened to be cycling past at that moment. A little smile flickered across Bongo's face at the sight of the soaking wet Piffle.

Next, Bongo and Piffle pretended to be cooking, and Bongo tripped while carrying two huge custard pies. Both landed right in Piffle's face. Bongo let out a huge chuckle of laughter when he saw Piffle's face covered in custard.

At the end of their act, the clowns were pretending to be decorators, painting up a ladder. Of course, you've guessed it. The ladders fell down and all the pots of paint landed on the two clowns. Bongo looked across at Piffle, who had a big paint pot stuck on his head, with paint dripping down his body. Bongo threw back his head and roared with laughter. Piffle thought Bongo looked just as funny with paint all over his body, too. And as for the crowd – well, they thought two clowns were even funnier than one and they clapped and cheered and filled the big top with laughter.

After that Bongo was never a sad clown again.

This Little Piggy

This little piggy went to market,
  This little piggy stayed at home,
This little piggy had roast beef,
  This little piggy had none,
And this little piggy cried,
  Wee-wee-wee-wee-wee,
All the way home.

To Market, to Market, to Buy a Fat Pig

To market, to market, to buy a fat pig,
  Home again, home again, dancing a jig;
Ride to the market to buy a fat hog,
  Home again, home again, jiggety-jog.

To Market, to Market

To market, to market,
  To buy a plum bun;
Home again, come again,
  Market is done.

Two Little Men in a Flying Saucer

Two little men in a flying saucer
  Flew round the world one day.
They looked to the left and right a bit,
  And couldn't bear the sight of it,
And then they flew away!

I Can ...

I can tie my shoe lace,
I can brush my hair,
I can wash my hands and face
And dry myself with care.

I can clean my teeth too,
And fasten up my frocks.
I can say, "How do you do?"
And pull up both my socks.

Higgledy Piggledy

Higgledy piggledy,
Here we lie,
Picked and plucked,
And put in a pie!

Two Fat Gentlemen

Two fat gentlemen met in a lane,
Bowed most politely, bowed once again.
How do you do? How do you do?
How do you do again?

Two thin ladies met in a lane,
Bowed most politely, bowed once again.
How do you do? How do you do?
How do you do again?

Two tall policemen met in a lane,
Bowed most politely, bowed once again.
How do you do? How do you do?
How do you do again?

Two little schoolboys met in a lane,
Bowed most politely, bowed once again.
How do you do? How do you do?
How do you do again?

Tumbling

In jumping and tumbling
We spend the whole day,
Till night by arriving
Has finished our play.

What then? One and all,
There's no more to be said,
As we tumbled all day,
So we tumble to bed.

Small and Pink

One morning, Percy the pig strutted proudly through the farmyard. "Today's the day," he told everyone he passed.

"What is he on about?" asked Doris the duck.

"Percy is expecting some piglets," clucked Jenny the hen.

"I didn't think boy pigs could have babies," said Doris, looking puzzled.

"No, no," Jenny clucked, flapping her wings. "They are coming from another farm to live here as part of his family."

Doris smiled. "Like Tilly and George and their new foal?" she said. "Oh, how lovely."

Percy had tripped and trotted from one end of the farmyard to the other more times than he cared to remember, but Old MacDonald still hadn't returned with the new arrivals.

Percy went back to his sty and checked it one more time. It was spotless. The straw was piled up neatly along one wall and the water trough was clean and full.

"I must make sure that everything is ready for my piglets," said Percy, brushing a speck of dust from the doorway.

Just as Percy finished cleaning, brushing and tidying he heard Old MacDonald's truck rumbling into the farmyard – they were here at last!

Percy was so excited! He hurried from his sty, but before he could reach the truck...

Whoosh! Something very small, very pink and very fast shot past his nose.

Whizzz! Something just as small and pink and even faster scuttled under his tail.

Wheeeee! Another small and pink and noisy thing zoomed straight under Percy's tummy.

"What's going on?" gasped Percy, as he spun round on his trotters.

"Eeeeeeeeee!" shrieked seven little piglets, dashing in every direction around the farmyard.

Late that night, a very tired Percy stood at the doorway of his sty – it was a tip. The straw was everywhere and the water trough was upside down. But seven little piglets were fast asleep in the corner.

"Tired, Percy?" asked Jenny the hen.

"Yes," sighed Percy.

"They never stand still from morning till night, do they?" added Maria the sheep.

"No," sighed Percy.

"Are you having second thoughts, Percy?" asked Old George the horse.

But Percy gave the kind of grin that only a very happy and contented proud pig can give. “Shhhhhhh!” he whispered. “My babies are sleeping!”

Not Another Bear

William loved teddy bears. When asked what he would like for his birthday, or for Christmas, William's answer was always the same, "I'd like a teddy bear, please."

"Not another bear!" his parents would say. "Look at your bed, William. There's no room for any more!" It was true. There were bears all over William's bed. Every night William had to squeeze into the tiny space that was left. But William didn't mind at all.

"We've got to do something about this," said William's dad, marching into William's bedroom with a pile of wood and a bag of tools. "We'll make some shelves, so that you can have some room." By tea time there were three shelves on William's bedroom wall. And a row of bears sat neatly on each one. When William went to bed that night there was plenty of room. But it just didn't feel right.

Next day, at the school fair, Mum gave William some pocket money. "Find something you'd like," she said. William noticed a small bear on the White Elephant stall. He bought it and when they got home he ran straight upstairs. "What did you buy, William?" Mum called up. William grinned.

"Not another bear!" sighed Mum.

"But there's plenty of room now," William answered. He winked at the new bear, and William was sure that the bear winked back.

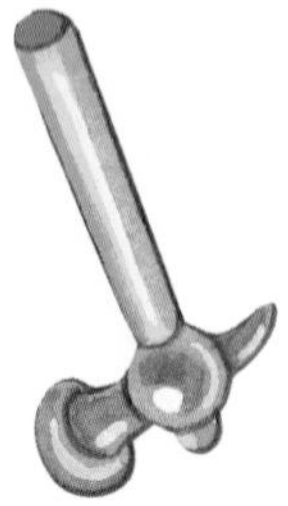

Yes, You Can!

Ozzie sat on the river bank watching the other otters having fun. He wished he could splash in the water like them. But Ozzie didn't dare to go down into the river, because he couldn't swim! Once, he climbed to the top of the bank and looked at the water below. But he had been really scared so, since then, he always sat by the river on his own.

"What's the matter, Ozzie?" asked his mum.

"I wish I could swim so I could have fun with my friends," said Ozzie.

"But you can," laughed Mum. "Come on," she said. "Climb on my back and hold tight." So, with Ozzie holding on to his mum's back, they slipped into the water and swam round in small circles. At first, Ozzie was frightened. Then, he began to enjoy the water, lapping at his sides.

"This is fun!" he cried. "Can we do it again?" But there was no answer. Ozzie's mum wasn't there. She was on the river bank, smiling at him.

"Help!" yelled Ozzie, in panic. "I can't swim!"

"Yes, you can," called his mum. "Pretend you're running!" Suddenly, he felt himself moving forward – he was swimming! Round and round he went, splashing and diving.

On the bank, he found a tiny otter shivering. "What's the matter?" asked Ozzie.

"I can't swim," said the otter.

"Yes, you can!" smiled Ozzie. "Come on, climb on my back and I'll show you!"

Fire! Fire!

The sun was shining in the higgledy-piggledy, messy alley.

"It's much too hot!" Hattie thought to herself, as she tried to find a nice shady spot for a snooze. Her kittens, Lenny and Lulu, were cat-napping under the apple tree and she knew from the loud snoring that Uncle Bertie and Auntie Lucy were fast asleep in their dustbins. Everyone was hiding from the sun – everyone except Cousin Archie!

Archie was lying on top of the fence, slurping his third bottle of milk! He didn't notice the sun's rays shining through the glass of those empty milk bottles. It was focused right onto Hattie's dustbin full of old newspapers – the perfect place for a fire to start!

Suddenly, Hattie's nose twitched. "What's that?" she wondered. "It smells like smoke."

"It is smoke!" she gasped, as she saw bright red and yellow flames leaping out of her dustbin.

"F-Fire!" she cried. "Help!"

"Wake up, Bertie!" cried Hattie. "My dustbin's on fire!"

Uncle Bertie's sleepy head popped up from his dustbin.

"I must have been dreaming, Hattie!"

he yawned. "I dreamt that your bin was on fire."

"It wasn't a dream," cried Hattie. "My bin *is* on fire."

Cousin Archie fell off the fence in shock! He landed right on top of poor Bertie!

"Hurry!" urged Hattie. "We must put the fire out."

All the shouting woke the twins from their dreams.

"Mummy! Mummy!" they meowed, "what's happening?"

Hattie grabbed her kittens and put them on the top of the fence, well away from the dangerous fire.

"You'll be safe here," she told them.

Uncle Bertie knew he had to find some water quickly.

"Over there!" Hattie said, pointing to an old bucket by the fence.

"Hooray!" cried Bertie, finding the bucket half full of water. "It might just be enough to put out the fire."

"Cousin Archie!" he cried. "Come and help me."

The two cats ran down the alley, carrying the bucket between them.

Then, with smoke billowing all around, Archie and Bertie aimed the bucket of water and let go...

SPLOSH! There was a huge sizzling sound.

"Hooray!" Bertie cried, with a sigh of relief. "We've done it!"

But suddenly, a spark from the fire landed on the rubbish next to the dustbin.

"Oh no, we haven't!" wailed Archie. "Now the rubbish is on fire!"

"Quick," Hattie said to Archie. "We need more help. Go and wake up the dogs."

At the other end of the alley, the dogs were all fast asleep.

"Help!" shrieked Archie, as he hurtled towards them. "Hattie's bin is on fire. It's spreading down the alley and we can't put it out."

But no one stirred. Archie was always playing tricks on the Alley Dogs and today it was just too hot to bother. Harvey opened one eye lazily.

"That's a good one, Archie," he said. "But you'll have to try harder than that."

"It's true!" Archie shouted, desperately. "Look!"

Harvey sat up slowly. "This had better not be one of your tricks, Archie," he growled. Then he shaded his eyes from the sun and looked up the alley. As soon as he saw the billowing smoke, he knew the Alley Cat was telling the truth.

"Archie's right!" barked Harvey. "Quick, everyone to the rescue!"

The dogs raced up the alley towards the fire. Even little Puddles wanted to help. But Harvey scooped her up and placed her on the fence by the kittens.

"You can't do a thing, Puddles!" he said. "Just stay here."

The alley was filled with smelly black smoke. All the cats were coughing and choking. But Harvey knew just what to do.

"Quick!" he said. "Everybody to the water-barrel. Use anything you can to gather the water."

Grabbing old buckets and cans, the cats and dogs formed a long line. Auntie Lucy stood by the barrel to fill up the containers. Then, splishing and splashing, they passed the water along the line to Harvey, who threw it over the fire.

Suddenly, Lucy gave a cry. "The water's run out!"

"Oh no!" said Archie. "We'll never put the fire out now."

The Alley Cats and Dogs stared in dismay. What could they do? They must have more water.

"Oh, no! We're going to lose our lovely home," wailed Hattie, bursting into tears.

Suddenly, Lenny had an idea. "I know what to do," he coughed. Grabbing his sister and Puddles, he pulled them over the fence.

"I've just remembered what's in this garden," said Lenny, disappearing into the long grass.

When he came back, he was pulling a hose.

"Mummy!" cried Lenny. "Look what we've got."

Hattie peered through the smoke and gasped. Harvey grabbed the nozzle, as Bertie leapt over the fence and raced to turn on the tap.

With a mighty spurt, the water sploshed out, drenching the blazing boxes and soaking the smouldering bins. Everyone cheered! Some of the water splashed over the cats and dogs – but they didn't care. The fizzling, sizzling fire was out!

"You little ones deserve a treat for saving our alley!" barked Harvey. "Puppy snacks for you, Puddles, and kitty nibbles for the twins."

"Three cheers for Lenny, Lulu and Puddles!" cried Archie.

"Hip-hip-hooray!"

Polly Piglet's Surprise Party

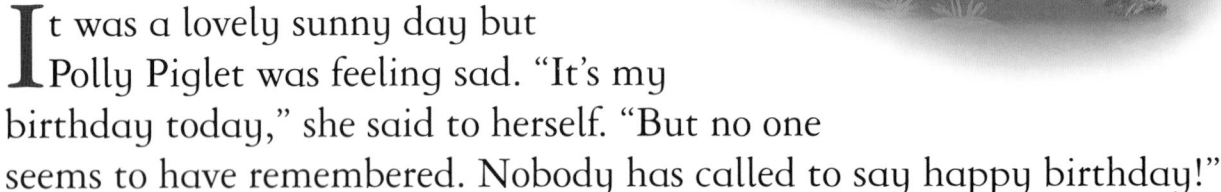

It was a lovely sunny day but Polly Piglet was feeling sad. "It's my birthday today," she said to herself. "But no one seems to have remembered. Nobody has called to say happy birthday!"

Polly decided to go for a walk. "Maybe my friends will remember if they see me," she told herself and went out into the farmyard.

"There's Holly Horse!" thought Polly. Holly was inside the stables looking very busy. But, as soon as she saw Polly, she stopped what she was doing and began whistling.

"Hello Polly, nice day for a walk!" said Holly.

"Yes it is," said Polly. She waited a minute to see if Holly was going to wish her happy birthday. But Holly just went on whistling.

Just then, five little chicks came rushing past. They looked as if they were on their way somewhere very important. "Hello Polly, we must rush, lots to do, have a nice walk!"

"Everyone's forgotten!" thought Polly crossly. "I was going to make a cake to share with my friends, but now I won't bother."

"There's Lolly Lamb," thought Polly. "She always remembers my birthday!" But, as soon as Lolly saw Polly, she ran off to the barn.

"What is going on?" wondered Polly. But then she saw that Lolly was beckoning Polly to follow her.

A tiny thought crept into Polly's mind, "Mmm, I wonder...?" And off she raced towards the barn, wagging her little curly tail. Dolly Cow was standing at the barn door.

"You've found us at last!" said Dolly smiling, and she stood back to let Polly step inside...

"Happy Birthday, Polly!" shouted Holly Horse, the five little chicks, Lolly Lamb, Dolly Cow and all of Polly's farmyard friends.

"Welcome to your surprise birthday party!"

The Dreamy Bunny

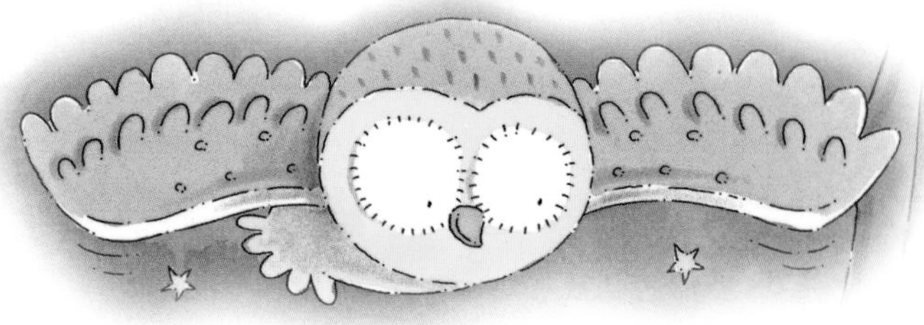

When bunnies should be fast asleep,
The dreamy bunny comes to peep.
He looks up at the moonlit sky
And sighs, "How I wish I could fly!
I'm tired of being a bouncy bunny,
To be an owl would be more funny."

"I'd soar up high, then swoop down low.
To far-off places I would go,
Then, hiding in a leafy tree,
I'd hoot all night and sound spooky!
But best of all," the bunny said,
"I wouldn't have to go to bed!"

Binks, Silly-Billy Bunny!

Binks the bunny was so funny.
She was in a tizzy.
She raced around and around the wo
Until she felt quite dizzy!

She couldn't find her pretty hat,
The one for the parade.
"I've put it somewhere safe!" she cried
"It's the best I've ever made!"

Her friend, Old Bertie, came to help.
He took one look and said,
"You silly-billy bunny, Binks,
Your hat is on your head!"

The Bunnies' Sunny Day

It was a beautiful, bright, sunny day,
So all the bunnies came out to play,
Hopping and skipping and
having great fun,
While Grandpa Bunny just snoozed
in the sun!

And when they all got too sticky and hot,
A dip in the stream cooled them
down quite a lot!
At tea time, into the field they hopped,
And feasted on carrots – they nearly popped!
When the sun went to bed,
They skipped home down the lane,
But tomorrow they'd come out and
do it again!

I Wonder...

How a worm finds its
way underground.
Is it by feeling,
Or is it by sound?

I wonder...
How a bee can find
a flower so well.
Is it the colours,
Or is it the smell?

I wonder...
How a bat can find
its way at night.
How does it manage
To always be right?

I wonder...
How a polar bear knows
where to go
When there's nothing around
But snow, and more snow?

Do you know?

Fierce Tiger

Tiger wasn't really a tiger. He was a fierce stray kitten. People called him Tiger because he hissed and arched his back whenever they came near. "You really should be nicer to people," said his friend Tibbles. "They're not so bad once you train them."

But Tiger didn't trust people. If they came too near, he would show his claws and even give them a scratch. That soon taught them not to mess with Tiger. Tiger looked after himself. He didn't need anyone. At night he wandered the streets, searching dustbins for scraps and stealing food put out for pets. During the day, he slept wherever he could – under a bush, on top of a garage, and sometimes under the cars in an old scrap yard.

One cold winter's night, Tiger was wandering the streets when it began to snow. He spotted an open window.

"Aha," thought Tiger. "I bet it's warm and dry in there." He jumped through the window and found himself in a dark porch.

"This will do," thought Tiger. Tiger curled into a ball and was soon fast asleep. He was so comfortable that he slept all through the night. When he finally awoke, there was no one around. But beside him were a bowl of food and a dish of water.

"Don't mind if I do," purred Tiger. He gobbled down the whole lot, then drank some water before leaving through the window again. That day was colder than any Tiger had ever known so, when night fell and he saw the window open once more, he didn't hesitate to sneak in. This time, Tiger could see that the door from the porch was slightly ajar. He pushed it open and found himself in a warm kitchen. So he settled down and had a wonderful night's sleep. When he awoke in the morning, he found a bowl of delicious fish and a dish of water beside him.

"Don't mind if I do," purred Tiger. And he wolfed down the fish and lapped up the water before leaving. That night it was still snowing. Tiger returned once more. This time, when he went to settle himself beside the fire, he found a cosy basket there.

"Don't mind if I do," purred Tiger. And he crawled in and went to sleep. Tiger had never slept so well. In the morning, Tiger was woken by a rattling sound. Someone was in the kitchen. Tiger opened his left eye just a crack. A little boy was placing a bowl beside the basket. Tiger opened his eyes and stared at the little boy. The little boy stared at Tiger. Tiger leapt to his feet and got ready to hiss and scratch.

"Good boy," whispered the little boy, gently.

Tiger looked at the bowl. It was full of milk. "Don't mind if I do," he purred, and he drank the lot.

After that, Tiger returned to the house every night. Before long, he never slept anywhere else. The little boy always gave him plenty to eat and drink. And, in return, Tiger let the little boy stroke him and hold him on his lap.

One morning, Tiger was playing with the little boy in the garden, when his old friend Tibbles strolled past.

"I thought you didn't like people," meowed Tibbles.

"Oh," smiled Tiger, "they seem to be okay once you train them."

Tiger was no longer a fierce stray kitten!

Mummy's Having a Baby

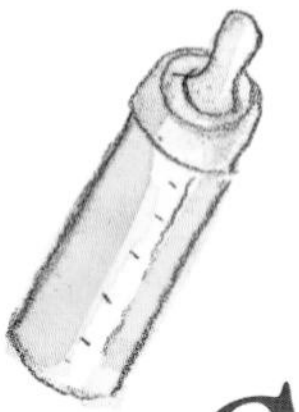

Josh was helping his mum to do the washing-up. "Guess what, Josh?" said Mum. "Soon, you're going to have a baby brother or sister to play with." She bent down and wiped some bubbles off his nose.

"Will the baby look like me?" asked Josh.

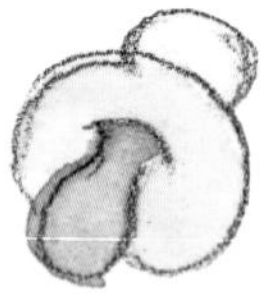

Mum laughed. "Oh, I hope so," she said. "Now, you'll have to help me. We've got *lots* to do before baby arrives."

The very next day, Josh and his mum went shopping. They chose some stripy baby-grows, a furry teddy bear and a brand new car seat – *all* for the baby! "What about *me*?" thought Josh.

Just then, Mum gave Josh a present. "Here you are," she said. "Thanks for helping me."

"Thanks, Mum!" cried Josh.

When they got home, Dad had brought Josh's old cot and buggy down from the attic. Josh lay in the buggy and ate his tea.

"But what about *me*?" he said, sadly. "That's *my* cot."

"You don't need this any more," laughed Dad. "You're a big boy now." Josh smiled.

As the weeks went by, Josh waited... and waited... and waited! Was this baby *ever* going to arrive? Then, one day, Mum said, "I'm going to the hospital, Josh. I think baby is coming today."

"But what about *me*?" asked Josh.

"Don't worry," said Mum. "Granny is here to look after you."

"I love Granny, but I don't want you to go," sniffed Josh. "I'll miss you."

"I'll miss you, too," said Mum and she hugged him tightly. "Don't worry. I'll be back soon."

Later that day, Dad came home from the hospital. "Josh!" he called. "You've got a beautiful baby sister. Come on, I'll take you to meet her. We've called her Molly." When they got to the hospital Dad took lots of photos – of baby Molly!

"What about *me*?" grumbled Josh, quietly. He was feeling left out.

Then, Dad said, "Let's have a picture of Josh and Molly together." He took the photo... then another... and another! Josh felt much better.

When Mum and Molly came home, lots of friends came to visit. They all wanted to see Josh's sister and they brought lots

of presents – for the baby! “What about *me*?” thought Josh.

“Look what Molly has bought for you,” said Mum. And there, in Molly’s cot, was a big parcel, tied up with a bow.

“Thanks for my train,” said Josh and he gave his sister a big kiss.

Little babies take a lot of looking after! Molly always seemed to be hungry and her nappy needed changing a lot! She liked being cuddled, too. “What about me?” thought Josh. “Will someone cuddle me, please!”

When Dad came home, he scooped Josh up and cuddled him. “I need a hug, too,” said Dad. “Who will give me one?”

“I will,” squealed Josh, laughing.

When they walked in the park, everyone wanted to look at baby Molly. No one seemed to notice Josh, except Mrs Jackson. “Molly looks just like you,” she said. Josh smiled, proudly. “I think her nose is like mine,” he said. Mum was getting tired.

“Looking after Molly is very hard work,” said Dad.

“What about *me*?” said Josh. “I can help Mum.” So, when Molly was upset, Josh pulled funny faces and made his sister laugh. When Molly wanted to play, Josh built brick towers and let her knock them down,

again… and again… and again! And when Molly dropped her rattle, Josh *always* picked it up for her.

At the supermarket, Mum let Josh push the buggy, which made him very happy. Everyone stopped to talk to him and his sister. "You really *are* Mummy's little helper, aren't you, Josh?" they said. And Josh was the only one who could get Molly off to sleep. He sang all his favourite songs to her. With Josh's help, Mum had more time to spare.

"Who wants a story and a nice, big cuddle?" she asked, sitting on the sofa.

"I do," laughed Josh. Mum started to read a story. Suddenly, Josh asked, "What about Molly? Can she hear the story, too?"

"Of course, she can," laughed Mum and went to fetch her. Then, Mum started to read again.

"What about *me*?" asked Dad, as he sat on the sofa. "Can I listen?"

"Of course, you can," laughed Josh. "Molly and I want *everyone* to join in."

Way Down Yonder in the Maple Swamp

Way down yonder in the maple swamp
  The wild geese gather and the ganders honk;
The mares kick up and the ponies prance;
  The old sow whistles and the little pigs dance.

Old Roger is Dead

Old Roger is dead and
  gone to his grave,
H'm ha! gone to his grave.

They planted an apple tree
  over his head,
H'm ha! over his head.

The apples were ripe
  and ready to fall,
H'm ha! ready to fall.

There came an old woman
  and picked them all up,
H'm ha! picked them all up.

Old Roger jumped up and
  gave her a knock,
H'm ha! gave her a knock.

Which made the old woman
  go hippity hop,
H'm ha! hippity hop!

Follow My Bangalorey Man

Follow my Bangalorey Man,
  Follow my Bangalorey Man;
I'll do all that ever I can
  To follow my Bangalorey Man.
We'll borrow a horse, and steal a gig,
  And round the world we'll do a jig,
And I'll do all that ever I can
  To follow my Bangalorey Man!

See-saw, Sacradown

See-saw, Sacradown,
  Which is the way to London Town?
One foot up and one foot down,
  That's the way to London Town.

Over the Hills and Far Away

When I was young and had no sense
I bought a fiddle for eighteenpence,
And the only tune that I could play
Was "Over the Hills and Far Away".

As I Was Going Along

As I was going along, long, long,
A singing a comical song, song, song,
The lane that I went was so long, long, long,
And the song that I sung was as long, long, long,
And so I went singing along.

A Sailor Went to Sea

A sailor went to sea, sea, sea,
To see what he could see, see, see,
But all that he could see, see, see,
Was the bottom of the deep blue sea, sea, sea.

From Wibbleton to Wobbleton

From Wibbleton to Wobbleton is fifteen miles,
From Wobbleton to Wibbleton is fifteen miles,
From Wibbleton to Wobbleton,
From Wobbleton to Wibbleton,
From Wibbleton to Wobbleton is fifteen miles.

King Neptune's Day Off

Trini the little mermaid was happy working in King Neptune's palace. It was beautiful, with fountains and a statue of King Neptune in the courtyard. Trini was happy working there. But some fierce sharks guarded the palace.

On his birthday King Neptune called Trini to see him.

"I'm taking the day off," he said. "I'd like you to organise a birthday banquet for me this evening. So, until then, you will be in charge." And off he went!

The sharks were delighted! They thought they would have some fun while King Neptune was away.

"I'm in charge, so you must do as I say," Trini told them sternly, after the king had left. The sharks just sniggered at her and didn't answer.

Trini set to work. She asked a team of fish to collect shrimps and special juicy seaweed. She told the crabs to collect smooth, pearly shells to use as plates. Then she sent her mermaid friends to collect pieces of coral to decorate the tables.

But the sharks were determined to spoil everything. Soon they saw the fish carrying a net of delicious food. "Give us that," they snapped, and gulped the food down. As soon as the crabs came back with their shell plates, the sharks took the shells and began throwing them to each other.

"Stop it at once!" cried Trini. But the sharks ignored her.

Then the sharks saw the mermaids watching close by. They started to chase them all around the courtyard. "Stop it!" cried Trini. But the sharks just laughed and carried on chasing the mermaids.

Then Trini had an idea. She would trick the sharks! While the sharks were having great fun chasing the mermaids, Trini squeezed through a crack in the hollow statue of King Neptune. The mermaids dropped all their pretty coral and swam away – the sharks couldn't stop laughing. They gathered around King Neptune's statue to plan some more mischief.

Suddenly, a voice like thunder boomed, "Behold, it is I, King Neptune, Emperor of all the Seas and Oceans." The sharks were very frightened. Then the voice bellowed, "Do as Trini commands or you will be banished from the kingdom!"

Then the voice from inside the statue told the sharks to pick up the plates and fetch more food and lay the tables for the banquet. And, while they were busy, Trini crept out from inside the hollow statue where she had been hiding!

So Trini's banquet was a great success. Everyone was there, even the sharks! But they had to stand guard outside the palace, while everyone inside enjoyed themselves. King Neptune had a marvellous time and asked Trini if she would always be his special helper.

"I'd be delighted," she answered, blushing!

Tiger Tales

Louis and Lisa Lion were just learning to pounce, and their dad had told them to practise as much as they could. So they were prowling through the jungle, looking for prey to pounce upon.

"There's something orange and blue and fluttery," whispered Lisa. "Here I go..." As Lisa pounced on the butterfly, Louis spotted something green and jumpy. He crept up and... POUNCED! As the two little cubs bounded through the jungle, Louis suddenly saw a flash of orange and black in some bushes.

"A stripey snake!" he whispered. "It's too good to pass up!" So, at just the right moment, he... POUNCED!

"Owwww!" came a voice from the bush. "What's got my tail?" The snake turned out to be attached to a stripey cub, just the same size as Louis and Lisa.

"Who are you?" they asked.

"I'm Timmy Tiger," said the little cub. "I've just moved here from The Other Side of the Jungle!"

"We're Louis and Lisa Lion," said Lisa. "Why don't we show you our side of the jungle?"

"Here's our river," said Louis proudly.

"It's nice," said Timmy, "but it's kind of small. Our river on The Other

Side of the Jungle is as wide as fifty tall palm trees laid end to end! And I can swim across that river – and back – without stopping once!"

"We can't even swim," said Lisa. "Will you show us how?"

"Err... maybe another time," said Timmy. "I'm just getting over the sniffles, and Mum said I shouldn't swim for a while."

A little farther along, Louis and Lisa saw Howard Hippo wallowing merrily in the mud.

"Meet our new friend, Timmy Tiger!" they called.

Howard opened his mouth in a big grin. "Nice to meet you!" he called.

"Er... same here," said Timmy, keeping his distance.

As the cubs scampered on, Timmy said, "On The Other Side of the Jungle, there's a hippo with a mouth as big as a cave. Three tigers can sit in it!"

As the cubs walked on, something from a branch above dropped down in front of them. Timmy jumped, but Louis and Lisa smiled. "Hi, Seymour! Meet our new friend, Timmy Tiger."

"Greetingssss," hissed Seymour Snake. "Niccce to make your aquaintancccccce!"

"Nice to meet you, too," said Timmy, a little uncertainly. "Well, ssso long," said Seymour, as he slithered off. "Sssssee you ssssoon I suppose!"

As Seymour slithered off, Timmy said, "On The Other Side of the Jungle, there are snakes as thick as tree trunks. Once, one of them swallowed me!"

"Oh, no!" cried Louis and Lisa.

"Yes," Timmy said, "but my dad hit the snake on the head and made him spit me out! My dad's really, really strong, and he's twice as big as an elephant, and he can carry six gorillas on his back! And my mum can stand on her front paws and juggle coconuts with her hind legs, and… "

"…and what?" asked two smiling, normal-sized tigers on the path in front of them.

"…and, here they are," said Timmy, sheepishly. "Mum and Dad, meet my friends, Louis and Lisa."

"Happy to meet you," said Mr and Mrs Tiger.

"As you can see," Mrs Tiger added, "we are very ordinary and normal tigers."

"But what about all those amazing things Timmy told us?" asked Louis. "What about The Other Side of the Jungle?"

"It's just like this side," said Mr Tiger.

"So the river isn't as wide as fifty palm trees?" asked Lisa.

"And there's no hippo with a mouth as big as a cave, or a snake who swallowed Timmy?" asked Louis.

"No, indeed!" laughed Mrs Tiger. Timmy looked embarrassed. "Well, they were good stories," he said.

"Yes," said Mrs Tiger, "but they were just stories." She turned to Louis and Lisa. "Timmy had no friends to play with in our old home, he spent his time imagining amazing adventures."

"But now that he's got friends like you two to play with," said Mr Tiger, "perhaps he'll have some real adventures!"

"And there are more friends to meet, Timmy," Lisa said, "like Mickey and Maxine Monkey, and Chico Chimp!"

"You know, there are monkeys and chimps on The Other Side of the Jungle, too," said Timmy.

"Really?" said Lisa, glancing at her brother.

"Yes," said Timmy, "but I didn't know them. I can't wait to meet Mickey, Maxine and Chico!"

"Well, what are we waiting for?" said Louis, and they all raced off, ready for fun and excitement on This Side of the Jungle.

Cheeky Chick

Cheeky Chick was a playful little chick. He was always playing tricks on his brothers and sisters. He would hide in the long grass, then jump out on them in surprise, shouting, "Boo!" One day they decided to get their own back. "Let's play hide and seek," they said.

They left Cheeky Chick to count to ten, while they all went to hide. Cheeky Chick hunted high and low for his brothers and sisters. He looked in all his favourite hiding places but they were nowhere to be found.

"Come out," he called. "I give up!" But no one came.

So Cheeky Chick carried on looking. He searched carefully all through the farmyard, through the vegetable patch and in all the empty flower pots. He searched along the hedgerow at the edge of the field. He even looked in the haystack, which took a very long time, but there was

no sign of his brothers and sisters to be found amongst the hay.

By now it was getting dark, and Cheeky Chick was feeling scared and lonely. "It's no use," he said to himself. "I'll have to go home."

He hurried to the henhouse and opened the door. "Surprise!" came a loud chorus. His brothers and sisters had been hiding there all along! It was a long time before Cheeky Chick played tricks on them again.

Night Sounds

Midnight's bell goes ting, ting, ting, ting, ting,
  Then dogs do howl, and not a bird does sing
But the nightingale, and she cries twit, twit, twit;
  Owls then on every bough do sit;
Ravens croak on chimneys' tops;
  The cricket in the chamber hops;
The nibbling mouse is not asleep,
  But he goes peep, peep,
    peep, peep, peep;
And the cats cry mew,
  mew, mew,
And still the cats cry mew,
  mew, mew.

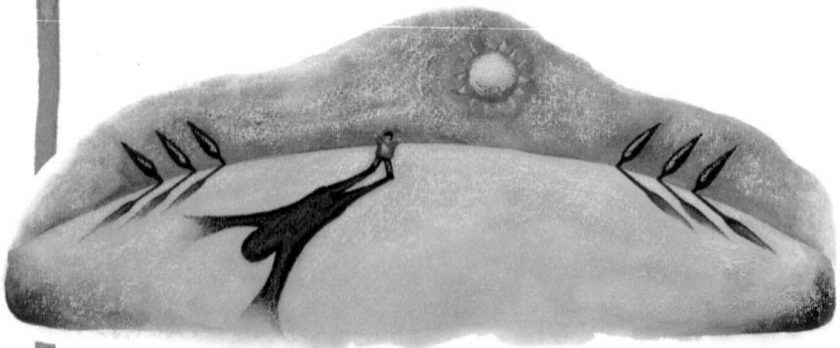

In Dreams

Beyond, beyond the mountain line,
  The grey-stone and the boulder,
Beyond the growth of dark green pine,
  That crowns its western shoulder,
There lies that fairy land of mine,
  Unseen of a beholder.
Ah me! they say if I could stand
  Upon those mountain ledges,
I should but see on either hand
  Plain fields and dusty hedges:
And yet I know my fairy land
  Lies somewhere o'er their hedges.

My Shadow

I have a little shadow that goes in and out with me,
  And what can be the use of him is more than I can see.
He is very, very like me from the heels up to the head;
  And I see him jump before me, when I jump into my bed.

One morning, very early, before the sun was up,
  I rose and found the shining dew on every buttercup;
But my lazy little shadow, like an arrant sleepyhead,
  Had stayed at home behind me and was fast asleep in bed.

Spellbound

The night is darkening round me,
The wild winds coldly blow;
But a tyrant spell has bound me
And I cannot, cannot go.

The giant trees are bending
Their bare boughs weighed
with snow.
And the storm is fast descending,
And yet I cannot go.

Clouds beyond clouds above me,
Wastes beyond wastes below;
But nothing drear can
move me;
I will not, cannot go.

From a Railway Carriage

Faster than fairies, faster than witches,
Bridges and houses, hedges and ditches;
And charging along like troops in a battle,
All through the meadows the horses and cattle:
All of the sights of the hill and the plain
Fly as thick as driving rain;
And ever again, in the wink of an eye,
Painted stations whistle by.
Here is a child who clambers and scrambles,
All by himself and gathering brambles;
Here is a tramp who stands and gazes;
And there is the green for stringing the daisies!
Here is a cart run away in the road
Lumping along with man and load;
And here is a mill, and there is a river:
Each a glimpse and gone for ever!

The Wind

Who has seen the wind?
Neither I nor you;
But when the leaves
hang trembling
The wind is
passing through.

Who has seen the wind?
Neither you nor I;
But when the trees bow
down their heads
The wind is passing by.

Maria's Haircut

One spring day, Maria the sheep stood by the pond in Old MacDonald's farmyard, gazing sadly into the water.

"What is she doing?" whispered Doris the duck to her friend Dora. "You don't often see sheep near water."

Meanwhile, ducklings were swimming across to see who the visitor was.

"Sheep don't eat ducklings, do they?" asked Dora, anxiously. She was not a clever duck!

"Of course not!" replied Doris. "They are quite safe with Maria."

But, just then, Maria gave such a big sigh that she blew the ducklings right across the pond and they had to be rescued by their mothers!

Old George the horse couldn't bear to see another animal on the farm feeling unhappy. He clip-clopped across the yard and rubbed his big head against Maria's woolly back. "What's the trouble, my dear?" he asked. "Has your lamb run away again?"

"No," sighed Maria. "It isn't that. Just look at me!"

Old George looked carefully at Maria. "Well, you look even more, er, wonderfully woolly than usual," he said, gallantly.

"I look a fright," said Maria. "My coat should have been trimmed weeks ago, but Old MacDonald seems to have forgotten."

"Hmmmm. He can be a little forgetful," said Old George. "I'll speak to the other animals and see what they suggest."

The animals were most interested in Maria's problem. "Perhaps I could nibble her coat," said Percy the pig, who would eat almost anything! A general chorus of disapproval greeted this idea.

"No, we must remind Old MacDonald to give Maria a haircut," said Poppy the cow.

"Old MacDonald is always so busy," added Henrietta the hen. "I don't know how we can make him notice Maria's problem!"

And that gave Poppy a very good idea. "No," she mooed, "it's Mrs MacDonald that notices things. Perhaps you should do some nibbling after all, Percy."

So, Percy did a little nibbling, then the hens scurried away with the tufts of wool in their beaks, and determined looks on their faces, searching for the farmer.

When Old MacDonald went into the farmhouse for his lunch that day, Mrs MacDonald threw up her hands in horror!

"MacD!" she cried. "You're covered in wool! Don't bring all those fluffy bits into my clean kitchen! It's obviously time those sheep were shorn."

The very next day, Maria's haircut was the talk of the farmyard. And she and her friends strutted happily around, looking as smart and as stylish as any sheep you've ever seen.

Troublesome Sister

In the higgledy-piggledy, messy alley it was tidy-up time! Harvey and the gang had worked hard all morning, scribbling and scrabbling in the heaps of junk trying to clean up their home.

At last, the skip was full of rubbish and they could have a break. All the gang settled down for a snooze, except for Puddles, Harvey's little sister.

"Where's my teddy?" she wondered. "And where's my ish?" Puddles' 'ish' was a blanket she'd had since she was a baby. It was full of holes and rather smelly, but she loved it lots.

She looked round the alley. "Teddy! Ish!" she called. "Where are you?" She didn't see them peeping out from the top of the skip.

Puddles was always getting into lots of mischief and today she scampered off down the alley, sure that she would find her teddy and ish down there somewhere. Spotting a hole in the fence, she peeped through and saw an old box of toys. "Are teddy and ish in there?" she wondered.

She squeezed and squashed herself through the gap and crept up to the toybox.

"Teddy! Ish! Are you in there?" she called. But they weren't. She did find an old toy mouse, hidden away at the back. "Doesn't anyone love you?" she asked. "You're very soft and cuddly – I'll love you! Come on, Mousey," she giggled. "You come home with me." Puddles was feeling much happier.

But Lulu the kitten wasn't. The mouse was her favourite toy and as Puddles trotted off she began to wail.

"Mummy! Mummy! Come quickly!" she cried.

Hattie, Lulu's mum, appeared through a gap in the fence. "What a terrible noise you're making," she purred. "What is the matter?"

Lulu sobbed and sniffed. "Mummy! Puddles has taken my Mousey!" cried the kitten.

"There, there," purred Hattie, trying to stop the sobs. "Don't you worry, Lulu, we'll soon get Mousey back."

But Lulu just screamed even louder.

Puddles didn't hear poor Lulu crying. She was dancing around the garden with her new friend. "We are having fun, aren't we, Mousey!" she laughed as she skipped along. "Now all I need is an ish."

As she skipped through the garden next door, Puddles saw a tatty, old scarf hanging down from the branch of an apple tree.

"Oh look, Mousey!" she cried. "A cuddly ish with no one to love it."

"Well, it's not really an ish," she thought, "but it is very, very soft." She reached up and took one end in her mouth. With a pull and a tug, the scarf floated down. Puddles picked it up and cuddled it. Now she was really happy. She didn't see Lenny, Lulu's brother, fast asleep in the flowerbed nearby.

Lenny woke up with a start and suddenly saw Puddles skipping off along the garden with his favourite scarf – the one he had hung in the tree to use as a swing! He couldn't believe his eyes and began to cry. "Mummy! Mummy!" he wailed, loudly.

Hattie and Lulu squeezed through the hedge.

"That naughty Puddles has stolen my scarf," sobbed Lenny.

Hattie sighed. Oh dear, now both her twins were crying. Something would have to be done about that pup!

Just then, Puddles popped through the hedge and ran straight into the angry Alley Cats.

"Oh no!" gulped Puddles. "Someone's in trouble, and I think it's *me*!"

Lulu and Lenny were hiding behind Hattie who looked very cross. Puddles was suddenly scared and she began to cry. "H-H-Harvey!" she croaked. "Help me!"

Puddles' wailing woke up Harvey and the gang.

"Is that Puddles I can hear?" said Ruffles. "Yes! Run, Harvey, *run*! Puddles needs your help!"

"Hang on, Puddles," woofed Harvey. "I'm coming!" And off he ran, as fast as he could go...

Harvey burst through the hedge. "Okay, guys!" he gasped. "What's all the fuss about?"

The angry Alley Cats began shouting all at once.

Puddles hid behind her big brother and shivered and shook. Whatever had she done?

There was so much noise that Harvey couldn't hear a word that anyone was saying.

"QUIET!" he barked. And they were – even the kittens!

"Thank you," said Harvey. "Now then, Hattie, tell me, what is all the noise about?"

"That scallywag sister of yours has stolen my twins' favourite toys," grumbled Hattie.

"Did you, Puddles?" asked Harvey, sternly.

"I didn't mean to, Harvey," she cried. "I thought that no one wanted them."

She gave back little Mousey and the tattered and torn scarf. "Sorry, Lulu," she whimpered. "Sorry, Lenny. I only wanted to love them."

"That's okay, Puddles," smiled the twins. "But you see, we love them – lots and lots."

Hattie looked at Puddles and shook her head, she really was an annoying puppy. Harvey gave a huge sigh – panic over!

"Puddles, you're such a scamp," smiled Harvey.

"But I was only looking for my teddy and my ish,"cried Puddles.

"I don't know where they are."

"Oh, is that what this is all about?" said Harvey.

He scooped them from the skip and gave them back to Puddles with a hug and a kiss. "Now, no more trouble today," he said. "Let's all have a dog-nap."

Puddles hugged her teddy and stroked her ish; she was happy again. "Well," said Puddles, looking at Harvey with a naughty grin, "Ish and I will be good, but Teddy might not!"

The Princess who Never Smiled

A long time ago, in a far off land, a princess was born. The king and queen called her Princess Columbine. They thought she was the most precious child ever to be born. And, to make sure that she was watched over every minute of every day, they hired a nurse to look after her.

One day the queen came to the nursery and found the nurse asleep and the little princess crying. The queen was very cross and called for the king who told off the nurse for not watching the baby.

But what the king and queen didn't know was that the nurse was really a wicked enchantress, and she cast a spell over the baby princess:

"Princess Columbine will not smile again until she learns my real name!"

The king and queen were devastated. From that day on, the princess never smiled! Names were collected from all over the land. They tried all the usual names such as Jane, Catherine, Amanda. They tried more unusual names such as Araminta, Tallulah, Leanora. They even tried quite outlandish names such as Dorominty, Truditta, Charlottamina. But none broke the spell.

Princess Columbine grew up to be a sweet and beautiful girl. Everybody loved her. But her face was always so sad, it made the king and queen unhappy. They tried everything to make her smile. They bought her a puppy. They even hired a court jester who told the silliest jokes you've ever heard.

"Why did the pecans cross the road?" asked the jolly jester. The princess shrugged.

"Because they were nuts!" the jester guffawed.

"Why did the ice cream?" the jester tried again. The princess just gazed politely.

"Because the jelly wobbled!"

One day an artist called Rudolpho came to the palace and asked the king if he could paint the princess's portrait. The king agreed on condition that he painted the princess smiling. Rudolpho set up his easel beneath a large mirror and began painting. The princess sat opposite watching him paint in the mirror behind him. He had soon painted the princess's portrait, all except for her smile.

Rudolpho tried some funny drawings to make the princess smile. He drew silly pictures of the king and queen while the princess looked on politely. Then he drew a picture of her old nurse and gave her a moustache, and underneath he wrote NURSE.

Princess Columbine gazed at the picture in the mirror. There, underneath the picture, was the word NURSE spelled out back to front. "ESRUN," Princess Columbine said quietly. And then she smiled.

"Her name is ESRUN!" laughed Princess Columbine. At last the spell was broken! When the king and queen heard her laughter they rushed to see what was happening. Everyone was so happy that soon they were all laughing too – but Princess Columbine laughed the loudest.

Dance, Thumbkin, Dance

Dance, dance, thumbkin, dance.
Dance ye merrymen everyone.
Thumbkin he can dance alone,
He can dance alone.

Dance, dance, foreman, dance.
Dance ye merrymen everyone.
Foreman he can dance alone,
He can dance alone.

Dance, dance, longman, dance.
Dance ye merrymen everyone.
Longman he can dance alone,
He can dance alone.

A Face Game

Here sits the Lord Mayor; (Forehead)
Here sit his two men; (Eyes)
Here sits the cock; (Right cheek)
Here sits the hen; (Left cheek)
Here sit the little chickens; (Tip of nose
Here they run in, (Mouth)
Chinchopper, chinchopper,
Chinchopper, chin! (Chuck the chin)

Clap Hands

Clap hands for Daddy coming
Down the wagon way,
With a pocketful of money
And a cartload of hay.

Wash, Hands, Wash

Wash, hands, wash,
Daddy's gone to plough;
If you want your hands wash'd,
Have them wash'd now.

Here's the Lady's Knives and Forks

Here's the lady's knives and forks.
  Here's the lady's table.
Here's the lady's looking glass.
  And here's the baby's cradle.
Rock! Rock! Rock! Rock!

My Hands

My hands upon my head I place,
  On my shoulders, on my face;
On my hips I place them so,
  Then bend down to touch my toe.

Now I raise them up so high,
  Make my fingers fairly fly,
Now I clap them, one, two, three.
  Then I fold them silently.

Ten Little Fingers

I have ten little fingers,
  And they all belong to me.
I can make them do things,
  Would you like to see?

I can shut them up tight,
  Or open them all wide.
Put them all together,
  Or make them all hide.

I can make them jump high;
  I can make them jump low.
I can fold them quietly,
  And hold them all just so.

Row, Row, Row Your Boat

Row, row, row your boat,
  Gently down the stream,
Merrily, merrily, merrily, merrily,
  Life is but a dream.

Lizzie and the Tractor

Little Yellow the tractor came to a halt next to Lizzie the cow. The farmer leaned out of the tractor cab.

"Come on Lizzie, get up!" said the farmer. "We have the big farm show in one week. How are you going to win the Best Cow prize if you laze around all day getting plump? You're so lazy!"

"I like lying here!" said Lizzie the cow. "I have all the grass I need right here next to me. I don't even have to get up!"

"Wouldn't you like to be pride of the show, Lizzie!" wailed the farmer.

"No!" said Lizzie, as she munched on her mouthful and thought about it.

The farmer did not know what to do. All his animals won prizes except Lizzie. Perhaps they would know how to make Lizzie fit and lovely again.

He drove Little Yellow around the farm to ask their advice. Gorgeous the pig said, "She is too dull! Paint her pink with brown spots… it always works for me."

Reckless the goat said, "She eats too much grass. Get her to eat newspapers… it always works for me!"

Flash the cockerel said, "Her tail is too small. Stick lots of big bright feathers on her bottom… it always works for me!" Then Little Yellow said, "I can make Lizzie into the Best Cow again."

The animals snorted with laughter. How could a tractor do anything they could not? But the farmer just said, "Please do everything you can, Little Yellow!"

So Little Yellow bustled around in his barn, humming to himself and trying on all the bits and pieces that a tractor can make use of. First he put on his big bulldozer bucket and went over to Lizzie.

"Please Lizzie, move into the small field."

"Shan't!" said Lizzie, rolling on to her back.

So Little Yellow scooped her up and took her into the field in the bucket. "It's for your own good," said Little Yellow.

Then Little Yellow put on his plough and, to everyone's amazement, ploughed up the grass in the middle of the field.

Next day, Little Yellow ploughed another strip in the middle of the field, and the day after that too. The ploughed bit was getting bigger and the grassy bit was getting smaller.

Lizzie cried, "There's not enough grass left to eat! I'm getting thinner!"

Then Little Yellow put on his grass cutter. He mowed all the grass that was left. If Lizzie lay down again she would not get enough to eat. She was smaller now, and the exercise was making her coat glossy.

But the tractor was not finished. He put on his back forks and took Lizzie a bale of hay to eat but, as she rushed to eat it, he drove away, and she had to trot behind to keep up. By the end of the day she was very tired, but fit and healthy too.

By this time, Little Yellow had used nearly every tool he had! The last thing he used was a power spray to wash her down, and… Ta-ra!… there stood Lizzie, more beautiful than ever before!

Lizzie went to the show, and of course was declared Best Cow. The farmer was given a silver cup to put on his sideboard. And all thanks to Little Yellow the tractor!

The Greedy Hamster

There was once a hamster named Harry. He was a very greedy hamster. As soon as his food was put in his cage he gobbled it all up, and then he would push his little nose through the bars in the hope that something else to eat might come within reach. From his cage he could see all manner of delicious food on the kitchen table – and the smells! The scent of freshly baked bread was enough to send him spinning round in his exercise wheel with frustration.

"It's not fair!" he grumbled to himself. "They're all eating themselves silly out there and here am I simply starving to death!" (At this point he would usually remember the large meal he had just eaten and that his tummy was indeed still rather full.)

"If only I could get out of this beastly cage, I could feast on all the food I deserve," he announced to himself, and the thought of all those tasty morsels made his mouth water.

One night after the family had gone to bed, Harry was having one last spin in his wheel before retiring to his sawdust mattress. As he spun around, he heard an unfamiliar squeaky noise.

"That's funny," thought Harry. "The little girl oiled my wheel only today.

It surely can't need oiling again." He stopped running and got off the wheel, but the squeak continued. Harry sat quite still on his haunches and listened intently. Then he realised it was the door to his cage squeaking. The door! The door was flapping open. The little girl had not closed it properly before she went to bed. Harry did a little dance of glee. Then he went to the door and looked cautiously out in case there was any danger. But all seemed to be well. The cat was asleep on a chair. The dog was sleeping soundly on the floor.

Now, as well as being a greedy hamster, Harry was clever. Once outside the cage, the first thing he did was look at the catch to see how it worked. Yes! He was pretty sure he could work out how to open it from the inside now. Harry sniffed the air. There were some tasty titbits left over from a birthday party on the table. He could smell the sugar icing, and soon he was on the table, cramming his mouth with odds and ends of cheese sandwiches and pieces of chocolate cake. When he had eaten his fill, he stuffed his cheek pouches with ginger biscuits and ran back into his cage, closing the door behind him.

"Good!" thought Harry. "Now I will never be hungry again."

The next night Harry let himself out of his cage and helped himself to food, and again the next night and the night after that.

He feasted on everything and anything – nuts, bananas, pieces of bread, left-over jelly and slices of pizza were all pushed into his greedy mouth. Each time he returned to his cage he filled his cheeks with more and more food. He did not notice that he was getting fatter and fatter, although he was aware that he could no longer run round in his wheel without falling off! Then, one night, he undid the door catch but found he was simply too wide to get through the door!

For a while Harry sat in a very bad temper in the corner of the cage. His cheeks were still bulging with food from his last midnight feast, but the greedy hamster wanted more. Then he had an idea. "I'll get that lazy cat to help," he thought. He squealed at the top of his voice until the cat, who had been dreaming of rats, woke up with a start.

"What do you want?" she hissed at Harry. Harry explained his problem.

"Of course, I'd be only too pleased to help," said the crafty cat, thinking to herself here was an extra dinner! With her strong claws she bent back the door frame of the cage, until there was just enough room for Harry to squeeze through. Then, with a mighty swipe of her paw, she caught him and gobbled him whole. She felt extremely full, what with Harry and all his food inside her. She could barely crawl back to her chair and soon she was fast asleep again and snoring loudly with her mouth open. Inside her tummy Harry, too, felt very uncomfortable. Every time the cat snored, it sounded like a thunderstorm raging around his head.

"I must get out of here," he thought, and headed for the cat's open jaws. But he was far too fat to get out again. Then he had another idea. Through the cat's jaws he could see the dog lying on the floor.

"Help! Help!" he squeaked. The dog woke up to a very strange sight. There was the cat lying on the chair snoring, but she also seemed to be squeaking, "Help!" The dog put his head on one side. He was very perplexed. Then he saw a pair of beady eyes and some fine whiskers inside the cat's mouth. It was Harry!

"Get me out of here, please," pleaded Harry.

Now the dog did not very much like the cat, so he was quite willing to help the hamster.

"I'll stick my tail in the cat's mouth. Then you hang on while I pull you out," said the dog. "But mind you don't make a sound and wake the cat, or she'll surely bite my tail!" The dog gingerly put the tip of his tail inside the cat's open jaws, just far enough for Harry's little paws to grab hold. Then he pulled with all his might. Out popped Harry and out of Harry popped all the food he'd stored in his cheeks – peanuts, an apple core and a slice of jam tart!

"Thank you, thank you," gasped Harry as he made a dash for his cage and slammed the door shut. "I think I'll stay in my cage from now on and just eat all the food that I'm given!"

Round and Round the Garden

Round and round the garden,
Like a teddy bear.
One step, two steps,
Tickly under there!

Round and round the haystac
Went the little mouse.
One step, two steps,
In this little house.

Teddy Bear, Teddy Bear

Teddy bear, teddy bear,
Turn around.
Teddy bear, teddy bear,
Touch the ground.
Teddy bear, teddy bear,
Show your shoe.
Teddy bear, teddy bear,
That will do.
Teddy bear, teddy bear,
Go upstairs.
Teddy bear, teddy bear,
Say your prayers.
Teddy bear, teddy bear,
Turn out the light.
Teddy bear, teddy bear,
Say good night.

The Wheels on the Bus

The wheels on the bus go round and round,
Round and round, round and round,
The wheels on the bus go round and round,
All day long.

The wipers on the bus go swish, swish, swish,
Swish, swish, swish, swish, swish, swish,
The wipers on the bus go swish, swish, swish,
All day long.

The horn on the bus goes beep! beep! beep!
Beep! beep! beep! beep! beep! beep!
The horn on the bus goes beep! beep! beep!
All day long.

The people on the bus go chat, chat, chat,
Chat, chat, chat, chat, chat, chat,
The people on the bus go chat, chat, chat,
All day long.

The children on the bus bump up and down,
Up and down, up and down,
The children on the bus bump up and down,
All day long.

Hey, Diddle, Diddle

Hey, diddle, diddle, the cat and the fiddle,
  The cow jumped over the moon;
The little dog laughed to see such sport,
  And the dish ran away with the spoon!

Dingle Dangle Scarecrow

When all the cows were sleeping
  And the sun had gone to bed,
Up jumped the scarecrow
  And this is what he said:

I'm a dingle dangle scarecrow
  With a flippy floppy hat!
I can shake my arms like this,
  I can shake my legs like that!

When the cows were in the meadow
  And the pigeons in the loft,
Up jumped the scarecrow
  And whispered very soft:
Chorus

When all the hens were roosting
  And the moon behind a cloud,
Up jumped the scarecrow
  And shouted very loud:
Chorus

If You're Happy and You Know It

If you're happy and you know it,
  Clap your hands.
If you're happy and you know it,
  Clap your hands.
If you're happy and you know it,
  And you really want to show it,
If you're happy and you know it,
  Clap your hands.

If you're happy and you know it,
  Nod your head, etc.

If you're happy and you know it,
  Stamp your feet, etc.

If you're happy and you know it,
  Say "ha, ha!", etc.

If you're happy and you know it,
  Do all four!

Ducks for a Day

One hot, sunny day, Becky and Bobby Chick waddled out of the farmyard, in search of some fun. They wandered down to the stream, where they saw Duck swimming by. "Be careful by the water, chicks," she quacked, cheerily.

"We will, Duck," said Becky, as she watched the big duck swim gracefully past. "Oh, I wish we could swim, Bobby. It must be nice to be a duck."

Mummy had said that they mustn't play by the stream but, when the little chicks spotted a large leaf bobbing gently up and down in the reeds, they just had to hop on for a game. "Let's pretend we're ducks!" laughed Bobby.

The two little chicks played happily on the leaf all morning. "Quack, quack! I wish we could paddle far away like real ducks!" laughed Bobby, jumping up and down. Suddenly, the leaf broke free of the reeds and started to float downstream!

"On, no!" cried Bobby, looking very worried. "How are we going to get off?"

"We'll have to swim!" sobbed Becky.

"But we can't!" said Bobby. "We're not real ducks! Help! Help!" The leaf-boat floated

gently downstream, past the meadow where all the animals from Buttercup Farm were grazing.

"Don't worry, Becky, the farm animals will save us!" cheeped Bobby, waving his wing, trying to get the animals' attention. "Help!"

"Oh look everyone!" mooed Cow. "The little chicks are waving to us!" All the animals laughed and waved their tails back – everyone except Duck. She could see the chicks' frightened faces, as well as the waterfall up ahead! The chicks were in danger. "They're not waving!" she cried. "They're floating away!"

Duck leapt into the water and began paddling after the chicks, as fast as she could! When she reached the leaf she tried to pull it to the bank but the current was too strong and they were getting closer and closer to the waterfall.

Then, Duck had an idea. "Quick," she quacked to the two chicks. "Hop on to my back!" Becky and Bobby leapt on to Duck's back, then Duck swam back upstream to safety.

When they reached the farm, they jumped off Duck's back and thanked her for saving them. Mummy Hen was waiting, anxiously. "We're so sorry, Mummy!" cried Becky, rushing over to her. "We'll never disobey you again!"

"It was nice being a duck for a while!" sniffed Bobby. "But being a chick is better!"

"And much safer!" clucked Mummy Hen, giving them both a big hug.

The Mean King and the Crafty Lad

There was once a king who was as mean as he was rich. He lived in a great palace where he spent his days counting his bags of gold coins. Meanwhile his subjects lived in great poverty. Sometimes the king would summon his page to prepare the royal carriage. Then the king would set forth in his great, golden coach to survey his kingdom.

Now not only was the king extremely rich, but he was very vain. As he passed his subjects working in the field, he liked them to bow to him and pay him compliments. "How handsome you look today, Your Majesty!" they would call, or "How well the colour pink suits you, Sire!"

His head would swell with pride as he moved on. "My people truly adore me!" he would say.

But, for all their complimentary words, the people hated their king. They resented the fact that the king lived in splendour while his subjects toiled hard all their lives. At last a secret meeting was called among the peasants. "Let's sign a petition demanding our rights!" cried one man.

"And fair pay!" shouted another. They all cheered and clapped their hands.

"Who's going to write down our demands?" called an old woman. Now the crowd was hushed, for none of them knew how to read or write.

"I know what we can do instead," called a voice from the back. Everyone turned round to see a young lad in rags. "Let's march on the palace!" he cried.

"Yes!" roared the crowd.

As the angry mob reached the palace, the king saw them and sent out his guard dogs. The peasants were forced to flee for their lives with the dogs snapping at their ankles. Not until the last peasant was out of sight did the king call off his dogs.

"Good work!" he cried. From then on, however, life became even harder for the people because the king was on his guard in case they marched on the castle again. Now, when he went out and about in his kingdom, he was always accompanied by his hounds.

Eventually, another secret meeting was called. "What can we do?" the people said. "We will never be able to get past those savage dogs."

"I've got an idea," came a familiar voice. It was the ragged lad again. For a while there was uproar as folk accused him of having nearly lost them their lives. "Please trust me," pleaded the lad. "I know I let you down, but this time I've got a well thought-out plan to get the king to give up his money." In the end, the peasants listened to the boy's scheme and they decided to let him try.

The next day, the boy hid in a branch of a tree that overhung the palace garden. With him he had some dog biscuits, in which he had hidden a powerful sleeping pill. He threw the biscuits on to the palace lawn and waited. Some time later, as the boy had hoped, the king's hounds came out on to the lawn. They headed straight for the biscuits and gobbled them up. Soon they were fast asleep, one and all.

Quickly the lad slid out of the tree and, donning a large black cape, he ran round to the front of the palace and rapped on the door. A sentry opened the door. "Good day," said the lad, "I am Victor, the world-famous vet. Do you have any animals requiring medical attention?"

"No," replied the sentry, slamming the door in the lad's face. Just then voices could be heard from within the palace and the sentry opened the door again saying, "Actually, we do have a problem. Step inside."

The sentry led the lad out to the lawn where the king was weeping over the dogs' bodies. "Oh, please help," he cried. "I need my dogs. Without them I may be besieged by my own people."

The lad pretended to examine the dogs. He said to the king, "I have seen one case like this. The only cure is to feed the animals liquid gold."

"Liquid gold?" exclaimed the king. "Where shall I find it?"

"Fear not," said the lad, "I have a friend – a witch – who lives in the mountains. She can turn gold coins into liquid gold. If you let me take all the dogs to her she will cure them. But you will have to give me a bag of gold to take to her."

Well, the king was so worried that he readily agreed. The sleeping dogs were loaded on to a horse-drawn cart, and the king gave the lad a bag of gold saying, "Hurry back, my dogs are most precious."

The lad went home. His parents helped him unload the dogs, who by now were beginning to wake up. They took great care of the dogs and the next day the lad put on the cloak again and returned to the palace.

"The good news is," he said to the king, "that the cure is working. The bad news is that there was only enough gold to revive one dog. I'll need all the gold you've got to cure the others."

"Take it all," screamed the king, "only I must have my dogs back tomorrow!" He opened the safe and threw his entire stock of gold on to another cart, which the young lad dragged away.

That night the lad gave each of the king's subjects a bag of gold. The next morning he led the dogs back to the palace. To his surprise, the king didn't want them back. "Now I have no gold," he said, "I don't need guard dogs."

Then the lad saw that the king had learned his lesson, and he told the king what had really happened. And, to everyone's joy, the king said the peasants could keep their bags of gold. As for the king, he kept the dogs as pets and became a much nicer person.

I Love Thee, Betty

I love thee, Betty,
Do'st thou, Johnny?
Hey, but I wonder where!
In my heart, Betty.
In thy heart, Johnny?
Thou never made it appear.

But I'll wed thee, Betty.
Wed me, Johnny?
Hey, but I wonder when!
On Sunday, Betty.
On Sunday, Johnny?
Hey, I wish it was Sunday then.

The Girl in the Lane

The girl in the lane,
That couldn't speak plain,
Cried, "Gobble, gobble, gobble."
The man on the hill,
That couldn't stand still,
Went hobble, hobble, hobble.

A Squabble

Moll-in-the-wad and I fell out,
What do you think it was all about?
I gave her a shilling, she swore it was bad,
It's an old soldier's button, says Moll-in-the-Wad.

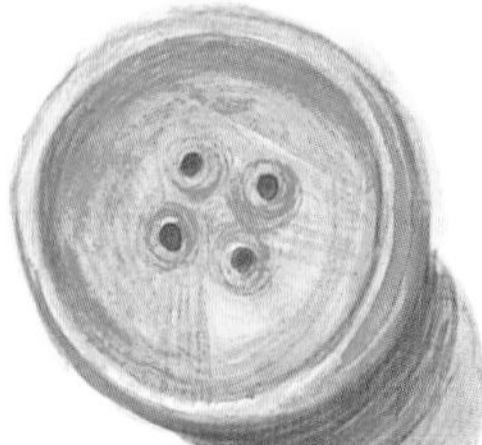

This Pig

This pig got in the barn,
This ate all the corn,
This said he wasn't well,
This said he'd go and tell,
And this said – weke, weke, weke,
I can't get over the bran door sill

Gift for the Queen

Pretty maid, pretty maid,
Where have you been?
Gathering roses
To give to the Queen.
Pretty maid, pretty maid,
What gave she you?
She gave me a diamond,
As big as my shoe.

One-ery, You-ery

One-ery, you-ery, ekery, Ann,
Phillisy, follysy, Nicholas, John,
Quee-bee, quaw-bee, Irish Mary,
Stinkle-em, stankle-em, buck.

The Squirrel

The winds they did blow,
The leaves they did wag;
Along came a beggar boy,
And put me in his bag.

He took me to London,
A lady me did buy,
Put me in a silver cage,
And hung me up on high.

With apples by the fire,
And nuts for me to crack,
Besides a little feather bed
To rest my little back.

My Small Cow

One, two, three, four,
My small cow's legs are feeling poor,
Let's pull her by the tail,
That'll cure what ails.

Praise

Praised is he who siteth on an anthill,
For he shall surely rise.

A Gentleman

If you are a gentleman,
As I suppose you be,
You'll neither laugh nor smile
At the tickling of your knee.

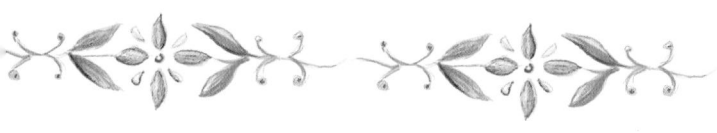

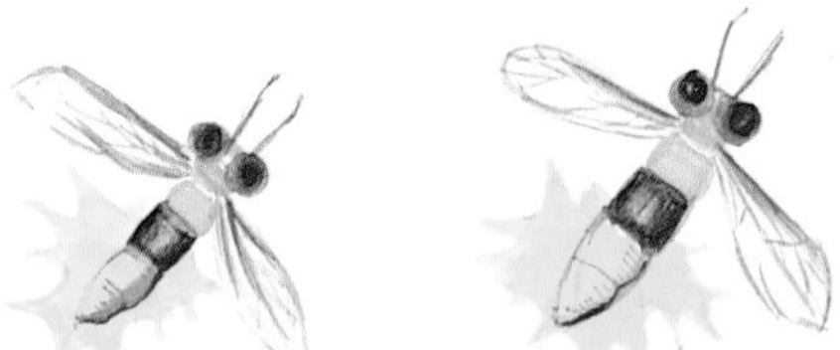

Firefly, Firefly

Firefly, firefly, yellow and bright
Bridle the filly under your light,
The son of the king is ready to ride,
Firefly, firefly, fly by my side.

To Sleep Easy

To sleep easy at night.
Let your supper be light,
Or else you'll complain
Of a stomach pain.

A Scary Adventure

It was a sunny morning at Faraway Farm. Danny and Rosie were sitting on the grass. "I'm bored," yawned Danny. "There's nothing to do. I want to have an adventure."

"I want to have one too," exclaimed Rosie. Then added, "But not too scary."

"It has to be a bit scary to be exciting," insisted Danny. He whistled to Conker. "Here boy!" he called. "We're off to the woods."

"Can I come too?" asked Rosie.

"No," replied Danny. "Adventures are just for big people and dogs."

On their way to the woods, Danny and Conker stopped to say hello to Archie who was happily munching grass in his field. "Come on, Conker," said Danny. "Let's make a den. It will be our secret place where we can watch out for enemies." Danny and Conker hid in the den and kept watch. "Ssssh!" whispered Danny. "Someone's coming." They sprang out. Conker barked and Danny shouted "Gotcha!"

"It's only me, silly," said Rosie. "I want to have an adventure too." Danny thought for a moment.

"All right," he agreed. "If you bring some food and drink, you can come in the den." Danny and Conker settled down to wait while Rosie ran back to the farm to see what she could get from Mum.

"It's a bit quiet, Conker," whispered Danny nervously. "Quite scary, really." Suddenly, Conker sat up. The hair on Danny's neck stood on

end. Rustle! Rustle! A twig snapped and then the roof of the den began to shake. "What's that noise?" whispered Danny. Conker began to bark. "Let's get out of here, Conker!" yelled Danny. They raced out of the den as fast as they could and bumped straight into Rosie.

"What's the matter? Where are you going?" asked Rosie, picking herself up.

"There's a monster attacking the den!" gasped Danny. "It's enormous! It climbed on the roof and..."

Rosie started to giggle. "What's so funny?" demanded Danny.

"It's only Archie," Rosie laughed, pointing. "He's eaten a great big hole in the roof." Danny looked around and began to laugh as well. "Aah, Archie," Rosie sighed, "did you want to join in our adventure too?"

"Come on, Rosie," said Danny. "Let's fix the den. But this time we'll leave a little window at the back so that Archie doesn't have to eat the roof to join in!"

I Wish...

I wonder what you would be if you weren't you. I like to sit and think of all the things I would like to be...

Sometimes I wish I was an elephant because it would make me laugh to sit in the bath and use my nose as a hose to rinse off all my bubbles.

Or I wish I was a chameleon because then I could change the colour of my skin to hide anywhere, and no one would be able to see me!

If I was a hippo I would be able to mess about all day and get as dirty as I liked, and no one would tell me off.

Or if I could be a dolphin I would be able to leap and splash about in the water having fun all day, and swim with the fish.

I suppose I could be an ostrich, but I am not sure that if I was frightened I would really want to hide my head in the sand!

I think that I will stay as me – but I won't stop wondering about being something else!

A Whale of a Time

Have you heard the story of Wendy Bligh? She was a remarkable whale who loved to fly!

One day Wendy was sleeping peacefully, bobbing along in the sea, when a hot-air balloonist flew by her. He looked down from his balloon basket and spotted her hump.

“I think I will land on that rock,” he said to himself. He tied up his balloon, and all the time Wendy carried on sleeping completely unaware of the balloonist.

But then a tornado whirled over the sea and blew the balloon and Wendy upwards as high as can be.

“What a wonderful feeling” cried Wendy in glee. “I am floating above the sparkling blue sea.”

The hot-air balloonist took her for a spin, then dropped her back in the sea at the end of the day.

“Oh thank you!” smiled Wendy and swam away.

Rumpelstiltskin

Once upon a time there was a boastful miller. One day, he told the king that his daughter was so clever that she could spin gold out of straw.

"I must meet this remarkable girl," said the king. "Bring her to the palace at once."

The king took the miller's daughter to a room filled with straw. In one corner stood a spinning wheel. "You must spin all this straw into gold before morning," the king told the girl, "or you will be put to death." Then he went out and locked the door behind him.

The poor girl sat at the spinning wheel and wept. However could she make gold from straw? Suddenly, the door flew open, and in leapt a funny-looking little man.

"Why are you crying?" he asked.

When the girl told him what the king had said, the strange man replied, "What will you give me

if I spin this straw into gold for you?"

"My pearl necklace," said the girl.

So the little man sat down at the spinning wheel and quickly spun all the straw into gold. Then he magically vanished from the room.

The next morning, the king was amazed at all the gold – but now he wanted even more. He took the girl to a bigger room, and had it filled with straw. Once again, he told her to spin the straw into gold by morning, or she would die. Then he left.

The poor girl sat down and wept. Suddenly, the odd little man appeared. "What will you give me if I help you this time?" he asked.

"My pretty ring," the girl replied.

So the little man began to spin, and soon all the straw had been turned into gold. Then he vanished.

The next morning the greedy king was astounded but still not satisfied. He took the girl to an even bigger room, piled to the ceiling with straw. "If you succeed this time, you will become queen," the king said. "If you

fail, you know what will happen."

As soon as the girl was alone, the little man appeared. "I have nothing left to give you," said the girl.

"Then promise me your first-born child when you become queen," said the man.

"I might never become queen and I may never have a child," the girl thought, and so she promised.

So the strange little man sat down at the spinning wheel and began to work. He spun for many hours and the pile of gold grew higher and higher.

"At last," said the little man, "my task is done." Then he vanished. The girl gazed around the room. It was stacked from floor to ceiling with glistening gold that shone like the sun.

At dawn, the king was overjoyed. He kept his promise and soon married the miller's daughter.

The whole kingdom rejoiced, and the king and his new queen were very happy together.

A year later, the king and queen had a baby. By this time, the queen had forgotten all about her promise – but the funny little man had not. One night, he appeared in the queen's bedchamber. "I have come for your baby!" he announced gleefully.

"No!" cried the queen. "I will give you jewels, gold, anything you wish! But please do not take my baby." She wept so miserably that the little man took pity on her.

"Very well," he said. "If you can guess my name within three nights you may keep your baby. If not, the child is mine!" Then he disappeared.

The queen sent messengers out to gather names from every town and village in the kingdom. They returned with thousands of suggestions. Over the next two evenings, when the little man arrived, the queen questioned him again and again:

"Is your name Tom?"

"No," replied the strange little man.

"Jack? Dick? Peter?" she asked. The strange man shook his head. "Could it be Brutus or Clarence, then?"

Each time, the reply was the same: "No, Your Majesty."

By the third day, only one messenger had not returned. Late that afternoon, he was on his way back to the palace when he saw a hut in a forest clearing. In front of it, an odd little man was dancing around a fire, singing:

"I'll be the winner of this game!
The queen will never guess my name!
She will lose, and I will win,
Because my name is...
Rumpelstiltskin!"

The messenger galloped back to the palace and told the queen what he had seen and heard. She was so grateful that she rewarded the messenger with a huge sack of gold.

That night, the queen eagerly waited in her throne room for the little man. When he appeared, the queen asked, "Is your name Guzzletum?"

"No, it's not!" laughed the little man.

"Is it Bumblebottom? Jigglejoggle? Tickletooth or Wigglewoggle?"

"No! No!" he cackled. "Your time's running out, Your Majesty!"

The queen smiled. "Could it be… Rumpelstiltskin?"

The little man could not believe his ears and flew into a rage. "Who told you? Who told you?" he shrieked. "How did you find out?"

He cried and squealed and beat the floor with his fists.

"You've won! You've won!" he wailed, and disappeared in a shower of sparks.

The little man never came back to worry the queen again, and they all lived happily ever after.

Bunny Tails

Bunnies come in all different colours and sizes. Some have long ears and some have floppy ears. But all bunnies have fluffy tails. All except Alfie, that is. He had no tail at all and his friends teased him badly.

"Never mind, dear," said his mummy. "I love you, tail or no tail."

But Alfie did mind and at night he cried himself to sleep. Then one night he dreamt he met a fairy and told her all about his problem.

"A little fairy magic will soon fix that!" said the fairy. She took some dandelion clocks and sewed them together to make a lovely fluffy tail. "Turn around!" she said and fixed it in place in a flash.

Alfie woke with a start.

"If only my dream could come true," he thought sadly and looked down at his back. And there, to his astonishment, was a fine fluffy white tail!

"I'm a real bunny at last!" he said proudly, running off to show his new tail to his friends.

Cross Patch

Cross patch,
  Draw the latch,
Sit by the fire and spin;
  Take a cup,
And drink it up,
  Then call your neighbours in.

A Thorn

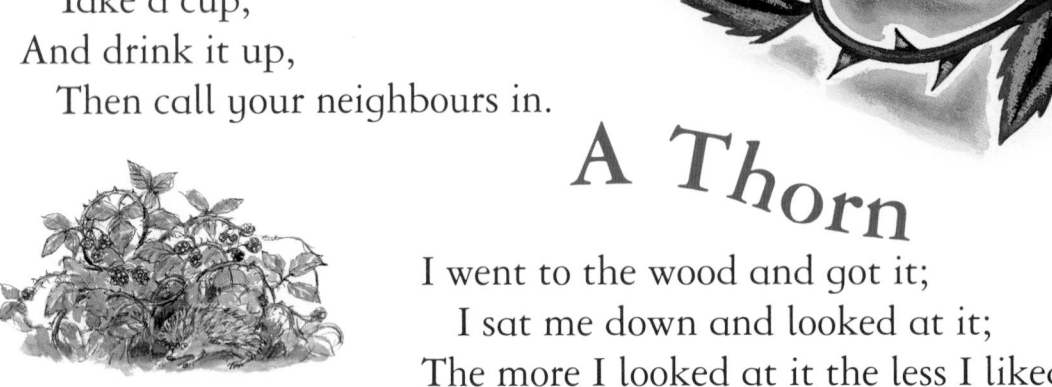

I went to the wood and got it;
  I sat me down and looked at it;
The more I looked at it the less I liked it;
  And I brought it home because I couldn't help it.

I Met a Man

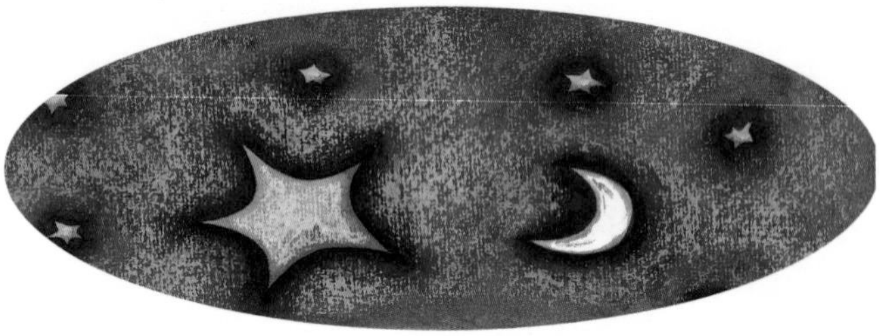

As I was going up the stair
  I met a man who wasn't there.
He wasn't there again today –
  Oh! how I wish he'd go away!

A Star

I have a little sister, they call her Peep, Peep
  She wades the waters deep, deep, deep;
She climbs the mountains high, high, high;
  Poor little creature she has but one eye.

Teeth

Thirty white horses upon a red hill,
  Now they tramp, now they champ,
Now they all stand still.

My Mother and Your Mother

My mother and your mother
Went over the way;
Said my mother to your mother,
It's chop-a-nose day!

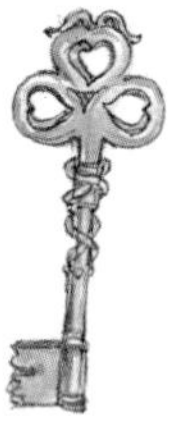

I Went Up One Pair of Stairs

I went up one pair of stairs.
Just like me.
I went up two pair of stairs.
Just like me.
I went into a room.
Just like me.
I looked out of a window.
Just like me.
And there I saw a monkey.
Just like me.

I Am a Gold Lock

I am a gold lock.
I am a gold key.
I am a silver lock.
I am a silver key.
I am a brass lock.
I am a brass key.
I am a lead lock.
I am a lead key.
I am a monk lock.
I am a monk key!

Forever Friends

Daisy Duckling had lots of friends but her best friend of all was Cilla Cygnet. Every day they played together, chasing each other through the reeds. "When I grow up, I'll be a beautiful swan like my mummy!" said Cilla.

"And I'll be a dull little brown duck," said Daisy. She worried that Cilla would only want to play with her pretty swan friends when she grew up.

Then one day, they were playing hide and seek when something dreadful happened. While Daisy hid amongst some large dock leaves, a sly fox crept up and snatched her in his mouth!

Before she had time to quack he was heading for his lair. But Cilla had been watching. Without hesitating she rushed after the fox and caught the tip of his long tail in her sharp beak.

As the fox spun round, she pecked him hard on the nose. His mouth dropped open and Daisy fell out. Now he was really mad and rushed at them. But Mrs Duck and Mrs Swan flew at him hissing furiously, and off he ran. Daisy couldn't thank them enough.

"That's what friends are for!" said Cilla. And Mrs Swan and Mrs Duck, who were the best of friends, could not agree more.

Bottoms Up!

The time had come for Doris the duck to teach her ducklings to dive.

"It's easy, little ducklings," she quacked. "You bob your heads under the water and put your bottoms in the air. Just remember that – heads down, bottoms up!"

The ducklings nodded excitedly and had a go. Quite a few managed it first time.

"Oooh!" squeaked one. "There are lots of interesting things down there!"

"Exactly!" cried Doris. "And that is why you must all learn to dive. Only we ducks know what goes on under the water."

All afternoon, the ducklings practised. Heads down! Bottoms up! One by one, they got the hang of it.

"Oh, Mummy, look! There are tiny fishes flashing about under here!" squealed one.

"And there's an old bucket, too!" called out another.

"I've found a squiggly thing," quacked a third, "and it tastes lovely!"

By teatime, all the ducklings could dive except for one.

"What's the matter, Dylan?" asked Doris.

"I'm afraid I might not come up again," whispered the little duckling.

"But, Dylan," quacked Doris, "to pop right up again, all you have to do is put your head up and your bottom down!"

Even so, Dylan still didn't want to try. Doris was as encouraging as she could be, but, when the sun began to set, even she was becoming a little bit impatient.

"All ducks dive, Dylan," she said. "You just have to do it. Go on! One, two, three, DIVE!"

But still Dylan hesitated. "I'm going to be one of those ducks who doesn't dive," he said. "I can't see the point. I'm not sure I want to stick my head under the water, it's cold down there. And I might not be able to put my head up again when my tail is up in the air. And I don't want to catch lots of squiggly wiggly things, even if they do taste nice, they might tickle my beak!"

Doris didn't say a word. Then she had an idea...

"Supper time!" called Doris. All the little ducklings bobbed their heads up.

"We're not hungry!" they called. "We've been eating fishes and squiggly things and delicious duckweed all day."

"I haven't," said Dylan. "I'm really hungry."

So Doris dived down and found him a nice fish.

"Here you are, Dylan," she quacked as she bobbed up. "Oops!"

As Doris spoke, the fish dropped from her beak and disappeared into the water.

"My supper!" cried Dylan. Down went his head! Up went his bottom! And he dived quickly down and caught his dinner.

"I did it!" he cried, bobbing up again.

"Well done!" laughed Doris, happily. "But please don't talk with your mouth full, dear!"

Johnny Morgan

Little Johnny Morgan,
Gentleman of Wales,
Came riding on a nanny-goat,
Selling of pigs' tails.

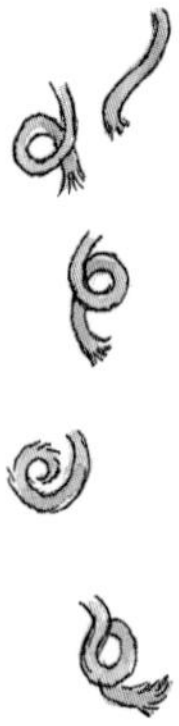

Banbury Fair

As I was going to Banbury,
Upon a summer's day,
My dame had butter, eggs and fruit,
And I had corn and hay.
Joe drove the ox, and Tom the swine,
Dick took the foal and mare;
I sold them all – then home to dine,
From famous Banbury fair.

Pettitoes

The pettitoes are little feet,
And the little feet not big;
Great feet belong to the grunting hog,
And the pettitoes to the little pig.

Churning

Come, butter, come,
Come, butter, come;
Peter stands at the gate
Waiting for a butter cake.
Come, butter, come.

Buttons

Buttons, a farthing a pair,
Come, who will buy them of me?
They are round and sound and pretty
And fit for the girls of the city.
Come, who will buy them of me?
Buttons, a farthing a pair.

Little Moppet

I had a little moppet,
I kept it in my pocket
And fed it corn and hay;
There came a proud beggar
And said he would wed her,
And stole my little moppet away.

Shoe a Little Hors

Shoe a little horse,
Shoe a little mare,
But let the little colt
Go bare, bare, bare.

Four Wrens

There were two wrens upon a tree,
  Whistle and I'll come to thee;
Another came, and there were three,
  Whistle and I'll come to thee;
Another came and there were four,
  You needn't whistle any more,
For being frightened, off they flew,
  And there are none to show to you.

Jeremiah, Blow the Fire

Jeremiah, blow the fire,
  Puff, puff, puff!
First you blow it gently,
  Then you blow it rough.

Washington Square

From here to there
  To Washington Square;
When I get there
  I'll pull your hair.

Father Short

Father Short came down the lane;
  Oh! I'm obliged to hammer and smile
From four in the morning till eight at night,
  For a bad master, and a worse dame.

Trit Trot

Trit trot to market
  to buy a penny doll;
Trit trot back again,
  the market's sold them all.

Little General Monk

Little General Monk
  Sat upon a trunk,
Eating a crust of bread;
  There fell a hot coal
And burnt in his clothes a hole,
  Now little general Monk is dead.

So Here We Go

So here we go around, around,
  And here we go around;
Here we go around, around,
  Till our skirts shall touch the ground.

Fancy Flying

Penelope Parrot and her mum, Portia, were having a wonderful afternoon, watching the Fancy Flying Display Team. Penelope could hardly believe her eyes as she saw the birds swoop and speed through the sky, doing their amazing tricks and wonderful stunts.

That night, Penelope dreamt about doing magnificent stunts with the other birds and, in the morning, she decided she would try to make her dream come true!

"I'm going to practise flying, Mum," she said. "I want to be the best!" Before Portia could say a word, Penelope had zoomed off.

"The first thing I have to do is learn to fly really fast," Penelope told herself. So she flapped her wings as hard as she could, to get up some speed. But Penelope had only just learned to fly – so she didn't know how fast or how far she could go. Soon she was huffing and puffing and panting, and her wings were flopping instead of flapping! "Oh, nooooo!" she cried, as she felt herself falling down… down… down… until… SPLASH! She landed right beside Howard Hippo, who had been enjoying his morning wallow. "Gracious, Penelope," said Howard, trying to shake the water out of his eyes and ears. "You must be more careful!"

"Sorry, Howard," said Penelope. "I didn't plan that. I was just seeing how fast I could fly and my wings got tired. I want to be a Fancy Flyer!"

"Then you'll need expert help," said Howard.

"But I don't know any experts," said Penelope.

"But I do," came a voice from the bank. It was her mum, Portia. "I've been trying to find you to tell you some special news," said her mum. "My uncle Percy has just arrived for a visit. He was a member of the original Fancy Flying team! He can give you the training you need."

Uncle Percy was delighted to hear that Penelope wanted to be a Fancy Flyer. "I'll teach you lots of stunts first," he said, "and then we'll work on one that will be your very own. Every Fancy Flyer has a speciality!"

Uncle Percy and Penelope went right out to start her training programme.

"We'll begin with the Twisting Take Off," Uncle Percy said. "Watch me and do as I do."

"Now, straighten up and fly forward!" Percy called. But Penelope couldn't stop spinning and spinning!

"Whoa!" she shouted. "I'm getting dizzy, Uncle Percy!"

Luckily, Penelope grabbed a branch and managed to stop spinning.

Jeremy Giraffe, who was nibbling leaves nearby, helped Penelope up as Uncle Percy flew back.

"Never mind," said Uncle Percy. "You'll soon get the hang of it."

Just then, Penelope's friends, Mickey, Maxine and Chico, came swinging by.

"Want to play Mango-Catch with us?" they called.

"Great!" said Penelope, flying over to join them.

"Wait!" said Uncle Percy. "A Fancy Flyer in training can't waste her energy on games!"

"Sorry, Uncle Percy," said Penelope. "I guess I'll see you all later," she said, a little sadly.

"In fact," said Uncle Percy, "I think it's time you were in your roost."

"But Uncle Percy," Penelope said, dismayed, "it's so early!"

"A Fancy Flyer needs her sleep, my dear!" said Uncle Percy. "Those wing muscles need lots of rest to prepare for all the work they must do."

"Better do what Uncle Percy says," said Portia, as she helped Penelope settle on to her bedtime branch. "He's the expert!"

The next morning, Uncle Percy woke Penelope up very early. "Time for your pre-dawn practice!" he squawked.

"But Uncle Percy, it's so early!" Penelope yawned. "The sun's not even up yet!"

"That's the best time to train!" said Uncle Percy. "Follow me!"

"We'll start with some speed exercises," Uncle Percy said. "This was my speciality when I was a Fancy Flyer. Just move in and out through the trees – like this!"

Penelope watched her uncle weave gracefully through the jungle. It looked easy, but when she tried...

THUH-WHACK! "Ouch!"cried Penelope.

Uncle Percy came rushing back to look at Penelope's head. "Nothing serious," he said. "A Fancy Flyer in training has to expect a few bumps and bruises! Best thing to do is keep going. Let's try it again."

All day, Uncle Percy tried to teach Penelope stunts. And all day, Penelope bashed... and crashed... and smashed... and splashed... into trees and other animals!

It was a very tired and worn-out Penelope who headed for home with Uncle Percy that afternoon.

"Well, Penelope," said Portia, when the two arrived back, "are you ready to be a Fancy Flyer?"

"Oh, yes," said Penelope. "And I know exactly what my speciality will be!"

"What?" asked Portia and Uncle Percy together.

"Watching from the audience!" laughed Penelope.

Ebby, the Smallest Pup

Ebby was the smallest puppy in the litter. His brothers and sisters were all bigger than he was. He wouldn't have minded, but they were always teasing him.

"Out the way, titch!" they laughed, as they pushed him to the side at meal times.

"Last one's a baby," they barked, as they rushed out to play. And, of course, Ebby lost every time.

"You're small because you were the last to be born," explained his mum. "And that's why you're so special." But Ebby didn't feel very special. In fact, he just felt sad.

One day, a family came to see the puppies. "Look smart," said their mother. "They've come to take one of you home."

Of course, all the puppies wanted to be chosen but only one could go – and it wasn't Ebby.

After that, lots of people came to the house. Each of them left with a puppy of their own, but nobody chose Ebby. Eventually, Ebby was the only puppy left.

"Nobody wants me," sniffed Ebby. "I'm not as good as other dogs."

"Don't be silly," said his mum. "You're just special, you'll see."

The next day, a little girl came to the house. "Oh, goody! They saved him for me," she laughed.

Ebby looked around to see who she was talking about. But, of course, nobody else was there.

Suddenly, Ebby was lifted into the air and whirled around. "You are the cutest puppy in the whole wide world!" smiled the little girl.

Ebby felt a bit giddy but he smiled back anyway. It seemed that somebody did want him, after all.

"I wonder where we're going," thought Ebby, as he waved goodbye to his mum. But he soon found out because his new home was just next door!

When Ebby was old enough, Helen and her daddy took him for a walk in the woods, and he was very pleased when his mum came too. There were other dogs walking in the woods and Ebby felt shy. He hid behind his mum. He didn't want everyone to see how small he was.

Suddenly, something small and soft hurtled into him. "Hiya, titch!" barked a familiar voice. It was his biggest brother, but he seemed to have shrunk. He was only as high as Ebby's shoulder.

"He hasn't shrunk," laughed his mum, when Ebby whispered in her ear. "You've grown, silly. It's all that food Helen gives you."

After that, Ebby and his brother had great fun playing together. They had even more fun when they were joined by two of their sisters.

Their mum watched proudly as they raced around the trees. And she couldn't help smiling when Ebby turned around and barked, "Last one's a baby!"

Diddle, Diddle, Dumpling

Diddle, diddle, dumpling, my son John
 Went to bed with his trousers on;
One shoe off, the other shoe on,
 Diddle, diddle, dumpling, my son John.

With my Hands on Myself

With my hands on myself, what have we here?
 This is my brainbox, nothing to fear.
Brainbox and wibbly wobbly woos,
 That's what they taught me when I went to school.

With my hands on myself, what have we here?
 These are my eye-peepers, nothing to fear.
Eye-peepers, brainbox and wibbly wobbly woos,
 That's what they taught me when I went to school.

With my hands on myself, what have we here?
 This is my nose-wiper, nothing to fear.
Nose-wiper, eye-peepers, brainbox and wibbly wobbly woos,
 That's what they taught me when I went to school.

With my hands on myself, what have we here?
 This is my chest-protector, nothing to fear.
Chest-protector, nose-wiper, eye-peepers, brainbox
 and wibbly wobbly woos,
That's what they taught me when I went to school.

Go to Bed, Tom

Go to bed, Tom,
 Go to bed, Tom,
Tired or not, Tom,
 Go to bed, Tom.

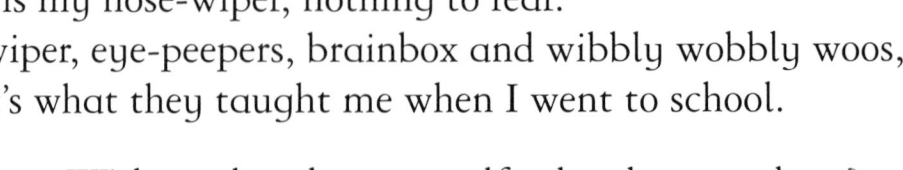

The Man in the Moon

The man in the moon,
Came tumbling down,
And asked his way to Norwich.
He went by the south,
And burnt his mouth
With supping cold pease-porridge.

Come to Bed, says Sleepy-head

Come let's to bed,
Says Sleepy-head;
"Tarry a while," says Slow;
"Put on the pot,"
Says Greedy-gut,
"Let's sup before we go."

Peter Works with One Hammer

Peter works with one hammer, one hammer, one hammer,
Peter works with one hammer, this fine day.

Peter works with two hammers, two hammers, two hammers,
Peter works with two hammers, this fine day.

Peter's very tired now, tired now, tired now,
Peter's very tired now, this fine day.

Peter's going to sleep now, sleep now, sleep now,
Peter's going to sleep now, this fine day.

Peter's waking up now, up now, up now,
Peter's waking up now, this fine day.

You're Not My Best Friend

Gabriella Goat, Chicken Charlotte, Sam the Sheepdog, Penfold Pig, Sally the Sheep and Jersey Cow all lived on Willow Farm. In the late afternoon when all the farm work had been done, they liked to meet in the paddock next to the farmyard to talk.

Gabriella was a very self-important goat, because she thought she was more useful on the farm than all the other animals. Not only did she provide milk for the farmer's wife to make cheese, but she also nibbled all the nettles and weeds and kept the farmyard neat and tidy. As far as she was concerned, that was much more important that just laying eggs or looking after sheep, or helping the farmer look for truffles, growing wool, or making milk.

Each morning, when Chicken Charlotte had finished laying eggs and all the other animals were still hard at work, she would flutter over the picket fence that kept the foxes away and strut over to visit Gabriella.

One very hot day when the sun was shining down on the garden, Gabriella decided she and Chicken Charlotte should go down to the duck pond and soak their feet in the clear, cool water. Chicken Charlotte didn't like this idea at all! "I'm afraid I might fall in and drown," said Chicken Charlotte. "I can't swim."

"You can't swim?" gasped Gabriella Goat. "How can you be any fun if you can't swim?" And she turned her back on Chicken Charlotte. Gabriella thought about who liked swimming, then she smiled. "Sam the Sheepdog can swim," she said. "Sam will be my very best friend."

Sam the Sheepdog had just finished chasing Sally the Sheep into the field when Gabriella Goat called out to him, "How about taking a break now and coming to the duck pond with me?"

"Why not?" Sam asked when he'd got his breath back. "It's a boiling hot day and I could do with a nice long swim to help me cool down."

Gabriella and Sam had tremendous fun all day splashing around in the water, and at the end of the day Gabriella said to Sam, "You're my very best friend. Let's do this again tomorrow!"

Sam agreed. He was delighted that Gabriella liked him the best of all the animals.

The next day, Gabriella went to fetch Sam so that they could play. Sam was in the field chasing Sally but, when Gabriella beckoned for him to come and play, Sam shook his head. "It's too early," said Sam. "I've got to make sure Sally grazes all this field, and the pond is all muddy now. The farmer won't like it if I get too dirty."

"What?" squealed Gabriella Goat in disbelief. "Whoever heard of a dog that didn't like mud?" And with that she turned her back on Sam the Sheepdog. Gabriella thought for a while about who else might like mud, and then smiled triumphantly. "Penfold Pig likes getting muddy," she said. "Penfold Pig will be my very best friend."

Penfold Pig was snuffling around in the hot yard when Gabriella Goat found him. "Come and roll in the mud with me," said Gabriella.

They had such fun that Penfold wanted to do this again the following day, but Gabriella said that she'd had enough of basking now, and tomorrow she wanted to lie in the field and chew juicy grass. Penfold Pig was distraught. He didn't like chewing grass – he liked pig-swill. Sadly, he told Gabriella Goat that he'd not be able to join her.

"You'll never make a good best friend if you can't eat grass," huffed Gabriella. And with that she turned her back on Penfold Pig. She thought about who else liked eating grass, and then smiled triumphantly. "Jersey Cow likes eating grass," thought Gabriella Goat. "Jersey Cow will be my very best friend."

The following morning, Gabriella went to find Jersey Cow, who was just about to be milked by the farmer's wife. She told Jersey Cow her plans for the day. Jersey Cow said that she would be honoured to have Gabriella to talk to as they chomped and lazed the day away. "I'll be with you in just a tick," said Jersey Cow. "I need to be milked first."

Gabriella Goat stared at Jersey Cow, and then turned and walked away! "What's wrong with all these silly animals?" she asked herself. "Why do they have to do something else first, or can't even do something at all?" And with that she decided to go alone to the juicy green field.

When Gabriella got to the field, she spied Sally the Sheep grazing away. Sally the Sheep was very pleased to be chosen as Gabriella's friend, and they spent the next hour talking and munching away. Before very long, Jersey Cow came to join them.

"Friendship is all about giving and taking," remarked Gabriella to Sally the Sheep (so that Jersey Cow could overhear), "and being a very best friend means giving a lot." But, when Jersey Cow moved off to chew some grass a little further away, Sally the Sheep followed her. Gabriella Goat snorted in disgust, and then chewed some more. "Who needs friends anyway?" she thought. "They're no good to anyone."

Gabriella Goat started to feel bored. She wanted to play a game. All the animals were together in the paddock. But, when Gabriella got close, all the animals turned their backs.

Just then she heard Jersey Cow remark to Sally the Sheep, "You know, friendship is all about giving and taking. If a friend of mine wouldn't give as well as take, she'd be no friend of mine."

Gabriella was very upset. She skulked off to the farmyard and was utterly miserable. The more she thought, the more miserable she became. The more miserable she became, the more she realised what a terrible friend she had been. The next day when she saw all her former friends, she sobbed, "I'm so sorry, won't you all forgive me?"

Chicken Charlotte flew to her side and gave her a big hug, and then all the other animals joined in. Nobody had liked seeing her so sad, and they all wanted to be friends again. "I've been so silly," said Gabriella, "but now I realise that you are ALL my very best friends."

Maud and the Monster

Maud was a very cheerful but quite mischievous little girl. She also thought she was very brave. All the things which frightened other children were her favourites – slimy eggs, spider's legs, and even the fuzzy bits from Grandpa's razor.

One day, as Maud walked past the cellar door, she noticed that the light was on. Maud thought of all the fun she could have down there exploring and playing games. Without a second thought, she dashed down the stairs. But, as Maud reached the bottom step, she heard the cellar door bang shut – which turned the light off! It was completely dark, and Maud began to feel rather frightened.

Then Maud noticed a strange humming sound. She crept forwards, feeling along the wall, and peered slowly into the darkness. Round the corner she saw a bright, white monstrous shape! Maud screamed!

The cellar door burst open and the light came on. Maud's mum came rushing down the stairs, looking very worried.

"Help, Mum! There's a monster!" cried Maud – but then, as they both looked at where she was pointing, Maud realised it was the freezer!

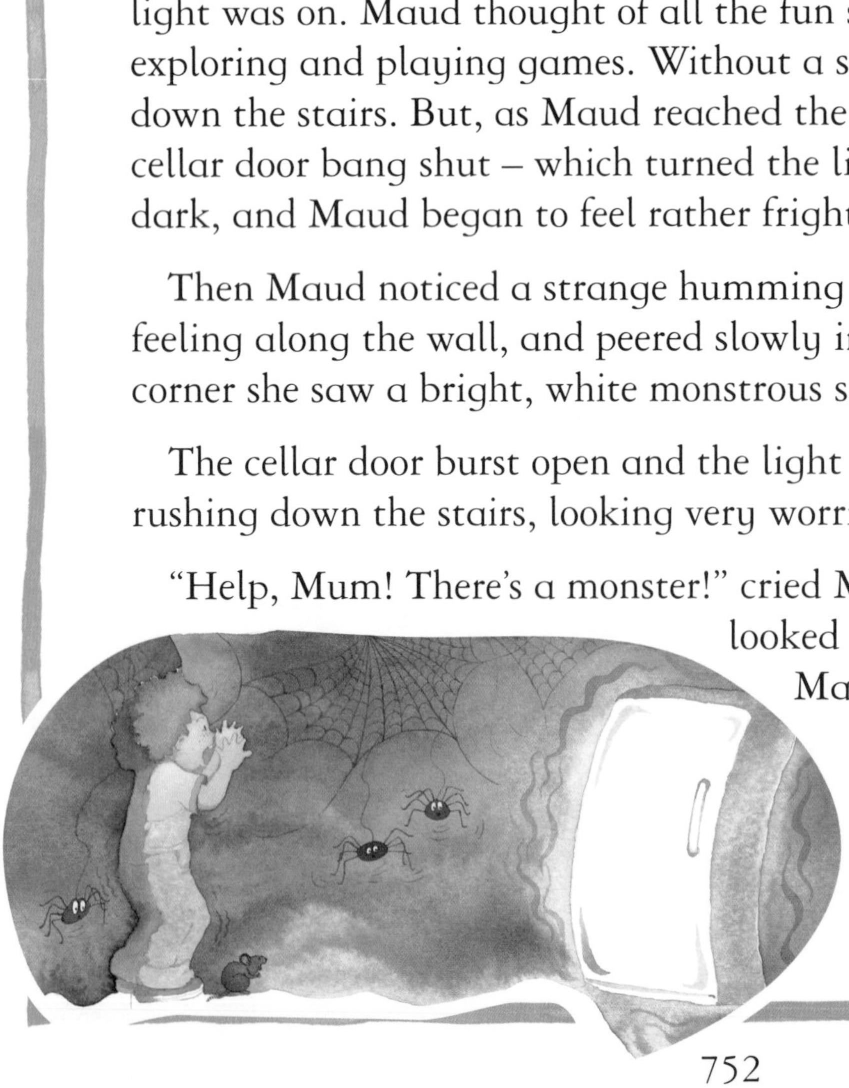

Maud's mum laughed and Maud felt rather silly. After that she didn't boast about her braveness any more.

When Monsters go to Fancy Dress Parties

We all know what a fancy dress party is. Everyone dresses up as something they are not – a pirate, a king, a princess or a monster. Dressing up as a monster is especially good fun – you can make loud noises and be rude and blame it all on the monster. But what do monsters dress up as when they go to a fancy dress party?

Do they dress up like us? Do they put on their best clothes and think of polite things to say to each other? Do they make sure that they are well mannered, eat delicately and dance modestly?

Oh no! Monsters aren't any good at pretending, they gulp down their food in huge mouthfuls and drop it all over the floor. When they dance they leap about and stamp the floor until it shakes. They hate playing musical chairs because they slip and fall on the messy floor.

So monsters might go to a party dressed like us, but they cannot hide what's inside. They behave in a monstrous way – which I am sure you never do, do you?

Mr Mole Gets Lost

Mr Mole poked his little black nose out from the top of one of his molehills and took a great big sniff of the air. Then he sniffed again. And then a third time, just to make sure. "Oh dear," he thought, "it smells like it's going to rain."

Mr Mole didn't like the rain one bit. Every time he got caught in the rain his plush little velvet fur coat got all wet and drippy, and he left muddy footprints all over his underground burrow. But worse still, the rain got in through the holes in his molehills and then everything got all soggy and took days to dry out.

Well, the skies got darker and darker, and very soon little spots of rain began to fall. Then the spots became bigger. And then bigger still. Before long, all you could see before your eyes were big, straight rods of rain bouncing off the leaves on the trees, pounding the ground and turning everything muddy and wet.

Mr Mole had never seen rain like it. He sat in his burrow in the middle of the meadow wishing it would stop. But it just kept raining and raining. Soon the rain started entering his burrow. First it went drip, drip, drip through the holes in his molehills, and then it became a little river of water in the bottom of his burrow. Then the little river became a bigger, faster-flowing river and suddenly Mr Mole was being washed along by it. Through the tunnels of his burrow he went, this way and then that, as the water gushed and poured through his underground home.

The next thing he knew he was being washed out of his burrow completely as the rain water carried him off down the meadow. Down he went, not knowing which way up he was or where he was going. Now he was being washed through the woods at the bottom of the meadow, but still the water carried him on, bouncing and turning him until he was dizzy and gasping for breath.

Suddenly, he came to a halt. The rain water gurgled and trickled around him and then flowed onwards, as he found himself stuck firmly in the branches of a bush.

"Oh dear," Mr Mole said as he got himself free. "Goodness me, where can I be?" he thought. Mr Mole looked around him, but being a very short-sighted mole – as most moles are – he couldn't make out any of the places that were familiar to him. Worse still, he couldn't smell any smells that were familiar to him. He was completely lost, far from home, and had no idea how to get back again. Now, to make things worse, it was starting to get dark.

"Woo-oo-oo-oo-oo!" said a voice suddenly. Mr Mole nearly jumped out of his moleskin with fright. "I wouldn't stay here if I were you," said the voice. Mr Mole looked up and found himself face to face with a huge owl. "Don't you know it's not safe in the woods at night?" asked the owl.

"There are snakes and foxes and weasels and all sorts of nasty creatures, that you really wouldn't like to meet."

"Oh dear!" was all Mr Mole could think of saying. He told the owl of his terrible watery journey and how he was lost and didn't know how to get back home again.

"You need to talk to Polly Pigeon," said the owl. "She is a homing pigeon and she lives near your meadow. She can show you the way home. But we'll have to find her first. Stay close to me, mind, and look out for those snakes, foxes and weasels I told you about."

Mr Mole didn't need telling twice. He stayed so close to the kindly owl that, every time the owl stopped or turned round to talk to Mr Mole, Mr Mole bumped right into him!

Through the dark, dangerous woods they went. Every now and again, there would be an unfriendly noise, such as a deep growl or a hiss, coming from the dense, tangled trees, but Mr Mole didn't want to think about that too much, so he just made sure that he never lost sight of the owl.

Finally, just when Mr Mole thought that he couldn't go a step further, they came to a halt by an old elm tree.

"Hallo-oooo," called the owl.

They were in luck. Polly Pigeon was waking up, and they found her just in time for she was about to continue her journey home.

"Please," said Mr Mole, "I'm afraid I'm terribly lost and don't know how to get back to my meadow. Will you take me there?"

"Of course I will," said Polly Pigeon. "We'd better let you rest here a while first, though. But we must go before it gets light."

So Mr Mole was soon trudging wearily back to his meadow, following as closely behind Polly Pigeon as he was able. Just as the first rays of sun lit the morning sky, Mr Mole smelled a very familiar smell. It was his meadow! He was almost home!

Soon, he was back in his own burrow. It was so wet and muddy, however, that the first thing he did was build some new tunnels higher up the meadow so that the rain wouldn't wash down into them so easily. Then he settled down to eat one of his supplies of worms, and fell into a deep, well-earned slumber.

The Yellow Bluebells

The fairies at Corner Cottage were always busy. The garden was full of flowers and it was the fairies' job to look after them. You never saw them because they worked at night and hid during the day. Blossom, the youngest fairy, was also one of the busiest. It was her job to paint all the bluebells. Corner Cottage had a lot of bluebells. They spread out under the apple tree like a deep, blue carpet. One evening, Blossom was sick.

"I've got a terrible cold," she told her friend Petal, sniffing loudly. "I don't think I can work tonight."

"I wish I could help," said Petal, "but I've got to spray the flowers with perfume or they won't smell right. You'll have to ask the gnomes."

Oh dear! Nobody liked asking Chip and Chuck, the garden gnomes. All they liked doing was fishing and windsurfing on the pond and playing tricks. Blossom was very worried about asking them.

"No problem!" said Chip and Chuck when she asked them. "Just leave it to us." But when Blossom got up the next morning the gnomes had painted some of the bluebells... YELLOW! She couldn't believe it.

"Have you seen what they've done?" she said to Petal. "What will Jamie think?" Jamie lived in Corner Cottage

with his mum and dad, and he played in the garden every day. That morning he came out as usual and made for the apple tree. As he sat on his favourite branch, he looked down. Something looked different.

"I'm sure those flowers were blue," he thought. "Mum," he said, going into the kitchen, "I've picked you some flowers."

"Yellowbells?" said Mum, putting them into a jam jar. "I don't remember planting those."

That night, Blossom was still feeling ill. "You'll have to paint the yellowbells," she told the gnomes, but Chip and Chuck just chuckled.

In the morning, Jamie ran out to the garden and climbed the apple tree. This time the flowers were pink! He picked a bunch for his mum and she put them in the jam jar with the yellowbells. When Petal told Blossom what had happened, Blossom groaned.

"I just knew something like this would happen." But she was still feeling too sick to work. "Don't worry," said Petal. "Leave it to me." Petal made the naughty gnomes paint all the pinkbells again. And this time she watched them carefully. The gnomes grumbled loudly.

The next morning, all the bluebells were blue again. Blossom was feeling much better. "I'll be glad to get back to work!" she told Petal.

When Jamie and his mum went into the garden, everything was as it should be. The bluebells were the right colour. And there was no sign of the yellowbells or pinkbells.

"It must have been the fairies!" joked Mum.

"Maybe it really was the fairies," thought Jamie as he drifted off to sleep that night.

When I Was a Bachelor

When I was a bachelor I lived by myself,
And all the meat I got I put upon a shelf;
The rats and the mice did lead me such a life
That I went to London to get myself a wife.

The streets were so broad and the lanes were so narrow,
I could not get my wife home without a wheelbarrow;
The wheelbarrow broke, my wife got a fall,
Down tumbled wheelbarrow, little wife, and all.

The Dark Wood

In the dark, dark wood, there was a dark, dark house,
And in that dark, dark house, there was a dark, dark room,
And in that dark, dark room, there was a dark, dark cupboard,
And in that dark, dark cupboard, there was a dark, dark shelf,
And on that dark, dark shelf, there was a dark, dark box,
And in that dark, dark box, there was a
GHOST!

At the Siege of Belle-isle

At the siege of Belle-isle
I was there all the while,
All the while, all the while,
At the siege of Belle-isle.

Doctor Foster Went to Gloucester

Doctor Foster went to Gloucester,
In a shower of rain;
He stepped in a puddle, up to his middle,
And never went there again.

Leg, Over Leg

Leg over leg,
  As the dog went to Dover;
When he came to a stile,
  Jump he went over.

Jeremiah

Jeremiah
  Jumped in the fire.
Fire was so hot
  He jumped in the pot.
Pot was so little
  He jumped in the kettle.
Kettle was so black
  He jumped in the crack.
Crack was so high
  He jumped in the sky.
Sky was so blue
  He jumped in a canoe.
Canoe was so deep
  He jumped in the creek.
Creek was so shallow
  He jumped in the tallow.
Tallow was so soft
  He jumped in the loft.

The House that Jack Built

This is the house that Jack built.

This is the malt
  That lay in the house that Jack built.

This is the rat,
  That ate the malt,
That lay in the house that Jack built.

This is the cat,
  That killed the rat,
That ate the malt,
  That lay in the house that Jack built.

This is the dog,
  That worried the cat,
That killed the rat,
  That ate the malt,
That lay in the house that Jack built.

Tommy Trot

Tommy Trot, a man of law,
  Sold his bed and lay upon straw:
Sold the straw and slept on grass,
  To buy his wife a looking-glass.

Tiger Tricks

Tiger loved to play tricks. Every time he found a new one, he couldn't wait to try it out on all of his friends. His latest one was – tying knots!

So, when Elephant was sleeping, Tiger tied a knot in his trunk! When Monkey was dozing, Tiger tied a knot in his tail! And when Snake was snoozing, Tiger tied a knot in – Snake!

Tiger thought it was great fun. The other animals didn't – they were fed up with Tiger, and his tricks.

"I've had enough of this!" said Elephant, rubbing his sore trunk.

"Something has to be done," said Monkey, rubbing his sore tail.

"He's gone too far this time!" said sore Snake.

"We need to catch him before he can try out his tricks on us," said Monkey.

"But that's the problem," said Snake. "We never see him coming in time."

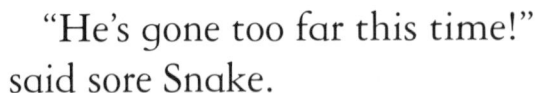

The others agreed. They never spotted Tiger sneaking up on them because, in the

jungle, Tiger's stripes made him really difficult to see! So all the animals thought really hard. Monkey scratched his head. Snake wriggled and writhed and Elephant swung his trunk.

Suddenly Elephant said, "I've got an idea!" He led them all to a fruit tree near the water hole.

When Elephant had explained his plan, a huge smile spread across Monkey's face, and Snake began to snigger. Monkey quickly scampered up the tree, and carried down some of the bright red fruits. Snake wriggled around in the soft earth, until he made a smooth hollow. Then Elephant squeezed the fruits with his trunk, until the bright red juice filled the hollow that Snake had made – and then the animals waited.

It wasn't long before Tiger came strolling along to the water hole, giggling. He started drinking...

Elephant dipped his trunk into the fruit juice and sucked hard. Then he pointed his trunk at Tiger and blew. The juice flew across the clearing, spattering Tiger all over, soaking into his coat. He looked as if he had bright red spots! Tiger jumped with shock.

"That'll take weeks to wear off," Elephant laughed.

"Yes, we'll see you coming for miles," said Monkey.

"So you won't be able to sneak up on us and play any more tricks," added Snake.

And all the animals laughed – except for bright red Tiger!

Snowy and Blowy

Old MacDonald peered out of his window and decided to put on three extra jumpers.

"That's very sensible," said Mrs MacDonald. "You need to keep warm when it's snowy."

"What worries me," said Old MacDonald, "is that it's snowy *and* blowy. I must make sure that the sheep are safe. They really don't like it when the snow gets blown into heaps in the fields. It's time they came down from the meadow."

Old MacDonald puffed and panted as he put on his boots and set off for the meadow, taking Bruce the sheepdog with him.

But when they reached the meadow, the sheep were nowhere to be seen. They were completely hidden by the snow!

"On days like these," said Old MacDonald, "I wish I had black sheep instead of white ones."

Suddenly, Bruce started to behave in a very strange way, jumping up and down with his paws together, just like sheep do!

Old MacDonald understood, he laughed and patted Bruce's head. Then he shouted, "Today there is going to be a jumping competition to keep us all warm! I think the rabbits in the next field will win!"

Woosh! One energetic sheep jumped up, showering snow all around. Woosh! Woosh! Two more leapt into the air, shaking the snow from their coats. Suddenly, the field was full of leaping, jumping sheep!

Those sheep made quite sure that the rabbits in the next field didn't stand a chance. Actually, those rabbits were all snugly sleeping in their burrows, quite unaware that their honour as jumpers was at stake.

Back in the farmyard, the other animals saw how warm and happy the woolly jumpers were. Before long, everyone joined in, even Henry, much to the embarassment of the hen!. The farmyard was full of laughing, smiling animals bouncing up and down – a very strange sight.

Of course, Old MacDonald didn't join in. He was too busy puffing and panting again, trying to get his boots off. All he wanted to do was to get in the warm of the farmhouse and settle down by the fire. He could smell is lunch and all that walking in the wind and the snow had made him very hungry!

And of course Bruce was too busy thinking about his bone to stay out in the yard with all those bouncing animals. His empty tummy was far more important!

The Funny Bunny

The Funny Bunny's in a flap.
He'll never get it done!
Every year, it's just the same.
He's such a hot, cross bun!

When everyone is fast asleep,
He hops off to the farm,
Clutching an enormous list,
His basket on his arm!

He taps upon the hen house door.
He hopes that they've been busy.
The hens laugh at his worried face.
He's always in a tizzy!

They fill his basket to the brim,
With eggs of every hue.
There's brown and white
and speckled ones
And some are even blue!

"Now, off you go," they cluck at him,
"And mind that they don't break.
You've just time to deliver them,
Before they're all awake!"

He stops to peer at his long list,
Then hops up to a door.
There's two for here and one for there
And next door, they need four!

The busy bunny hops and skips,
All round and round the towns,
To make quite sure the children wake
With smiles and not with frowns!

Then, suddenly, the sun wakes up.
The cock crows, "Hey! It's dawn."
"At last, my job is finished!"
Sighs the bunny, with a yawn!

But what is this? There's one egg left
He checks his list to see
If anyone has been left out.
"Oh, yes!" he smiles. "It's me!"

Bertha Saves the Day

Bertha Bunny had a shiny nose,
But this she could not mend,
Because her little powder puff
Was at the other end!

She felt upset, because her chums
All chuckled at the sight
Of Bertha's pink and perky nose,
That shone just like a light!

One day, the bunnies hopped
and skipped
And wandered off to play
Too far into the Wicked Wood,
Then couldn't find their way!

"Oh, no! We're lost!" sobbed Little Bob,
Because he's only three.
"My mummy will be worrying,
If I'm not home for tea!"

It got so dark, they couldn't tell
Just which way they should go.
Then, Bertie spotted Bertha's nose,
All shiny and aglow!

"Bertha's nose will light our way!"
Cried Bertie Bun, with glee.
"Yippeeee!" the other
bunnies yelled.
"We'll soon be home for tea!"

They followed Bertha through
the wood.
"You're such a clever bunny,"
said Billy, as they got back home.
"And your nose isn't funny!"

"Without it, we would
all be lost
Forever in the wood.
Three cheers for Bertha's
shiny nose.
We think it's really good!"

Custard's New Home

Custard the little hippo lived where it was very hot. His home was a cool river that flowed into the sea. This was where he met Sid, the hermit crab. Sid and Custard were best friends.

This was a bit odd because they were as different as could be. Custard was a lot bigger than Sid for a start. Custard thought that being a hermit crab must be really cool. Instead of having one shell like ordinary crabs, they keep changing from one shell to another.

At the moment Sid had a bright pink, pointed shell. He carried it around with him everywhere he went. Custard thought this was really great. He wanted to carry his own home around with him! Then he wouldn't have to stay out in the hot sun. Hippos don't like getting hot. But there are no shells as big as a hippo. So they have to stay in the river to keep cool.

"Will you help me build my own home?" Custard asked Sid one day.

"Of course I will," said Sid. So they built a house of leaves and tied it to Custard's back. Custard was as pleased as could be. They went for a walk by the river. Sid wore a new round blue shell this time. He said it was the latest fashion. They passed a lion that had a bad cold. ATISHOO! The lion sneezed loudly and blew Custard's new house away!

"Bother!" said Custard.

So they built another house, this time of bamboo.

"This won't blow away," said Custard.

But an elephant appeared. And, oh dear! Bamboo is an elephant's favourite food.

"Yummy!" said the elephant. "Thanks for bringing me my breakfast!" And he stuffed Custard's house into his mouth!

"That was my new home," said Custard crossly.

"Oops! Sorry," said the elephant.

Sid was looking for a new home for himself. The blue one was getting too small. He thought a yellow one would be nice. A large bird flying lazily overhead spotted Sid without his shell.

"Ah, crab lunch!" it said, and, swooping low, it grabbed Sid in its claws. Sid wriggled and freed himself. He dropped to the ground with a thump.

Custard rushed to help, but was too big and slow. Looking round, he spotted a deckchair, a sunshade and a bucket and spade.

"Quick," he called to Sid, "over here!" Sid dived under the bucket. Just in time! The bird squawked angrily, and flew away. Custard wriggled his bottom into the stripy deck chair, and settled down under the shade of the green umbrella. It felt nice and cool.

If only his head and legs didn't stick out in front. He wriggled a bit more trying to get comfortable.

"Sid, I've been thinking. I'll just keep cool in the river like I did before," said Custard.

"And I think I'll look for another shell," said Sid.

The two friends wandered back down to the river, happy to be going home together.

Birthday Bear

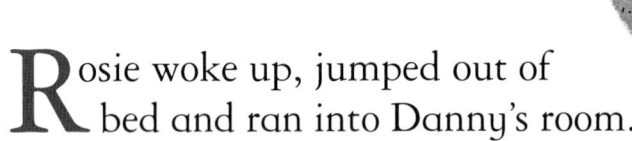

Rosie woke up, jumped out of bed and ran into Danny's room. "Guess what day it is!"

"It's Saturday," muttered Danny, grumpily. "And it's raining too."

"I know it's Saturday, silly," exclaimed an excited Rosie. "But it's my birthday!" Rosie spotted Jack the postman coming up the path. She ran downstairs to meet him.

"There's nothing for you," he teased. But Jack's bag was bulging!

"You can open your cards when Daddy comes in," laughed Mum. "But the birthday girl needs her breakfast first."

After breakfast, they all watched while Rosie opened a great pile of cards and presents. "I've got a card from Conker," said Rosie and gave him a big kiss. "It's got his paw mark on!"

They spent the morning getting the house ready for Rosie's birthday party.

They blew up balloons and hung up streamers until everything looked perfect.

"That looks lovely," announced Mum, finally. "I can see Joe down by the pond. Why don't you go and feed the ducks while I finish everything else."

Danny and Rosie ran through the orchard and waved to Joe the farm worker. It had stopped raining but it was still very wet and muddy. "Happy birthday, Rosie," called Joe. When they reached the pond, Rosie noticed something floating at the edge of the water all tangled up in the weeds.

"What's that muddy blob over there?" she asked.

"I'll go in and see," said Danny, splashing into the pond and wading out towards the curious object. Dan took three steps, then stopped.

"Go on," called Rosie. "What's the matter?" Danny began to giggle.

"I can't move," he said. "My boots are stuck in the mud!" Rosie started to laugh too. Danny wriggled, pulled, twisted and turned, trying to free his boots from the mud. Suddenly, Danny's foot slipped out of his boot and he sat in the water with a huge splash. Joe came across to see what all the laughter was about and held out his hand to Danny.

"What's that muddy mess you're holding?" he chuckled.

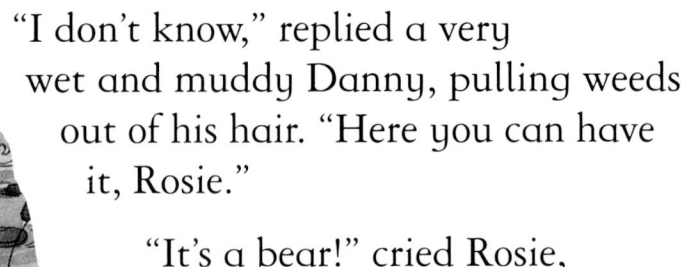

"I don't know," replied a very wet and muddy Danny, pulling weeds out of his hair. "Here you can have it, Rosie."

"It's a bear!" cried Rosie, cuddling the soggy bundle. "A poor muddy old bear."

"I wonder how he got there?" asked Danny. Dripping wet and covered with mud, Danny and Rosie walked back to the house.

"What have you been up to?" laughed Mum. "And who is this little fellow?" Mum took the bear from Rosie. "Oh dear! I think all three of you need a bath before the party starts." In no time at all, Rosie, Danny and the little bear were ready for the party.

"Wow! Look at the cake, Rosie," said Danny. "It looks brilliant!"

Rosie tied a big yellow bow around the bear's neck and sat him at the window sill to watch the party.

At bedtime, Rosie sighed, "That was the best birthday party ever. I love being five. Do you know what my best present was, Mummy?" she added.

"What was that?" asked Mum.

"It was that poor old muddy bear. I wish I could keep him."

"Well, we'll have to wait and see," said Mum. "He might belong to someone."

The next day, Rosie made a "Lost Bear" poster and Jack put it in the post office window. Nobody came to collect the bear, so Rosie adopted him. Rosie made up lots of stories about how the bear got into the pond. But they never did find out.

"It doesn't matter where you came from," she told him. "You can live with us now. Billy Rabbit can be your best friend."

"What will you call him?" asked Danny.

"Birthday Bear, of course!"

O Captain! My Captain!

O Captain! my Captain! our fearful trip is done,
The ship has weather'd every rack, the prize we sought is won,
The port is near, the bells I hear, the people all exulting,
While follow eyes the steady keel, the vessel grim and daring;

But O heart! heart! heart!
O the bleeding drops of red,
Where on the deck my Captain lies,
Fallen cold and dead.

O Captain! my Captain! rise up and head the bells;
Rise up – for you the flag is flung – for you the bugle trills,
For you bouquets and ribbon'd wreaths – for you the shores a-crowding,
For you they call, the swaying mass, their eager faces turning;

Here Captain! dear father!
This arm beneath your head!
It is some dream that on the deck,
You've fallen cold and dead.

My Captain does not answer, his lips are pale and still,
My father does not feel my arm, he has no pulse nor will,
The ship is anchor'd safe and sound, its voyage closed and done,
From fearful trip the victor ship comes in with object won;

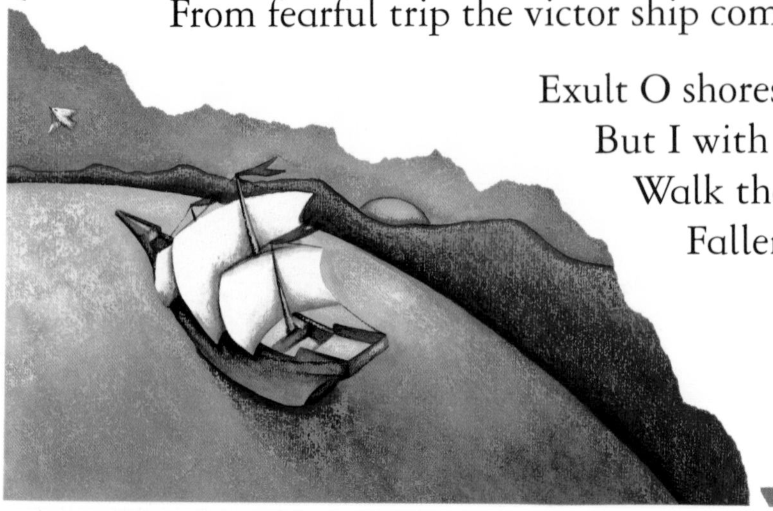

Exult O shores, and ring O bells!
But I with mournful tread,
Walk the deck my Captain lies,
Fallen cold and dead.

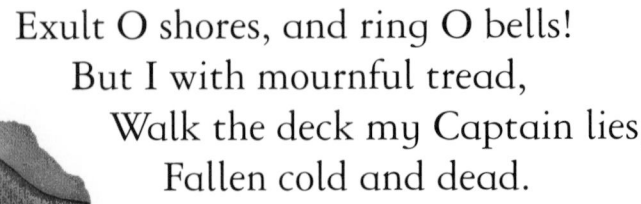

Walt Whitman

Meg Merrilees

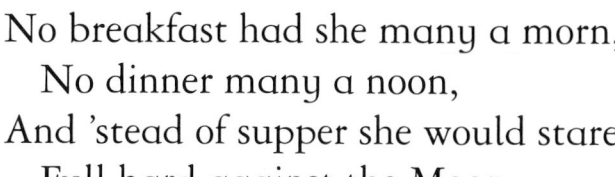

Old Meg she was a Gipsy,
And lived upon the moors:
Her bed it was the brown heath turf,
And her house was out of doors.

Her Brothers were the craggy hills,
Her Sisters larchen trees;
Alone with her great family
She lived as she did please.

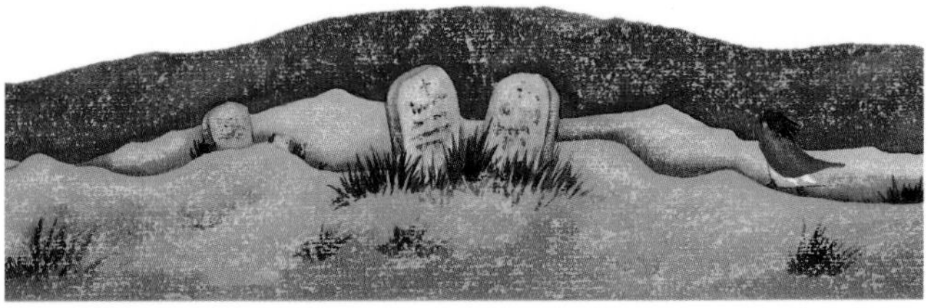

No breakfast had she many a morn,
No dinner many a noon,
And 'stead of supper she would stare
Full hard against the Moon.

But every morn of woodbine fresh
She made her garlanding,
And every night the dark glen Yew
She wove, and she would sing.

And with her fingers, old and brown,
She plaited Mats o' Rushes,
And gave them to the Cottagers
She met among the Bushes.

JOHN KEATS

The Lamb

Little lamb, who made thee?
Dost thou know who made thee?
Gave thee life, and bid thee feed
By the stream and o'er the mead;
Gave thee clothing of delight,
Softest clothing, woolly, bright;
Gave thee such a tender voice,
Making all the vales rejoice?
Little lamb, who made thee?
Dost thou know who made thee?
Little lamb, I'll tell thee,
Little lamb, I'll tell thee:
He is called by thy name,
For he calls himself a lamb.

He is meek, and he is mild;
He became a little child.
I a child, and thou a lamb,
We are called by his name.
Little lamb,
God bless thee!
Little lamb,
God bless thee!

The Yellow Digger

Crash! Bang! Clatter! There was a terrific noise in the yard at Faraway Farm. Rosie sat up in bed clutching Billy Rabbit. "What's happening?" she called. When she peeped out of the window, she saw an amazing sight. Down below, Joe the farm worker was driving the yellow digger round, scraping great holes in the yard. As Rosie watched, the digger took a mouthful of stones in its scoop. Then it spun round and clattered over to a huge dirt pile. The stones poured out making a roar like thunder. Rosie rushed downstairs, nearly tripping over Conker the dog in the hall.

"Joe's knocking down the house," she cried.

"Don't worry, Rosie," said Dad. "We're laying some new concrete in the yard. The old yard is cracked and muddy, so Joe is scraping it off. Get dressed and put your boots on. I've got a job for you and Danny."

Outside, the digger chugged backwards and forwards. "I wish I could drive it," sighed Danny.

"All in good time," said Dad. "Right now, I want you to run down to the gate and look out for the concrete truck. When it arrives, open the gate so we can get it right into the yard."

The children raced off. "I can see it!" shrieked Rosie, standing on the gate. Together, the children swung open the gate to let in a huge blue truck. The driver waved to them as he passed. The truck stopped in the yard but the concrete container went on turning with a loud scrunching sound.

"Why doesn't it stay still?" asked Rosie.

"Because all the concrete will go hard if it stops," said Dad.

The engine chugged and the concrete container churned slowly round and round. "What's going to happen now?" asked Rosie in excitement, as the driver pulled a lever and out poured the concrete. Dad and Joe spread the thick gooey mixture all over the yard.

Dad wiped his sweaty face with a handkerchief. "Phew! I'm boiling hot, now. Just make sure you don't step in the concrete while it's still wet."

While Dad and Joe went inside for a cold drink, Rosie and Danny gazed at the shiny, smooth yard. "When will it dry?" asked Rosie, poking the concrete with a little stick.

"Not till tomorrow," said Danny, drawing a round smiley face.

"I'd like to go paddling in it," said Rosie. "Wouldn't you?"

Joe came out of the house and started the digger. The sudden roar made Stan the cat leap up in fright. "Oh, no!" cried Danny. "Catch him quick." Rosie grabbed but Stan was too fast. He dashed across the yard, leaving a long trail of paw prints in the wet concrete. Conker barked madly and raced after him. The children watched in horror as Conker hurtled into the wet concrete. Stan leaped neatly on to the water butt. Conker slithered to a halt as his paws sank into the thick grey mixture. Gingerly he hopped a few more steps, then stood still with a puzzled look on his face.

"Uh oh!" said Danny, glumly. "Somebody's going to be in trouble."

When Dad came out of the house and saw Conker stranded in the concrete, his face went very red and cross-looking. "Who let those animals into the yard?" he asked sternly. "Look at my lovely concrete."

Conker whimpered and tried to wag his tail."He's very sorry," said Rosie, tugging at Dad's sleeve. "Will he have to stay there till it's dry?"

"Don't be silly," snorted Danny. "We'll never get him out then."

"I've got an idea," shouted Joe. Joe revved up the digger's engine and rumbled over to the edge of the yard. Slowly he stretched out the digger's arm, edging the scoop as near to Conker as he could. Everybody cheered. "Come on, Conker. Jump in." But Conker wouldn't budge.

"I know what to do," cried Rosie. She dashed indoors and returned with some of Conker's favourite biscuits. She put some into the digger's scoop. Then Joe stretched out the arm across the concrete again. Conker's eyes brightened. He sniffed the biscuits and then, very carefully, climbed into the scoop. Everyone held their breath.

"Up we go," said Joe, raising the digger's arm slowly. Conker started barking like mad.

"Stay still," called Rosie. For once, Conker did as he was told. When the scoop was lowered, he sprang out and shook himself, spraying everyone with wet concrete. They all laughed, even Dad.

"Ugh!" said Danny, as Conker leaped up to lick his face. "You're filthy."

"Make sure you wash those paws before you come indoors," said Dad.

Rosie slipped her hand into Dad's and whispered in his ear. "I like the yard better with all the footprints in it. Can I put my footprint in it too?" Dad smiled.

"Well, perhaps we could all put our footprint in it before it dries." Rosie clapped her hands and ran off to fetch Mum and Billy Rabbit.

Everybody put a footprint in the wet concrete. Billy Rabbit's was the smallest and Joe's enormous boot was the biggest. Then Dad got a stick and they each wrote their initials next to the footprint. "I'll write Conker's because he can't spell," said Danny.

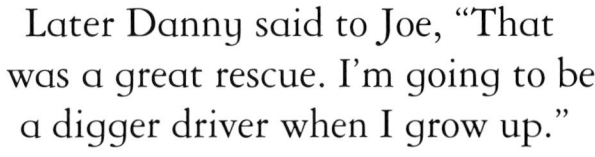

Later Danny said to Joe, "That was a great rescue. I'm going to be a digger driver when I grow up."

"I'm going to be a vet," said Rosie, hugging Conker.

"Come on then," laughed Mum. "I think it's time we gave that naughty dog a bath."

There's No Room Here!

It was a very hot day down on Apple Tree Farm. The chicks trotted off to sit in the cool barn – but the cows had got there first!

"There's no room in here for you chicks!" mooed Mrs Cow. "Try the duck pond." But the duck pond was full of splashing ducks!

"This is not a chick pond!" quacked Mrs Duck. So, the chicks waddled past the pigsty, where Mr Pig was rolling in a big, squidgy mudbath.

"That looks very cool," called the chicks, peeping round the fence.

"Yes!" grunted the greedy pig. "And it's all for me!"

Suddenly, Robbie Chick had an idea. "Come on!" he cried. "Follow me!" The three hot chicks followed him into the farmer's garden and, just at that moment, a fountain of water shot up in the air and splashed all the chicks! "Oooh! That's freezing!" giggled Rosie. "It feels great!"

The little chicks ran in and out of the cool water all afternoon, splashing and splishing about, until it was time for tea. On the way home, they saw that the sun had dried up Mr Pig's mudbath. The dippy ducks had splashed all the water out of the pond, and the cows had been taken for milking and were moaning in the hot milking parlour.

But the very cool chicks just chuckled and dripped their way back home to Mummy.

The Great Egg Hunt

On Sunnybrook Farm, there lived a very forgetful hen called Hetty. One day, Hetty laid a lovely clutch of five eggs, but then she couldn't remember where they were. She searched the farmyard. "Oh, where did I put my babies?" she cried. "I'm such a feather-brain!"

Dolly the duck rushed over to help. "Don't worry," quacked Dolly, kindly. "We'll soon find them." And she waddled off to get the other farm animals – the Great Egg Hunt had begun!

Jake the sheep found one of the eggs amongst the brambles! Gus the goat found another egg on top of an old cabbage leaf in the compost heap! Harry the horse found missing egg number three in a rabbit hole! Claudia the cow found egg number four in a cosy clump of hay!

"But there's still one missing! I laid five eggs!" squawked Hetty. Then, Penny the pig spotted something nestling under a very old wheelbarrow.

"Panic over," she oinked. "I've found it!"

"Hooray!" the other animals quacked, barked, neighed and mooed in delight. Sam the sheepdog scooped all the eggs on to an old sack and carried them back to the hen house. And so ended the Great Egg Hunt!

Hetty the hen was overjoyed! "Oh, thank you, thank you!" she clucked and quickly settled herself on top of the five eggs.

The next morning, one by one, five, fat, fluffy chicks hatched out! Hetty proudly took the baby chicks out of the hen house, to show the other farm animals.

The Frog Prince

There was once a king who had but one daughter. Being his only child, she wanted for nothing. She had a nursery full of toys, her own pony to ride and a wardrobe bursting with pretty dresses. But, for all this, the princess was lonely. "How I wish I had someone to play with," she sighed.

The princess's favourite toy was a beautiful golden ball. Every day she would play with her ball in the palace garden. When she threw the ball up in the air, it seemed to take off of its own accord and touch the clouds before landing in the princess's hands again.

One windy day. the princess was playing in the garden as usual. She threw her golden ball high into the air, but, instead of returning to her hands, the wind blew the ball into the fishpond. The princess ran to the pond, but to her dismay the ball had sunk right to the bottom. "Whatever shall I do?" wailed the girl. "Now I have lost my favourite toy." And she sat down beside the pond and cried.

All at once she heard a loud PLOP! and a large green frog landed on the grass beside her. "Eeeuugh! Go away you nasty thing!" screamed the princess.

To her astonishment, the frog spoke to her. "I heard you crying," he said in a gentle voice, "and I wondered what the matter was. Can I help you in any way?"

"Why, yes!" exclaimed the princess, once she had got over the shock of being addressed by a frog. "My ball has sunk to the bottom of the pond. Would you fish it out for me?"

"Of course I will," replied the frog. "But in return, what will you give me if I do?"

"You can have my jewels, my finest clothes and even my crown if you will find my ball," said the princess hastily, for she was truly eager to get her favourite toy back.

"I do not want your jewels, your clothes or your crown," replied the frog. "I would like to be your friend. I want to return with you to the palace and eat from your golden plate and sip from your golden cup. At night I want to sleep on a cushion made of silk next to your bed and I want you to kiss me goodnight before I go to sleep, too."

"I promise everything that you ask," said the girl, "if only you will find my golden ball."

"Remember what you have promised," said the frog, as he dived deep into the pond. At last he surfaced again with the ball and threw it on to the grass beside the princess. She was so overjoyed she forgot all about thanking the frog – let alone her promise – and ran all the way back to the palace.

That evening the king, the queen and the princess were having dinner in the great hall of the palace, when a courtier approached the king and said, "Your majesty, there is a frog at the door who says the princess has promised to share her dinner with him."

"Is this true?" demanded the king, turning to the princess and looking rather angry.

"Yes, it is," said the princess in a small voice. And she told her father the whole story.

"When a promise is made it must be kept, my girl," said the king. "You must ask the frog to dine with you."

Presently, the frog hopped into the great hall and round to where the princess was sitting. With a great leap he was up on the table beside her. She stifled a scream.

"You promised to let me eat from your golden plate," said the frog, tucking into the princess's food. The princess felt sick and pushed the

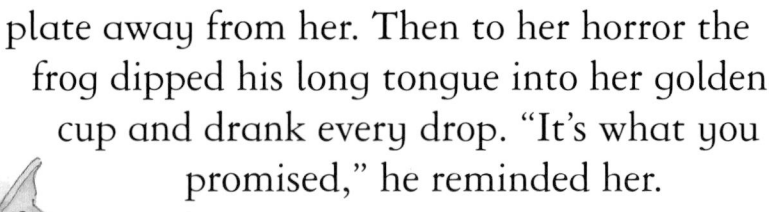

plate away from her. Then to her horror the frog dipped his long tongue into her golden cup and drank every drop. "It's what you promised," he reminded her.

When he had finished, the frog stretched his long, green limbs, yawned and said, "Now I feel quite sleepy. Please take me to your room."

"Do I really have to?" the princess pleaded with her father.

"Yes, you do," said the king sternly. "The frog helped you when you were in need and you made him a promise."

So the princess carried the frog to her bedroom. As they reached the door she said, "My bedroom's very warm. I'm sure you'd be more comfortable out here where it's cool."

But, as she opened the bedroom door, the frog leaped from her hand and landed on her bed.

"You promised that I could sleep on a silk cushion next to your bed," said the frog.

"Yes, yes, of course," said the princess looking with horror at the froggy footprints on her clean, white sheets. She called to her maid to bring a cushion.

The frog jumped on to the cushion and looked as though he was going to sleep. But then he opened his eyes and said, "What about my goodnight kiss?"

"Oh, woe is me," thought the princess as she closed her eyes and pursed her lips towards the frog's cold and clammy face and kissed him.

"Open your eyes," said a voice that didn't sound a bit like the frog's. She opened her eyes and there, standing before her, was a prince. The princess stood there in dumbstruck amazement.

"Thank you," said the prince. "You have broken a spell cast upon me by a wicked witch. She turned me into a frog and said the spell would only be broken if a princess would eat with me, sleep beside me and kiss me."

They ran to tell the king what had happened. He was delighted and said, "You may live in the palace from now on, for my daughter needs a friend." And, indeed, the prince and princess became the best of friends and she was never lonely again. He taught her to play football with the golden ball and she taught him to ride her pony. One day, many years later, they were married and had lots of children. And, do you know, their children were particularly good at leapfrog!

Elsie Elephant's Jungle Shower

Up above the jungle there wasn't a cloud in the sky. Deep down inside the jungle Elsie Elephant was feeling very hot.

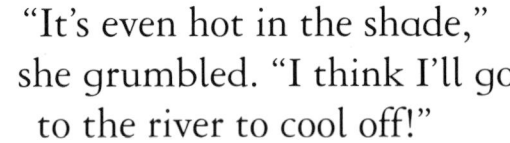

"It's even hot in the shade," she grumbled. "I think I'll go to the river to cool off!"

Tommy Monkey was swinging high up in the tree-tops. "I'm going swimming," Elsie told him. "You can come too, if you like." Tommy jumped out of the tree and skipped along with Elsie.

"You've got a very long trunk," said Tommy Monkey.

"What is it for?"

Elsie thought about it for a minute. "I'm not really sure," she said at last.

At the river they found Leo Lion standing at the edge of the water, looking in. "Hello Leo – are you coming for a swim?" asked Elsie.

"Lions don't like swimming," sighed Leo. "But I'm so hot! I'll come and watch you."

Soon Stripy Tiger arrived. She and Leo watched as Elsie and Tommy Monkey dived into the river and began splashing around.

"It's lovely and cold – jump in!" shouted Elsie.

"Tigers are a bit scared of water," called Stripy. "But it does look fun!"

Elsie saw how hot all her friends looked and had an idea. She filled her trunk with cool water and sprayed it all over Leo Lion and Stripy Tiger. Soon Tommy Monkey and even the jungle birds came to play under Elsie's shower.

"NOW I know what my long trunk is for!" said Elsie happily, and all the animals cheered!

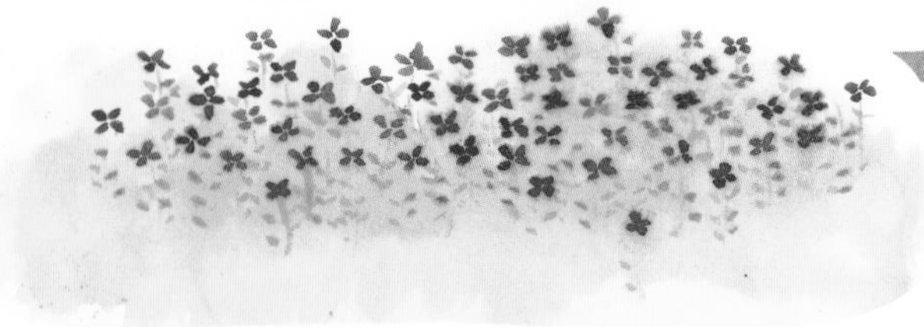

Lie A-Bed

Lie a-bed,
Sleepy head,
Shut up eyes, bo-peep;
Till day-break
Never wake:–
Baby, sleep.

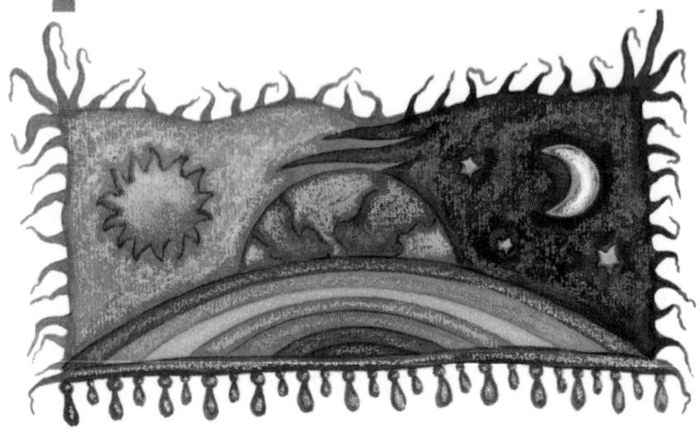

A Child's Evening Prayer

Ere on my bed my limbs I lay,
God grant me grace my prayers to say:
O God, preserve my mother dear
In strength and health for many a year;
And, O! preserve my father too,
And may I pay him reverence due;
And may I my best thoughts employ
To be my parents' hope and joy;
And O! preserve my brothers both
From evil doings and from sloth,
And may we always love each other
Our friends, our father,
and our mother.

Song of the Sky Loom

O our Mother the Earth, O our Father the Sky,
Your children are we, and with tired backs
We bring you the gifts that you love.
Then weave for us a garment of brightness;
May the warp be the white light of morning,
May the weft be the red light of evening,
May the fringes be the falling rain,
May the border be the standing rainbow.
Thus weave for us a garment of brightness,
That we may walk fittingly where birds sing,
That we may walk fittingly where grass is green,
O our Mother the Earth, O our Father the sky.

Putting the World to Bed

The little snow people are hurrying down
  From their home in the clouds overhead;
They are working as hard as ever they can,
  Putting the world to bed.

Every tree in a soft fleecy nightgown
  they clothe;
Each part has its night-cap of white.
  And o'er the cold ground a thick cover
they spread
  Before they say good-night.

And so they come eagerly sliding down,
  With a swift and silent tread,
Always as busy as busy can be,
  Putting the world to bed.

O Lady Moon

O Lady Moon, your horns point toward the east:
  Shine, be increased.
O Lady Moon, your horns point toward the west:
  Wane, be at rest.

Now the Day is Over

Now the day is over,
  Night is drawing nigh,
Shadows of the evening
  Steal across the sky.

Now the darkness gathers,
  Stars begin to peep,
Birds and beasts and flowers
  Soon will be asleep.

Jesu, give the weary
  Calm and sweet repose;
With thy tenderest blessing
  May our eyelids close.

Grant to little children
  Visions bright of thee;
Guard the sailors tossing
  On the deep blue sea.

When the morning wakens,
  Then may I arise
Pure and fresh and sinless
  In thy holy eyes.

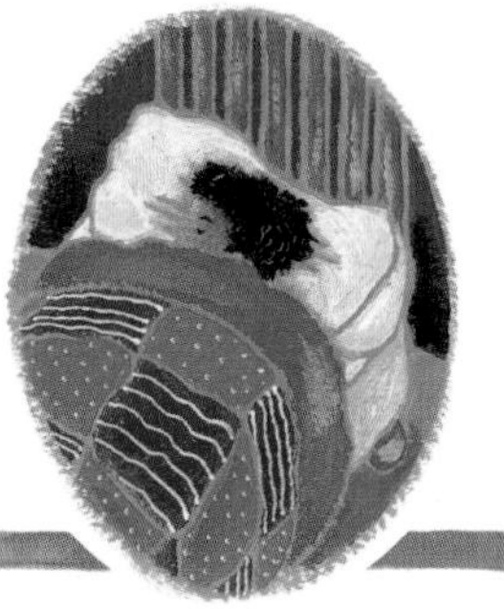

The Mermaid Fair

Jason loved diving and he was very good at it. He loved to dive for shellfish and sponges, but mainly he loved to look for pearls. Pearls are jewels of the sea and he collected even the tiniest one.

One day Jason was diving when he saw a sign on a rock. Jason was very surprised. He swam closer and was even more surprised to read the words: MERMAID FAIR TODAY!

Jason had heard of mermaids, of course, but he'd never seen one! Jason took a huge gulp of air and swam towards the fair. He hid behind a rock and watched. There was a crowd of mermaids at the fair, some were riding dolphins, some were swimming in races and some were playing games at the stalls. And there were pearls! There were stalls where you could win a pearl by throwing a hoop over it. Another where, if you pulled down a lever and saw three shells in a row, a hundred white pearls came out of a hole at the bottom! Two of the mermaids noticed Jason watching and came over to him.

"You're a strange sort of fish!" teased the fair-haired mermaid.

"I think it must be a boy!" laughed the dark-haired mermaid.

"Hello," said Jason. To Jason's amazement, he found he could talk

and breathe under water! "Can I take part in your fair? I'd love to win some pearls!"

"Oh, you don't want dull old pearls," said one. "What you want are these," and showed Jason a plastic comb with a flower on it. The mermaid had found it one day in a rock pool and thought it was the most beautiful thing she'd ever seen. Jason told her he would bring her many combs if she would show him how to win a pearl.

"That's easy!" she told him. "You just have to win the dolphin race!" So Jason entered the dolphin race. But it was not as easy as he thought. He found that dolphins are very slippery to ride, and jumping through a hoop underwater is impossible. Unless, of course, you are a mermaid!

It was nearly time to go and Jason had not won a single prize! At the very last stall there was the biggest pearl he had ever seen – almost as big as a coconut. He had to throw a sponge at the pearl to knock it over. If there was one thing Jason could do, it was throw a sponge.

The mermaids gathered round to cheer him on. He had one or two near misses and then, amidst lots of laughter, he knocked the huge pearl off the stand with his third try.

"You've won!" the mermaids shouted excitedly. "The pearl is yours!"

Jason swam back to his boat, delighted. The next day he returned clutching a box filled with pretty plastic combs. When the mermaids saw them they danced for joy in the waves and kissed him on both cheeks.

After that Jason saw the mermaids whenever he went diving, and he always took them a special plastic comb.

Buried Treasure

Jim lived in a big old house with a big rambling garden. The house was rather spooky, and Jim much preferred the garden. He would spend hours kicking a football around the overgrown lawn, climbing the old apple trees in the orchard or just staring into the pond in case he might spot a fish. It was a wonderful garden to play in, but Jim was not really a happy child because he was lonely. How he wished he had someone to play with! It would be such fun to play football with a friend, or have someone to go fishing with. He had plenty of friends at school, but it was a long bus journey to his home and, besides, his school friends found his house so spooky that they only came to visit once.

One day Jim was hunting about in the garden with a stick. He hoped he might find some interesting small creatures to examine. Every time he found a new creature he would draw it and try to find out its name. So far, he had discovered eight types of snail and six different ladybirds.

As he was poking about under some leaves he saw a piece of metal sticking out of the ground.

He reached down and managed to pull it free. In his hand lay a rusty old key. It was quite big, and, as Jim brushed away the soil, he saw that it was carved with beautiful patterns.

Jim carried the key indoors and cleaned it and polished it. Then he set about trying to find the lock that it fitted. First he tried the old garden gate that had been locked as long as Jim could remember. But the key was far too small. Next he tried the grandfather clock in the hall. But the key did not fit the clock's lock. Then he remembered an old wind-up teddy bear that played the drum. Jim hadn't played with the toy for a long time and he eagerly tried out the key, but this time it was too big.

Then Jim had another idea. "Perhaps the key fits something in the attic," he thought. He was usually too scared to go into the attic on his own because it really was scary. But now he was so determined to find the key's home that he ran up the stairs boldly and opened the door. The attic was dimly lit, dusty and full of cobwebs. The water pipes hissed and creaked and Jim shivered. He began to look under a few dustsheets and opened some old boxes, but didn't find anything that looked like it needed a key to unlock it. Then he caught sight of a large book sticking out from one of the shelves. It was one of those sorts of books fitted with a lock. Jim lifted down the book, which was extremely heavy, and put it on the floor.

His fingers trembled as he put the key in the lock. It fitted perfectly! He turned the key and the lock sprang open, releasing a cloud of dust. Jim slowly opened the book and turned the pages.

What a disappointment! The pages were crammed with tiny writing and there were no pictures at all. Jim was about to shut the book when he heard a voice coming from the book! "You have unlocked my secrets," it said. "Step into my pages if you are looking for adventure."

Jim was so curious that he found himself stepping on to the book. As he put his foot on the pages he found himself falling through the book. The next thing he knew he was on the deck of a ship. He looked up and saw a tattered flag with a skull and crossbones flying from a flagpole. He was on a pirate ship! He looked down and saw that he was dressed like a pirate.

The pirate ship was sailing along nicely, when suddenly Jim saw some dangerous-looking rocks in the water – and they were heading straight for them! Before he could shout, the ship had run aground and all the pirates were jumping overboard and swimming to the shore. Jim swam, too.

The water felt deliciously warm and when he reached the shore he found warm sand between his toes. He couldn't believe it! Here he was on a desert island. The pirates went in all directions, searching for something to make a shelter.

Jim looked, too, and under a rock he found a book. The book looked familiar to Jim. He was sure he'd seen it somewhere before. He was still puzzling over it when one of the pirates came running towards him waving a knife. "You thief, you stole my rubies!" cursed the pirate in a menacing voice. What was Jim to do?

Then he heard a voice call from the book, "Quick! Step back here!"

Without thinking twice, Jim stepped into the book and suddenly he was back in the attic again.

Jim peered closely at the page from which he'd just stepped. "The Pirates and the Stolen Treasure" it said at the top of the page. Jim read the page and found he was reading exactly the adventure he had been in. He turned excitedly to the contents page at the front of the book and read the chapter titles. "Journey to Mars", he read, and "The Castle Under the Sea". Further down it said: "The Magic Car" and "Into the Jungle". Jim was thrilled. He realised that he could open the book at any page and become part of the adventure, and he only had to find the book and step into it to get back to the attic again.

After that, Jim had many, many more adventures. He made lots of friends in the stories and he had some narrow escapes. But he always found the book just in time. Jim was never lonely again.

Okey Cokey

You put your left arm in, your left arm out,
In, out, in, out, you shake it all about,
You do the okey cokey, and you turn around,
And that's what it's all about.

Oh, the okey cokey,
Oh, the okey cokey,
Oh, the okey cokey,
Knees bend, arms stretch,
Ra, ra, ra!

These are Grandma's Glasses

These are Grandma's glasses,
This is Grandma's hat;
Grandma claps her hands like this
And rests them in her lap.

These are Grandpa's glasses,
This is Grandpa's hat;
Grandpa folds his arms like this,
And has a little nap.

Mousie

Mousie comes a-creeping, creeping.
Mousie comes a-peeping, peeping.
Mousie says, "I'd like to stay,
But I haven't time today."
Mousie pops into his hole
And says, "ACHOO!
I've caught a cold!"

I'm a Little Teapot

I'm a little teapot short and stout,
Here's my handle, here's my spout,
When I get my steam up hear me shout,
Tip me up and pour me out.

Ride a Cock-horse

Ride a cock-horse to Banbury Cross,
To see a fine lady ride on a white horse,
Rings on her fingers and bells on her toes,
She shall have music wherever she goes.

I Am the Music Man

I am the music man,
I come from far away,
And I can play.
What can you play?
I play piano.
Pia, pia, piano, piano, piano,
Pia, pia, piano, pia, piano.

I am the music man,
I come from far away,
And I can play.
What can you play?
I play the big drum.
Boomdi, boomdi, boomdi boom,
Boomdi boom, boomdi boom,
Boomdi, boomdi, boomdi boom,
Boomdi, boomdi, boom.
Pia, pia, piano, piano, piano,
Pia, pia, piano, pia, piano.

Build a House with Five Bricks

Build a house with five bricks,
One, two, three, four, five.
Put a roof on top,
And a chimney too,
Where the wind blows through!

Turn Around

Turn around and touch the ground,
Turn around and touch the ground,
Turn around and touch the ground,
And fall right down.

Aunty and the Flowers

Every year on the farm, the animals had a competition. Everyone liked to join in the fun, and there was a prize for the winner. The prize could be for anything. One year, it was for growing the best purple vegetables. Once it was for having the knobbliest knees. (Gladys the duck won that, of course.)

This year they decided the prize would be for the best display of flowers. But who would choose the winner?

If Nelly the hen were the judge, she would make herself the winner. She always did. Bramble the sheep caught her wool on everything. She pulled the tables and chairs down behind her wherever she went.

Blink the pig covered everything in mud and Rambo the big horse couldn't even get into the tent!

But Aunty the goat wanted the job. She told the others how much she liked flowers. So why not? Aunty had never been a judge before and so she was chosen.

The big day came. Everyone had been busy for days. The tent was full of flowers, colour and light. Perfect!

The judge, Aunty, came in first. She looked very important and was taken to the first display made by Bramble the sheep.

"So I just choose which flowers I like best?" Aunty asked.

"Yes, we walk along the table, and whichever display you think is best wins the prize. This is Bramble's display. He has spent all morning getting it right," said Blink the pig.

"It's called 'Daisies and Dandelions'," said Bramble proudly. The flowers were white and yellow and looked very pretty in a blue mug. Aunty looked at them carefully. She sniffed them. And then she ate them.

The others were so surprised, that they couldn't speak! They just stared as Aunty went to the next one, "Buttercups and Roses". She ate them too!

The goat tilted her head back, half closed her eyes in a very thoughtful sort of way, and compared "Buttercups and Roses" with "Daisies and Dandelions".

Moving along the line, she ate "Cowslips and Honeysuckle". Then she ate "Chrysanthemums and Poppies". Aunty wrinkled up her nose.

"Bit sour, that," she said. She turned at last and saw all the others looking at her with their mouths open. She looked from one to the other, red poppies drooping from the sides of her mouth.

"What?" she said, puzzled. "What!"

Rambo said, "You were supposed to judge how pretty the flowers are!"

"Flowers are pretty as well?" asked Aunty.

Everyone burst out laughing. They had to explain it all to Aunty. She thought the whole idea of just looking at flowers was very odd.

There was no time to pick more flowers and start again. Instead, they gave Bramble the prize... Aunty had decided that Bramble's flowers tasted the best!

At the end, the judge is always given a bunch of flowers as a small, thankyou gift. Aunty was very pleased... She ate it!

Good Teamwork

It had been raining heavily for so long on Old MacDonald's farm that even the ducks wished the sun would come out.

"I shall have to take the tractor down to the bottom meadow and see if the stream is overflowing. I can't have my sheep getting wet feet!" said the farmer one morning at breakfast.

Old MacDonald set off on the tractor, but he didn't get very far. The gateway to the farmyard had become very muddy. Brrrrm! Vrrrrm! Brrrrm! The tractor did its very best, but it was soon stuck fast in the mud!

The rain trickled off Old MacDonald's nose as he climbed down from his tractor. He shook his head when he saw the mud. "Only my old friend George can help me now," he said.

Old George the horse didn't want to go out in the rain, but he stood patiently as the farmer harnessed him to the tractor.

"Now pull, George, PULL!" he cried. Old George pulled with all his might – the tractor wouldn't budge.

"I need two horses," said Old MacDonald, and he went to fetch Tilly.

Tilly and Old George pulled as hard as they could – the tractor wouldn't move. The ducks stood in a long line, watching with interest.

"If only I had another horse," said Old MacDonald. Then, before you could say "You must be joking!" the farmer had brought out his four cows to help! He tied the cows to the tractor in front of the horses and then Old George, Tilly, Annabel, Poppy, Heather and Emily pulled and pulled and pulled – the tractor still refused to move.

Old MacDonald was getting desperate. One by one, he called on Percy the pig, Maria the sheep, Bruce the sheepdog and his two cats, Milly and Lazy – and even Mrs MacDonald!

The rain continued to pour down. The MacDonalds and their animals tugged and pulled. But the tractor stayed exactly where it was!

The cows looked very dejected. They were sad that they hadn't been able to help.

Old MacDonald decided to have one more try. He tied everyone on to the tractor again.

Then along came Jenny the hen. "I'll help!" she clucked, and she took a very firm hold of Milly the cat's tail in her beak.

Milly howled. Lazy yowled. Bruce yelped. Maria bleated. Percy oinked. The cows mooed and the horses neighed.

Then Old MacDonald and his wife shouted above the noise of all the animals. "One, two, three, *heave*!"

And the tractor went *Squelch! Slurp! Splodge!* and rolled slowly out of the mud at last. Everyone cheered in delight and relief – and tried not to fall over in the mud!

Just at that moment, the rain stopped and a beautiful rainbow filled the sky.

"You can't beat good teamwork," beamed Old MacDonald.

"Or hens!" clucked Jenny, proudly.

Just As Well, Really!

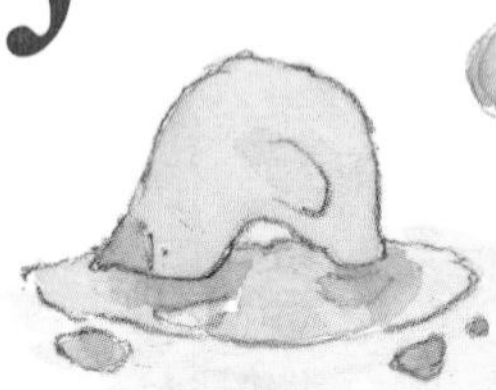

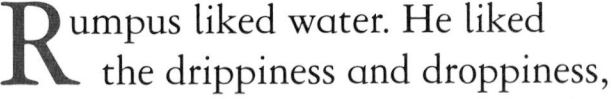

Rumpus liked water. He liked the drippiness and droppiness, the splashiness and sloppiness of it!

He liked it so much that, whenever there was water around, Rumpus somehow always managed to fall into it!

But Mum loved Rumpus, so every time she simply sighed and she mopped up the mess.

Rumpus loved mud.
He loved the
way you could
plodge in it.
splodge in it,
slide in it and
glide in it!
Rumpus somehow always managed to get covered in it!

But Dad loved Rumpus, so every time he simply sighed and he sponged off the splatters.

Rumpus enjoyed paint. He liked to splatter and dash it, to spread and splash it! Rumpus somehow managed to get it everywhere!

But Rumpus' brother loved him, so every time he simply sighed and cleaned himself up.

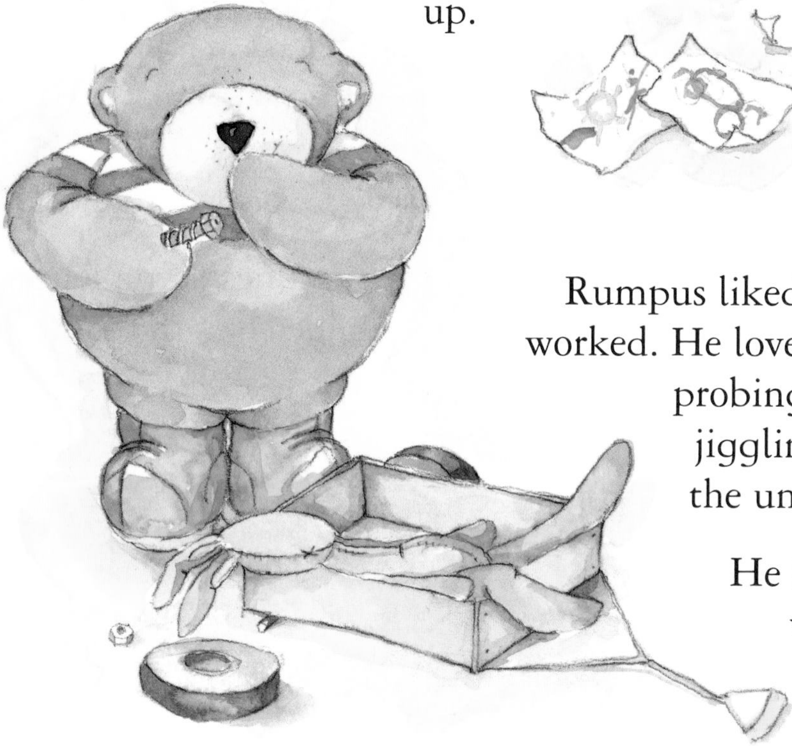

Rumpus liked to find out how things worked. He loved the prodding and probing, the wiggling and the jiggling, the unscrewing and the undoing!

He loved it so much that, whenever Rumpus was around, things didn't work for long!

But Granny loved Rumpus, so she simply sighed and she tidied away the clutter.

Rumpus loved his mum, dad, brother and granny. Rumpus' mum, dad, brother and granny loved Rumpus… just as well, really!

A Christmas Carol

In the bleak mid-winter
Frosty wind made moan,
Earth stood hard as iron,
Water like a stone;
Snow had fallen, snow on snow,
Snow on snow,
In the bleak mid-winter
Long ago.

Our God, heaven cannot hold Him,
Nor earth sustain;
Heaven and earth shall flee away
When He comes to reign:
In the bleak mid-winter
A stable-place sufficed
The Lord God Almighty,
Jesus Christ.

What can I give him,
Poor as I am?
If I were a shepherd
I would bring a lamb;
If I were a wise man
I would do my part –
Yet what I can, I give Him,
Give my heart.

Christmas Bells

I heard the bells on Christmas Day
Their old familiar carols play,
And wild and sweet
The words repeat
Of Peace on earth, Good-will to men!

And thought how, as the day had come,
The belfries of all Christendom
Had rolled along
The unbroken song
Of Peace on earth, Good-will to men!

Then from each black accursed mouth,
The cannon thundered in the South,
And with the sound
The carols drowned,
The Peace on earth, Good-will to men!

And in despair I bowed my head;
"There is no peace on earth," I said,
"For hate is strong
And mocks the song
Of Peace on earth, Good-will to men!"

Then peeled the bells more loud and deep:
"God is not dead, nor doth he sleep!
The Wrong shall fail,
The Right prevail,
With Peace on earth, Good-will to men!"

The Shepherd Boy's Song

He that is down, needs fear no fall,
He that is low, no pride;
He that is humble, ever shall
Have God to be his guide.

I am content with what I have,
Little be it, or much:
And, Lord, contentment still I crave,
Because thou savest such.

Fullness to such a burden is
That go on pilgrimage:
Here little, and hereafter bliss
Is best from age to age.

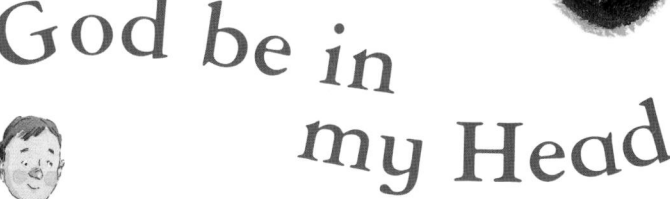

God be in my Head

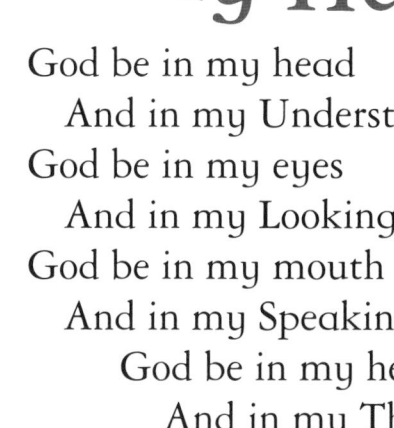

God be in my head
And in my Understanding.
God be in my eyes
And in my Looking.
God be in my mouth
And in my Speaking.
God be in my heart
And in my Thinking.
God be at mine end
And at my Departing.

Now Thrice Welcome Christmas

Now thrice welcome, Christmas,
Which brings us good cheer,
Minc'd pies and plum porridge,
Good ale and strong beer;
With pig, goose, and capon,
The best that can be,
So well doth the weather
And our stomachs agree.

Observe how the chimneys
Do smoke all about,
The cooks are providing
For dinner, no doubt;
For those on whose tables
No victuals appear,
O may they keep Lent
All the rest of the year!

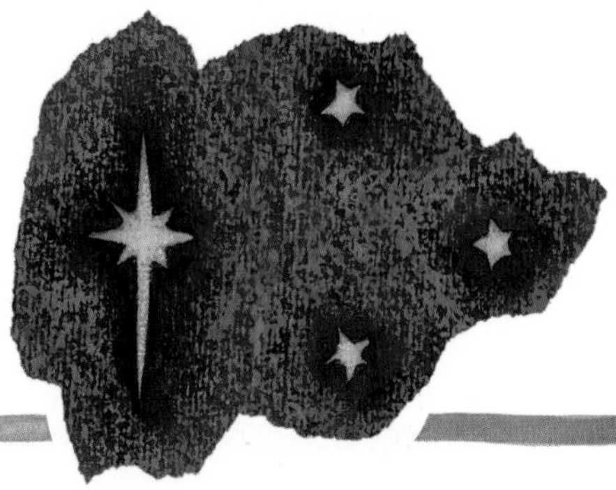

Bouncy Bunny

Mummy Rabbit had four beautiful babies. Three of them were tiny, soft balls of fluff – they were cuddly, quiet and very, very cute. They never made a noise and always did exactly what their mummy told them.

And then there was Benny!

Benny wasn't like his brother and sisters at all. He was large and loud and he had the biggest bunny feet in the whole world. And he loved to bounce! From dawn to dusk, Benny bounced everywhere – THUMP! THUMP! THUMP! Benny never did what Mummy Rabbit told him, but she loved him just the same.

Early one morning, Mummy Rabbit was woken by a very loud noise that made the whole burrow wibble and wobble. Soon, everyone was wide awake. What was that noise?

It was Benny, of course, bouncing and boinging around the burrow on his big, flat feet! "I'm *sure* he doesn't mean to be so noisy," said Mummy Rabbit, with a big yawn.

Benny bounced outside. Mummy Rabbit followed him, twitching her nose and checking for danger – *where had he disappeared to?*

Suddenly, there was a loud THUMP! THUMP! THUMP!

"I'm hungry," said Benny, bouncing past her. "I want my breakfast now, Mummy!" By the time all the bunnies had come out of the burrow and into the sunshine, Benny had bounced round the meadow three times!

"Benny, stop jumping around!" said Mummy Rabbit. "Stay with the others. It's dangerous out here."

"Now then, children," whispered Mummy Rabbit. "We're going over to the carrot field for breakfast. You must all stay very close to me and don't wander from the path."

But, of course, Benny didn't listen. With one huge bounce he disappeared through a hole in the hedge and was gone!

"Oh, dear! Oh, dear! Oh, dear!" said his mother. "What is he up to now?"

"Benny Bunny!" said Mummy Rabbit. "Where did you get that lettuce?"

"In that field!" replied Benny.

"You might have been caught," said Mummy.

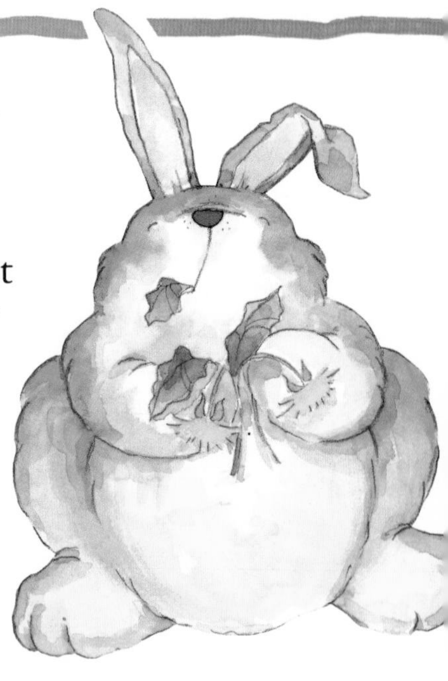

"I'm much too fast!" said Benny.

"Hurry, children," said Mummy Rabbit. "We must get to the carrot field before the farmer starts work."

But, of course, Benny wasn't listening. He was nibbling a dandelion. "Hmm, tasty!" he mumbled to himself.

"Benny Bunny!" called Mummy Rabbit, crossly. "Stop that munching and follow me!" Mummy Rabbit hopped under the gate and into the field. She collected lots of crunchy carrots. "Remember," she warned her bunnies. "Eat as much as you can, but stay close to me and watch out for the farmer."

The carrots were wonderful – fat and juicy and crisp. Soon, Benny's brother and sisters were all chewing happily. Benny bounced around on his big, flat feet, nibbling and munching as he went. Boing! Boing! Boing!

Mummy Rabbit and her bunnies munched their way across the field, nibbling a leaf here, crunching a carrot there. No one noticed that little Tufty, Benny's baby brother, wasn't following them.

Suddenly, Mummy Rabbit heard the roar of the tractor. "Quick!" she cried. "The farmer's coming!" Everyone hopped into the hedge – except Tufty!

Mummy Rabbit saw the tractor heading straight for Tufty. Its big wheels were squashing everything in its path. Her little baby crouched by the fence, his paws over his eyes, too terrified to move.

What could Mummy Rabbit do? Suddenly, Benny Bunny bounced past! In one huge bound, Benny was by Tufty's side. He bounced his brother out of the way, just before the tractor ran over him!

"I told you I was fast," giggled Benny.

"Benny Bunny!" said Mummy Rabbit, hopping over to Tufty and Benny. "You're so… "

"I know! I know!" said Benny. "I'm so *bouncy*!"

"Oh, yes!" said Mummy Rabbit. "I'm so glad that you *are* such a bouncy bunny!" and she gave him a great big kiss.

Cinderella

Once upon a time, there lived a very pretty girl. Sadly, when she was young, her mother died. Her father remarried, but the girl's stepmother was a mean woman with two ugly daughters. These stepsisters were so jealous of the young girl's beauty that they treated her like a servant and made her sit among the cinders in the kitchen.

They called her Cinderella, and before long everyone, even her father, had forgotten the poor girl's real name. Cinderella missed her real mother more and more each day.

One day, an invitation arrived from the royal palace. The king and queen were holding a ball for the prince's twenty-first birthday, and all the fine ladies of the kingdom were invited.

Cinderella's stepsisters were very excited when their invitations to the ball arrived.

"I will wear my red velvet gown!" cried the first stepsister. "And the black pearl necklace that Mother gave to me."

"And I will wear my blue silk dress with a silver tiara!" cried the other.

"Come, Cinderella!" they called. "You must help us to get ready!"

Cinderella helped her stepsisters with their silk stockings and frilly petticoats. She brushed and curled their hair and powdered their cheeks and noses. At last, she squeezed them into their beautiful ball-gowns.

But, even after all this, the two ugly stepsisters weren't nearly as lovely as Cinderella was in her rags. This made them very jealous and angry, and they began to tease Cinderella.

"Too bad you can't come to the ball, Cinders!" sneered the first stepsister.

"Yes," laughed the other one. "They'd never let a shabby creature like you near the palace!"

Cinderella said nothing, but inside, her heart was breaking. She really wanted to go to the ball. After her stepsisters left, she sat and wept.

"Dry your tears, my dear," said a gentle voice.

Cinderella was amazed. A kind old woman stood before her. In her hand was a sparkly wand that shone.

"I am your fairy godmother," she told Cinderella. "And you shall go to the ball!"

"But I have nothing to wear! How will I get there?" cried Cinderella.

The fairy godmother smiled.

The fairy godmother asked Cinders to fetch her the biggest pumpkin in the garden. With a flick of her magic wand she turned it into a golden carriage and the mice in the kitchen mousetrap into fine horses. A fat rat soon became a handsome coachman.

Cinderella could not believe her eyes.

Smiling, the fairy godmother waved her wand once more and suddenly Cinderella was dressed in a splendid ball-gown. On her feet were sparkling glass slippers.

"My magic will end at midnight, so you must be home before then," said the fairy godmother. "Good luck."

When Cinderella arrived at the ball, everyone was dazzled by her beauty. Whispers went round the ballroom as the other guests wondered who this enchanting stranger could be. Even Cinderella's own stepsisters did not recognise her.

As soon as the prince set eyes on Cinderella, he fell in love with her. "Would you do me the honour of this dance?" he asked.

"Why certainly, sir," Cinderella answered. And from that moment on he only had eyes for Cinderella.

Soon the clock struck midnight. "I must go!" said Cinderella, suddenly remembering her promise to her fairy godmother. She fled from the ballroom and ran down the palace steps. The prince ran after her, but when he got outside, she was gone. He didn't notice a grubby servant girl holding a pumpkin. A few mice and a rat scurried around her feet.

But there on the steps was one dainty glass slipper. The prince picked it up and rushed back into the palace. "Does anyone know who this slipper belongs to?" he cried.

The next day, Cinderella's stepsisters could talk of nothing but the ball, and the beautiful stranger who had danced all night with the prince. As they were talking, there was a knock at the door.

"Cinderella," called the stepmother, "quick, jump to it and see who it is." Standing on the doorstep was His Highness the Prince and a royal footman, who was holding the little glass slipper on a velvet cushion.

"The lady whose foot this slipper fits is my one and only true love," said the prince. "I am visiting every house in the kingdom in search of her."

The two stepsisters began shoving each other out of the way in their rush to try on the slipper. They both squeezed and pushed as hard as they could, but their clumsy feet were far too big for the tiny glass shoe.

Then Cinderella stepped forward. "Please, Your Highness," she said, shyly, "may I try?"

As her stepsisters watched in utter amazement, Cinderella slid her foot into the dainty slipper. It fitted as if it were made for her!

As the prince gazed into her eyes, he knew he had found his love – and Cinderella knew she had found hers.

Cinderella and the prince soon set a date to be married.

On the day of their wedding, the land rang to the sound of bells, and the sun shone as the people cheered. Even Cinderella's nasty stepsisters were invited. Everyone had a really wonderful day, and Cinderella and her prince lived happily ever after.

A Home for Archie

Archie, the black and white kitten, wasn't pleased. His owner, Tessa, hadn't given him his favourite fish for breakfast. All he had in his dish when he looked was some biscuits left over from the day before.

"Out you go," said Tessa, who was busy mopping the kitchen floor. And she pushed Archie out the door. Now Archie was quite cross. He flicked his tail and swished his head. "I know when I'm not wanted," he thought. "I'll find someone who knows how to look after me!"

He jumped on to the garden fence and into the neighbour's garden. Mrs Green always gave him a treat. But, as soon as his paws touched the ground, he heard a loud bark. Archie had forgotten about Bouncer, Mrs Green's playful new puppy. Bouncer raced across the lawn and started to bounce around Archie.

"It's far too rough here," thought Archie, scrambling up a handy tree. He jumped into the next garden. It belonged to Mr Reed. He didn't have a playful dog.

Archie strolled across the lawn and jumped up on to a window ledge. He was just about to squeeze through the open window, when he heard a squawk, followed by, "Who's a pretty boy?" Archie had forgotten about Mr Reed's parrot.

"It's far too noisy here," thought Archie. He made a quick escape through the hedge.

The next garden belonged to Granny Smith. She lived on her own and didn't have any pets. "Meow!" called Archie. Granny Smith always had something nice to eat.

"Pussy!" cried a little voice from inside. Archie stopped in his tracks as he heard the patter of little feet running along the hall carpet. Oh, dear! Granny Smith's grandson was visiting. He always pulled Archie's tail. Archie decided to disappear before he got outside.

Archie squeezed through a broken panel in the fence. The next garden was rather overgrown. Some new people had just moved in and Archie hadn't met them yet. He hoped they liked kittens.

Archie strolled towards the house. He hadn't got far before he heard a hiss behind him. He turned around just in time to see a Siamese cat preparing to pounce. Archie, who knew better than to get in a fight with a Siamese, didn't stop to say hello. He flew through the grass, leapt on to the fence and ran as fast as his paws would carry him.

"I don't think I'll bother going there again," thought Archie, when he stopped for breath. He sat on the fence and thought what to do next. As he sat there, a wonderful fish smell drifted past. Archie sniffed and followed his nose, his tail twitching at the thought of a wonderful fish breakfast.

Archie wandered past garden after garden where children screamed, birds squawked, dogs barked and cats wailed. At last his nose gave an extra big twitch and he stopped by a garden that was wonderfully quiet.

"Archie, there you are!" a voice called. It was Tessa. "I've finished cleaning, and I've got a lovely piece of fish for you!"

Archie purred. "Good old Tessa!" he thought. "She does know how to look after me, after all!"

I Saw a Slippery, Slithery Snake

I saw a slippery, slithery snake
  Slide through the grasses,
Making them shake.
  He looked at me with his beady eye.
"Go away from my pretty green garden," said I.
  "Sssss," said the slippery, slithery snake,
As he slid through the grasses,
  Making them shake.

Foxy's Hole

Put your finger in
  Foxy's hole.
Foxy's not at home.
  Foxy's out at the
back door
  A-picking at a bone.

Head, Shoulders, Knees and Toes

Head, shoulders, knees and toes, knees and toes,
  Head, shoulders, knees and toes, knees and toes,
And eyes and ears and mouth and nose.
  Head, shoulders, knees and toes, knees and toes.

Round About There

Round about there,
  Sat a little hare,
A cat came and chased him,
  Right up there!

Clap, Clap Hands

Clap, clap hands, one, two, three,
Put your hands upon your knees,
Lift them up high to touch the sky,
Clap, clap hands and away they fly.

Tall Shop

Tall shop in the town.
Lifts moving up and down.
Doors swinging round about.
People moving in and out.

Shoes

Baby's shoes,

Mother's shoes,

Father's shoes,

Policeman's shoes,

GIANT'S SHOES!

Five Little Soldiers

Five little soldiers standing in a row,
Three stood straight,
And two stood – so.
Along came the captain,
And what do you think?
They ALL stood straight,
As quick as a wink.

Who's Afraid of...?

The woodland animals were arguing...
"I scare everyone when I flutter around," said Bat.

"Rubbish," said Owl. "I'm much scarier than you. You should see animals freeze when I swoop down on them, hooting."

"That's nothing," scoffed Badger. "When I come trundling through the wood, everyone gets out of my way – fast!"

The animals turned to look at Mouse. "You decide," they said. "Tonight, we'll all try to frighten you, and you can judge who is the scariest animal."

"No problem," said Mouse, and he smiled. That evening, Mouse settled down under a tree and waited. Soon, he heard a flapping sound above his head.

"Hi, Bat," he said. "Out for your evening flight, are you?" Bat was surprised that Mouse hadn't been frightened.

"TWIT-TWHOOOO," came a sound from a branch nearby. Then Owl swept down, staring straight at Mouse with his piercing eyes.

"I know it's you, Owl," said Mouse. "You try the same old trick every night." Owl was amazed that Mouse hadn't been scared.

Then the ground began to shake and rumble, and Badger came charging out of the undergrowth, grunting and growling.

"Really, Badger," said Mouse. "You are so clumsy. You've snapped all those branches." Badger was stunned that Mouse hadn't been shocked.

"Well, who is the scariest animal in the wood?" asked Bat, Owl and Badger. "If it's none of us?"

"Well..." said Mouse. "You're not going to believe me but it's..."

Just at that moment, Bat felt something soft brush against his wing. He began to shiver.

Owl felt something dangly touch the top of his head. He began to tremble.

Badger felt something hairy running along his back. He began to shake.

"Help!" yelled the three animals.

"That," laughed Mouse, "is the scariest animal in the wood – it's Spider."

The Naughty Broom

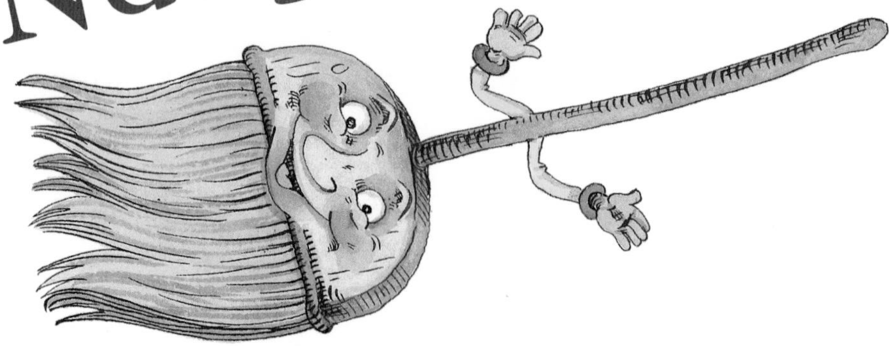

"Goodness me, what a lot of dirt and dust there is all over this kitchen floor," said the maid. She was a very house-proud maid, and didn't like dirt and dust on her floor one little bit. Out came the broom from its place in the cupboard in the corner, and soon the maid was busily sweeping the floor and brushing all the dirt and dust into a big dustpan.

Unfortunately, this kitchen also had elves living in it. They were too tiny to see, of course, but if you upset them they were very mischievous. As the broom worked away, it swept into one dark corner where the elves were having a party. Suddenly the king elf was swept away from their little table and into the dustpan! The next thing he knew he was being thrown, with all the other rubbish, on to the rubbish tip.

Coughing and spluttering with rage, the king elf finally climbed out from under all the rubbish and stood on top of it. He picked the dirt and dust out of his ears and nose, pulled a fish bone from out of his trousers and tried to look as king-like as he could, having just been thrown on to a rubbish tip. "Who did this?" he squeaked at the top of his voice. "I'll make someone very, very sorry indeed," he vowed.

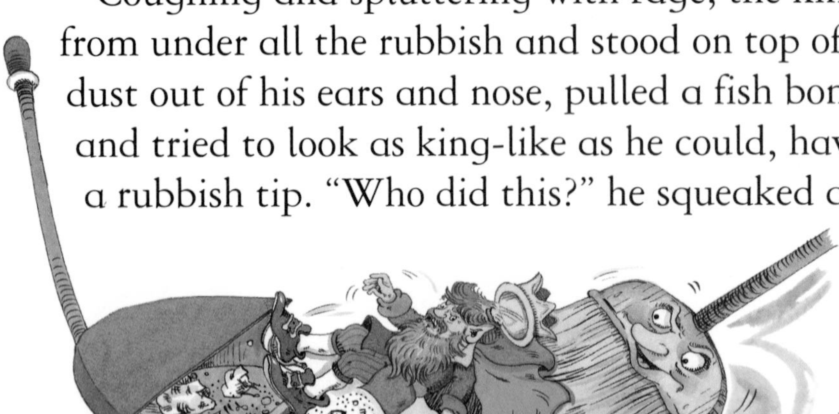

Eventually he made his way back to the house, and into the kitchen again.

The other elves looked at the king elf and did their best not to laugh, for the king elf was still looking very dirty and untidy, with bits of rubbish stuck all over him. But the other elves knew better than to laugh at the king, because he was likely to cast a bad spell on them.

"It was the broom that did it," chorused all the other elves.

"Right," said the king elf, "then I shall cast a bad spell on the broom."

The broom was by now back in its cupboard. The king elf marched over to the cupboard and jumped in through the keyhole. The king elf pointed to the broom and said,

"Bubble, bubble, gubble, gubble,
Go and cause a lot of trouble!"

And with that the broom suddenly stood to attention, its bristles quivering. It was night time now and everyone in the house was asleep. The broom opened its cupboard door and sprang into the kitchen. It then unlocked the kitchen door and went outside. Straight to the rubbish tip it went, and, with a flick of its bristles, swept a huge pile of rubbish back into the kitchen. Tin cans, dirt, dust, chicken bones and goodness knows what else all got swept on to the kitchen floor.

When the maid came into the kitchen, she couldn't believe her eyes. "Who has made this awful mess?" she said. She took the broom from the cupboard and swept all the rubbish back outside again.

The next night, the same thing happened. Once it was quiet and everyone in the house was asleep, out of its cupboard came the broom, and into the house came all the rubbish again, swept there as before by the naughty broom. This time, there were fish heads, old bottles and the soot from the fireplaces.

The maid was speechless. She cleaned up again, and then she got the gardener to burn all the rubbish, so that nothing else could be brought in – although she still had no idea how it had happened.

But that night, the naughty broom decided it would make a mess in a different way. Instead of sweeping in rubbish from outside, the broom flew up to the shelves and knocked all the jars to the ground. With a crash they fell to the floor and their contents went everywhere.

"Stop this AT ONCE!" shouted a voice suddenly. "What do you think you are doing?" said the voice again.

The voice had come from a very stern-looking fairy who was now standing on the draining board, with her hands on her hips. What the broom did not know was that one of the bottles it had knocked down contained a good fairy, imprisoned by the elves. Now she was at last free, the spell was broken and it was her turn to cast a spell.

"Broom, broom, sweep this floor,
Make it cleaner than ever before.
Find the elves that cast your spell,
And sweep them off into the well."

The broom went to work. It swept so fast that its bristles just became a blur. It swept in every corner, and every nook and cranny. Every bit of dirt and dust, and all the broken bottles, were swept into the dustpan and then out of the house. Then it came back and swept all the elves down into the well where they couldn't do any more mischief.

In the morning, the maid came down to find a spotlessly clean kitchen. She was puzzled to find some of the jars missing, but between you and me she was also rather pleased. It just meant that there were fewer things to dust.

Two Little Kittens

Two little kittens
  One stormy night,
Began to quarrel,
  And then to fight.

One had a mouse
  And the other had none;
And that was the way
  The quarrel begun.

"I'll have that mouse,"
  Said the bigger cat.
"You'll have that mouse?
  We'll see about that!"

"I will have that mouse,"
  Said the tortoise-shell;
And, spitting and scratching,
  On her sister she fell.

I've told you before
  'Twas a stormy night,
When these two kittens
  Began to fight.

The old woman took
  The sweeping broom,
And swept them both
  Right out of the room.

The ground was covered
  With frost and snow,
They had lost the mouse,
  And had nowhere to go.

So they lay and shivered
  Beside the door,
Till the old woman finished
  Sweeping the floor.

And then they crept in
  As quiet as mice,
All wet with snow
  And as cold as ice.

They found it much better
  That stormy night,
To lie by the fire,
  Than to quarrel and fight.

JANE TAYLOR

Epigram

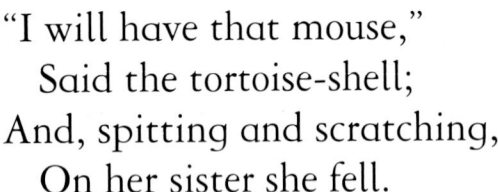

Engraved on the Collar of a Dog which I Gave to His Royal Highness

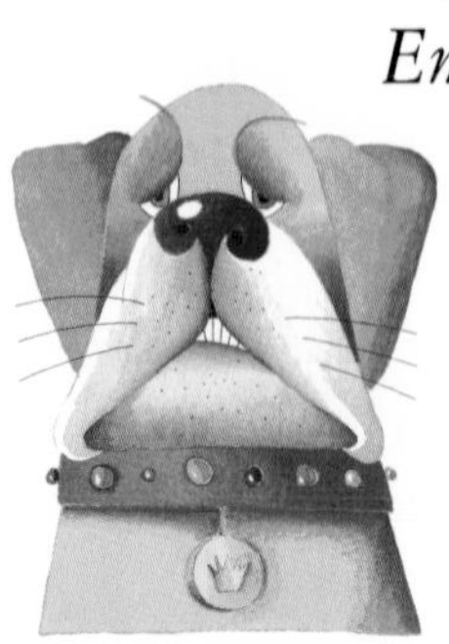

I am his Highness' Dog at Kew:
  Pray tell me, sir, whose dog are you?

ALEXANDER POPE

Mother Tabbyskins

Sitting at a window
  In her cloak and hat
I saw Mother Tabbyskins,
  The *real* old cat!
Very old, very old,
  Crumplety and lame;
Teaching kittens how to scold –
  Is it not a shame?

Kittens in the garden
  Looking in her face,
Learning how to spit and swear–
  Oh, what a disgrace!
Very wrong, very wrong,
  Very wrong and bad;
Such a subject for our song,
  Makes us all too sad.

Old Mother Tabbyskins,
  Sticking out her head,
Gave a howl, and then a yowl,
  Hobbled off to bed.
Very sick, very sick,
  Very savage, too;
Pray send for a doctor quick –
  Any one will do!

Doctor Mouse came creeping,
  Creeping to her bed;
Lanced her gums and felt her pulse,
  Whispered she was dead.
Very sly, very sly,
  The *real* old cat
Open kept her weather eye –
  Mouse! beware of that!

Old Mother Tabbyskins,
  Saying "Serves him right",
Gobbled up the doctor, with
  Infinite delight.
Very fast, very fast,
  Very pleasant, too –
"What a pity it can't last!
  Bring another, do!"

ELIZABETH ANNA HART

The Cat of Cats

I am the cat of cats. I am
  The everlasting cat!
Cunning, and old, and sleek as jam,
  The everlasting cat!
I hunt the vermin in the night –
  The everlasting cat!
For I see best without the light –
  The everlasting cat!

Wibble and the Earthlings

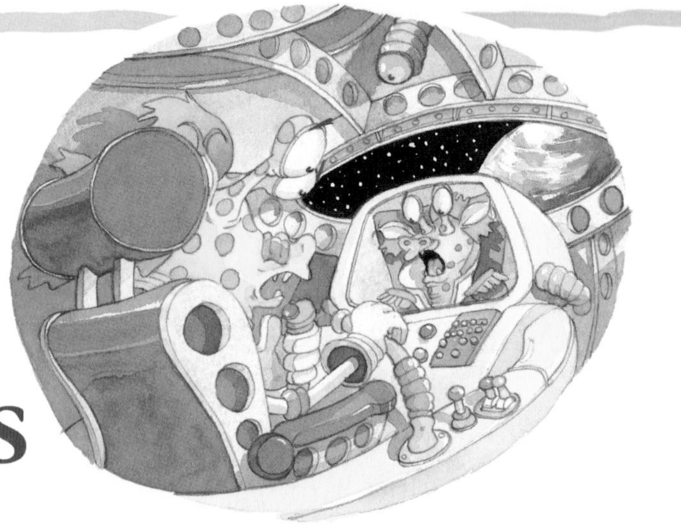

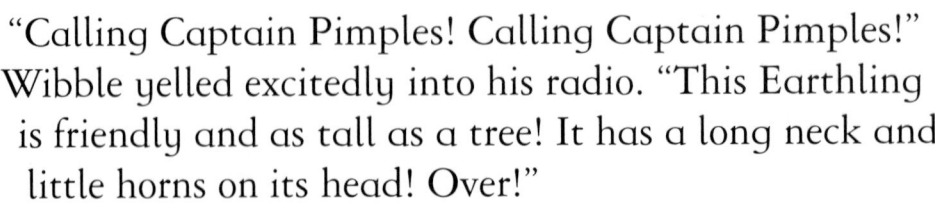

Wibble was from the planet Xog. He was on a mission. He'd been sent secretly to Earth to find out about Earthlings.

Wibble's spaceship wobbled on landing, but there wasn't too much damage. He radioed back to Xog to tell them his camera was broken.

"Just tell us what the Earthlings look like," said Captain Pimples, the leader of the Xogs, "and I'll draw them. Over!"

"I will," said Wibble. "Over and out!" He climbed down from the spaceship and looked around. There was a big sign saying ZOO.

"I wonder what that means," thought Wibble.

Wibble wobbled over to the nearest building and opened the door. He went up to a big wooden fence and saw his first Earthling. With its long neck, it leaned over the fence and gave Wibble a huge lick.

"Calling Captain Pimples! Calling Captain Pimples!" Wibble yelled excitedly into his radio. "This Earthling is friendly and as tall as a tree! It has a long neck and little horns on its head! Over!"

Wibble read the sign on the pen. GIRAFFE. Wibble, of course, didn't understand the signs and thought it must be an Earthling. Captain Pimples drew an Earthling with a long neck and two horns.

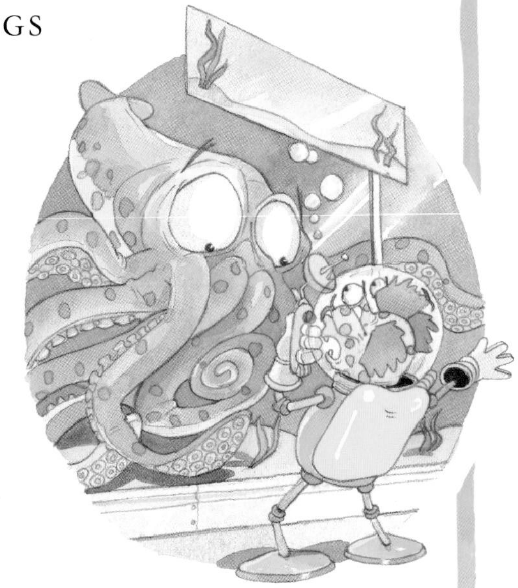

"Sounds okay so far!" said the captain. "Tell me more. Over"

Wibble wandered into the next fence, marked ELEPHANT. He switched on the radio.

"It's an enormous Earthling! It has huge ears and a long spout on the front like a teapot! Over!"

Captain Pimples quickly added the big ears and the spout to his drawing.

Next, Wibble went into a building marked AQUARIUM. He gazed around at the water tanks. One had a sign that said SQUID. "This Earthling has two huge eyes and is covered in orange spots! Over!" Wibble said into his radio. Captain Pimples added two huge eyes and orange spots to the drawing.

"Okay!" said Captain Pimples. "We've heard enough. Earthlings are big, hairy, have enormous ears and a spout, two huge eyes and orange spots. A bit like us really! Over and out!"

So Captain Pimples led an expedition to Earth. That is when Mr Brown the Zoo-keeper walked by.

Mr Brown had quite a shock seeing them, but not half as much as the Xogs had seeing him.

"Aargh!" cried the Xogs, and ran back to their spaceship. They took off and didn't stop until they reached planet Xog. Captain Pimples found Earth on his map, crossed it off and wrote underneath, "BEWARE – MONSTERS!"

Trampling Trotters

Mrs MacDonald had a little garden near the farmhouse. She was usually very busy on the farm, but she always managed to find time to look after the flowers. But the hens loved the flowers – for different reasons!

"Marigolds are delicious," Henry would mutter, talking with his beak full as usual.

Mrs MacDonald watched the hens through the kitchen window. If they tip-toed into the garden, she would rush out, waving a tea towel. "Shoo, you greedy birds!" she would call. "Leave my flowers alone!" And Henry and the hens would flutter away – for a while.

Early one morning, before Old MacDonald and Mrs MacDonald set off for the market, Mrs MacDonald had a word with the hens. "There is plenty of grain in the henhouse," she said. "There is no need for you to go into my garden. Do you understand?"

The hens eagerly nodded and clucked but, whether this meant that they agreed or not, Mrs MacDonald wasn't quite sure.

As Old MacDonald's van disappeared down the lane, Henry the cockerel strutted towards a particularly beautiful clump of marigolds.

Jenny the hen scuttled anxiously after him. "Henry," she warned, "if we peck at those flowers, Mrs MacDonald is going to be very angry. Remember what happened last time!"

Henry was just thinking about those dreadful scenes when something large and pink dashed past him.

It was Percy the pig!

In his hurry, Old MacDonald had left the gate of the pigsty slightly open. Percy loved to have a run around the farmyard, and now he was heading for Mrs MacDonald's lovely garden.

That naughty pig rolled over and over on the flower beds. He rooted under the begonias. He jumped on to the marigolds. The garden was in a terrible mess!

"Are you thinking what I'm thinking?" asked Henry glumly.

"Yes," gulped the hens, looking very worried and sad. "Mrs MacDonald will think it was us!"

Hens are not known for hard work, but Jenny, Henrietta, Mary, Victoria and Henry all worked very hard indeed. They propped up the squashed flowers and stamped down the uprooted earth. They tried very hard to clear up all the mess made by Percy's trampling trotters. But, when they heard Old MacDonald's van trundling down the lane, the garden still looked a sorry sight. There was no way that the hens could disguise Percy's mess. Henry and the hens had done their best, but the garden was ruined.

The hens and Henry lined up beside the garden, shifting nervously from foot to foot. There was a long silence as Mrs MacDonald surveyed the scene. The hens and Henry became more and more worried.

Finally, Mrs MacDonald said, "Don't worry, ladies. Don't worry, Henry. I can see that someone bigger and bulkier than you has been bouncing in my begonias. We'll all have a special snack before I deal with that pig!"

The Broom Song

Here's a large one for the lady,
  Here's a small one for the baby;
Come buy, my pretty lady,
  Come but o' me a broom.

Chairs to Mend

If I'd as much money as I could spend,
  I never would cry, "Old chairs to mend.
Old chairs to mend! Old chairs to mend!"
  I never would cry, "Old chairs to mend!"

My Maid Mary

My maid Mary,
  She minds the dairy,
While I go a-hoeing and mowing each morn;
  Merrily runs the reel,
And the little spinning wheel,
  Whilst I am singing and mowing my corn.

The Gossips

Miss One, Two, and Three
  Could never agree,
While they gossiped around
  A tea-caddy.

Cock-crow

The cock's on the wood pile
  Blowing his horn,
The bull's in the barn
  A-threshing the corn,
The maids in the meadow
  Are making hay,
The ducks in the river
  Are swimming away.

Puss in the Pantry

Hie, hie, says Anthony,
  Puss is in the pantry,
Gnawing, gnawing,
  A mutton, mutton bone;
See how she tumbles it,
  See how she mumbles it,
See how she tosses
  The mutton, mutton bone.

Buff

I had a dog
  Whose name was Buff,
I sent him for
  A bag of snuff;
He broke the bag
  And spilt the stuff,
And that was all
  My penny's worth.

Puss at the Door

Who's that ringing at my door bell?
A little pussy cat that isn't very well.
Rub its little nose with a little mutton fat,
That's the best cure for a little pussy cat.

Three Ghostesses

Three little ghostesses,
Sitting on postesses,
Eating buttered toastesses,
Greasing their fistesses,
Up to their wristesses.
Oh what beastesses
To make such feastesses!

Grig's Pig

Grandpa Grig
Had a pig,
In a field of clover;
Piggy died,
Grandpa cried,
And all the fun was over.

Cock Robin's Courtship

Cock Robin got up early
At the break of day,
And went to Jenny's window
To sing a roundelay.
He sang Cock Robin's love
To little Jenny Wren,
And when he got unto the end
Then he began again.

Washing Day

The old woman must stand
At the tub, tub, tub,
The dirty clothes to rub, rub, rub;
But when they are clean,
And fit to be seen,
She'll dress like a lady
And dance on the green.

Engine, Engine

Engine, engine, number nine,
Sliding down Chicago line;
When she's polished she will shine,
Engine, engine, number nine.

Thank You

Thank you for your portrait,
I think it's very nice.
I've put it in the attic
To scare away the mice.

Super Snakes

One morning, Seymour Snake's dad, Seymour Senior, said, "I have a surprise, son! Your cousin Sadie is coming to visit!"

"SSSensational!" said Seymour. "We'll have so much fun playing together, just like we did when we were little!"

"Sadie may have changed a bit since you last saw her," said Seymour Senior. "She's been going to Madame Sylvia's Snake School."

Later that day, Seymour slithered down the path to greet his cousin. "Sadie!" cried Seymour. "It's so good to see you! Come and meet my friends!" Seymour said eagerly. "You can play games with us, and..."

"Oh, I can't play games," Sadie interrupted. "Madame Sylvia always says, 'A well-behaved snake may slither and glide and wriggle and slide, but we DON'T swing or sway, or climb or play!'"

"You don't climb trees and swing from branches?" asked Seymour.

"Certainly not!" said Sadie.

"Well, will you come and meet my friends?" Seymour asked hopefully.

"Oh course," said Sadie. "It would be rude not to!"

"HEY, SEYMOUR!" shouted Maxine Monkey. "Come and play with us!"

"Sure!" said Seymour. "By the way, this is my cousin Sadie."

"HI, SADIE!" shouted Mickey. Maxine and Mickey always shouted! "You can come and play, too."

"No, thank you," said Sadie. "I'll just watch. I don't swing or sway, or climb or play." Sadie watched as Seymour climbed a tree, hooked his tail round a branch, and hung down with his mouth open.
Mickey and Maxine threw coconuts for him to catch.

"It really is fun, Sadie," Seymour called to his cousin. "Are you sure you don't want to try?"

"It looks good," Sadie admitted, "but no. Thank you anyway."

The game had just finished when Penelope Parrot arrived. After Seymour had introduced her to Sadie, Penelope asked if they would help her practise her stunt flying.

"Sure, Penelope!" said Seymour and wound himself round the branch to make two loops. With a whooosh Penelope zoomed through the loops.

Seymour spent hours hanging and swinging and climbing – he even climbed to the very top of a tree to talk to Jeremy Giraffe. Each time, Seymour invited Sadie to join him. And each time, Sadie looked more tempted – but she always said the same thing: "I mustn't swing or sway, or climb or play."

Later, Seymour spoke to his dad. "I'm sure Sadie wants to play with me and my friends," he said. "But she insists on only watching. How can I get her to join in?"

"The only way," said Seymour Senior, "is to get Sadie to see for herself how much fun she could be having."

Suddenly, Seymour had an idea.

"Thanks, Dad," he said. "That's just what I'll do!"

The next morning, Sadie was showing Seymour how gracefully she could glide, when suddenly there was a cry of "OH, NO!" Ellen, Emma and Eric Elephant were staring up into a tree. They looked very upset.

"What's wrong?" Sadie asked.

"We were playing Fling the Melon," said Ellen, "and it got stuck in the tree. Our trunks aren't long enough to reach it!"

"Oh, dear," said Sadie. "I'm sure Seymour will be happy to climb up and get it back for you. Won't you, Seymour? Seymour, where are you?"

Seymour had disappeared!

"Can't you help us, Sadie?" asked Emma.

"I'm sorry," said Sadie, "but I DON'T swing or sway…"

"…or climb or play," Emma finished. "We know about Madame Sylvia's rules. But didn't she also teach you that it's important to help others?" she asked.

"Well," said Sadie, "she did say that we must never pass up a chance to do a good deed."

"And this would be a good deed!" said Eric. "We would be so grateful!"

"I'll do it!" Sadie decided.

Up Sadie went, winding round the trunk, weaving her way up into the branches, until she reached the melon at the very top.

"Here it comes!" she shouted to the elephants, giving the melon a shove with her nose. It fell straight down into Ellen's waiting trunk. Then, with a quick wriggle, Sadie coiled herself round the branch and hung upside down above the elephants.

"This is SSSTUPENDOUS!" Sadie shouted. "I haven't had so much fun in years!"

She swung herself over to another tree, "WHEEEEEE!" she cried.

"I knew you'd enjoy this," said Seymour, slithering out from his hiding place. "You just had to try!"

"Come up, Seymour!" Sadie called. "We can swing and sway together."

"Here I come, Sadie," said Seymour, whizzing up the tree. "But what will you tell Madame Sylvia when you go back to school?"

"I'll tell her," said Sadie, "that we MUST climb and play, and swing and sway – ALL DAY!"

To which Seymour and his friends could only add a loud, "Hip-hip-HOORAY!"

Witches on the Run

At night, when it's all dark and scary, as you peek out over the bed covers, you might see shapes on the wall that will give you a fright! The thought of witches high on the ceiling, with broomsticks, pointed hats and capes can keep you awake all night.

If you think about it for too long, it just gets worse – you can hear their ear-piercing cackles and screams, and the bubbling of their cauldron. If you look really hard, you can see the cauldron glowing with a strange light as the witches cast their spells. They stir the dreadful mixture with a huge wooden spoon, adding slimy green bits. And as you lie there shaking, the smell from the spell gets stronger and the bubbling gets louder!

But there is one thing on the planet that all real witches hate, and that is anything that is clean, particularly clean children! Of course witches never wash, and the thought of children with clean skin makes them feel very ill. They much prefer to be smelly and grimy.

So, the next time you think there are witches flying on your ceiling, remember all you need is clean skin and they will vanish as quick as a flash!

Lonely Hearts

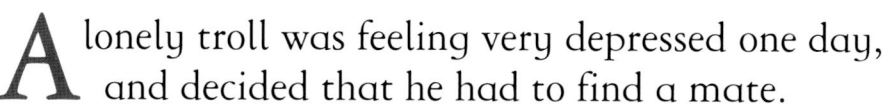

A lonely troll was feeling very depressed one day, and decided that he had to find a mate.

Although this was a good idea, it gave the troll a problem – where does a troll go to find a mate? After thinking for ages he decided the best thing to do was to advertise for someone in the local paper. This is what he wrote:

Fun-loving troll, dirty and smelly,
With damp slimy skin and big hairy belly
Nice muddy fingers and grubby wet toes,
Hot steamy breath and rings through each nose.
With stains on his shirt and holes in his socks,
Teeth that need cleaning and knots in his locks,
Tears in his trousers and scuffs on his shoe.
He's waiting to meet someone lovely like you.
He likes dirty ditches and hiding in holes,
Is certain to win when he fights other trolls.
Is very attentive, will woo you with roses,
After he's used them to pick both his noses!
He lives on his own, in a dark stinking pit,
Oozing with slime and covered in spit.
Now feeling lonely, he hopes there's a chance
He can meet someone similar for fun and romance!

Do you know anyone who will reply?

Goldilocks and the Three Bears

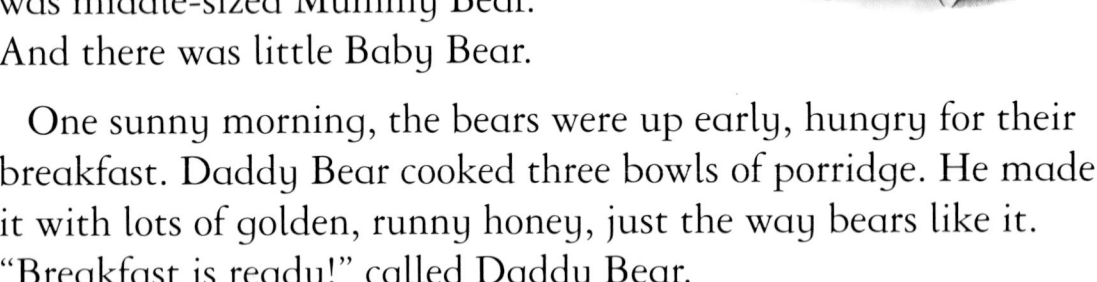

Once upon a time, deep in a dark green forest, there lived a family of bears. There was great big Daddy Bear. There was middle-sized Mummy Bear. And there was little Baby Bear.

One sunny morning, the bears were up early, hungry for their breakfast. Daddy Bear cooked three bowls of porridge. He made it with lots of golden, runny honey, just the way bears like it. "Breakfast is ready!" called Daddy Bear.

But, when he poured it into the bowls, it was far too hot to eat!

"We'll just have to let our porridge cool down for a while before we eat it," said Mummy Bear.

"But I'm hungry!" wailed Baby Bear.

"I know, let's go for a walk in the forest while we wait," suggested Mummy Bear. "Get the basket, Baby Bear. We can gather some wild berries as we go."

So, leaving the steaming bowls of porridge on the table, the three bears went out into the forest. The last one out was little Baby Bear, and he forgot to close the front door behind him.

The sun was shining brightly through the trees that morning and someone else was walking in the forest. It was a little girl called Goldilocks, who had long, curly golden hair and the cutest nose you ever did see.

Goldilocks was skipping happily through the forest when suddenly she smelt something yummy and delicious – whatever could it be?

She followed the smell until she came to the three bears' cottage. It seemed to be coming from inside. The door was open, so she peeped in and saw three bowls of porridge on the table.

Goldilocks just couldn't resist the lovely, sweet smell. So, even though she knew she wasn't ever supposed to go into anyone's house without first being invited, she tiptoed inside.

First, she tasted the porridge in Daddy Bear's great big bowl. "Ouch!" she said. "This porridge is *far* too hot!" So she tried the porridge in Mummy Bear's middle-sized bowl. "Yuck!" said Goldilocks. "This porridge is *far* too sweet!" Finally, she tried the porridge in Baby Bear's tiny little bowl. "Yummy!" she said, licking her lips. "This porridge is *just right*!" So Goldilocks ate it *all* up – every last drop!

Goldilocks was so full up after eating Baby Bear's porridge that she decided she must sit down. First, she tried sitting in Daddy Bear's great

big chair. "Oh, dear!" she said. "This chair is *far* too hard!" So she tried Mummy Bear's middle-sized chair. "Oh, no!" said Goldilocks. "This chair is *far* too soft!" Finally, she tried Baby Bear's tiny little chair. "Hurray!" she cried. "This chair is *just right*!" So she stretched out and made herself very comfortable.

But Baby Bear's chair wasn't *just right*! It was *far* too small and, as Goldilocks settled down, it broke into lots of little pieces!

Goldilocks picked herself up off the floor and brushed down her dress. Trying out all of those chairs had made her *very* tired. She looked around the cottage for a place to lie down and soon found the three bears' bedroom.

First, Goldilocks tried Daddy Bear's great big bed. "Oh no, this won't do!" she said. "This bed is *far* too hard!" So she tried Mummy Bear's middle-sized bed. "Oh, bother!" said Goldilocks. "This bed is *far* too soft!" Finally, she tried

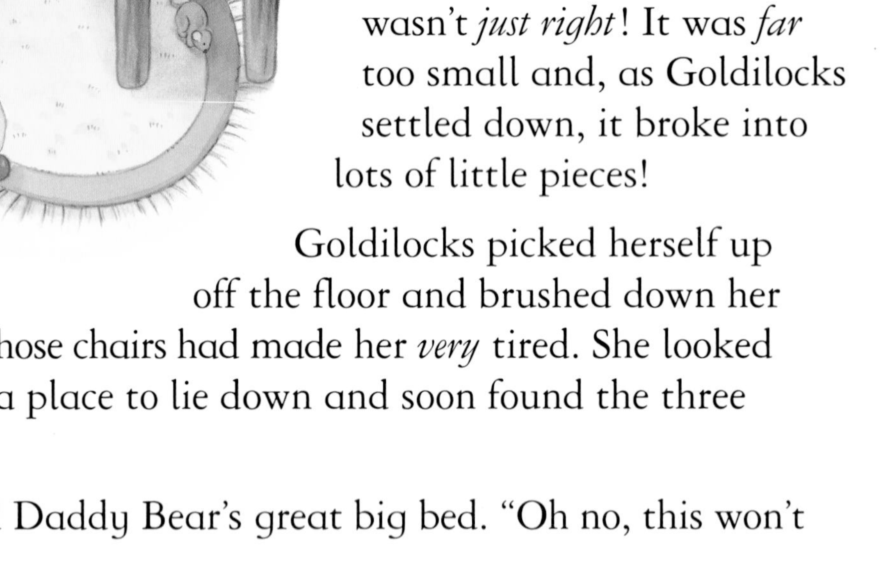

Baby Bear's tiny little bed. "Yippee!" she cried. "This bed is *just right*!" So Goldilocks climbed in, pulled the blanket up to her chin and fell fast, fast asleep.

Not long after, the three bears came home from their walk, ready for their yummy porridge. But, as soon as they entered their little cottage, they knew something wasn't quite right.

"Someone's been eating my porridge!" said Daddy Bear, when he looked at his great big bowl.

"Someone's been eating my porridge!" said Mummy Bear, looking at her middle-sized bowl.

"Someone's been eating *my* porridge," cried Baby Bear, looking sadly at his tiny little bowl. "And they've eaten it *all up*!"

Then Daddy Bear noticed that his chair had been moved. "Look, Mummy Bear! Someone's been sitting in my chair!" he said in his deep, gruff voice.

"Look, Daddy Bear! Someone's been sitting in my chair," said Mummy Bear, as she straightened out the cushions on it.

"Someone's been sitting in *my* chair, too," cried Baby Bear. "And look! They've broken it all to pieces!" They all stared at the bits of broken chair. Then Baby Bear burst into tears.

Suddenly, the three bears heard the tiniest of noises. Was it a creak? Was it a groan? Where was it coming from? No, it was a snore, and much to their surprise, it was coming from their bedroom. They crept up the stairs very, very slowly and quietly, to see what was making the noise…

"Someone's been sleeping in my bed!" cried Daddy Bear.

"Someone's been sleeping in my bed," said Mummy Bear.

"Someone's been sleeping in *my* bed!" cried Baby Bear. "And she's still there!"

All this noise woke Goldilocks up with a start.

When she saw the three bears standing over her, Goldilocks was very scared. "Oh, dear! Oh, dear! Oh, dear!" she cried, jumping out of Baby Bear's bed. She ran out of the bedroom, down the stairs, out of the front door and all the way back home – and she never ever came back to the forest again!

Leo Makes a Friend

Leo was quite a shy lion. His mum and dad, and brothers and sisters were all much bolder. Sometimes he was sad because he didn't have any friends.

"Mum," he said one day, "why will no one play with me?"

"They think you're frightening because you're a lion," said Mum.

It was a lovely day. Leo felt sure he would make a new friend today. He came to some trees where a group of small monkeys were playing. When the monkeys saw Leo they scampered to the top of the tallest trees.

"Hello," called out Leo. There was no answer. "Hello," he called again. "Won't you come down and play with me?"

There was silence. Then one of the monkeys blew a loud raspberry.

"Go away," he said rudely, "we don't like lions! Your teeth are too big," said the monkey, and giggled noisily.

Leo walked on until he came to a deep pool where a hippopotamus and her baby were bathing. Leo watched them playing in the water.

"Hi!" called out Leo. "Can I come in the water with you? I'd like to play," said Leo.

"So would I!" said Baby Hippo.

"No, you wouldn't," said Mummy Hippo firmly. "You don't play with lions."

Puzzled, Leo walked on. He came to an ostrich with its head buried in the sand. "What are you doing?" asked Leo in surprise.

"Hiding from you!" said the ostrich gruffly.

"But I can still see you!" said Leo.

"But I can't see you!" said the ostrich.

"Come and play with me instead," said Leo.

"Not likely," said the ostrich. "I don't play with lions, they roar!"

Leo walked on. He saw a snake sunbathing on a rock. He touched the snake gently with his paw. "Play with me," he said.

"Ouch!" said the snake. "Your claws are too sharp."

"I shall just have to get used to playing by myself," he thought.

Suddenly, he heard a small voice say, "Hello!"

Leo looked round. He could see a pair of yellow eyes peeping at him from behind a tree. "You won't want to play with me," said Leo grumpily, "I've got a loud roar, and sharp claws, *and* big teeth!"

"So have I," said the voice.

"What are you?" asked Leo, interested now.

"I'm a lion, of course!"

And into the clearing walked another little lion.

"I'm a lion, too," said Leo, grinning. "Would you like to share my picnic?"

"Yes, please!" said the other lion. They ate the picnic and played for the rest of the afternoon.

"I like being a lion," said Leo happily. He had made a friend at last!

The Story of Flying Robert

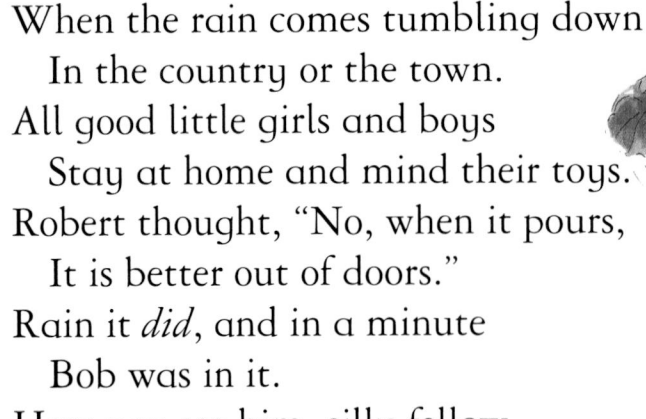

When the rain comes tumbling down
  In the country or the town.
All good little girls and boys
  Stay at home and mind their toys.
Robert thought, "No, when it pours,
  It is better out of doors."
Rain it *did*, and in a minute
  Bob was in it.
Here you see him, silly fellow,
  Underneath his red umbrella.

What a wind! Oh! how it whistles
  Through the trees and flowers and thistles!
It has caught his red umbrella;
  Now look at him, silly fellow,
Up he flies
  To the skies.

No one heard his screams and cries,
  Through the clouds the rude wind bore him,
And his hat flew on before him.
  Soon they got to such a height,
They were nearly out of sight!
  And the hat went up so high
That it really touched the sky.

No one ever yet could tell
  Where they stopped or where they fell:
Only, this one thing is plain,
  Bob was never seen again!

DR HEINRICH HOFFMANN

Little Wind

Little wind,
  blow on the hill-top;
Little wind,
  blow down the plain;
Little wind,
  blow up the sunshine;
Little wind,
  blow off the rain.

KATE GREENAWAY

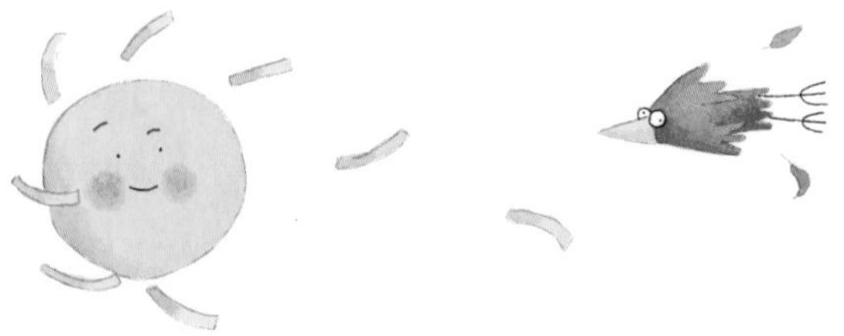

Ozymandias

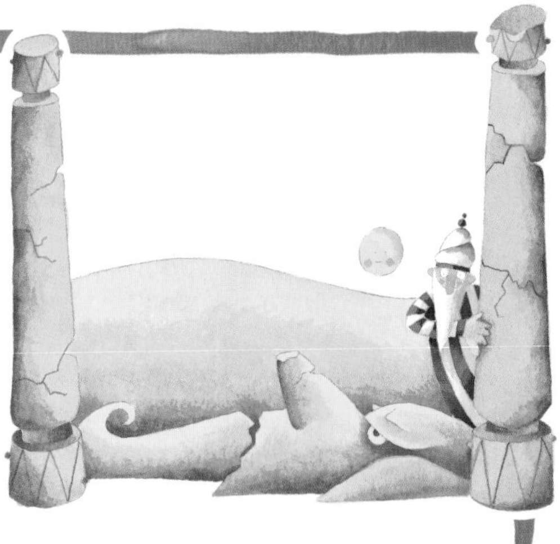

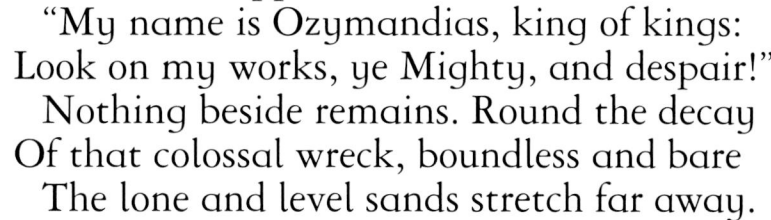

I met a traveller from an antique land
Who said: Two vast and trunkless legs of stone
Stand in the desert... Near them, on the sand,
Half sunk, a shattered visage lies, whose frown,
And wrinkled lip, and sneer of cold command,
Tell that its sculptor well those passions read
Which yet survive, stamped on these lifeless things,
The hand that mocked them, and the heart that fed:
And on the pedestal these words appear:
"My name is Ozymandias, king of kings:
Look on my works, ye Mighty, and despair!"
Nothing beside remains. Round the decay
Of that colossal wreck, boundless and bare
The lone and level sands stretch far away.

PERCY BYSSHE SHELLEY

When that I Was and a Tiny Little Boy

When that I was and a little tiny boy,
With hey, ho, the wind and the rain;
A foolish thing was but a toy,
For the rain it raineth every day.

But when I came to man's estate,
With hey, ho, the wind and the rain;
'Gainst knaves and thieves men shut their gate,
For the rain it raineth every day.

A great while ago the world begun,
With hey, ho, the wind and the rain;
But that's all one, our play is done,
And we'll strive to please you every day.

WILLIAM SHAKESPEARE

Oh Bear!

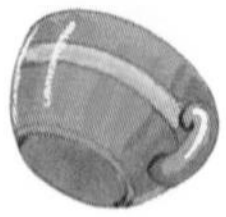

Bear and Rabbit had been shopping. There were posters all over town about the circus that was coming.

"I think I might join the circus," said Bear, as they reached his gate.

"What would you do?" asked Rabbit.

"I'd walk the tightrope," said Bear. "It's easy peasy." And he leapt on to the clothes line. He began well. He glided gracefully. He somersaulted superbly. He bowed beautifully. Then disaster struck! He wavered and wobbled. He teetered and tottered. He lost his grip and began to slip...

"Oh, Bear!" laughed Rabbit.

"Oh, well," said Bear, as he picked himself up. "Perhaps I'll ride a unicycle instead."

"But you haven't got a unicycle," said Rabbit.

"I can fix that," said Bear. And he disappeared into his shed. Soon, Rabbit heard tools clanging and banging.

"There," called Bear, as he cycled out of the shed. He began quite well. He pedalled up and down. He pirouetted round and round. Then disaster struck!

"Oh, Bear!" laughed Rabbit, as he watched Bear get tangled and the cycle get mangled.

"Oh, well," said Bear, as he picked himself up. "Perhaps I'll juggle instead."

"But there's nothing to juggle," said Rabbit.

"I'll find something," said Bear. And he disappeared into the kitchen. Rabbit waited patiently. He heard crockery clinking and clattering.

"There," said Bear, as he juggled down the path. He began quite well. He whirled the cups and twirled the plates. Higher and higher they went. Then disaster struck! The cups and plates crashed and the whole lot smashed.

"Oh, Bear!" laughed Rabbit.

"I'm not sure the circus is a good idea," Rabbit told Bear.

"Nonsense!" said Bear. "Of course it is."

"But Bear," said Rabbit. "You've tried walking the tightrope. You've tried riding a unicycle. You've tried juggling. And look what happened."

"Yes," said Bear. "Look what happened. I made you laugh. Now I know exactly the right job for me," and quickly he ran indoors.

It wasn't long before he was back.

"Oh, Bear!" laughed Rabbit. "You're right. You make a perfect clown!"

Pigs will be Pigs

Everyone on Old MacDonald's farm knew that it would soon be Old George's birthday. The horse had reached a great age – most of the animals couldn't even count that high!

"We must organise a special party with lots of games," Maria the sheep whispered.

"That would be fun for us," said Poppy the cow, "but George is a very old horse. I don't think he'd like it that much."

Now, a pig's mind is never far from food, so it was not surprising when Percy suggested that they have a feast! "If we all keep some of our food back each day, we'll have lots saved up by George's birthday!" he said.

Everyone agreed that a feast was a good idea. The animals found a place at the back of the barn to hide the food – well away from Old MacDonald's prying eyes!

Soon, they had a huge pile of the most tasty, delicious and scrummy things ready for the party – and they were all getting very excited as the day drew nearer.

The evening before the feast, the pile of food was massive! The animals knew that Mr and Mrs MacDonald would be going to market early the next morning – they would have the whole farmyard all to themselves.

As night fell, some of the little animals were too excited to sleep.

As the moon rose over Old MacDonald's farm, Percy found himself wide awake. He tossed and turned, and turned and tossed, trying very hard not to think about the piles of delicious food.

Now, there is nothing that makes a pig so hungry as knowing that there are good things to eat nearby. Even though he knew that the food was meant for the party, and no matter how hard he tried, Percy simply could not forget that food.

"Just a mouthful or two wouldn't matter," he said to himself. "No one would miss the odd juicy apple, or a handful of corn, would they?" Percy's mouth began to water.

Percy crept out of his sty, walking on trotter tiptoes. He reached the door of the barn. Creeeaaaaaak! He pushed it open with his nose and went inside.

"GOT YOU, PERCY PIG!" clucked Jenny the hen, jumping up from behind a bale of straw. "Percy, old thing," she grinned, "we knew you wouldn't be able to resist all this gorgeous food, so we've been on guard all week. Go straight back to bed and wait until morning." Percy blushed – he had been caught out!

The next morning, as all the animals tucked in to the fabulous feast, Percy told the others that he was sorry.

"Never you mind," they said. "Pigs will be pigs! Here, have another apple, Percy!"

Naughty Chester Chick

Chester was a naughty chick,
He really was quite bad
And every day, the things he did
Would make his mum go mad!

He'd yell, "Ooh, quickly, Mary-Lou,
There's something you should see!"
But while his sister took a look,
He'd gobble up her tea!

He'd climb up on the hen house roof
And crow just like his dad,
But Chester's screechy-scratchy yells
Just drove the whole farm mad!

He's wait until his poor, old mum
Had settled for a nap
And then he'd run and, with a jump,
He'd land right in her lap!

"All right! That's it! I've had enough!"
His angry mummy cried.
"The others all can have a treat,
But you must stay inside!"

So, Chester missed out on
the treat,
Which really was so sad,
Because they all had
sunflower seeds,
"My favourites!" moaned the lad.

"Mum, from now on,
I'll be good! I promise!"
Chester cried.
"I'm sorry I have been so bad.
Please may I come outside?"

"All right," his mum said,
"out you come!
But, Chester, don't forget,
I don't give treats to naughty boys
So, was Chester good? You bet!

The Chirpy Chatty Chicks

Poor Billy Bull can't get to sleep!
Those chicks keep chirping, "Cheep!
Cheep! Cheep!"
Each time he shuts his weary eyes,
They wake him up with their
loud cries.
"We're hungry, Mum!" they shout
and yell.
"Our tums are empty! Can't you tell?"

So, Billy Bull gets really mad.
"I've had enough! I'll tell their Dad!
All day long, they chirp and cheep.
I wouldn't mind – but
I can't sleep!
I'll never get to
rest my head
Until these noisy
chicks are fed!"

The mighty bull
stomps from his stall.
His great, big face peers
round the wall.
But, just as he begins to shout,
Five fluffy chicks come
trotting out
And run around
big Billy's feet.
"Oh!" Billy cries.
"You're really sweet!"

So now the chicks have a new mate,
Who thinks that they
are really great
And doesn't mind that
he can't sleep,
Because they always cry,
"Cheep! Cheep!"
He smiles now when they
call to say,
"Hey Billy! Please come
out to play"

Esmerelda the Rag Doll

At the back of the toy cupboard on a dark and dusty shelf lay Esmerelda the rag doll. She lay on her back and stared at the shelf above, as she had done for a very long time. It seemed to Esmerelda that it was many years since Clara, her owner, had taken her out of the cupboard. Now her lovely yellow hair was all tangled and her beautiful blue dress was creased, torn and faded. Clara always played with the newer toys at the front of the cupboard. Every time Clara put the toys back in the cupboard, Esmerelda felt herself being pushed further towards the back – poor Esmerelda might have suffocated if it wasn't for a hole at the back of the cupboard, which enabled her to breathe.

These days Esmerelda felt very lonely. Until recently a one-eyed teddy bear had been beside her on the shelf. But one day he had fallen through the hole at the back of the cupboard. Esmerelda missed him dreadfully. Now she, too, could feel herself being pushed towards the hole. She felt a mixture of excitement and fright at the prospect of falling through it.

Sometimes she imagined that she would land on a soft feather bed belonging to a little girl who would really love her. At other times she thought that the hole led to a terrifying land full of monsters.

One day Esmerelda heard Clara's mother say, "Now Clara, today you must tidy up the toy cupboard and clear out all those old toys you no longer play with."

Esmerelda could see Clara's small hands reaching into the cupboard. She couldn't bear the thought of being picked up by the little girl and then discarded. "There's only one thing to do," she said to herself. She wriggled towards the hole, closed her eyes and jumped. Esmerelda felt herself falling, and then she landed with a bump on something soft.

"Watch out, my dear!" said a familiar voice. Esmerelda opened her eyes and saw that she had landed on One-eyed Ted.

The two toys were so overjoyed to see each other again that they hugged one another. "What shall we do now?" cried Esmerelda.

"I have an idea," said Ted. "There's a rusty old toy car over there. I wanted to escape in it, but I can't drive with only one eye. What do you think? Shall we give it a go?"

"Yes, yes!" exclaimed Esmerelda, climbing into the driver's seat.

One-eyed Ted had found the key and was winding up the car. "Away we go!" he called as they sped off.

"Where are we going?" shouted Esmerelda.

"To the seaside," replied Ted.

"But I don't know the way, we'll have to ask someone."

The rusty car sped along. When they reached the top of a mountain they met a sheep. Now, as you know, sheep never listen properly. "Excuse me," said Esmerelda, "where can we find the beach?"

Well, the silly sheep thought Esmerelda was asking where they could find a peach! "Down there," she bleated, nodding at an orchard in the valley below.

Esmerelda and Ted leaped back into the car and sped off down the mountainside, but when they reached the orchard there was no sign of water, of course – just a lot of peach trees. They were very puzzled. Just then a mole popped his head out of the earth. "Excuse me," said Ted, "would you happen to know how we can find the seaside?"

Now the mole was very wise, but unfortunately moles are also, as you know, very short-sighted. He peered at Esmerelda's blue dress. "That patch of blue must surely be a river, and rivers run into the sea," he thought.

"Just follow that river," he said, "and you'll end up at the seaside. Good day!" And with that he disappeared underground again – which left Esmerelda and Ted even more puzzled, for there was no sign of a river in the orchard.

"Don't give up," said Ted, and they climbed back in the rusty car and set off again.

After a short while the car started to splutter and then it came to a complete halt at the side of the road. "What shall we do now?" cried Esmerelda.

"We'll just have to wait here," said Ted. After a very long time they heard footsteps, and then Esmerelda felt herself being picked up.

"Look – it's a dear old tatty rag doll," said a voice. Esmerelda looked up and saw that she was being carried by a little girl.

Ted and the rusty car had been picked up by the girl's father. "Let's take them home and look after them," the man said.

Soon the toys found themselves in a house. The little girl carried Esmerelda, One-eyed Ted and the rusty car upstairs to her bedroom and put them down on a window sill. "I'll be back soon," she whispered.

Esmerelda looked out of the window and nearly danced for joy. "Look, look Ted," she shouted. For out of the window she could see the road, and beyond the road was a beach and then the sea. "We reached the seaside after all," she cried.

Esmerelda, Ted and the rusty car lived happily in the house beside the sea. Esmerelda's hair was brushed and plaited and she was given a beautiful new dress and Ted had a new eye sewn on. The rusty car was painted and oiled. Most days the little girl took her new toys down to the beach, and the days in the dark toy cupboard were soon forgotten. The little girl told her friends the story of how she had found her three best toys lying beside the road. As for the toys, they sometimes talked about that strange day when they had such an adventure – and they'd burst out laughing.

Like a Duck to Water

Mrs Duck swam proudly across the farm pond followed by a line of fluffy ducklings. Hidden in the safety of the nest Dozy Duckling peeked out and watched them go. He wished he was brave enough to go with them but he was afraid of the water! Instead, he pretended to be asleep, and Mrs Duck told the others to leave him alone.

When they returned that night they told him tales of all the scary animals they had met by the pond.

"There's a big thing with hot breath called Horse," said Dotty.

"There's a huge smelly pink thing called Pig," said Dickie.

"But worst of all," said Doris, "there's a great grey bird, called Heron. Pig says he gobbles up little ducklings for breakfast!"

At that all the little ducklings squawked with fear and excitement.

Next morning, Mrs Duck hurried the ducklings out for their morning parade. Dozy kept his eyes shut until they had gone, then looked up to see a great grey bird towering over him! He leapt into the water crying, "Help, wait for me!" But the others started laughing!

"It's a trick! Heron won't eat you. We just wanted you to come swimming. And you've taken to it like a duck to water!"

I Remember, I Remember

I remember, I remember
The house where I was born,
The little window where the sun
Came peeping in at morn;
He never came a wink too soon
Nor brought too long a day;
But now, I often wish the night
Had borne my breath away.

I remember, I remember
The fir trees dark and high;
I used to think their slender tops
Were close against the sky:
It was a childish ignorance,
But now 'tis little joy
To know I'm farther off from Heaven
Than when I was a boy.

Meet-on-the-Road

"Now, pray, where are you going?" said Meet-on-the Road.
"To school, sir, to school sir," said Child-as-it-Stood.
"What have you in your basket, child?" said Meet-on-the-Road.
"My dinner, sir, my dinner, sir," said Child-as-it-Stood.

"What have you for dinner, child?" said Meet-on-the-Road.
"Some pudding, sir, some pudding, sir," said Child-as-it-Stood.
"Oh, then I pray, give me a share," said Meet-on-the-Road.
"I've little enough for myself, sir" said Child-as-it-Stood.

"Pray, what are those bells ringing for?" said Meet-on-the Road.
"To ring bad spirits home again," said Child-as-it Stood.
"Oh, then I must be going, child!" said Meet-on-the-Road.
"So fare you well, so fare you well," said Child-as-it-Stood.

The Dumb Soldier

When the grass was closely mown,
  Walking on the lawn alone,
In the turf a hole I found
  And hid a soldier underground.

Spring and daisies came apace;
  Grasses hid my hiding-place;
Grasses run like a green sea
  O'er the lawn up to my knee.

Under grass alone he lies,
  Looking up with leaden eyes,
Scarlet coat and pointed gun,
  To the stars and to the sun.

When the grass is ripe like grain,
  When the scythe is stoned again,
When the lawn is shaven clear,
  Then my hole shall reappear.

I shall find him, never fear,
  I shall find my grenadier;
But, for all that's gone and come,
  I shall find my soldier dumb.

Robert Louis Stevenson

A Child's Laughter

All the bells of heaven may ring,
  All the birds of heaven may sing,
All the wells on earth may spring,
  All the winds on earth may bring
All sweet sounds together;
  Sweeter far than all things heard,
Hand of harper, tone of bird,
  Sound of woods at sundawn stirred,
Welling water's winsome word,
  Wind in warm wan weather.

Golden bells of welcome rolled
  Never forth such notes, nor told
Hours so blithe in tones so bold,
  As the radiant mouth of gold
Here that rings forth heaven.
  If the golden-crested wren
Were a nightingale – why, then,
  Something seen and heard of men
Might be half as sweet as when
  Laughs a child of seven.

Tractor Trouble

Old MacDonald loves his tractor, but it can be as troublesome as the naughtiest piglet. One cold and frosty morning, it sat in the barn and refused to start.

"I must plough the far field before the new lambs are born," groaned Old MacDonald, "while I still have the time."

But the tractor did not start. It coughed and wheezed, and a few puffs of black smoke came out of the exhaust. But there was none of the roaring noise that Old MacDonald liked to hear.

"I'll just have to call the mechanic," he said crossly, stomping towards the farmhouse.

Unfortunately, the mechanic was busy for the rest of the week.

"Listen carefully while I tell you what to do," he told Old MacDonald helpfully.

So the farmer trudged back to the barn, his head full of thoughts of pipes, plugs and pumps – not at all sure he had understood what the mechanic had said!

But, the moment Old MacDonald opened up the engine's bonnet, he knew exactly what the problem was – and he wasn't angry at all. A little mouse had made her nest there and was busy taking care of six tiny babies!

"Don't worry," whispered Old MacDonald, "I'll find you somewhere better to live."

So Old MacDonald started searching the barn for a special place for the mouse and her family to make their home. It had to be warm and cosy. It had to be somewhere that Milly and Lazy the cats couldn't reach.

Looking through all the junk and clutter stored in the barn was hot work, so Old MacDonald hung his coat from a beam. By the end of the morning, the barn looked a lot tidier, but he still hadn't found a home for the mouse family.

"Come and have your lunch," called his wife. "And don't even think about bringing those mice into my kitchen!"

But, as Old MacDonald went to take his coat down from the beam, he suddenly had a good idea…

Ten minutes later, the mouse family had a lovely new home, and Old MacDonald was enjoying his lunch at last. All that work to tidy the barn had made him hungry, and he was very pleased to have found a home for the mouse family.

"I'm off to do the ploughing now," he said to his wife when he had finished. "Where is my old jacket?"

Mrs MacDonald looked surprised. "Why?" she began. Then she smiled. "I suppose you've lent your coat to someone else for a while."

Old MacDonald found his old coat and went back to the barn. This time the tractor roared into life.

"A little less noise until we get outside, old friend," smiled Old MacDonald. "We don't want to wake the babies."

Lion

It was Lion's birthday.

"The animals must have forgotten," said Lion. "No one has wished me happy birthday."

Lion walked slowly through the jungle, feeling very sad.

"Let's surprise Lion with a birthday party!" said Elephant.

"We'll bring our birthday presents," said Giraffe...

..."and we will think of lots of games to play," said Monkey.

"We'll dance and have fun," said Zebra.

"HAPPY BIRTHDAY, LION!" called Hippo.

"Happy birthday!" sang the animals.

"What a SURPRISE!" roared Lion.

The animals had fun all afternoon, it was the best party ever!

Monkey

Tiny Monkey looked sad. He did not know how to climb.

The animals decided they would try to cheer him up.

"I'll bring some leaves to shade you from the sun," said Giraffe.

"I will bring feathers to make a cosy bed for you," said Parrot.

"And a long bedtime story will help you to sleep," yawned Lion.

"But I don't want to sleep," said Tiny Monkey. "I want to learn to climb."

"I will teach you, Tiny Monkey," said Big Monkey.

"Just follow me. Cling with your feet, and swing your tail – like this!"

Taking a deep breath, Tiny Monkey raced up the tree, clinging to the branches.

"Look at me! I'm the best climbing monkey in the forest!" he called.

Morag the Witch

Morag was just an ordinary witch – until the day she enrolled for a course of advanced spell casting at the Wizard, Witch and Warlock Institute of Magic. For that was where she met Professor Fizzlestick. Now Professor Fizzlestick was a very wise old man indeed. Morag, on the other hand, was a very vain young witch who didn't know as much as she thought she did. She could turn people into frogs if they really deserved it, and do other simple spells like that, but she still had a lot to learn. The problem was, Morag thought she was the most perfect little witch in the whole wide world.

Morag's adventure started on her very first day at school. At the beginning of the day, after all the young witches and wizards had made friends and met the teachers, they were called in one by one to talk to Professor Fizzlestick.

"Now, young Morag Bendlebaum, I taught both your mother and your father," said the professor in a very serious voice, "and a very fine witch and wizard they turned out to be, too. So, what kind of witch do you think you are going to be?"

Without giving this any thought at all, Morag blurted out, "I'm better than my parents, and I'm probably better than you!"

This answer surprised even Morag, for although she thought this was true, she didn't actually mean to say it.

"Don't be surprised by your answers," said Professor Fizzlestick, "there is a truth spell in this room, and whatever you truly believe you must say. And I have to say that you appear to have an enormously high opinion of yourself. Why don't you tell me what makes you so very good?"

"I'm clever," said Morag, "and I'm good, and I'm always right."

"But what about your dark side?" said Professor Fizzlestick.

"I'm sorry to disappoint you," replied Morag quite seriously, "but I'm afraid I simply don't have a dark side."

"Well in that case I would like you to meet someone very close to you," said Professor Fizzlestick with a smile on his lips.

Morag looked over to where Professor Fizzlestick pointed, and was startled to see on the sofa next to her… herself!

As Morag stared open-mouthed with astonishment, the professor explained that if, as she believed, she was without a dark side, then there was absolutely nothing to worry about. "If, however," he continued, "you have deceived yourself, then I'm afraid you are in for a few surprises."

With that the professor dismissed them both from the room and told them to get to know each other. As Morag and her dark side stood outside the professor's room, Morag's dark side jumped and whooped for joy.

"At last," she cried, "I'm free. I don't have to sit and listen to you telling me what's right all day;

I don't have to keep persuading you to choose the biggest slice of cake before your brother – in fact, I don't, I repeat don't, have to do anything that you tell me, at all."

So saying, she broke into a run and rushed down the corridor, knocking over chairs and bumping into other little witches and wizards along the way. Morag was horrified. She would have to follow her dark side and stop her from causing trouble. Morag chased after her dark side and finally caught up with her at the chocolate machine. "Don't eat all that chocolate," cried Morag. "You know it's bad for your teeth and will ruin your appetite for lunch!"

"Tsk!" scoffed her dark side. "You might not want any chocolate but I certainly do!" And with that she ran off once more, dropping chocolate on to the freshly polished floor as well as pushing a big piece into her mouth.

Just then, the bell sounded for lunch. Although Morag felt she ought to find her dark side, she also knew that the bell was a command to go to the dining hall, and she mustn't disobey it. Morag sat down to lunch next to her friend, Topaz. She was just about to tell her what had happened, when she saw that Topaz was not eating her vegetables! Morag scolded Topaz for this, and gave her a lecture on eating healthily.

Topaz stared at Morag in amazement, then peered closely at her. "What's happened to you?" she asked.

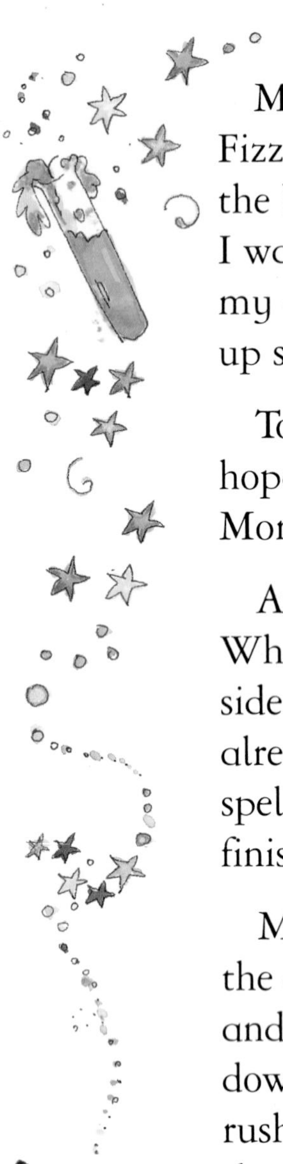

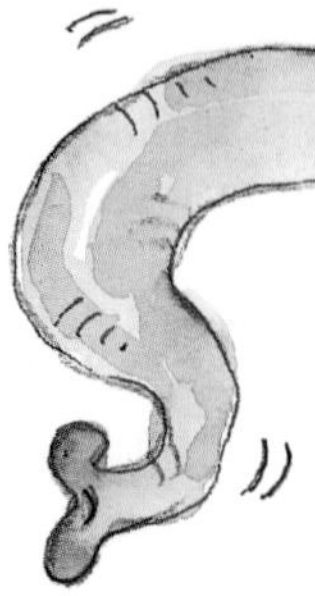

Morag explained what had happened in Professor Fizzlestick's office, and then declared, "And you know, it's the best thing that has ever happened to me. I thought I was good before, but now I'm even better. I never want my dark side back again, but we must find her and lock her up so that she can do no harm."

Topaz agreed that they must find her dark side, but secretly hoped that she and Morag would be re-united. Morag wasn't Morag without her dark side.

After lunch, Morag went for her first lesson of the afternoon. When she walked into the classroom she discovered her dark side already there, busy preparing spells! Morag's dark side had already prepared a "turning a nose into an elephant's trunk" spell and a "turning skin into dragons' scales" spell and was just finishing off a "turning your teacher into stone" spell!

Morag suddenly heard a trumpeting noise from the back of the classroom. She turned to find that the wizard twins, Denzil and Dorian Dillydally, had both sprouted huge grey trunks down to the ground where their noses had been. Morag rushed over to her dark side to make her change them back, but before she could reach her she tripped over a creature crouching down on the floor. It looked just like a dragon and it was wearing a purple and white spotted dress last seen on Bettina Bumblebag. Morag's dark side was casting spells all over the place. "Oh, why doesn't the teacher stop her!" cried Morag to Topaz.

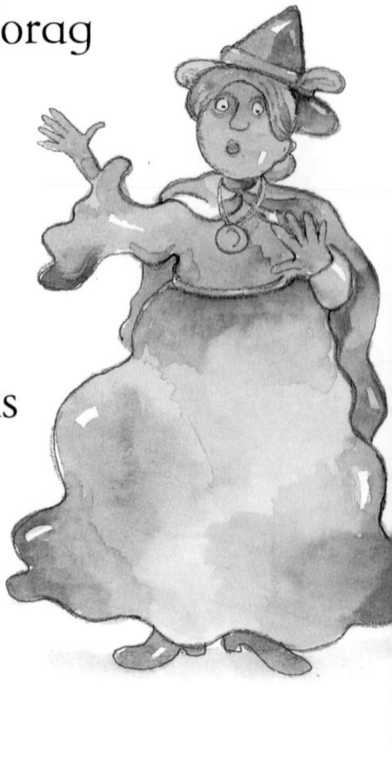

I'm sure you've guessed by now. Nice Miss Chuckle was entirely turned to stone from head to foot!

Just then Professor Fizzlestick walked into the classroom. Morag pointed to her dark side, still making spells at the front of the classroom.

"Lock her up immediately," Morag begged the professor.

"I'm afraid that you are the only one who can do that," said the wise old man. "The two of you are inseparable and you need each other. Without your dark side you would be unbearable and without you she is dreadful. Have I your permission to lock her back inside you?"

Even though Morag didn't want any part of her dark side back, she agreed reluctantly. Her dark side instantly disappeared, and Morag felt... wonderful! Oh, it was so good to be back to normal, to be basically good, but occasionally mischievous.

"Thank you," said Morag to the professor. "I think I've learned something very valuable today."

"There is good and bad in everyone," replied the professor, "even the most perfect of witches."

Morag blushed when she remembered what she had said earlier that morning. Then she realised that she was so relieved to find she was normal that she really didn't mind. Morag and Topaz went back to the classroom to undo all the bad things Morag's dark side had done, but on the way they both felt a huge urge for a snack, so they stopped at the chocolate machine first!

The Tale of Two Princesses

Long ago there were twin princesses called Charmina and Charlotte. Even though they were twins, they were opposites. Princess Charmina was gracious and charming to everyone. She curtsied politely to the king and queen. And she remained quite still while the dressmakers came to fit her new ball gown. Princess Charlotte was very different!

"Why do I have to dress like a puffball?" grumbled Princess Charlotte when it was her turn to have a new ball gown fitted.

"How dare you speak to us like that!" her parents cried. But she did dare. She dared to run barefoot through the gardens until her hair looked like a bush. She dared to wear her shabbiest clothes. In fact, she didn't behave like a princess at all!

One day there was to be a ball at the palace. The guests of honour were two princes from the next kingdom. The two princesses, dressed in their new ball gowns, kept getting in the way of the preparations. "Why don't you go for a walk until our guests arrive," suggested the queen. "But stay together, don't get dirty and don't be late!"

The two princesses walked to the bottom of the palace gardens. "Let's go into the forest," said Princess Charlotte.

"I don't think we should," said Princess Charmina. "Our gowns will get dirty." But Princess Charlotte had already set off.

"I think we should go back," Princess Charmina told her sister. "We'll be late for the ball." Just then they heard a strange noise. "Let's turn back!" said Princess Charmina.

"It may be someone in distress!" said Princess Charlotte. "We must go and help!" Although Princess Charmina was scared she agreed. "But we must get back in time for the ball."

They set off again going even deeper into the forest. Finally, they came upon two horses in a clearing, but there was no sign of their riders. Just then they heard voices calling out, "Who's there?"

At first, the two princesses couldn't see where the voices were coming from. In the middle of the clearing there was a large pit. They peered over the edge. Princess Charmina stared in astonishment. Princess Charlotte burst out laughing. There at the bottom of the pit were two princes.

"Well don't just stand there," said the princes. "Help us out!"

The two princesses found ropes and threw one end down to the princes. They tied the other end to the horses. Soon the princes were rescued.

On their return they found the king and queen furious that their daughters had returned late looking so dirty. But their anger turned to joy when the two princes explained what had happened.

Everyone enjoyed the ball. The two princesses danced all night with the two princes. From that time on, Charlotte paid more attention to her gowns and hair. And Charmina became a little more playful and daring than before!

Don't-Care

Don't-care didn't care;
Don't-care was wild.
Don't-care stole plum and pear
Like any beggar's child.
Don't-care was made to care,
Don't-care was hung:
Don't-care was put in the pot
And boiled till he was done.

The Oxen

Christmas Eve, and twelve of the clock.
"Now they are all on their knees,"
An elder said as we sat in a flock
By the embers in hearthside ease.

We pictured the meek mild
creatures where
They dwelt in their strawy pen,
Nor did it occur to one of us there
To doubt they were kneeling then.

So fair a fancy few would weave
In these years! Yet, I feel,
If someone said on Christmas Eve,
"Come; see the oxen kneel

"In the lonely barton by yonder coomb
Our childhood used to know,"
I should go with him in the gloom,
Hoping it might be so.

Where Go the Boats?

Dark brown is the river,
Golden is the sand.
It flows along for ever,
With trees on either hand.

Green leaves a-floating,
Castles of the foam,
Boats of mine a-boating –
Where will all come home?

On goes the river,
And out past the mill,
Away down the valley,
Away down the hill.

Away down the river,
A hundred miles or more,
Other little children
Shall bring my boats ashore.

ROBERT LOUIS STEVENSON

Eldorado

Gaily bedight
  A gallant knight,
In sunshine and in shadow,
  Had journeyed long,
Singing a song,
  In search of Eldorado.

But he grew old –
  This knight so bold –
And o'er his heart a shadow
  Fell as he found
No spot of ground
  That looked like Eldorado.

And, as his strength
  Failed him at length,
He met a pilgrim shadow:
  "Shadow," said he,
"Where can it be,
  This land of Eldorado?"

"Over the mountains
  Of the Moon,
Down the valley of
  the Shadow,
Ride, boldly ride,"
  The shade replied,
"If you seek for Eldorado."

The Mouse's Lullaby

Oh, rock-a-by, baby mouse, rock-a-by, so!
When baby's asleep to the baker's I'll go,
And while he's not looking I'll pop from a hole,
And bring to my baby a fresh penny roll.

The Duel

The gingham dog and the calico cat
  Side by side on the table sat;
'Twas half-past twelve, and
  (what do you think!)
Nor one nor t'other had slept a wink!
  The old Dutch clock and the Chinese plate
Appeared to know as sure as fate
  There was going to be a terrible spat.
(I wasn't there; I simply state
  What was told to me by the Chinese plate!)

The gingham dog went "Bow-wow-wow!"
  And the calico cat replied "mee-ow!"
The air was littered, an hour or so,
  With bits of gingham and calico,
While the old Dutch clock in the
  chimney-place
Up with its hands before its face,
  For it always dreaded a family row!
(Now mind: I'm only telling you
  What the old Dutch clock declares is true!)

Cuddles to the Rescue

Cuddles was a very smart little poodle. Her hair was snowy white and fell in perfect curls. Her claws were always neatly trimmed and polished. She wore a crisp red bow on top of her head. And she never, ever went out without her sparkly jewelled collar.

Once a week Cuddles was sent to the poodle parlour, where she was given a wash, cut and blow dry. And every morning Gilly, her owner, brushed and styled her hair until she looked exactly like herself.

But although Cuddles was the smartest, most pampered pooch around, she was not happy. You see, she didn't have any doggy friends.

Whenever Gilly took her walking in the park, Cuddles tried her best to make friends but the other dogs didn't want to know her.

"Here comes Miss Snooty," they would bark. Then they'd point and snigger, before racing away to have some playful puppy fun.

And Cuddles was never let off her velvet lead. "Those other dogs look rough," explained Gilly. "You're far safer walking with me."

Cuddles would have loved to run around with the other dogs. She thought that chasing sticks and balls looked like brilliant fun. And she was sure that she'd be able to swim in the lake if only Gilly would let her.

But the other dogs didn't know that Cuddles wanted to be one of them.

They just took one look at her snowy white curls and sparkly collar and thought that she was too posh for them.

"She doesn't want to get her paws dirty," Mrs Collie explained to Skip, her youngest pup, when he asked why Cuddles was always on a lead.

Then one day, Cuddles was walking with Gilly in the park, when she saw Skip chasing ducks beside the lake.

"Careful!" barked Cuddles, as Skip bounced up and down excitedly.

But Skip was far too busy to listen. Then, as a duck took off, Skip took an extra large bounce, and threw himself into the lake.

"Stop!" barked Cuddles. But it was no good, Skip was already up to his chin in water.

"Help, help!" barked Skip, as he splashed about wildly in the lake. Cuddles gave a loud bark, and then, using all her strength, pulled the lead from Gilly's hand.

Cuddles was already in the water. Gilly looked on in horror as Cuddles caught the struggling pup by the scruff of his neck and pulled him ashore.

Once on dry land, Cuddles gave herself a big shake, then started to lick Skip dry.

"Cuddles," breathed Skip, who was quickly recovering from his ordeal.

"Cuddles!" cried Gilly, pointing in horror at her soaking wet curls and muddy paws.

"Will you play with me?" barked Skip, wagging his tail hopefully.

After that, Gilly always let Cuddles play with the other dogs in the park, and Cuddles was the happiest little poodle around.

Silly Goose Chase

One morning, Dad came out of his surgery with something large, white and noisy in his arms. "Oh, wow! Is that a goose?" asked Joe.

"Yes, Joe," said Dad, trying not to get a mouthful of feathers! "Her wing is damaged, but I think she'll be fine, with a little rest."

"Where will she live?" asked Sally.

"Well, I'll put her with the ducks for now," said Dad, "but I expect she'll soon decide where she wants to go." The young goose swam in the duck pond, honking very loudly.

"Do you think she'll keep that noise up forever?"asked Sally, covering her ears with her hands.

"At least we know what to call her," said Joe. "Noisy!" Next, Noisy decided to explore the duck house. One or two ducks flew out in a hurry. Then, she tried to squeeze out again.

"Oh, no! Look, Joe!" cried Sally. Noisy couldn't get out of the duck house! And it didn't matter how much she honked, she was stuck tight!

The children managed to free Noisy and carefully gave her a clean. As soon as they had finished, the goose waddled away from the pond to explore some of the farm buildings. "Come on, Sally," said Joe. "We'd better catch her, before she gets into any more trouble!"

Suddenly, they all heard a faint honking noise. "That sounds like she's found the stables," said Sally. "Come on, Joe!" Joe and Sally ran as fast as they could to the stables. Hearing the noise, Old Major looked over his stall. This silly goose chase looked like great fun!

"Honk! Honk!" went the naughty goose.

"She's in the tack room!" cried Joe. This was where they kept the saddles and bridles for the horses and all the cleaning equipment. They found Noisy tangled up in tack, leather polish and dusters, trying to eat one of the grooming brushes!

"Oh, no!" said Sally. "She's knocked everything down from the shelves. It's going to take ages to put everything away again." Joe and Sally untangled Noisy and put her into an empty horse box, while they tidied the tack room. However, Noisy didn't want to be shut away. There were lots more places she wanted to explore!

"Phew! I don't know about you, Joe," said Sally, "but I'm getting really tired!"

"Well, she's safe in the box now," said Joe. "Besides, there aren't any other places she can go, are there?" Then, they both had the same idea – the barn! Too late! Noisy had already escaped!

Noisy had waddled round the side of the house and discovered a new place, full of interesting things. Dad had just parked his tractor and left the barn doors open. Noisy slipped inside, honking curiously – where should she start? She hopped on to the bench and pecked at some tools, an oily cloth and a big sponge in a yellow bucket. Then, a box of shiny nuts and bolts caught her eye…

"Noisy! Here, goosey, goosey!" called Joe and Sally. They looked everywhere, but couldn't find the silly goose. Patch the dog came along to help, trotting round the farm, his nose to the ground.

"It's funny we can't hear her any more," said Sally. "Do you think something's happened?" Suddenly, Patch picked up the goose's scent and ran ahead, barking.

"Look!" said Joe. "Patch is heading for the barn." And, inside the barn, they found Noisy looking really sorry for herself. Beside her was a nearly empty nuts and bolts tin! With a bit of a struggle, Joe and Sally grabbed Noisy and quickly took her to the surgery. Once there, they told Dad all about the silly goose chase.

"I can give her some medicine, which will help get rid of all those nuts and bolts," said Mr Haven. "With any luck, we won't need to operate on her. But I'll keep her safe, here in the hospital, until tomorrow!"

Luckily for Noisy, Dad's medicine worked and Noisy was soon feeling much better. "Do you think she's learnt her lesson?" asked Sally, when they were all having breakfast one morning.

"Oh, yes," said Mum, smiling. "She knows just where to go for the right kind of food now!"

"Honk! Honk!" Joe and Sally looked round. There, at the door, was Noisy – waiting for Mum to give her a bowl of grain and some vegetables. "She's not such a silly goose after all!" laughed Joe.

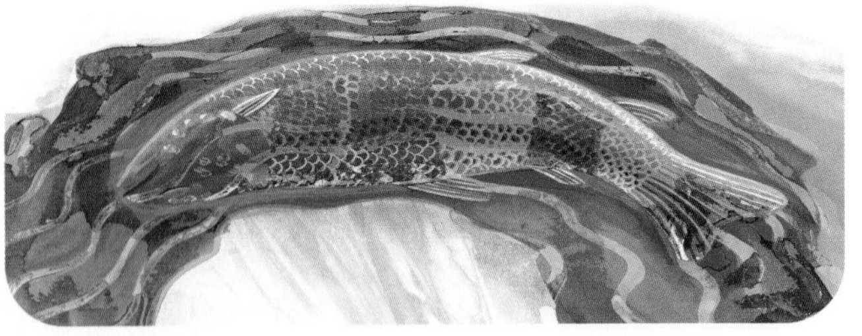

A Boy's Song

Where the pools are bright and deep,
Where the grey trout lies asleep,
Up the river and o'er the lea,
That's the way for Billy and me.

Where the blackbird sings the latest,
Where the hawthorn blooms the sweetest,
Where the nestlings chirp and flee,
That's the way for Billy and me.

Where the mowers mow the cleanest,
Where the hay lies thick and greenest;
There to trace the homeward bee,
That's the way for Billy and me.

Where the hazel bank is steepest,
Where the shadow falls the deepest,
Where the clustering nuts fall free,
That's the way for Billy and me.

Why the boys should drive away
Little sweet maidens from their play,
Or love the banter and fight so well,
That's the thing I never could tell.

But this I know, I love to play
Through the meadow, among the hay;
Up the water and o'er the lea,
That's the way for Billy and me.

Minnie and Mattie

Minnie and Mattie
And fat little May,
Out in the country,
Spending a day.

Such a bright day,
With the sun glowing,
And the trees half in leaf,
And the grass growing.

Minnie and Mattie
And May carry posies,
Half of sweet violets,
Half of primroses.
Give the sun time enough,
Glowing and glowing,
He'll rouse the roses
And bring them blowing.

Violets and primroses
Blossom to-day
For Minnie and Mattie
And fat little May.

CHRISTINA ROSSETTI

A Good Play

We built a ship upon the stairs
  All made of the back-bedroom chairs,
And filled it full of sofa pillows
  To go a-sailing on the billows.

We took a saw and several nails,
  And water in the nursery pails;
And Tom said, "Let us also take
  An apple and a slice of cake";
Which was enough for Tom and me
  To go a-sailing on, till tea.

We sailed along for days and days,
  And had the very best of plays;
But Tom fell out and hurt his knee,
  So there was no one left but me.

ROBERT LOUIS STEVENSON

If a Pig Wore a Wig

If a pig wore a wig,
  What could we say?
Treat him as a gentleman,
  And say "Good-day".

If his tail chanced to fail,
  What could we do?
Send him to the tailoress
  To get one new.

CHRISTINA ROSSETTI

The Swing

How do you like to go up in a swing,
  Up in the air so blue?
Oh, I do think it the pleasantest thing
  Ever a child can do!

Up in the air and over the wall,
  Till I can see so wide,
Rivers and trees and cattle and all
  Over the countryside –

Till I look down on the garden green,
  Down on the roof so brown –
Up in the air I go flying again,
  Up in the air and down!

ROBERT LOUIS STEVENSON

Kiss It Better

Rumpus was romping around the living room. He cartwheeled across the carpet. He turned a somersault on the sofa. "Be careful!" called Mum.

Too late! Rumpus slipped from the sofa, crumpled on to the carpet and banged his head on the floor. "My head hurts!" he groaned.

"Come here and I'll kiss it better," said Mum. She hugged Rumpus and planted a kiss on his forehead. "Now, go and find something less rowdy to do," she said.

Rumpus rushed out into the garden and began to ride his bike. Round and round he raced. "Watch out!" called Mum.

Too late! Rumpus crashed into the corner of the wheelbarrow and tumbled to the ground and grazed his knee. "My leg hurts!" he wailed.

"Come here and I'll kiss it better," said Mum. She hugged Rumpus and planted a kiss on his knee.

"Now, go and find something safer to do," she said.

Rumpus ran up the grassy slope. Then he rolled down. "Roly poly, down the hill," he sang. "Look where you're going!" called Mum.

Too late! Rumpus rolled right into the rose bush. The thorns scratched him all along his arm. "My arm's sore!" cried Rumpus.

"Come here and I'll kiss it better," said Mum and she planted kisses all up his arm.

"Now, try and keep out of trouble," she said.

Mum went into the kitchen. "I need a break," she thought. She made a cup of tea. She cut herself a slice of cake. Then, she sat down for five minutes. Just as she picked up her cup, Rumpus zoomed into the kitchen on his skateboard.

"Rumpus!" said Mum. "Can't you find something more sensible to do?" Mum moved into the living room. "I need a rest," she thought. She sat down on the sofa and picked up the paper.

"Boom! Boom! Boom!" In marched Rumpus, banging on his drum. Mum sighed a loud sigh. "Is anything wrong?" asked Rumpus.

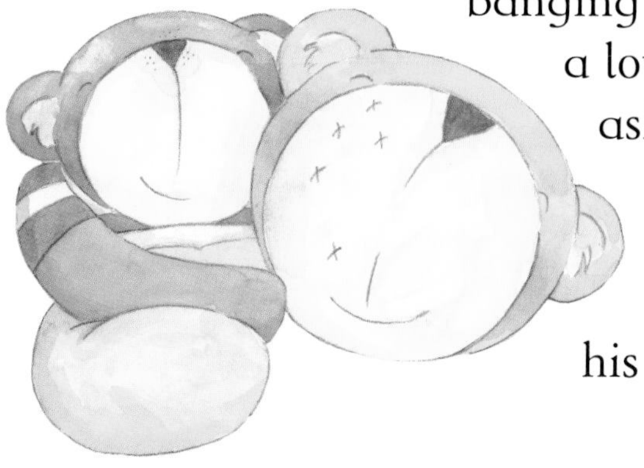

"I've got a headache!" said Mum.

"Never mind," smiled Rumpus, throwing his arms around her. "I'll soon kiss it better."

Lucy and the Green Door

Lucy Jenkins lived in an ordinary house, in an ordinary street, in an ordinary town. At the back of Lucy's house was an ordinary garden with ordinary flowers and an ordinary path. But down the path at the bottom of the garden was a tree that was not ordinary at all! It was a huge old oak tree, and at the bottom of the tree was a very small green door, only just big enough for Lucy to squeeze through. This was Lucy's secret, because only she knew about the door. But what lay behind the door was Lucy's best secret of all!

Each afternoon Lucy would knock lightly on the door. On the third knock the door would swing open wide, and the chief elf would be there to welcome her inside.

"Come in for tea, little Lucy," the elf would always say.

Inside, Lucy would meet some very special friends indeed! First there were Penelope and Geraldine, two of the gentlest and sweetest fairies it was possible to imagine.

Then there were Basil and Granville, who were rather mischievous imps. And there were the storytellers, who would sit for hours with Lucy and tell her the greatest tales from all the corners of the world. And of course there was the chief elf, who would make the most delicious milkshakes and scones with heaps of cream for Lucy to eat.

The world behind the green door was a wonderful place, and Lucy would always go home afterwards feeling very cheerful and jolly. On one particular visit to the world behind the green door Lucy had just finished a scrumptious tea of cocoa and toasted marshmallows with the chief elf, when she went off to play games with Basil and Granville.

Now just recently, Lucy had been feeling down in the dumps because very soon she would be going to school and would only be able to visit her friends at weekends. But they assured her that they would never forget her, and that as long as she was always a true friend to them she could visit as often or as little as she liked. This cheered up Lucy considerably, and then they took her to visit the storytellers so that her happiness was complete. Of all the delights behind the green door, the storytellers were Lucy's favourite. They told her stories of how the whales had learned to sing, and of where the stars went when the sun had risen in the sky and they had slipped from view.

Because of the assurances of the fairies, Lucy was not too worried when the day came for her to start school. Lucy would go to school each day and then afterwards would visit her friends behind the green door. As winter came round and the days grew dark she only visited at weekends, and looked forward to the holidays when she could visit them every day again.

Meanwhile, at school, Lucy had made friends with a girl called Jessica, and, although she told Jessica all about her family and her home, she didn't at first tell her about her special tree with the little green door and its magic world. But Lucy did tell Jessica the stories that she was told by the storytellers, and Jessica grew very curious about where she had heard all the wonderful tales. Every day, Jessica would ask more questions, and Lucy found it harder to avoid telling her about her secret. Eventually, Lucy gave in and told Jessica all about her adventures behind the green door.

Jessica scoffed and laughed. She howled with laughter at the thought of the wonderful teas and the stories that followed. Jessica thought that Lucy was making the whole thing up! When Lucy protested Jessica told her that it simply wasn't possible – that there were no such things as elves and fairies and imps and strange and wonderful worlds behind doors in trees. So Lucy decided to show Jessica.

On the way home Lucy started to worry. What if she really had imagined it all? But, if her wonderful friends didn't exist, how could she possibly know them? Jessica walked beside Lucy, still teasing her and laughing about Lucy's "invisible" friends!

Lucy and Jessica reached the bottom of the garden. Just as Lucy was about to tap lightly on the green door she suddenly noticed the door had disappeared. She rubbed her eyes and looked again, but it had gone!

Jessica laughed at Lucy, calling her silly and babyish to believe in magic and fairy tales, and then ran off back to school.

Lucy could not face going back to school that afternoon, and when her mother saw her she thought she must be ill – she looked so upset! Lucy went up to bed and she cried herself to sleep.

And when Lucy slept she started to dream. All the imps, elves, fairies and the storytellers were there in the dream. Then they hugged her and asked why she hadn't been to see them for so long. Lucy explained what had happened on her last visit, and then Geraldine spoke. "Little Lucy," she said, "you are special. You believe in magic and you believe in the little people. And, because you believe, you are able to see us and live among us. But those who don't believe will always be shut out from our world. You must keep your belief, little Lucy."

With a huge surge of happiness Lucy woke up, dressed quickly and ran out of her ordinary house, down the ordinary path in the ordinary garden up to the extraordinary tree, and was delighted to see the green door once more! She knocked very lightly and, after the third tap, the door swung open to reveal the chief elf. "Come inside, little Lucy," the elf said happily, "and have some tea."

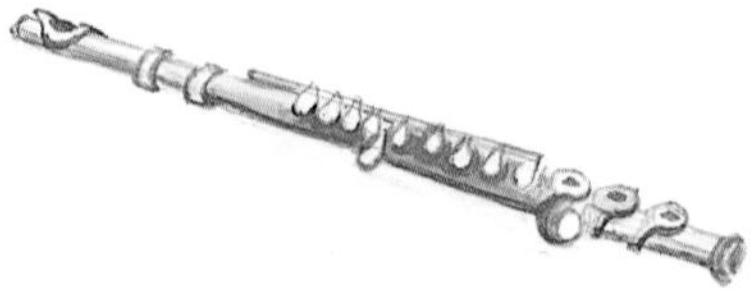

Many More Terrible

A Tudor who tooted a flute
tried to tutor two tooters to toot.
Said the two to their tutor,
"Is it harder to toot
or to tutor two tooters to toot?"

Nine nice night nurses
nursing nicely.

A tree toad loved a she-toad
Who lived up in a tree.
He was a two-toed tree toad
But a three-toed toad was she.
The two-toed tree toad tried to win
The three-toed she-toad's heart,
For the two-toed tree toad loved the ground
That the three-toed tree toad trod.
But the two-toed tree toad tried in vain.
He couldn't please her whim.
From her tree toad bower
With her three-toed power
The she-toad vetoed him.

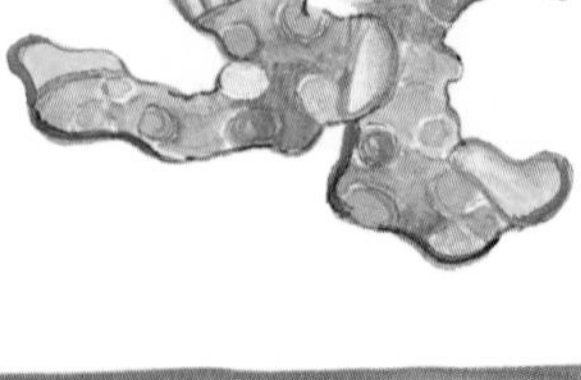

Sam's shop stocks
short spotted socks.

The myth of Miss Muffet.

One smart fellow, he felt smart.
Two smart fellows, they felt smart.
Three smart fellows, they all felt smart.

Flee from fog to
fight flu fast!

We surely shall see
the sun shine soon.

Two toads, totally tired.

Lovely lemon liniment.

Tongue Twisters

Fat frogs flying past fast.

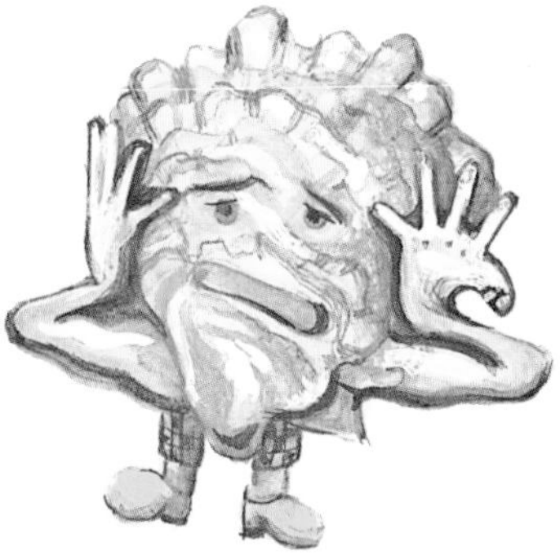

A noisy noise annoys
an oyster.

Many an anemone sees
an enemy anemone.

The blue bluebird blinks.

You've no need to light a night-light
On a light night like tonight,
For a night-light's light's a slight light,
And tonight's a night that's light.
When a night's light, like tonight's light,
It is really not quite right
To light night-lights with their slight lights
On a light night like tonight.

Friendly Frank flips
fine flapjacks.

The boot black bought
the black boot back.

The two-twenty-two train
tore through the tunnel.

Twelve twins twirled
twelve twigs.

Shy Shelly says she shall sew sheets.

Which witch wished
which wicked wish?

Tim, the thin twin tinsmith

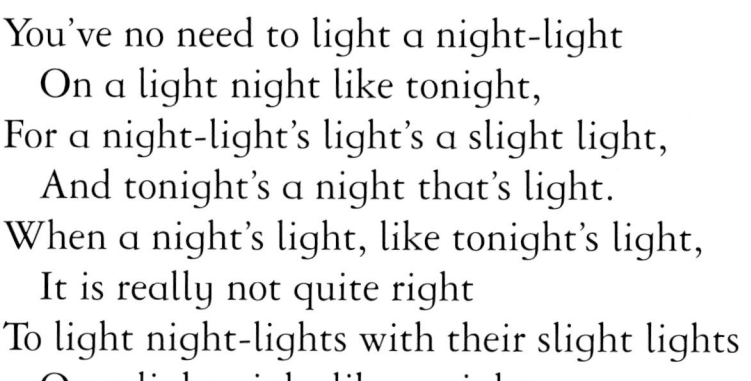

While we were walking, we
were watching window washers
wash Washington's windows
with warm washing water.

See's saw would not have sawed
Soar's seesaw.
So See's saw sawed Soar's seesaw.
But it was sad to see Soar so sore
Just because See's saw sawed
Soar's seesaw!

Sugarplum and the Butterfly

"Sugarplum," said the Fairy Queen, "I've got a very important job for you to do." Sugarplum was always given the most important work. The Fairy Queen said it was because she was the kindest and most helpful of all the fairies. "I want you to make a rose-petal ball gown for my birthday ball next week."

"It will be my pleasure," said Sugarplum happily.

Sugarplum began to gather cobwebs for the thread, and rose petals for the dress. While she was collecting the thread she found a butterfly caught in a cobweb.

"Oh, you poor thing," sighed Sugarplum. Very carefully, Sugarplum untangled the butterfly, but his wing was broken. Sugarplum laid the butterfly on a bed of feathers, then she gathered some nectar from a special flower and fed him a drop at a time. Then she set about mending his wing with a magic spell.

After six days, the butterfly was better. He was very grateful. But now Sugarplum was behind with her work!

"Oh dear! I shall never finish the Fairy Queen's ball gown by tomorrow," she cried. "Whatever shall I do?" The butterfly comforted her.

"Don't worry, Sugarplum," he said. "We'll help you."

He gathered all his friends together. There were yellow, blue, red and brown butterflies. He told them how Sugarplum had rescued him from the cobweb and helped to mend his wing.

The butterflies gladly gathered up lots of rose petals and dropped them next to Sugarplum. Then the butterflies flew away to gather more cobwebs, while Sugarplum arranged all the petals. Back and forth went Sugarplum's hand with her needle and thread making the finest cobweb stiches. Sugarplum added satin ribbons and bows. When she had finished, Sugarplum was very pleased.

"Dear friend," she said to the butterfly, "I couldn't have finished the dress without your help."

"And I could never have flown again without your kindness and help," said the butterfly.

The Fairy Queen was delighted with her new ball gown. And, when she heard the butterfly's story, she wrote a special Thank You poem for Sugarplum:

Sugarplum is helpful,
Sugarplum is kind.
Sugarplum works hard all day,
But she doesn't mind.
She always does her
very best,
To make sick creatures well.
She brings such joy
and pleasure
As she weaves her
magic spell!

So Many Colours

Old MacDonald looked out over his field of yellow corn with pride. "It will be ready for cutting in a couple of days," he said to Mrs MacDonald. "And, although I say it myself, I've never seen such a fine crop."

"That's more than you can say for this gate," said his wife. "Look at the way the paint is peeling off! It's a disgrace."

"Then my first job today will be to paint it," declared Old MacDonald. "Just leave it to me, my dear!" And he hurried off to the farmyard to find the old pots of paint and brushes he kept in the barn.

It wasn't long before Old MacDonald was back at the gate with lots of paint. A long line of curious animals had followed him to see what was going on.

"Give me some room, Jenny!" he told the hen, as she poked her

beak into the first pot of paint he opened – it was a bright red colour.

"That will do nicely," said Old MacDonald. "There is plenty here to finish the job."

But Jenny couldn't resist taking another look into the paint pot while the farmer was busy painting. And when he turned back to dip in his brush again...

Squawk! The pot overturned, spilling the paint everywhere! Jenny's little yellow legs were bright red!

"Well, never mind," said Old MacDonald, as Jenny hopped back to the farmyard. "I'll open another pot."

The farmer was soon busy painting again, this time using a bright green. What a pity that Annabel the cow chose just that moment to race over to see what was happening. But she didn't see the pot of paint. Clang! It went flying up into the air. Clunk! It landed on Percy the pig's head.

"That's it!" cried Old MacDonald. "Back to the farmyard everyone, and let me get on in peace."

Jenny and Percy wandered away with paint dripping off them. Now Old MacDonald would have another job to do as soon as he had painted the gate – unpaint the animals!

Meanwhile, Old MacDonald opened a pot of yellow paint and set to work. "This is much better," he said, as he admired his handiwork. "How am I doing?"

The farmer took a step back and – whoops! One more pot was spilt, and guess who now had very yellow boots!

When Mrs MacDonald came to see how he was getting on, Old MacDonald was putting the finishing touches to the last rail, this time using a pot of blue paint!

"Is that better?" asked Old MacDonald.

Mrs MacDonald blinked. She had never seen so many colours before! "I'll tell you as soon as I put on my sunglasses!" she laughed.

The Night Carnival

Jim was a boy who hated the night, it made him feel lonely and gave him a fright. One night a bright light seemed to be coming from outside, so he pulled back the curtains – and gasped in surprise…

There was a bright, shiny lantern outside his window! "It's carnival time!" cried the lantern, grinning. "There's an adventure for everyone, why don't you join in?"

"I'm on my way!" cried young Jim, and with a skip and a jump, he slide down the drainpipe. Jim joined in the fun, dancing all night. But when it was time to go back to his room, Jim looked sad.

"Whatever is the matter?" asked the lantern.

"My room is full of monsters, and I'm scared of the dark," replied Jim.

"They aren't monsters at all," the lantern replied. "They are carnival folk – so there's no need to hide!"

The lantern and his friends left, and the room grew dark, but when Jim looked out from behind his hands he didn't see monsters, he saw carnival bands!

The Queen of the Monsters

Towards the end of every year all the monsters meet in a huge cave to vote for their new queen. The tales of their misbehaviour made the headlines in the newspapers every year but, this time Mog decided she would see for herself.

As she arrived, Mog heard Trundle the Troll let out one of his infamous roars in the depths of the cave. The sound was so loud that it knocked her over! As she picked herself up Hagar the Hairy, who was terribly scary, strode past. The huge claws on the ends of his paws scratched the ground, and he left a trail of digusting dribble.

Slod the Slimeball was the favourite to win – she was a disgrace, even for a monster! But the monsters all crowded round little Mog. They were fasinated by her, she was so small and sweet. She had four dainty feet and a charming smile – not very monstrous at all!

After they had voted, the monsters sat down for a banquet. The noise was appalling as they discussed who should win and Mog felt sure that Slod the Slimeball would be the new queen.

But when the decision was announced, Mog was amazed to hear that she was to be the new queen! For once the monsters had decided that they didn't want a queen they would dread – so they voted for little Mog instead!

Guess What I Want?

"Guess what I want?" said Ruff to Rufus.

"Something from me?" asked Rufus. "Now, let me see – what could it be?"

"You've got to guess," said Ruff.

"You want me to tie a string to the moon, so you can pull it around like a giant balloon?" said Rufus.

"We could tie the moon to the post of your bed, to shine through the night above your head."

"Would you really get me the moon?" asked Ruff.

"Well, it would be quite hard to climb up that high, but for you, of course, I'd give it a try," said Rufus.

"Guess again," laughed Ruff.

"You want me to catch you a shining white star, and capture its bright light for you in a jar?" said Rufus.

"It would twinkle all night and light up your dreams, and dance round your room, mixed with yellow moonbeams."

"Would you really fetch me a star?" asked Ruff.

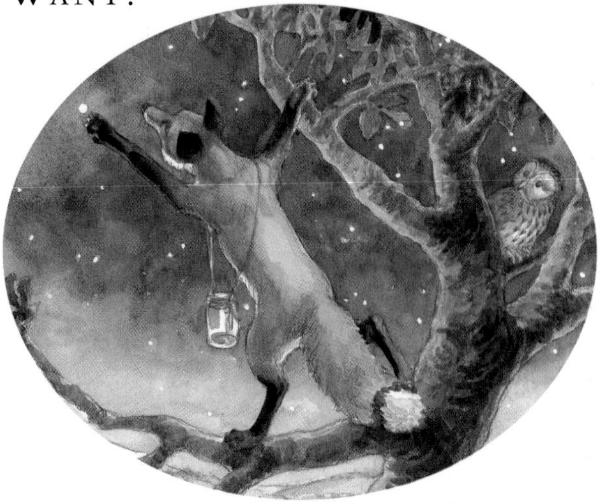

"Well, catching a star isn't easy to do, but I'd give it a try, because I love you," said Rufus.

"Guess again," laughed Ruff.

"You want me to capture the song of the breeze, as it lulls its way gently through leaves on the trees?" said Rufus.

"You'd be able to turn on the breeze's soft tune, for the starlight to dance along with the moon."

"Would you really bring me the song of the breeze?" asked Ruff.

"Well, the breeze moves so fast, it isn't easy to do, but I'd find a way to do it for you," said Rufus.

Ruff thought hard.

"To tie down the moon, wouldn't be right. And the sky is the place to leave the starlight. It wouldn't be fair to stop the wind's song. Now, try one more guess – your first three were wrong!"

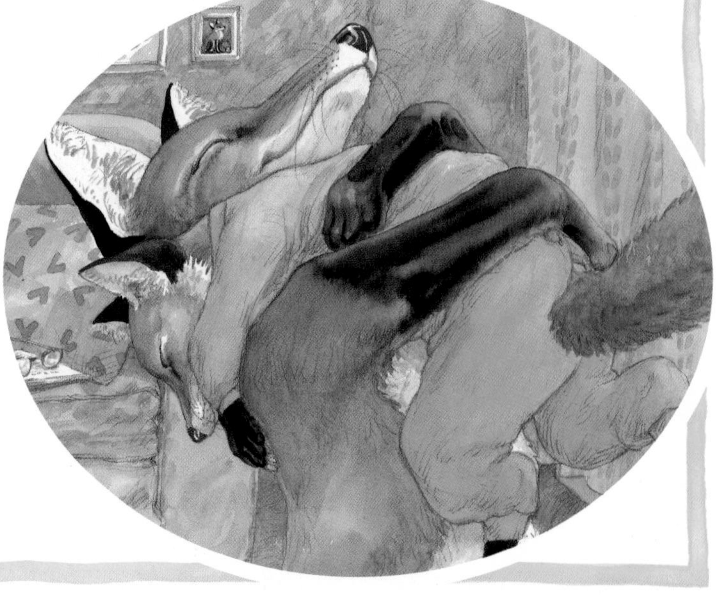

"I know. I was teasing. I think you want this... a huge great big cuddle, and a lovely big kiss!"

The Fox and the Grapes

One warm summer's day, Red Fox went out into the forest. He was a handsome young fox and very proud of his thick red coat and fine bushy tail. He was strolling along the forest path, looking for something to do, when he spotted some fluffy little bunnies just coming out of their burrow. "Perfect for chasing!" thought Red Fox and scampered after them. But they were too fast for him.

"You can't catch us!" they giggled, as they darted away.

"Who cares about a bunch of silly bunnies?" thought Red Fox. "Rabbits are never any fun. I'll look for something else to chase!"

So, Red Fox plodded slowly along the path, until he spotted two bushy-tailed squirrels, busily burying acorns. But the squirrels heard Red Fox and scampered quickly away before he could get near them!

"You can't catch us!" they chuckled, as they pelted him with acorns.

"Oh, who cares about a couple of silly squirrels?" thought Red Fox. "If I had caught them, they would have given me nothing but trouble anyway. I'll find something else to do!"

So, Red Fox continued until he came to the edge of the forest. "I've never been out in the big, wide world," he thought. "I'll bet I can have lots of fun out there!" Red Fox strolled across a field until he came to a wide, dusty road. "I wonder where this leads," he thought, so he decided to follow it.

As he walked, Red Fox looked all around him. He saw some fuzzy field mice, scurrying through the tall grass and then suddenly he heard a loud rumbling and clattering that made the ground shake and his toes tingle. Red Fox was frightened! He'd never heard such a terrible noise before and he wondered if the earth was going to swallow him up! But it was only a farmer's cart. As soon as it passed, everything was quiet again and Red Fox went on his way. As Red Fox trudged along, the blazing sun beat down on his back.

He soon grew hot and thirsty and, before long, his empty tummy began to rumble and grumble. "I haven't eaten anything for hours,"

moaned Red Fox. "And the hot sun and dusty road have made my mouth *so* dry, I wish I could find something sweet and juicy to eat." Suddenly, Red Fox smelled something wonderful. It was sweet and tempting and it made his mouth water.

He followed his nose across the road, right to where the smell was coming from. Red Fox found himself in the garden of a tiny house. At the side of the house was a leafy grape vine, with big bunches of ripe, purple grapes hanging down. Red Fox couldn't believe his luck!

"Yum, yum!" said Red Fox, licking his lips. "Those grapes look *so* sweet and juicy. They are just what I need to quench my thirst and fill my empty tummy!"

"I'll have to really stretch myself to reach those grapes," said Red Fox, "but I'm *sure* I can do it!" He stood under the grape vine and reached up as far as he could. He stretched and stretched and stretched. But even standing on the very tip-toes of his hind legs, Red Fox couldn't reach the grapes.

"Stretching won't work," grumbled Red Fox. "I know, I'll just have to jump!" So, he jumped high into the air. But he *still* couldn't reach the grapes. Once again, Red Fox looked up at the grapes, which hung just out of his reach. They looked more delicious than

ever and Red Fox *knew* he had to have some, no matter what it took.

"I must jump higher this time," he thought. So, he leapt up into the air, just as high as he could. But he *still* couldn't reach those plump, juicy grapes! Red Fox was tired with thirst and hunger, but he couldn't give up now. The grapes looked sweeter and juicier than ever.

"I'll try one more time," he said. "And this time, I'm *sure* to reach them!" Red Fox reared back on his hind legs and sprang high into the air. But *still* he could not reach those gorgeous grapes. Exhausted and miserable, Red Fox gave up at last. With his head hanging down, he slowly slunk off down the hot, dusty road.

"Oh, who wants a bunch of silly grapes?" he said. "They were probably sour, anyway!"

And, hungrier and thirstier than ever, he trudged wearily back to the forest.

All the Bells were Ringing

All the bells were ringing
  And all the birds were singing,
When Molly sat down crying
  For her broken doll.

O you silly Moll!
  Sobbing and sighing
  For a broken doll,
When all the bells are ringing
  And all the birds are singing.

CHRISTINA ROSSETTI

Alone

From childhood's hour I have not been
  As others were, – I have not seen
As others saw, – I could not bring
  My passions from a common spring.
From the same source I have not taken
  My sorrow; I could not awaken
My heart to joy at the same tone;
  And all I loved, I loved alone.
Then – in my childhood – in the dawn
  Of a most stormy life was drawn
From every depth of good and ill
  The mystery which binds me still:
From the torrent, or the fountain,
  From the red cliff of the mountain,
From the sun that round me rolled
  In its autumn tint of gold, –
From the lightning in the sky
  As it passed me flying by, –
    From the thunder and the storm,
      And the cloud that took the form
    (When the rest of Heaven was blue)
      Of a demon in my view.

EDGAR ALLAN POE

There was an Old Man with a Beard

There was an old Man with a beard,
  Who said, "It is just as I feared! –
Two Owls and a Hen, four Larks and a Wren
  Have all built their nests in my beard!"

EDWARD LEAR

Hurt No Living Thing

Hurt no living thing,
  Ladybird nor butterfly,
Nor moth with dusty wing,
Nor cricket chirping cheerily,
Nor grasshopper, so light of leap,
  Nor dancing gnat,
  Nor beetle fat,
Nor harmless worms that creep.

CHRISTINA ROSSETTI

Bread and Milk for Breakfast

Bread and milk for breakfast,
  And woollen frocks to wear,
And a crumb for robin redbreast
  On the cold days of the year.

CHRISTINA ROSSETTI

Going Downhill on a Bicycle

With lifted feet, hands still,
  I am poised, and down the hill
Dart, with heedful mind;
  The air goes by in a wind.

Swifter and yet more swift,
  Till the heart with a mighty lift
Makes the lungs laugh,
    the throat cry:–
  "O bird, see; see, bird, I fly.

"Is this, is this your joy?
  O bird, then I, though a boy,
For a golden moment share
Your feathery life in air!"

Say, heart, is there aught like this
  In a world that is full of bliss?
'Tis more than skating, bound
  Steel-shod to the level ground.
Speed slackens now, I float
  Awhile in my airy boat;
Till, when the wheels scarce crawl,
  My feet to the treadles fall.

Alas, that the longest hill
  Must end in a vale; but still,
Who climbs with toil, wheresoe'er,
  Shall find wings waiting there.

HENRY CHARLES BEECHING

The Bee Who Wanted More Stripes

Bertie the bee was a rather vain young bee. Every morning, as soon as he woke up, he would find a large dewdrop in which to admire his reflection. The thing that Bertie liked best about himself was his stripes. He thought stripes were the smartest, flashiest fashion accessory any animal could have. He just wished he had more stripes. But he only had a couple. "Still," he thought, "they are very fine stripes."

Then he had an idea. What if he could get some more stripes? He would be the stripiest bee around, and then everyone else would admire him, too. "I know what I'll do," he said. "I'll ask some other very stripy animals how they got all their stripes, and maybe I can copy them."

He buzzed off through the wood, looking for striped animals to ask. He flew across the fields and then the sea and at last he reached a place where there seemed to be quite a few striped animals. The first animal he approached looked like a striped horse. "Hello, neddy!" said Bertie, landing on the beast's nose.

"I'm not a horse – I'm a zebra. And get off my nose!" said the zebra crossly.

"I do beg your pardon," said Bertie. "I am sorry to bother you, but I just wanted to ask you how you got your stripes."

"Well," said the zebra, "I used to be all brown. Then one day I came across a piano in the middle of the plain. As I walked past the piano, its black and white keys started to play a tune all by themselves. Then I looked down and found I had turned black and white, too. And if you believe that you'll believe anything!" And with that the zebra laughed and trotted off.

Bertie continued on his way. Now he could see a large striped cat. "Hello, puss!" said Bertie, landing on the creature's back.

"I'm not a cat – I'm a tiger. And get off my back!" growled the tiger.

"Sorry!" said Bertie. "I wanted to ask you how you got your stripes."

"Well," said the tiger, "I used to be all yellow. Then one day, when I was a cub, I was playing with a ball of black string and I got all tangled up in it. And that's how I got my stripes. And if you believe that you'll believe anything!" And the tiger started to laugh as he stalked off.

Bertie continued on his way. Soon he could see a long striped worm slithering through the grass. "Hello, little worm!" called Bertie, landing on the worm's tail.

"I'm not a worm – I'm a snake. And get off my tail!" hissed the snake.

"Oh dear. I didn't mean to upset you," said Bertie. "I just wanted to ask you how you got your stripes."

"Well," said the snake, "I used to be all brown. Then one day I was crossing a road just as the traffic lights were changing from red to green, and when I reached the other side I found that I was striped red and green from head to tail. And if you believe that you'll believe anything!" And the snake started to laugh as he slithered away.

Bertie continued on his way once more. Then, in a tree, he spotted a squirrel with a striped tail. "Hello, squirrel!" he said, landing on the animal's paw.

"I'm not a squirrel – I'm a ring-tailed lemur. And get off my paw!" said the ring-tailed lemur angrily.

"I do apologise," said Bertie. "I just wanted to ask you how you got your striped tail."

"Well," said the ring-tailed lemur, "my tail used to be all white. Then one day I was playing hoop-la with my friends. I said they could use my tail as a target, and so they threw all the rings on to my tail. But they got stuck. And that's how I got a striped tail. And if you believe that you'll believe anything!" And the ring-tailed lemur started to laugh as he scampered away.

"Well," thought Bertie, "I'd better give it a go!" First he looked for a piano on the plain, but to no avail. There just wasn't a piano to be found. Then he looked for a ball of string – but he couldn't find one of those, either. He did find a set of traffic lights and he buzzed backwards and forwards in front of them until he felt quite dizzy, but he still had the same number of stripes. Finally, he called out, "Anyone fancy a game of hoop-la?" But there was no reply. It was night time and all the animals were asleep.

"I'll just have to make my way home," thought Bertie sadly. He flew all through the night and arrived home exhausted in the morning.

Then he met Clarice, the wise old bee. "Clarice," said Bertie, "I really would like some more stripes but, although I've asked lots of stripy animals how they got their stripes, all they gave me were silly answers."

Clarice looked at Bertie rather sternly and said, "You only get the stripes you were born with, Bertie. And besides, do you know what you would be if you had more stripes? You would be a wasp!"

Bertie looked horrified. The last thing he wanted to be was a wasp. Wasps were always going around frightening and stinging everyone, and no one liked them at all.

Bertie thought for a few moments and then said, "Perhaps having just a few stripes but being liked by others is better after all."

Cuddly's Jumper

Cuddly Sheep and Stout Pig were going to show the others how to knit. Cuddly Sheep was really good at knitting. But she needed her friend, Stout Pig, to help with the wool. Stout Pig couldn't knit, not even a little bit, but he was very good at spinning the wool for Cuddly to use.

Wool has to be made into yarn before you can knit with it. Yarn is made by twisting it, like string. That is what Stout did. He collected all the loose bits of wool that caught on thorny bushes around the farm and made long, beautiful lengths of yarn out of them. Then Cuddly used Stout Pig's yarn to knit lots of pretty things. She could knit woolly socks. She could knit woolly hats. She could knit the best woolly jumpers in the world!

Cuddly and Stout sat close to each other. Stout Pig sat with his back against a low hedge and Cuddly sat on the other side. The pig pulled out lengths of wool from a pile under the hedge. He started to spin the wool on his wheel, until it was twisted into yarn. Then he gave the end to Cuddly.

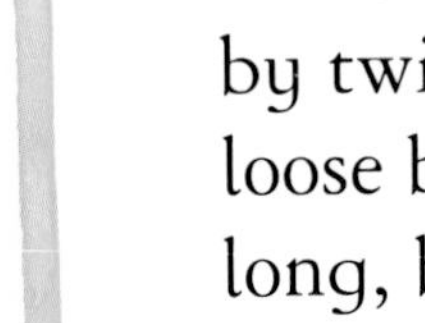

Cuddly made little loops of the wool and put them on two fat knitting needles. Then she started knitting.

"Knit one, purl one, knit two together," she whispered to herself. Only knitters know what these secret words mean. They must be magic words, because they are whispered over and over again.

"Knit one, purl one, knit two together."

The jumper quickly started to take shape. As it grew in size, the animals watching could see it was nearly all white, just like the colour of Cuddly's own woolly coat, with little bits in purple, like the berries on the hedge.

Stout had to work hard on the other side of the hedge to keep up with Cuddly Sheep.

Cuddly looked up. "Is it getting late? I'm getting a bit cold," she said. None of the others felt cold.

"You can put my blanket on," said Pebbles Horse. He pulled his blanket over Cuddly's shoulders. But Cuddly got colder. And colder!

"I keep warm in the straw," said Saffron Cow. She covered Cuddly with straw. But the more Cuddly knitted, the colder she got.

And the hotter Stout became. Cuddly was trying to finish the jumper quickly before she froze. The faster she knitted, the faster Stout Pig had to turn the spinning wheel, and he was soon in a sweat!

Then the jumper was finished… and Cuddly was shivering! Her teeth were chattering! Pebbles looked hard at Stout.

"Where did the wool come from that you were spinning?" he asked.

"I used that bundle of wool under the hedge," said Stout. "It was here when I came."

Pebbles' large head followed the wool from the spinning wheel over the hedge. There was only Cuddly there. "Cuddly," said Pebbles '…I think you have been knitting your own wool!"

Cuddly jumped up in surprise. The blanket and the straw fell off. She was bare all around her middle. No wonder she was cold. Her wool was all gone.

"Oh well," said Cuddly Sheep, taking out the needles from her knitting. "Never mind! I have a nice thick new jumper to keep me warm!"

The Walrus and the Carpenter

"The time has come," the Walrus said,
"To talk of many things:
Of shoes – and ships – and sealing-wax –
Of cabbages – and kings –
And why the sea is boiling hot –
And whether pigs have wings."

"But wait a bit," the Oysters cried,
"Before we have our chat;
For some of us are out of breath,
And all of us are fat!"
"No hurry!" said the carpenter.
They thanked him much for that.

"A load of bread," the Walrus said,
"Is what we chiefly need:
Pepper and vinegar besides
Are very good indeed –
Now if you're ready, Oysters dear,
We can begin to feed."

Lady Moon

Lady Moon, Lady Moon,
Where are you roving?
Over the sea.
Lady Moon, Lady Moon,
Whom are you loving?
All that love me.
Are you not tired with
rolling, and never
Resting to sleep?
Why look so pale,
And so sad, as for ever
Wishing to weep?

Ariel's Song

Full fathom five thy father lies;
Of his bones are coral made;
Those are pearls that were his eyes:
Nothing of him that doth fade,
But doth suffer a sea-change
Into something rich and strange:
Sea nymphs hourly ring his knell.
Ding-dong!
Hark! now I hear them,
Ding-dong, bell!

There's a Hole in the Middle of the Sea

There's a hole, there's a hole,
there's a hole in the middle of the sea.
There's a log in the hole in the middle
of the sea.
There's a hole, there's a hole,
there's a hole in the middle of the sea.
There's a bump on the log in the
hole in the middle of the sea.
There's a hole, there's a hole,
there's a hole in the middle
of the sea.

There's a frog on the bump on the
log in the hole in the middle of
the sea.
There's a hole, there's a hole, there's
a hole in the middle of the sea.
There's a fly on the frog on the bump
on the log in the hole in the middle
of the sea.
There's a hole, there's a hole, there's
a hole in the middle of the sea.

Small is the Wren

Small is the wren,
Black is the rook,
Great is the sinner
That steals this book.

The Children's Hour

Between the dark and the daylight,
When the night is beginning to lower,
Comes a pause in the day's occupations,
That is known as the Children's Hour.

I hear in the chamber above me
The patter of little feet,
The sound of a door that is opened,
And voices soft and sweet.

From my study I see in the lamplight,
Descending the broad hall stair,
Grave Alice, and laughing Allegra,
And Edith with golden hair.

A whisper, and then a silence:
Yet I know by their
merry eyes
They are plotting and
planning together
To take me by surprise.

Lost and Alone

Deep in the jungle, Mungo was trying to slip off through the trees. "Mungo, tell me where you're going, please," called Mum. "What are you planning to do today?"

"I'm just going to play," smiled Mungo.

"Okay," said Mum. "But no monkey business!"

Elephant was enjoying a drink, when Mungo crept up and yelled, "Hi, Elephant! Want to play?" Then he added, "I know a good game."

"Oh, yes?" said Elephant, suspiciously. "What's its name?"

"Funny faces!" said Mungo. "What do you say?"

"I'm not sure," said Elephant. "I don't know how to play."

"Easy," said Mungo. "All you have to do, is pull a funny face. Look, I'll show you." And he took hold of Elephant's trunk. Mungo wound Elephant's trunk round and slipped the end through. He pulled it into a knot. "Wow, Elephant!" he giggled. "What a funny face you've got!"

"Hey!" gurgled Elephant."How do I get out of this?" But Mungo was gone!

Lion was trying to have a laze in the sun, when Mungo swung down and asked, "Want some fun?" Then he added, "Come on. I know a good game."

"Yeah?" said Lion, suspiciously. "What's its name?"

"Funny faces," said Mungo. "What do you say?"

"I'm not sure," said Lion. "I don't know how to play."

"Easy," said Mungo. "All you have to do, is pull a funny face. Look, I'll show you." And he took hold of Lion's bottom lip. Mungo pulled the lip up over Lion's nose. "You see," he said, "that's the way it goes."

Then he ran off, smiling, through the trees. "Forget what Mum said," thought Mungo. "I'll do as I please." He swung through the branches, but, after a while, Mungo's face lost its smile. "I don't know where I am!" he wailed.

"That's a funny face," said Elephant. "He wins the game for sure."

"It's not a game," howled Mungo. "I'm lost and alone. I want my mum! How do I get out of here? This isn't any fun!"

"Well, shall we help him?" Lion roared. "What do you think?"

"I'm not sure," said Elephant. "He did disturb my drink."

"He wrecked my rest, too," Lion said. "You're not the only one."

"If we agree to help, Mungo," the animals said, "then no more funny faces. Can you get that into your head?"

Mungo looked much happier than he'd done in quite a while. "No more tricks!" Mungo promised, and he thanked both of them. "Being lost and alone wasn't any fun for me!"

Peter Meets a Dragon

Once upon a time there was a young boy named Peter. He lived in an ordinary house with an ordinary Mum and Dad, an ordinary sister and an ordinary pet cat, called Jasper. In fact, everything in Peter's life was so ordinary that he sometimes wished that something extraordinary would happen. "Why doesn't a giant come and squash the house flat with his foot?" he wondered. But, each day, Peter would wake up in the morning and everything was just the same as it had been the day before.

One morning when Peter woke up there was a very strange smell in the house. Looking out of his bedroom window, he saw that the front lawn was scorched and blackened. There was smoke drifting off the grass and, further away, he could see some bushes ablaze.

Peter rushed downstairs and out of the front door. He ran out of the

garden and down the lane following the trail of smoke and burning grass. He grew more and more puzzled, however, as there was no sign of anything that could have caused such a blaze.

Peter was about to run home and tell his Mum and Dad, when he heard a panting noise coming from the undergrowth. Parting the bushes, he found a young creature with green, scaly skin, a pair of wings and a long snout full of sharp teeth. Every now and again a little tongue of flames came from its nostrils, setting the grass around it on fire. "A baby dragon!" Peter said to himself, in great surprise. Big tears were rolling out of the dragon's yellow eyes and down its scaly cheeks as it flapped its wings desperately and tried to take off.

When the dragon saw Peter it stopped flapping its wings. "Oh, woe is me!" it sobbed. "Where am I?"

"Where do you want to be?" asked Peter, kneeling down on the scorched ground.

"I want to be in Dragonland with my friends," replied the dragon. "We were all flying together, but I got tired and needed a rest. I called to the others but they didn't hear me. I just had to stop and get my breath back. Now I don't know where I am, or if I'll ever see my friends again!"

"I'm sure I can help you get home," said Peter, but he had no idea how.

"You?" hissed a voice. "How could you possibly help? You're just a boy!" Peter looked round, and to his astonishment found Jasper sitting behind him. "I suppose you're going to wave a magic wand, are you?" continued Jasper. "You need to call in an expert."

Then he turned his back on Peter and the baby dragon and started washing his paws.

Peter was astounded. He'd never heard Jasper talking before. "W… w… what do you mean?" he stammered.

"Well," said Jasper, glancing over his shoulder at Peter, "I reckon that horse over there could help. Follow me."

Jasper leaped up on to the gate and called to the horse. Then he whispered in the horse's ear. The horse whispered back in Jasper's ear. "He's got a friend on the other side of the wood who'll help," said Jasper.

"But how?" said Peter, looking perplexed.

"Be patient! Follow me!" said Jasper as he stalked off through the grass. "And tell your friend to stop setting fire to everything!" he added.

"I can't help it," cried Flame, about to burst into tears again. "Every time I get out of breath I start to pant, and then I start breathing fire."

"Let me carry you," said Peter. He picked up Flame in his arms and ran after Jasper. The baby dragon felt very strange. He was cold and clammy, but his mouth was breathing hot smoke, which made Peter's eyes water. He followed Jasper's upright tail through the wood to a field, and in the field was a horse. But this was no ordinary horse. Peter stopped dead in his tracks and stared. The horse was pure milky white, and from its head grew a single, long horn. "A unicorn!" breathed Peter.

Jasper was talking to the unicorn. He beckoned with his paw to Peter.

"He'll take you both to his home, Peter." And with that, Jasper was off.

"Climb aboard," said the unicorn gently.

Peter and the little dragon scrambled up on to the unicorn's back. "What an adventure," thought Peter as they soared through the clouds. He saw a mountain ahead, then they descended through the clouds and landed right at the top of the mountain. "I'm home!" squeaked Flame joyously as they landed. Sure enough, several dragons were running over to greet him. They looked quite friendly, but some of them were rather large and one was breathing a great deal of fire.

"Time for me to go," said Peter a little nervously, as Flame jumped off the unicorn's back and flew to the ground. The unicorn took off again and soon they were back in the field once more. When Peter turned to thank the unicorn he saw that it was just an ordinary horse with no trace of a horn at all. Peter walked back home across the field, but there was no sign of burnt grass and his lawn was in perfect condition too. Peter felt rather perplexed. "I hope Jasper can explain," he thought, as the cat ran past him and into the house. "Jasper, what's happened to the burnt grass?" he blurted out. But Jasper didn't say a word, he ignored Peter and curled up in his basket.

When Peter wasn't looking, however, Jasper gave him a glance that said, "Well, was that a big enough adventure for you?"

The Naughty Mermaids

Of all the mermaids that lived in the sea, Jazz and Cassandra were the naughtiest. They were not supposed to swim above sea when there were people about. But their latest prank was to swim to the lighthouse and call out to the little boy, Jack, who lived there.

"Coo-ee," they would call and, when the little boy looked towards them, they giggled and dived under the waves. When King Neptune heard about it, he was very cross indeed!

One day, Jack's mum made him a picnic. Jack laid the food on a cloth on the rocks. He had pizza and crisps and fizzy drink and chocolate.

The two naughty mermaids popped up from the waves and saw all the food. "Hello!" they called to Jack. "Are you going to eat all this food by yourself?" Jack was surprised, he'd never seen the mermaids before.

"Yes," said Jack. "I mean, no! You can have some of my picnic, if you like." The mermaids had never had pizza or crisps or fizzy drink or chocolate before. They ate so much they felt sick! They swam home slowly, hoping King Neptune wouldn't spot them. But he did, and he summoned them to see him.

"Be warned!" said King Neptune. "Mermaids are not

like children. They cannot behave like children and they cannot eat the food that children eat!"

For a while Jazz and Cassandra ate mermaid food, like shrimps and seaweed, but they soon became bored. "I'm longing for some pizza," said Jazz to Cassandra one day.

"So am I," answered Cassandra, "and some crisps, and chocolate!" Then the naughty mermaids swam up to the surface.

Jack was there with another picnic. The mermaids ate everything, then they played hide and seek in the waves while Jack ran round the lighthouse trying to spot them. The mermaids enjoyed themselves so much, they came back the next day and the next. On the third day, the mermaids said goodbye and started to swim to the bottom of the sea. But, oh dear! Their tails had become stiff and heavy. They could not move! King Neptune was right. Mermaids can't behave like children. They clung on to the rocks around the lighthouse and began to cry.

"What's wrong?" shouted Jack, alarmed. "We're not supposed to eat children's food," they told him. Jack knew exactly what to do! He got his net and bucket and collected shrimps and seaweed from the rock pools.

For three days and three nights he fed the mermaids proper mermaid food. By the third day they could move their tails again and swim.

When they arrived home King Neptune was waiting for them.

This time, King Neptune wasn't angry – he was glad to see them back safely. "I hope you have learned a lesson," he said, quite gently. "Jack has been a good friend so you can play with him again. As long as you don't eat his food!"

Snap Happy

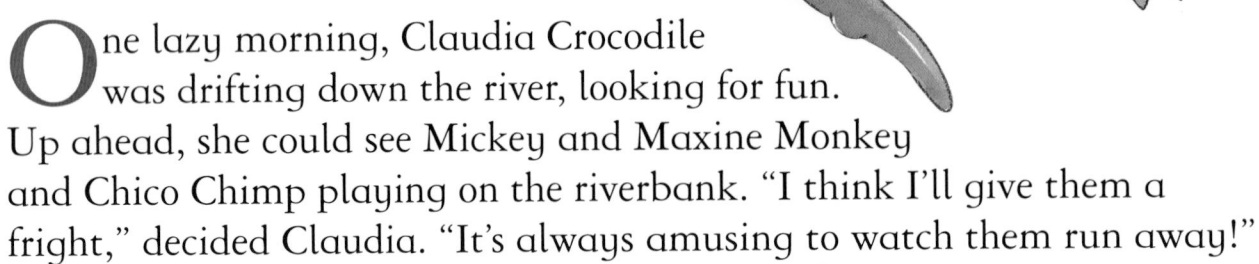

One lazy morning, Claudia Crocodile was drifting down the river, looking for fun. Up ahead, she could see Mickey and Maxine Monkey and Chico Chimp playing on the riverbank. "I think I'll give them a fright," decided Claudia. "It's always amusing to watch them run away!"

Flashing and gnashing her sharp teeth, she swam towards the three friends. Sure enough, the SNAP! SNAP! SNAP! of Claudia's jaws scared the little monkeys.

"RUN," cried Maxine, "before she snaps our tails off!"

They tumbled over each other as they climbed to safety.

"Hee, hee!" Claudia laughed as she watched them. "Scaring the monkeys is such fun!"

That afternoon, Claudia was bored again, so she looked for someone else to frighten. "Aha!" she said. "There's little Timmy Tiger, paddling all by himself. I'll give him a real fright!" And she set off down the river, SNAP-SNAP-SNAPPING as she went.

Timmy didn't hear Claudia, until she was right behind him! SNAP! SNAP! went her great big jaws. GNASH! GNASH! GNASH! went her sharp, pointy teeth.

"AAAAGGGGGHHH!" screamed Timmy, as he saw Claudia's mouth open wide. He tried to run away, but his paws were stuck in the mud!

Claudia came closer and closer. Timmy trembled with terror.

"You're supposed to run away!" Claudia whispered.

"I c-c-can't," stammered Timmy. "I'm stuck!"

"Oh," said Claudia, disappointed. "It's no fun if you don't run away."

"Aren't you g-going to eat me?" gulped Timmy.

"EAT YOU?" roared Claudia. "Yuck! You're all furry! I prefer fish."

"Really?" said Timmy. "Then why are you always snapping and gnashing and frightening everyone?"

"Because that's what crocodiles do!" said Claudia. "We're supposed to be scary. Er... you won't tell anyone I didn't eat you, will you?" she asked, helping Timmy climb out of the mud.

"Don't worry," laughed Timmy, "I won't tell!"

"Thanks for un-sticking me," Timmy said. "I never knew you could be nice. I like you!"

Claudia's green face blushed bright red!

"I think everyone would like you," went on Timmy, "if you just tried to be friendly, instead of scary."

"Oh, I don't think I can do that," said Claudia. "My jaws simply HAVE to snap and my teeth just MUST gnash! I can't help it."

"Wait!" said Timmy. "I know just how you can be friendly and helpful and snap and gnash at the same time! Here's your chance."

As Timmy and Claudia went along together, they saw Mickey and Maxine trying to smash open some coconuts.

Claudia swam towards the monkeys, SNAP-SNAP-SNAPPING with her jaws. As soon as they heard her, the monkeys ran for the nearest tree.

"I just want to help," said Claudia, climbing on to the bank. "Throw me a coconut!" And with a SNAP! SNAP! SNAP! quick as a flash, Mickey's coconut was open. Then Claudia opened Maxine's coconut, too and soon everyone was sharing the cool, refreshing milk and chewy chunks of coconut. Claudia had never shared anything and found that she liked it!

Chico Chimp came running towards his friends. He was carrying a big watermelon. Suddenly, Chico spotted Claudia, whose jaw was open, ready to SNAP! "Uh-oh!" he gulped, turning to run.

"Don't worry, Chico," said Maxine. "Throw Claudia the watermelon!"

Chico watched in amazement as Claudia SNAP-SNAP-SNAPPED the watermelon into neat slices for everyone. "Thanks, Claudia!" they all chorused. Chico gave Claudia the biggest slice.

Then Emma, Eric and Ellen Elephant came trundling down to the river with bundles of thick branches in their trunks. "We're going to make a raft!" said Emma – and then they saw Claudia.

As the frightened elephants galloped away, Claudia picked up the branches they had dropped. SNAP! SNAP! GNASH! GNASH! went Claudia's strong jaws and sharp teeth.

"Wow! Thanks, Claudia!" said Emma, as the elephants came back. "That was really helpful!"

Claudia grinned. Being friendly and helpful was rather nice!

"Here we go!" shouted the elephants, when their raft was ready. The friends on the riverbank watched them.

"That looks like so much fun!" said Chico. "Can you help us make a raft, too, Claudia?"

"I can do even better," said Claudia. "Hop on my back!"

"WHEEE! This is GREAT!" whooped Maxine as they sailed down the river on Claudia's back.

Happiest of all was Claudia, who had found that having friends was much more fun than scaring them!

The Little Doll

I once had a sweet little doll, dears,
The prettiest doll in the world;
Her cheeks were so red and so white, dears,
And her hair was so charmingly curled.
But I lost my poor little doll, dears,
As I played in the heath one day;
And I cried for her more than a week, dears;
But I never could find where she lay.

I found my poor little doll, dears,
As I played in the heath one day:
Folks say she is terribly changed, dears,
For her paint is all washed away,

And her arm trodden off
by the cows, dears,
And her hair not the least
bit curled:
Yet for old sakes' sake
she is still, dears,
The prettiest doll
in the world.

There was an Old Man from Peru

There was an old man from Peru
Who dreamed he was eating his shoe.
He woke in a fright
In the middle of the night
And found it was perfectly true.

Minnie and Winnie

Minnie and Winnie
Slept in a shell.
Sleep, little ladies!
And they slept well.

Pink was the shell within,
Silver without;
Sounds of the great sea
Wandered about.

Sleep, little ladies,
Wake not soon!
Echo on echo
Dies to the moon.

Two bright stars
Peeped into the shell.
"What are they dreaming of?
Who can tell?"

Started a green linnet
Out of the croft;
Wake, little ladies,
The sun is aloft!

ALFRED, LORD TENNYSON

Brother and Sister

"Sister, sister go to bed!
  Go and rest your weary head."
Thus the prudent brother said.

"Do you want a battered hide,
  Or scratches to your face applied?"
Thus his sister calm replied.

"Sister, do not raise my wrath.
  I'd make you into mutton broth
As easily as kill a moth!"

The sister raised her beaming eye
  And looked on him indignantly
And sternly answered, "Only try!"

Off to the cook he quickly ran.
  "Dear Cook, please lend a frying-pan
To me as quickly as you can."

"And wherefore should I lend it you?"
  "The reason, Cook, is plain to view.
I wish to make an Irish stew."
  "What meat is in that stew to go?"
"My sister'll be the contents!"
  "Oh!"
"You'll lend the pan to me, Cook?"
  "No!"

Moral: Never stew your sister.

LEWIS CARROLL

Skipping

Little children skip,
  The rope so gaily gripping,
Tom and Harry,
  Jane and Mary,
Kate, Diana,
  Susan, Anna,
All are fond of skipping!

The little boats they skip,
  Beside the heavy shipping,
And while the squalling
  Winds are calling,
Falling, rising,
  Rising, falling
All are fond
  of skipping!

I Eat my Peas with Honey

I eat my peas with honey,
  I've done it all my life,
It makes the peas taste funny,
  But it keeps them on my knife.

Catswhiskers

Catswhiskers was a pyjama case cat, and a very fine-looking pyjama case cat too! Susie's granny had made him when Susie was only four years old. It had taken Susie's granny quite a long time to make Catswhiskers. Every night she had sat by the fire carefully cutting and sewing, until he was perfect. Catswhiskers' body was made from the finest black velvet. He had beautiful red glass eyes, a bushy tail and the longest whiskers you have ever seen, which is how he got the name Catswhiskers. Catswhiskers sat on the end of Susie's bed, looking at all the toys in the bedroom in that slightly snooty way that cats have of looking at things.

When Susie was asleep, or playing in another room, Catswhiskers and all the toys would talk to each other. But Catswhiskers was bored with talking to the toys. Jenny the ragdoll was – well – just a ragdoll. "What could a ragdoll possibly have to say that would be of interest to a velvet pyjama case cat?" thought Catswhiskers.

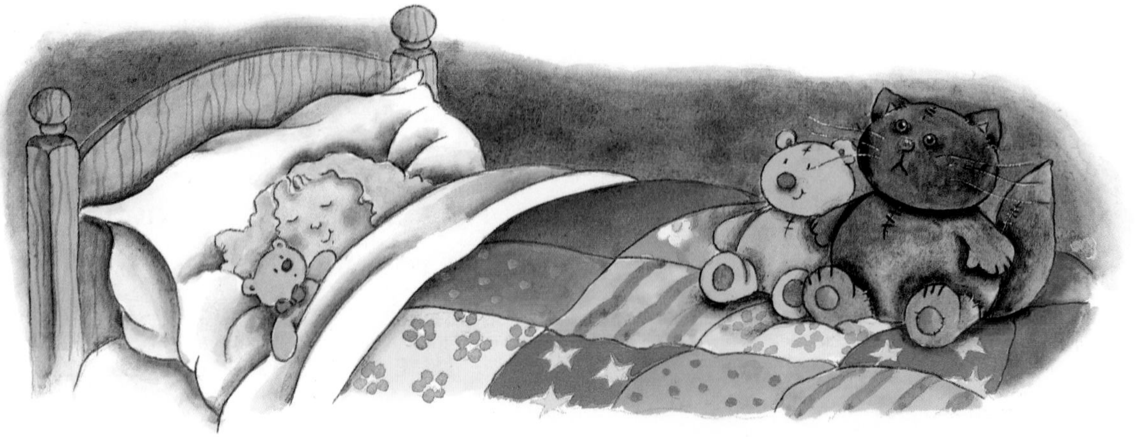

Then there was Neddy the rocking horse. He was a perfectly pleasant rocking horse as far as rocking horses went, but he only ever seemed to want to talk about how nice and shiny he was, and how he thought he was Susie's favourite toy. Even the alphabet bricks, the jack-in-the-box and the brightly coloured ball seemed to have nothing of interest to say to Catswhiskers. He sighed and looked at the window, wondering if life was more exciting outside.

One day, he decided he'd had enough of life in the bedroom with all the toys, and that he would venture outside to see if he could meet someone more interesting to talk to. So that night, when it was dark and Susie was asleep, he crept carefully to the open bedroom window and jumped out. It was a clear, cold, moonlit night. Catswhiskers shivered a little to find it so cold outside, and he maybe shivered a little more because he was also rather frightened. But he was very excited to be in the outside world, too, and he soon forgot about the cold and his fear.

He walked along the fence to the end of Susie's garden and jumped down into the garden next door. He had no sooner landed when he heard a fierce growl and saw two big, black eyes glinting in the moonlight. It was Barker, next door's dog – and he didn't like cats at all. With a loud bark, Barker came rushing towards Catswhiskers. His mouth was open wide and Catswhiskers could see his big, sharp teeth.

In fact, he thought that he could see all the way down into Barker's stomach! Catswhiskers only just had time to leap back on to the fence as Barker, jaws still snapping, gave chase.

"Phew, what a narrow escape," gasped Catswhiskers. "I didn't realise dogs were so unfriendly!"

He was wondering where it might be safe to go when he heard a low, hissing voice behind him. "Hey, velvet cat," hissed the voice. "What do you think you are doing on *our* patch?"

Catswhiskers turned round to see the biggest, meanest-looking cat he had ever set eyes on. And behind him were several more mean-looking cats, all coming towards Catswhiskers with their claws at the ready. Catswhiskers didn't wait a second longer. He simply ran for his life.

Now he was very frightened. He was also feeling cold and hungry. He wished that he was still in the warm safety of Susie's bedroom with the other toys.

Just as he was thinking that the outside world was perhaps a bit too exciting, he heard the sound of a van approaching. It suddenly stopped, its glaring headlights shining straight at him. On the side of the van were the words STRAY CAT CATCHER.

Out of the van stepped a man carrying a big net. Catswhiskers thought he knew just who that net was for, and decided that it was definitely time to go!

Without thinking about the dangers he might find himself in if he came face to face again with gangs of sharp-clawed cats or fierce, barking dogs, he ran back towards Susie's house as fast as his velvet legs could carry him. At last he reached the window and jumped thankfully back inside.

Snuggled down again on the warm bed with all his familiar friends around him, Catswhiskers decided that perhaps this was the best life for a pyjama case cat after all.

Catch Him

Catch him, crow! Carry him, kite
 Take him away till the apples are ripe;
When they are ripe and ready to fall,
 Here comes a baby, apples and all.

Wine and Cakes

Wine and cakes for gentlemen,
 Hay and corn for horses,
A cup of ale for good old wives,
 And kisses for the lasses.

Jack-a-Dandy

Nauty pauty Jack-a-Dandy
 Stole a piece of sugar candy
From the grocer's shoppy shop,
 And away did hoppy-hop.

Punctuate

Every lady in this land
 Has twenty nails upon each hand
Five and twenty on hands and feet
 All this is true without deceit.

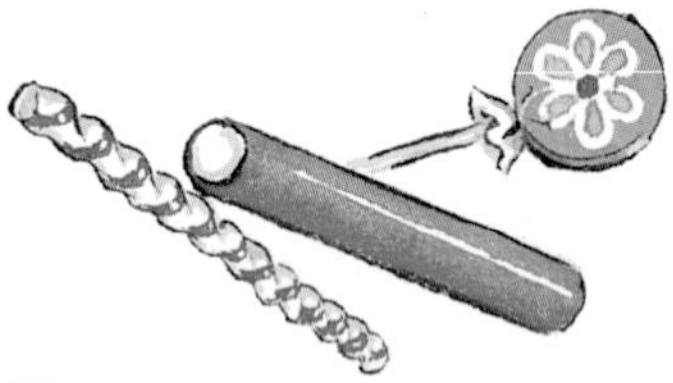

Marching

March, march, head erect,
 Left, right, that's correct.

Did You See My Wife?

Did you see my wife, did you see, did you see,
 Did you see my wife looking for me?
She wears a straw bonnet, with white ribbands on it,
 And diminity petticoats over her knee.

Rain

Rain, rain,
 go to Spain,
Never show
 your face again.

Tommy's Shop

Tommy kept a chandler's shop,
 Richard went to buy a mop;
Tommy gave him such a whop,
 That sent him out of the chandler's shop.

King Boggen

King Boggen, he built a fine new hall;
Pastry and piecrust, that was the wall;
The windows were made of black pudding and white,
Roofed with pancakes – you never saw the like.

Pit, Pat

Pit, pat, well-a-day,
Little Robin flew away;
Where can little robin be?
Gone into the cherry tree.

Bagpipes

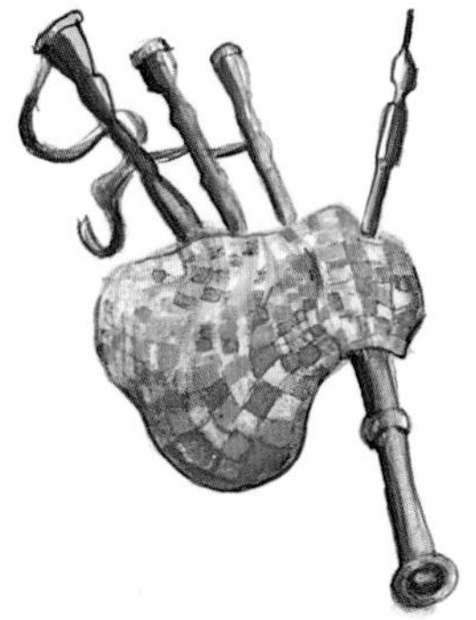

Puss came dancing out of
a barn
With a pair of bagpipes
under her arm;
She could sing nothing but,
Fiddle cum fee,
The mouse has married the humble-bee.
Pipe, cat – dance, mouse –
We'll have a wedding at our good house.

Green Cheese

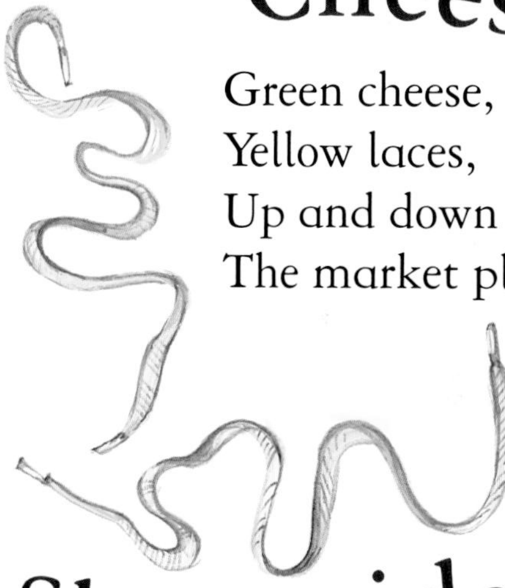

Green cheese,
Yellow laces,
Up and down
The market places.

The Priest

The little priest of Felton,
The little priest of Felton,
He killed a mouse within his house,
And nobody there to help him

Shrovetide

Once, twice, thrice,
I give thee warning,
Please to make pancakes
Again in the morning.

Mother?

"Mother, may I go out to swim?"
"Yes, my darling daughter.
Fold your clothes up neat and trim,
But don't go near the water."

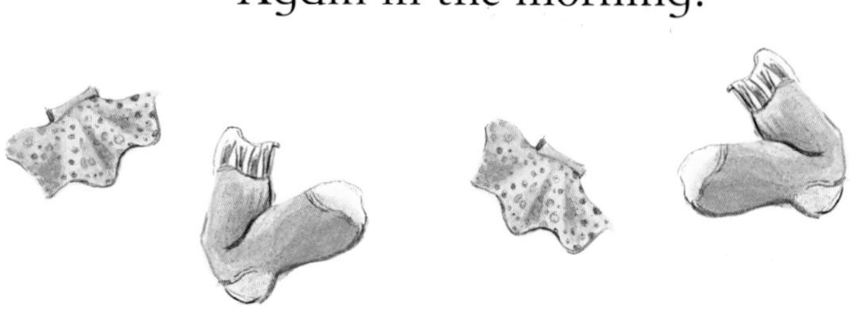

Lost for Ever

Sheep are lovely animals, but they are not the cleverest creatures. They follow one another without thinking too much about whether it is a good idea. When the leader is Maria, it very often isn't!

One day, Maria thought that the grass in the next meadow was much greener and juicier than the grass right under her nose.

"Come on, girls!" she baa-ed. "Follow me!"

With a skip and a jump, Maria was over the fence and into the meadow next door, and it wasn't long before the other sheep had followed Maria into the next field, too.

After an hour of munching grass in the new meadow, Maria happened to look over the wall on

the far side. The grass there looked even better. "Follow me!" she baa-ed again, and she was off! The other sheep were right behind her.

By the end of the afternoon, Maria and her friends found themselves a very long way from Old MacDonald's farm and seemed likely to be lost for ever!

"I don't know where we are," said Maria, looking all around her. "Oh, I can't think now. I'm going to sleep."

And, of course, all the other sheep were soon asleep, too.

Now, when sheep wake up, they are hungry! So the next morning, when Maria awoke, she forgot about trying to find her way home. Instead, she tucked into some tasty grass.

You can guess what the other sheep did!

Maria grazed her way across the meadow and came to a hedge. Over the hedge was another meadow, and the grass looked even tastier there. "Follow me, girls!" Maria baa-ed. So, with a skip, a jump and a leap, the flock bounded into the meadow and started on their mid-morning snack.

At lunch time, tea time and supper time, exactly the same thing happened.

It wasn't until it was bedtime that Maria remembered that they were a long way from home. "We must be even further now," she baa-ed, sadly.

"But maaamaaa..." bleated her little lamb.

"Tell me in the morning," Maria replied.

"But maaamaaa..." the lamb tried again.

"Go to sleep, little one," said Maria. "We'll get home tomorrow."

"But MAAAMAAA!" laughed the little lamb. "We are home already. Look! What can you see?"

And, sure enough, there before them was Old MacDonald's meadow.

The smoke from the farmhouse chimney drifted into the evening air. Old MacDonald stood by the gate. Without intending to, Maria had led them all the way back home again.

Although sheep are not clever creatures, sometimes they are silly in a very clever way – if you see what I mean!

The Bunny Olympics

Everyone on Fiddlestick Farm was really excited – today was the Bunny Olympics. Rabbits hopped and skipped from all around, to find out who would be the champion runner, jumper and muncher!

All the animals helped to get things ready. Goat and Pig put out the plant pots for the Hopping-In-and-Out Race. Then, it was time to start… READY, STEADY, GO!

BOING! BOING! BOING! Up and down and in and out of the plant pots went those bunnies, as fast as they could go! Charlie won easily, but then had to go back and rescue his little sister Bubbles, who was stuck inside the very first pot!

Next, it was time for the High Jump. Cow and Horse held the rope, while the bouncy bunnies jumped higher and higher until… WHEEEEEE! Ellie Bunny leapt right over Horse's back!

"No one will be able to jump higher than that!" mooed Cow. "Ellie wins the High Jump!"

Down in the meadow, near the stream, rabbits were competing in the Long Jump competition. Suddenly – SPLOOSH! Freddie Bunny leapt so far, he landed straight in the water! No one

else could jump that far, so Freddie Bunny was the winner!

The Munching Contest was next. Sheep was in charge of counting how many carrots and lettuces had been eaten.

Patty Bunny munched eight carrots. Little Bobo ate three lettuces and Nicky Bunny chomped through ten carrots and five lettuces.

Then – "BUUUUURP!" burped Harry, the biggest bunny, very loudly. "Pardon me," he said.

"Goodness!" said Sheep, in surprise. "Why, Harry, you've managed to gobble twenty carrots and ten whole lettuces! You are our Champion Muncher!"

Finally, it was time for the Obstacle Race. All the rabbits lined up at the start line. How the farm animals cheered, as the bunnies hopped, bounced and skipped over the stream, except little Bubbles, who wanted to stay and paddle! Then, Harry got stuck when he tried to bounce through the hollow log and everyone had to push him through! They squeezed under the strawberry nets, hopped over the bales of hay and, huffing and puffing, dashed back to the old tractor and past the finishing line. But who was the winner?

They all were! Every one of the bunnies had crossed the finish line together, so they all shared the first prize – a great, big, juicy carrot! And, as the sun began to set, everyone agreed it had been a great Bunny Olympics!

Where are you Going to My Pretty Maid?

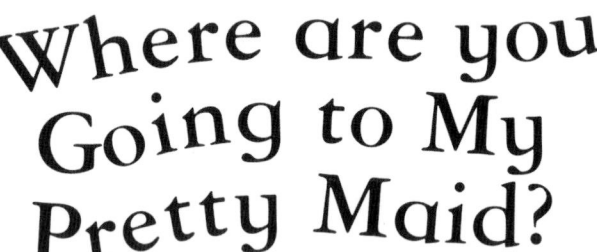

Where are you going to, my pretty maid?
Where are you going to, my pretty maid?
I'm going a-milking, sir, she said,
Sir, she said, sir, she said,
I'm going a-milking, sir, she said.

May I go with you, my pretty maid?
May I go with you, my pretty maid?
You're kindly welcome, sir, she said,
Sir, she said, sir, she said,
You're kindly welcome, sir, she said.

What is your fortune, my pretty maid?
What is your fortune, my pretty maid?
My face is my fortune, sir, she said,
Sir, she said, sir, she said,
My face is my fortune, sir, she said.

Then I can't marry you, my pretty maid,
Then I can't marry you, my pretty maid,
Nobody asked you, sir, she said,
Sir, she said, sir, she said,
Nobody asked you, sir, she said.

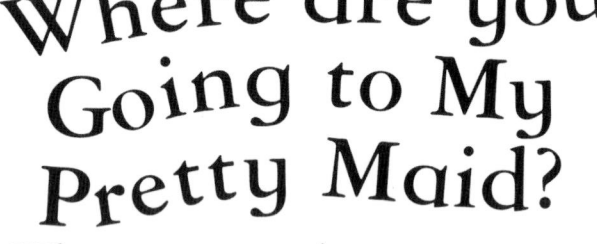

There was a Naughty Boy

There was a naughty boy,
A naughty boy was he,
He would not stop at home,
He could not quiet be –
He took
In his knapsack
A book
Full of vowels
And a shirt
With some towels,
A slight cap
For night cap,
A hair brush,
Comb ditto,
New stockings –
For old ones
Would split O!
This knapsack
Tight at's back
He rivetted close
And followed his nose
To the North,
To the North,
And followed his nose
To the North.

JOHN KEATS

A Frog he Would A-Wooing Go

A frog he would a-wooing go,
  Heigho! says Rowley,
Whether his mother would let him or no,
  With a rowley, powley, gammon and spinach.

A Candle

Little Nancy Etticoat
  In a white petticoat,
And a red rose.
  The longer she stands
The shorter she grows.

A Tisket, a Tasket

A tisket, a tasket,
  A green and yellow basket.
I wrote a letter to my love,
  And on the way I dropped it.

I dropped it, I dropped it,
  And on the way I dropped it.
A little girl picked it up
  And put it in her pocket.

The City Child

Dainty little maiden, whither would you wander?
  Whither from this pretty home, the home where mother dwells?
"Far and far away," said the dainty little maiden,
  "All among the gardens, auriculas, anemones,
Roses and lilies and Canterbury-bells."

Dainty little maiden, whither would you wander?
  Whither from this pretty house, this city house of ours?
"Far and far away," said the dainty little maiden,
  "All among the meadows, the clover and the clematis,
Daisies and kingcups and honeysuckle-flowers."

ALFRED, LORD TENNYSON

The Elves and the Shoemaker

Once upon a time there was a kind old shoemaker who lived in a tiny flat above his shop with his wife. He had many bills to pay, so he had to work from dawn to dusk to pay them off. The day came when he had only a few pennies left – just enough to buy leather for one final pair of shoes.

That evening, by candlelight, the shoemaker cut up the leather. Then, leaving it on his workbench, he picked up his candle and wearily climbed the stairs to his bed.

The next morning, when he came down to his shop, the shoemaker could not believe his eyes. There on his workbench, where the leather had been, was the finest pair of shoes he had ever seen.

The shoemaker went to the stairs and called to his wife to come and see what he had found.

"Did you make these shoes?" he asked her.

"Of course not," she replied.

The shoemaker was very puzzled and

scratched his head in amazement. "Then who could it have been?" he wondered.

The shoemaker put the shoes in his shop window. That afternoon, a fine gentleman came to try them on. He liked the shoes very much, and gave the shoemaker a good price for them.

With the money, the shoemaker was able to buy food for dinner, and had enough left over to buy leather to make two new pairs of shoes.

Later that night, the shoemaker cut up the leather and left it lying on his workbench. "I'll finish the shoes in the morning," he yawned, shutting up the shop. He picked up the candle and went up the stairs to bed.

The next morning, when he came downstairs, the shoemaker was truly amazed. There, sitting neatly on his workbench, were two fine pairs of beautiful new shoes! They were soft and delicate. He thought they were the best shoes he had ever seen.

Once again, the shoemaker called his wife and asked if she had made them. "Oh, husband," she said, "of course I didn't."

The shoemaker was confused, but once again he put them in his shop window, where everyone could see them. In no time at all, he had sold both pairs for a very good price.

That evening, the shoemaker and his wife had a marvellous dinner. There was also enough money left to buy leather to make four new pairs of shoes!

Once more, the shoemaker cut out the leather and left it neatly on his workbench. And, in the morning, there were more new shoes waiting for him when he came downstairs.

So it went on for weeks. Every night the shoemaker cut out the leather and left it on his workbench, and every morning there were splendid shoes waiting to be sold.

Soon the shoemaker and his wife were quite wealthy. But they still did not know who was making the smart shoes that appeared in the shop as if by magic.

One cold, wintry night, just before Christmas, the shoemaker and his wife decided that they had to solve the mystery once and for all. So, after the shoemaker left the leather on his workbench, he shut

up the shop and hid in a big cupboard with his wife. They left the door slightly open so that they could see, and waited... and waited... and waited.

At last, when the clock struck midnight, there was a tiny noise from the dark chimney. It grew louder. Suddenly, two tiny elves appeared in a shower of magical stars. They ran straight over to the workbench and began to stitch and sew, until they had made five beautiful pairs of shoes.

They sang as they worked:

"There isn't any time to lose,
We must make these fine new shoes!"

As soon as the shoes were finished, they hopped off the workbench and shot up the chimney. The shoemaker and his wife were amazed.

The shoemaker and his wife wanted to do something in return for the kind little elves. What could they do?

"They must be frozen in those thin, tattered clothes," said the shoemaker.

"Yes," said his wife. "And their feet are bare, although they make such beautiful shoes!"

So the shoemaker's wife made two little jackets and two pairs of trousers. She knitted four little woolly socks to keep their feet warm, and two tiny hats for their heads. The shoemaker made two pairs of small boots, fastened with shiny silver buckles.

That evening, they wrapped the little clothes in tissue paper and left them on the workbench. Then they hid in the cupboard and waited for the elves.

At the stroke of midnight, there was a noise from the chimney and the elves appeared in the shower of magical stars. They were puzzled when they saw parcels instead of leather. But, when they opened all the presents, they were overjoyed. They quickly put on their new clothes and danced happily all around the shop. As they danced they sang,

"See what handsome boys we are!
We will work on shoes no more!"

They danced happily across the room, flew up the chimney and were gone in a flash!

The elves did not return, but the man and his wife never forgot the two tiny men and all their hard work.

The shoemaker continued to make shoes which were fine and beautiful, and he became rich and famous across the land. But none compared to the beautiful, light and delicate shoes that the little elves had made!

Grandma Elephant's Birthday

"Boris," said his parents, "it's a special day today. Can you remember why?" They say elephants never forget, but Boris never remembered. He wrinkled his forehead and thought very hard.

"Do I start school today?" he said. "Is it my birthday?" asked Boris.

"Getting closer," said Mum. "It's Grandma Elephant's birthday! I want you to take her this basket of fruit. Can you remember where she lives?"

"Yes," nodded Boris. Mum gave him the basket and watched him leave.

Boris walked through the forest. It was very quiet and shady. "Boo!" shouted a voice suddenly. Boris looked round and saw a very strange animal. It looked like a mouse with wings. "Do I know you?" asked Boris

"I'm Fruit Bat, ninny," said the fruit bat.

"What do fruit bats do?" asked Boris.

"Eat fruit, of course," said the bat. "Where are you off to?"

"It's Grandma Elephant's birthday, but I can't remember how to get to her house," said Boris.

"If I tell you, will you give me some fruit?" asked the bat. Boris nodded. "That's the path over there," pointed the bat, taking an apple from Boris's basket.

The path was very narrow. Right in the middle, blocking the way, was a huge gorilla.

"I'm taking fruit to Grandma," said Boris bravely. "It's her birthday."

"Don't you remember who I am?" asked Gorilla.

"You're Rhinoceros," Boris guessed.

"If you can't remember who I am," said Gorilla, "you'll have to give me some fruit!" Boris couldn't remember so Gorilla took two bananas and let Boris pass.

Reaching a crossroads, Boris didn't know which path to take. "Take the left path," said a voice high above him. Looking up, Boris saw Giraffe with his head sticking out of the top of a tree. "Are you going to Grandma Elephant's? I can see her house from up here," said Giraffe.

"Thank you," said Boris. "Have some fruit!"

"That's very kind of you," said Giraffe. He took a pear from the basket.

When Boris arrived at Grandma's house, all that was left in the basket was one juicy plum! What would Grandma say? Would she be cross? He needn't have worried. Grandma hugged him and took him to the kitchen.

There, sitting round the table, were Fruit Bat, Gorilla and Giraffe, all wearing party hats. In the middle of the table was a big birthday cake, a large wobbly red jelly, and all the fruit from Boris's basket.

Grandma said it was the nicest birthday she could remember.

Boris couldn't remember the way home. So when the party was over his friends took him all the way back. His mum was so pleased to see him.

"Aren't you going to introduce me to your friends?" she asked.

"This is Bat Fruit, Crocodile and Giraffe," said Boris.

Everybody laughed. Silly Boris... what a memory!

In the Tree-Top

"Rock-a-by, baby, up in the tree-top!"
Mother his blanket is spinning;
And a light little rustle
that never will stop,
Breezes and boughs are beginning.
Rock-a-by, baby, swinging so high!
Rock-a-by!

"When the wind blows,
then the cradle will rock."
Hush! now it stirs in the bushes;
Now with a whisper, a flutter of talk,
Baby and hammock it pushes.
Rock-a-by, baby! shut, pretty eye!
Rock-a-by!

The Song of the Stars

We are the stars which sing,
We sing with our light.
We are the birds of fire
We fly over the sky,
Our light is a voice.
We make a road for spirits,
For the spirits to pass over.
Among us are three hunters
Who chase a bear;
There never was a time
When they were not hunting.
We look down on
the mountains.
This is the song of the stars.

Hush, Little Baby

Hush, little baby, don't say a word,
Papa's going to buy you a mocking bird.
If the mocking bird won't sing,
Papa's going to buy you a diamond ring.
If the diamond ring turn to brass,
Papa's going to buy you a looking-glass.
If the looking-glass gets broke,
Papa's going to buy you a billy-goat.
If that billy-goat runs away,
Papa's going to buy you another today.

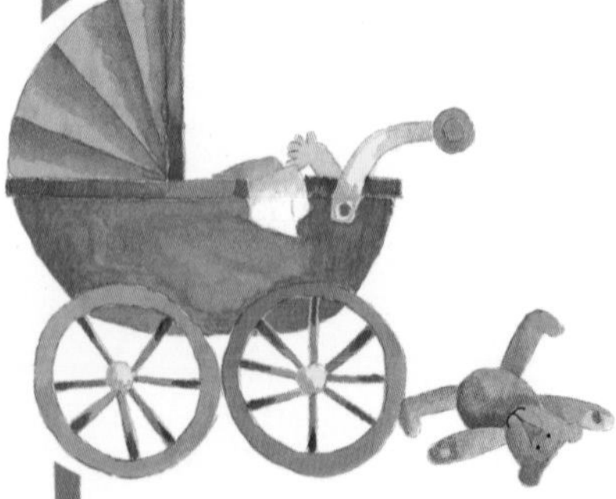

Humpty Dumpty's Poem

In winter, when the fields are white,
I sing this song for your delight –
In spring, when woods are getting green,
I'll try and tell you what I mean.
In summer, when the days are long,
Perhaps you'll understand the song:
In autumn, when the leaves are brown,
Take pen and ink, and write it down.

I sent a message to the fish:
I told them "This is what I wish."
The little fishes of the sea,
They sent an answer back to me.
The little fishes' answer was
"We cannot do it, Sir, because –"
I sent to them again to say
"It will be better to obey."

A Cradle Song

Golden slumbers kiss your eyes,
Smiles awake you when you rise.
Sleep, pretty wantons, do not cry,
And I will sing a lullaby:
Rock them, rock them, lullaby.

Care is heavy, therefore sleep you;
You are care, and care must
keep you.
Sleep, pretty wantons, do not cry,
And I will sing a lullaby:
Rock them, rock them, lullaby.

Frog went a-Courtin'

Mr Froggie went a-courtin' an' he did ride;
Sword and pistol by his side.
He went to Missus Mousie's hall,
Gave a loud knock and gave a loud call.

"Pray, Missus Mousie, air you within?"
"Yes, kind sir, I set an' spin."
He tuk Miss Mousie on his knee,
An' sez, "Miss Mousie, will ya marry me?"

Daisy the Dizzy Calf

One day, two special visitors were brought to Haven Farm – a poorly cow called Annie and her calf, Daisy. Sally and Joe helped their Dad settle them into the warm, comfortable barn. "You'll be fine now you've come to stay with us, Annie," said Joe, as he stroked the cow's soft nose. Sally gave the little calf a cuddle. "And you'll love it here, Daisy," she said. "Dad will soon make your mum much better."

That morning, Joe and Sally took Daisy into the meadow to meet the other animals. At first, Daisy found everything a bit scary. The chickens ran in and out of her feet. The horses were so big. The pigs were very noisy. And Billy the goat was so bouncy. He skipped, jumped and bounced everywhere! "Don't be afraid, Daisy," said Sally. "Billy just wants to play." The little calf wanted to join in, but her wobbly legs just wouldn't do what she wanted them to!

Billy gave her a playful nudge. Then, he bounced and skipped away to join the other animals. Poor Daisy was left stumbling after him.

"Don't take any notice, Daisy," said Joe. "He's just showing off!"

The little calf watched all the other animals having lots of fun, playing together. "Maybe if I practise," she thought to herself, "I won't be so wobbly."

That afternoon, Daisy ran round and round the meadow, jumping over the little stream at the bottom. "Hey, look!" laughed Joe, as he and Sally watched. "What a dizzy calf Daisy is!" The other animals also found the dizzy calf funny. Daisy was sure that everybody was making fun of her and she didn't like it. All she wanted to do was to join in!

As she walked away from the others, she saw the gate to the meadow wasn't closed properly. "I bet if I left the farm," Daisy thought to herself, "nobody would even notice I was gone." So, while no one was looking, Daisy squeezed through the gate and made her way up the hillside.

With each step, Daisy moved further and further away from the farm and it wasn't long before she was very tired, very hungry... and very lost! As Daisy climbed to the top of the hill, the skies darkened and rain drops started to fall. Shivering, the little calf ran under a big oak tree.

Suddenly, flashes of lightning lit the sky and thunder rumbled through the hills. "Mum!" mooed Daisy. "Where are you?" But the little calf was all alone and nobody could hear her cries.

Later that afternoon, Sally and Joe went to the meadow, to see how Daisy was settling in. But, when they arrived, there was no sign of her. "Can you see her, Joe?" asked Sally. They both looked round the meadow. Daisy was nowhere to be seen! "She's not here!" cried Sally. "Let's take Patch and look round the farm. He might be able to find her."

Patch the dog led Joe and Sally to the barn... then the milking shed... and then the chickens' pen. But still, they couldn't find Daisy. Suddenly, Patch started barking by the meadow gate. The children rushed over and saw that the gate had been left open. There were lots of muddy hoof prints everywhere. "We'd better tell Mum and Dad," said Joe. "Daisy's run away!"

Patch led Joe and Sally up the hillside, while Mum and Dad followed behind them. Patch ran with his nose to the ground, sniffing for signs of Daisy. He searched in the bushes... over the rocks... and round the trees. Suddenly, he lifted his

head and started to bark. Joe and Sally ran after Patch. "Good boy!" cried Joe. "Go find Daisy!"

At the top of the hill, they could see Daisy lying asleep under the shelter of the big oak tree. "Oh, Daisy!" cried Sally, kneeling down by the little calf. "I'm so glad we've found you!" Dad quickly made sure that Daisy was safe to move. With Mum's help, he picked up the tired calf and carried her carefully down the hillside.

Back at the farm, Daisy was safely tucked up next to her mum, Annie, who was feeling much better. "What's wrong with Daisy, Dad?" asked Joe.

"She's just very tired and cold," he said. "Nothing that rest, food and an extra bit of care can't put right." Joe and Sally gave the little calf a big hug.

"Daisy, we were so worried about you," said Sally. "Everybody missed you so much." Daisy looked up to see other farm animals by the barn door.

"I've been so silly," thought Daisy, as she snuggled up to her mum. "I won't ever run away again." Annie nuzzled her little calf. What a dizzy Daisy!

Billy Bunny's Shopping List

Billy Bunny wanted to play, but Mummy needed his help. "You can tidy the burrow or you can do the shopping," she said. Billy knew that if he went shopping he might see his friends on the way. "I'll do the shopping," he said. Mummy gave him a list. It read: five acorns, two carrots and some parsley.

As Billy went skipping through the woods, a gust of wind blew the list out of his paw and it floated away. "Never mind," said Billy. "I'm sure I'll remember everything!"

But he couldn't remember anything. He met his friend Fox, who said, "Get some flowers. Mummies always like flowers." So Fox and Billy Bunny picked a few bluebells that grew beside the stream.

"What else?" said Billy. "I know – I'll ask Dora Deer. Dora Deer was playing a leaping game near the fallen logs. Billy and Fox joined in, but after a while Billy remembered the shopping.

"If your mummy had written a list, what would be on it?" Billy asked. Dora thought

hard for a minute. "Leaves," she said at last. "Lots of nice fresh leaves to make my bed soft. I'm sure leaves were on your list."

Owl watched them gather a basket of leaves. "I know what your mummy wants," she said, blinking wisely. "All mummies like it when their friends come to visit. I bet your list said 'Invite all my friends to tea'."

"Are you sure?" asked Billy. "I think I would have remembered that." Owl just sniffed and said, "We owls know everything." So Billy ran around the woods and invited everyone he knew to come to tea that afternoon.

Billy went home with flowers and leaves. "Don't worry," he told his mummy. "I lost your list, but I remembered everything – and everyone is coming to tea this afternoon!" Mummy Bunny didn't have time to be cross – she had too much to do! Her friend Moose brought some berry cakes and, by the time everyone arrived for tea, Mummy had almost forgiven her silly Billy Bunny!

No Dabbling!

On Old MacDonald's farm, one group of animals caused more trouble than any other – the DUCKS! They waddled around, sticking their beaks in where they weren't wanted and quacked and flapped on the pond. They squabbled over slimy snails and quick little fish, and disagreed over delicious duckweed.

"I'm so glad I'm not a duck," said Henrietta the hen to her friend Jenny. "They are so loud!"

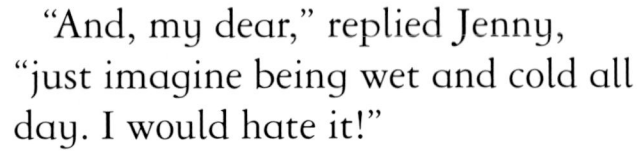

"And, my dear," replied Jenny, "just imagine being wet and cold all day. I would hate it!"

"*They* seem to enjoy it," clucked Henrietta. "I suppose it's just as well we're all different."

But, the next day, the hens woke up to a farm that seemed strange and different. Henrietta poked her beak out of the henhouse into the cold, frosty morning air. She couldn't work out what it was, but something was definitely wrong!

Percy the pig snuffled his snout. He was puzzled, too. What was missing? He called to Old George the horse, who was shuffling in the straw of his nice, warm stable. "George, something strange is going on."

"Something strange?" said Old George. "No, everything seems fine to me, Percy." And Percy, remembering that Old George was becoming hard of hearing, suddenly realised what it was – there was no sound from the duck pond!

It took only a few minutes for the news to spread round the farmyard. Shivering in the crisp, cold air, the animals hurried over to the pond to see what was wrong.

It was a sad sight that met their eyes. The pond was a solid sheet of ice. Huddled around it, looking very miserable, were the ducks.

There would be no splashing, no diving and no dabbling ducks that day. Without water, the ducks were still and sad.

"I never liked the squabbling," whispered Percy to Jenny, "but this quietness is awful."

"I know what you mean," replied the hen. "A place can be too quiet!"

"We must help them," declared Percy. "I can think of only one place where the water won't be frozen, but they'll have to be very, very quiet."

So, with Percy in the lead, a long line of miserable ducks waddled across the yard, into Old MacDonald's farmhouse and up the stairs to the bathroom.

Old MacDonald had just had a bath, and the water was still in the tub – warm and inviting. As the ducks dived in, they quacked and squawked in delight.

Downstairs, Old MacDonald was eating his breakfast when the happy quacking began. He looked up to the ceiling in surprise. But, outside in the yard, the animals were glad things were back to normal!

Little Kitten

Snuggle up, Kitten,
  warm in your bed.
Let moonlit dreams
  fill your head.

The little bunny
  curled up tight,
Dreams of carrots
  every night.

The baby mouse dreams
  in his nest,
Of cheese, the food
  that he loves best.

Shut your eyes, Kitten,
  sleep and dream,
Of balls of wool,
  and bowls of cream.

Mr Moon will guard
  your bed.
"Good night, sleep tight,
  dreamy head."

Little Puppy

Come, Little Puppy,
jump into bed,
Time to lay down
your sleepy head.

Yes, the sun still shines
and the sky is blue,
There are holes to dig
and bones to chew.

There are friends to make
and tails to chase,
You want to bark,
to jump and race!

But go to sleep, Puppy,
and dream away.
Tomorrow you can run
and play.

Shut your little eyes
up tight.
So Mr Moon can say
"Good night".

Mr Squirrel Won't Sleep

It was autumn. The leaves were falling from the trees in the forest and the air was cold. All the animals began to get ready for winter.

One night Mr Fox came back from hunting and said to his wife, "There's not much food about now it's getting colder. We'd better start storing what we can to help tide us over the winter."

"You're right, Mr Fox," replied his wife, gathering her cubs into their lair.

"I'd love to go fishing," said Mr Bear, "but I'll have to wait until spring now." He went into his den, shut the door tight and sealed it.

Mrs Mouse ran by with a mouthful of straw. "Must dash," she squeaked, "or my winter bed will never be finished in time." But soon she, too, was curled up with her tail wrapped around her for warmth.

Now only Mr Squirrel wasn't ready for winter. He danced about in his

tree, leaping from branch to branch and chasing his tail. "Ha, ha!" he boasted. "I don't have to get ready for winter. I have a fine store of nuts hidden away, a beautiful bushy tail to keep me warm and, besides, I don't feel in the least bit sleepy." And he carried on playing in his tree.

"Are you still awake?" snapped Mr Fox.

"Go to sleep!" growled Mr Bear.

"Please be quiet," squeaked Mrs Mouse, drawing her tail more tightly about her ears.

But Mr Squirrel wouldn't go to sleep. He danced up and down all the more and shouted, "I'm having SUCH FUN!" at the top of his voice.

Winter came. The wind whistled in the trees' bare branches, the sky turned grey and it became bitterly cold. Then it started to snow. At first Mr Squirrel had a grand time making snowballs – but there was no one around to throw them at and he began to feel rather lonely. Soon he felt cold and hungry, too.

"No problem!" he said to himself. "I'll have some nice nuts to eat. Now, where did I bury them?" He scampered down his tree to find that the ground was deep with snow. He ran this way and that trying to find his hiding places, but all the forest looked the same in the snow and soon he was hopelessly lost.

"Whatever shall I do?" he whimpered, for now he was shivering with cold and hunger and his beautiful, bushy tail was all wet and bedraggled.

All of a sudden he thought he heard a small voice. But where was it coming from? He looked all around but there was no sign of anyone. Then he realised that the voice was coming from under the snow.

"Hurry up!" said the voice. "You can join me down here, but you'll have to dig a path to my door."

Mr Squirrel started digging with his front paws and sure enough there was a path leading to a door under a tree stump. The door was just open enough for Mr Squirrel to squeeze his thin, tired body through.

Inside was a cosy room with a huge fire, and sitting by the fire was a tiny elf. "I heard you running around up there and thought you might be in need of a bit of shelter," said the elf. "Come and sit by the fire." Mr Squirrel was only too pleased to accept and soon he was feeling warm and dry.

"This isn't my house, you know," said the elf. "I think it might be part of an old badgers' sett. I got lost in the forest and so, when I found this place, I decided to stay here until spring. Though how I'll ever find my way home, I don't know." A fat tear rolled down the elf's cheek.

"I have been a very foolish squirrel," said Mr Squirrel. "If you hadn't taken me in I surely would have died. I am indebted to you and, if you will let me stay here until spring, I will help you find your way home."

"Please stay!" replied the elf. "I'd be glad of the company." So Mr Squirrel settled down with his tail as a blanket and soon he was asleep.

Days and nights passed, until one day the elf popped his head out of the door and exclaimed, "The snow has melted, spring is coming. Wake up, Mr Squirrel." Mr Squirrel rubbed his eyes and looked out. There were patches of blue in the sky and he could hear a bird singing.

"Climb on my back," Mr Squirrel said. "I'll show you the world."

They set off through the forest until they climbed to the top of the highest tree of all.

"You can look now," said Mr Squirrel, seeing that the elf had covered his eyes with his tiny hands. The elf had never seen anything like it in his whole life. Stretching in all directions, as far as the eye could see, were mountains, lakes, rivers, forests and fields. Suddenly the elf started to jump for joy.

"What is it?" said Mr Squirrel.

"I... I... can see my home," cried the elf, pointing down into the valley below the forest. "And there are my friends sitting in the sunshine. I must go home, Mr Squirrel. Thank you for showing me the world, for I should never have seen my home again without you." And with that he climbed down the tree and skipped all the way home.

Mr Squirrel made his way back to his own tree where Mrs Mouse, Mr Fox and Mr Bear were very pleased to see him.

"I've been very foolish, but I've learned my lesson," said Mr Squirrel. "Now let's have a party – I've got rather a lot of nuts to eat up!"

So the animals celebrated spring with a fine feast. And Mr Squirrel vowed not to be silly again next winter.

Sleepy the Farm Kitten

Sleepy, the farm kitten, was always tired. He liked nothing better than sleeping all day long, and all through the night. While all the other kittens were busy chasing mice or scaring away birds, he was normally fast asleep.

"Looks too much like hard work to me," he'd yawn, before strolling off to find a comfy spot for a snooze.

One day, while the other kittens were chasing mice around the corn shed, Sleepy stretched and looked around for somewhere to nap.

"You can't sleep here," said the farmer's wife, sweeping Sleepy out of the kitchen. "Today's cleaning day and you'll just be in the way."

"You can't sleep here," clucked the hens, flapping him out of the chicken run. "We're laying eggs and we certainly don't want you watching."

"You can't sleep here," mooed the cows, shooing him out of the milking shed. "We're busy being milked, and a kitten can never be trusted around milk."

"You can't sleep here," said the farmer, pushing him out of the dairy. "We're making ice cream and we don't want your hairs all over the place."

"I'm really tired," Sleepy complained to a passing mouse. "Can I sleep with you mice?"

"Don't be ridiculous," laughed the mouse. "Don't you know that kittens are supposed to chase mice?"

Just as Sleepy was about to give up hope of ever finding somewhere to sleep, he spotted the ideal bed – a soft bale of hay sitting on a trailer.

"Purrfect," he purred, curling into a sleepy ball. Within seconds, he was purring away in his sleep.

He was so comfortable, that he didn't even wake up when the tractor pulling the trailer chugged into life. And he still didn't wake up when the tractor and trailer bumped down the road leading to town.

It was only when the trailer shuddered to a halt that Sleepy woke with a start. He blinked his eyes sleepily, stretched, and looked around. Then he flew to his feet. He couldn't believe his eyes. He was at market and the farmer was driving away in the tractor.

"Wait for me," meowed Sleepy, leaping down from the trailer. But the farmer had gone. "Looks like I'll have to walk all the way home," moaned Sleepy, as he started to walk back towards the farm.

Sleepy walked all afternoon and all through the night. The cockerel was just beginning to crow the morning in when he eventually made it back to the farm.

"Hello, lazybones," called the other kittens when they saw him. "Where have you been sleeping all night while we've been chasing mice?"

But for once Sleepy really was tired – far too tired to explain where he had been all night. And it wasn't long before he was fast asleep!

Welcome Little Chick

With a scritch and a scratch and
  tippity tap,
The shiny shell begins to crack.
  A hole appears and then a beak,
Two beady eyes now take a peek.
  A head peeps through, it
starts to shout.
  It wiggles and wiggles,
And yells, "Let me out!"

He fluffs up his feathers
  And gives a big kick.
The shell breaks in two
  And there is a chick!

The Noisy Farm

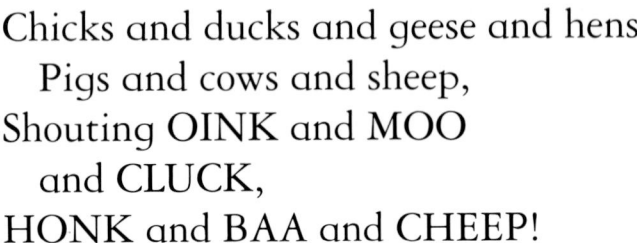

Chicks and ducks and geese and hens,
  Pigs and cows and sheep,
Shouting OINK and MOO
  and CLUCK,
HONK and BAA and CHEEP!

Down on Primrose Farm each day,
  Horses neigh and donkeys bray.

It's really such a noisy place,
  Till Mr Sunshine hides his face.
Then they snore and snooze and yawn,
  Until the cockerel crows, "It's dawn!"

Happy Hatching Day

Chicks are here,
Chicks are there,
Chicks are hatching everywhere!
Poking out their tiny beaks,
They open wide and call,
"Cheep! Cheep!"

So, is this a special day,
When all the chicks
come out to play?
Yes, it is! Hip,
hip hooray!
At last, it's Happy
Hatching Day!

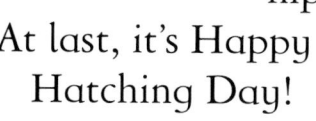

Second-hand Bear

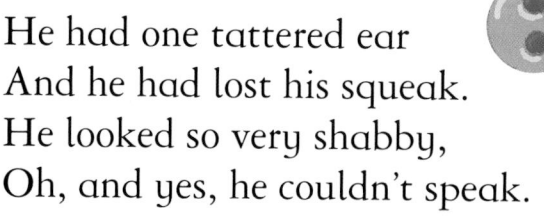

He had one tattered ear
And he had lost his squeak.
He looked so very shabby,
Oh, and yes, he couldn't speak.

His fur was worn and patchy.
He only had one eye.
There were a lot of other toys
In there that I could buy.

But he seemed so very tearful,
On the shelf all alone.
It looked like he was longing
For a best friend of his own.

So I took him home to my house
And I tried to fix his eye.
I put a patch upon his ear,
And now I'll tell you why.

I knew that all he needed
Was a little bit of care,
And I had fallen quite in love
With that second-hand old bear.

The Golden Bird

There was once a king who kept a golden bird in a gilded cage. The bird wanted for nothing. Every day the king's servant brought him food and water and groomed his fine yellow feathers. And each day the bird sang his beautiful song for the king. "How lucky I am," cried the king, "to have such a beautiful bird that sings such a fine song." However, as time passed the king began to feel sorry for the bird. "It really isn't fair," he thought, "to keep such a handsome creature in a cage. I must give the bird its freedom." He called his servant and ordered him to take the cage into the jungle and release the bird.

The servant obeyed, and took the cage deep into the jungle where he came to a small clearing. He set the cage down, opened the door and out hopped the golden bird. "I hope you can look after yourself," the servant said as he walked away.

The golden bird looked about him. "This is strange!" he thought to himself. "Still, I suppose someone will come along to feed me soon." He settled down and waited.

After a while he heard a crashing sound in the trees, and then he saw a monkey swinging from branch to branch on his long arms.

"Hello there!" called the monkey, hanging by his tail and casting the bird an upside down grin. "Who are you?"

"I am the golden bird," replied the golden bird haughtily.

"I can see you're new around here," said the monkey. "I'll show you the best places to feed in the tree tops."

"No thanks," replied the golden bird ungratefully. "What could an ape like you possibly teach me? You've got such a funny face. I expect you're envious of my beautiful beak," he added.

"Have it your own way," called the monkey as he swung off into the trees.

Some time later the golden bird heard a hissing noise and a snake came slithering by. "Well, hello," hissed the snake. "Who are you?"

"I am the golden bird," replied the golden bird proudly.

"Let me show you the jungle paths," said the snake.

"No thanks," replied the bird rudely. "What could a snake possibly teach me? With your horrid hissing voice, you must be jealous of my beautiful song," he said, forgetting that he had not sung yet.

"Very well," hissed the snake as he slithered and slipped his way into the undergrowth.

By now the golden bird was beginning to wonder when his food would arrive. He began to imagine the tasty morsel that he hoped he would soon be eating.

Just then he was aware of a movement on the tree trunk behind him. Looking up he caught a glimpse of a chameleon, lying camouflaged against the trunk.

"Good day," said the chameleon. "I've been here all the time, so I know who you are. You're the golden bird. It's a good idea to know where to hide in case of danger. Let me show you."

"No thanks," replied the golden bird. "What could an ugly brute like you possibly teach me? You must wish you had lovely feathers like me," he said, fluffing up his beautiful, golden plumage.

"Well, don't say I didn't warn you," muttered the chameleon as he darted away.

The golden bird had just settled down again when a great grey shadow passed over the jungle. He looked up to see a great eagle swooping low over the trees. The monkey swung up to hide in the densest foliage near the top of the trees. The snake slid off to hide in the deepest part of the undergrowth. The chameleon stayed quite still but his skin colour became a perfect match for the tree he was on and he became totally invisible.

"Aha!" thought the golden bird. "All I have to do is fly away and that stupid eagle will never catch up with me." He flapped his wings and flapped and flapped, but he did not know that his wings had grown weak through living a life of luxury in the palace. Now the bird regretted his golden plumage and wished that he had dull brown feathers that would not show up in the forest clearing. For his fine yellow feathers made him easy to see. He was sure the eagle would come and gobble him up. "Help!" he trilled. "Please help me someone." Now he could see the eagle swooping down towards him with eyes blazing like fire and talons drawn.

At that moment the golden bird felt something close around his legs and pull him into the undergrowth. It was the snake. Then he was lifted up into the trees by a long, hairy arm and saw he was being carried by the monkey. "Keep still," whispered the chameleon pushing him into the centre of a large yellow flower. "The eagle won't see you there." And sure enough, the golden bird found that he was precisely the colour of the flower and the eagle flew straight past him.

"How can I repay you all?" exclaimed the bird. "You saved my life!"

"You can sing for us," replied the animals. And so from then on, the monkey, the snake and the chameleon looked after the golden bird, and he sang his beautiful song for them every single day.

Puss in Boots

There was once a miller who had three sons. When he died, he left his mill to the eldest son, his cottage to his middle son and only his pet cat to his youngest son, William.

William went and sat under a tree, feeling very miserable and sorry for himself. "What will become of us, Puss?" he moaned.

To William's utter amazement, Puss answered him. "Don't worry, Master," said the cat. "Just do what I say and you will be far richer than either of your brothers!"

Puss told William to get him a fine suit of clothes, a pair of soft leather boots and a strong canvas sack. Then he caught a huge rabbit, put it in the sack, and took it to the palace.

No one there had ever seen a talking cat before, so he was granted an immediate audience with the king.

"Your Majesty," said Puss, "this fine rabbit is a gift from my master, the Marquis of Carabas."

The king had never heard of the Marquis of Carabas, but he was too embarrassed to admit this. "Please thank the Marquis," he said to Puss, "and give him my regards."

The next day, Puss caught some plump partridges and once more he took them to the king, with the same message: "These are from my master."

For several months, Puss went on bringing the king fine gifts.

One day, he heard that the king would be riding along the river bank that afternoon with the princess.

"Master," said Puss, "you must go swimming in the river today."

"Why?" asked William.

"Just do as I say, and you will see," answered Puss.

While William was swimming, Puss hid all his clothes. Then, when he saw the king's carriage approaching, he ran up to it shouting for help. "Help!" cried Puss. "Robbers have stolen my master's clothes!"

When the king recognised the cat, he immediately called to his chief steward and ordered him to bring a fine new suit from the palace.

"It must be of the finest cut," said the king, "and made from the softest cloth, do you hear! Only the very best will do for the Marquis of Carabas!"

Once he was dressed in his fine new suit, William looked quite handsome. The princess invited him to join her and her father in the carriage.

As William and the princess sat next to each other, they began to fall in love.

Meanwhile, Puss ran ahead until he came to a meadow where he saw some men mowing. "The king's carriage is coming," Puss told them. "When he asks whose meadow this is, say it belongs to the Marquis of Carabas – or you will have your heads cut off!"

The mowers didn't dare to disobey.

When the royal carriage came by, the king asked who the meadow belonged to. The mowers quickly replied, "The Marquis of Carabas."

"I can see that you are very well-off indeed," the king said to William, who blushed modestly. That made the princess love him even more!

Further on, Puss came to a field where men were harvesting corn.

"When the king asks whose corn this is," Puss told them, "say it belongs to the Marquis of Carabas – or you will have your heads cut off!"

The harvesters didn't dare to disobey.

Next, Puss came to an enormous castle which he knew belonged to a fierce ogre. Still he bravely knocked on the door.

When the ogre let him in, Puss bowed low and said, "I have heard that you have wondrous powers, and can change yourself into anything – even a lion or an elephant."

"That is true," said the ogre. And to prove it, he changed himself into a snarling, growling lion.

Puss was terrified and leapt up onto a cupboard. Then the ogre changed himself back again.

"That was amazing," Puss remarked. "But surely it cannot be too difficult for someone of your size to change into a creature as big as a lion. If you were truly the magician they say you are, you could turn into something tiny – like a mouse."

"Of course I can do that!" bellowed the ogre. In an instant he became a little brown mouse scurrying across the floor.

Quick as a flash, Puss leapt off the cupboard, pounced on the mouse and ate it in one big gulp!

Soon, Puss heard the king's carriage drawing near and rushed outside. As it approached, he bowed low and said, "Welcome, Your Majesty, to the home of the Marquis of Carabas."

The king was very impressed indeed. "May we come in?" he asked William.

"Of course, Your Majesty," replied William, looking a little confused.

As they walked through the castle, the king was delighted to see treasures of great value everywhere he looked. He was so pleased that he said to William, "You are the perfect husband for my daughter."

William and the princess were very happy and later that day they were married. They lived in the ogre's castle happily ever after. Puss, of course, lived with them – though he never chased mice again!

Kissable Kitten

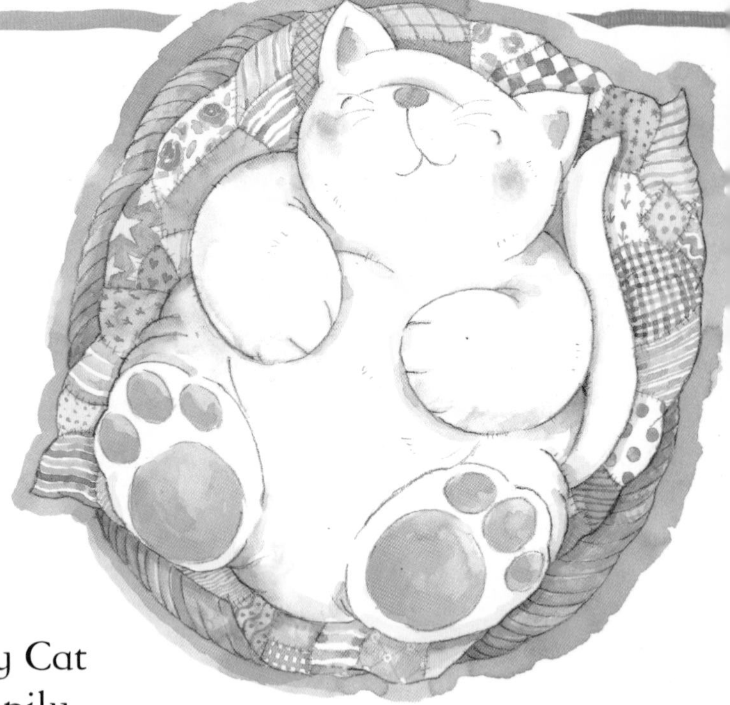

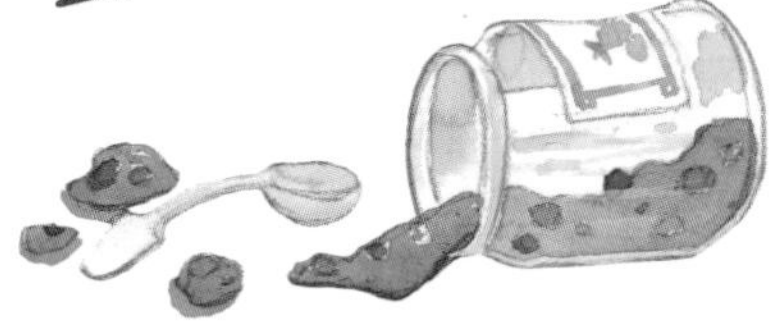

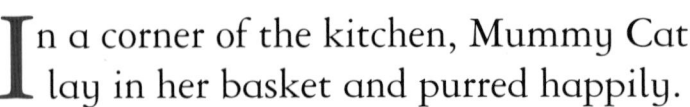

In a corner of the kitchen, Mummy Cat lay in her basket and purred happily. Curled up asleep beside her were four beautiful kittens – a grey kitten called Timmy, a black kitten called Winnie and a stripy kitten called Ginger.

And then there was Kissy, the softest, cutest kitten you ever did see!

Timmy had the biggest blue eyes. They spotted everything. When he and Kissy were in the garden, chasing bumble bees, it was Timmy who spied the water sprinkler.

"Watch out, Kissy!" said Timmy. "You'll get wet!"

"Splish, splash, flipperty-flash!" sang Kissy. "I don't care!" Kissy pushed through the flowers with her little pink nose and shrieked with laughter, as the water sprinkler suddenly covered them both with water.

"Kissy!" spluttered Timmy, shaking water drops from his ears. "Now look what you've done!" But Kissy just rolled around, laughing. "Oh, Timmy," she giggled. "That was so funny!"

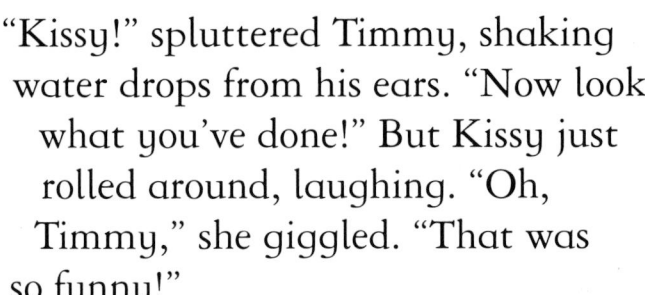

"Goodness me," said Mummy Cat, as her kittens dripped water on to the kitchen floor. "Timmy Kitten! You shouldn't have let Kissy get so wet! Now I shall have to dry you both!"

Kissy wriggled and giggled, as Mummy Cat's rough, pink tongue made her wet fur soft and white again. "Sugar and spice, that feels nice!" she sang.

But Timmy wasn't quite so happy. "Ow! Miaow!" he howled, as Mummy Cat's tongue licked him dry.

Kissy loved to explore with Winnie. Winnie had the cutest kitten nose ever and could sniff out all the best yummy food. "Mmm! Smells like jam and cream," said Winnie, her nose and whiskers twitching. Kissy reached up and gently pulled a corner of the tablecloth.

"Mind, Kissy!" said Winnie. "You'll pull everything over!"

"Yum, yum, yum, that cream should be in my tum!" sang Kissy as she pulled the cloth a bit more. Suddenly, the cream jug and jam pot fell to the floor with a crash!

"Oh, Kissy!" shrieked Winnie. "What have you done?"

Jam and cream went everywhere – what a mess! Kissy Kitten could hardly speak for laughing. "Oh, Winnie," she giggled. "That was so funny!"

Mummy Cat threw her paws in the air, when she saw the mess. "Goodness me," she said. "How could you let Kissy get so sticky, Winnie Kitten? Now I shall have to wash you both!"

Kissy giggled, as Mummy Cat licked her clean. "Bibble and bat, I like that!" she sang.

But Winnie wasn't happy at all. "Ow! Miaow!" she cried, as Mummy Cat's tongue lapped up the jam.

Kissy loved playing with Ginger because Ginger liked to pretend he was a fierce tiger, hunting wild animals or pouncing on Mummy Cat's twitching tail. Today, they were both hunting a Monster Mouse in the vegetable patch. "There's a dangerous mud puddle over there, Kissy," whispered Ginger. "Whatever you do, don't go in it!"

"Fiddle, fuddle, who cares for a puddle?" sang Kissy as she crawled right through the sticky, squelchy mud. Her beautiful white coat got muddier and muddier. She looked as if she was wearing brown boots!

Ginger hid his eyes. "I can't look!" he said. Kissy laughed and laughed. Then, she shook the mud off her dainty paws – all over Ginger!

Mummy Cat howled when she saw her two dirty kittens. "Ginger Kitten! How could you have let Kissy get so muddy?" she cried. "It will take me ages to clean you both!"

"Piddle and pud, that feels good!" sang Kissy.

Poor Ginger didn't feel good at all. "Ow! Miaow!" he wailed, as Mummy Cat cleaned up his coat.

Mummy Cat looked at her kittens and shook her head. "I just can't understand it," she said. "You've always been such good kittens!" Timmy, Winnie and Ginger all frowned at Kissy, who was fast asleep, purring in their basket.

"It wasn't us!" they cried. "We told Kissy Kitten to be careful! We don't like being bathed!" cried the kittens. "We don't like getting soaked or covered with sticky stuff or coated with mud!"

Mummy Cat looked into the basket. "Kissy?" she said. Kissy opened a bright, green eye and said, "But Mummy, I just love it when you kiss my nose and wash me every time I get messy!"

"What a funny Kissy Kitten you are!" said Mummy Cat, giving her a big lick. "You can have a kiss any time you want. You don't have to get really messy first!"

"No, we'd prefer it if you didn't!" said Timmy.

"But we forgive you," said Winnie and Ginger.

Kissy promised never to get them messy again. Then, they all cuddled up together in their basket and went fast asleep!

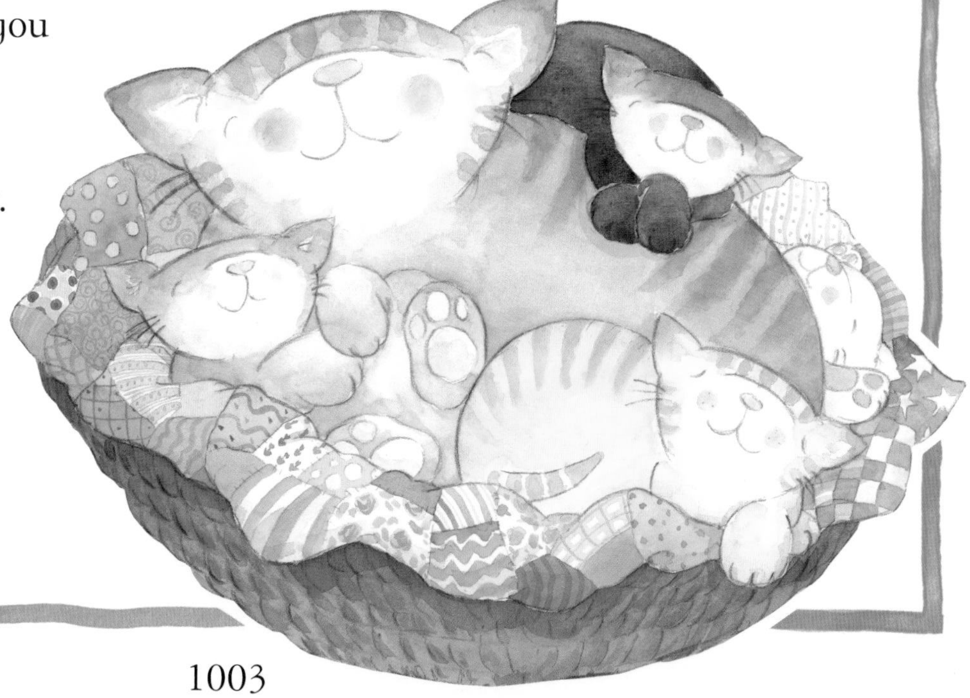

Little Bunny

Come, Little Bunny,
say "Good night".
There's lots to do
before you turn out the light.

Collect all your toys and
put them away.
Kiss them good night –
it's the end of the day.

Hop in the bath for a
rinse and a scrub.
Play with the bubbles –
rub-a-dub-dub-dub!

Finish your story and turn
out the light.
Time to tuck you in warmly
and kiss you goodnight.

Sweet dreams, Little Bunny,
we love you.
And Mr Moon says
"Good night" too.

Little Bear

Look through the window at the
moon shining bright.
Who can you see in the twinkling
starlight?

Up in the trees,
the grey doves coo.
Calling a friendly
"Good night" to you.

Good night, little squirrel.
Good night, little mouse.
Hurrying, scurrying to bed
in the house.

Close your eyes, Little Bear,
and turn out the light.
Fall asleep like your friends,
with eyes closed tight.

Listen to Owl calling
"Who-whoo-whooo!"
While old Mr Moon
watches over you.

Home Sweet Home

Old MacDonald always worked hard, but lately he had been extra busy in his workshop. One bright, sunny morning, he was ready to show everyone what he had been making. "Here you are, ladies!" he cried. "A new henhouse for you – and Henry the cockerel, of course. I didn't like to think of you shivering in your drafty old home.

Jenny and the other hens hurried over to look, clucking with curiosity.

Henry flapped up to the roof to see if it was a comfortable place for crowing.

"Cock-a-doodle-not-bad-at-all," he crowed, as Jenny, Henrietta, Mary and Victoria hopped into their new home.

For two days, the hens were happy in their new house. But the ducks, being rather jealous, squawked and squabbled and sulked in a rather obvious way!

On the third day, Jenny the hen said what the other hens had been thinking. "You know, there was

something to be said for the cracks in our old home," she clucked. "We could even keep an eye on those daft ducks without ever going outside." Henry crowed his agreement!

"Yes," agreed Henrietta. "And our old perches were much more comfortable, too."

"And," clucked Mary, "this place smells funny! I suppose it's the paint, but I'm not sure I'd want to bring up chicks in here."

Soon the hens and Henry decided they wanted to move back to their old home.

"I could cock-a-doodle-doo right over the pigsty from there," said Henry. "And I used to like chatting to Percy first thing in the morning."

That evening, when Mrs MacDonald came out to feed the hens, Old MacDonald came, too. "Doesn't that look better?" he said, proudly patting the henhouse roof.

"It's a bit too near the flower garden for my liking," said his wife, looking at Henry, who was very fond of eating her marigolds!

The hens knew that Old MacDonald was proud of the new henhouse. They couldn't bear to hurt his feelings by returning to their old home, so they would just have to make do with this one.

A few days later, it was Milly the farm cat – who wasn't the best of friends with any of the feathered folk on the farm – who solved the problem.

While the hens and Henry were in the barn, Milly crept into the brand new henhouse.

It was just the cosy place she was looking for. "Mmmmm, this is purr-fect," she said.

Later, Old MacDonald had a quiet word with Henry and the hens. "I'm sorry," he said, "but Milly has just had her kittens in your new home. We won't be able to disturb her for a few weeks. Could you…"

Before he could finish, they were scuttling through the door of their dear old home. It's amazing how helpful they can be sometimes!

A Goodnight Kiss

"It's bedtime now, Oakey," said Mum. Oakey curled up in the chair. His ears began to droop and he muttered, "Oh, that's not fair!"

"Have a drink first," smiled Mum, "then you must go."

"Five minutes more!" begged Oakey.

Mum answered, "No!"

Oakey's ears drooped and off he went. But he was back in a flash! "Where's your drink?" asked Mum. "You haven't been very long. You look scared, Oakey. Is there something wrong?"

"There's a monster in the kitchen, with long, white shaggy hair, lurking in the corner, behind the rocking chair," said Oakey.

Mum laughed. "Oh, Oakey, you've made a mistake. That's no monster. It's a mop." And she gave the mop a shake.

Oakey's ears drooped and off he went. But he was back in a flash! "What's the matter?" asked Mum.

"There's a ghost in the hallway, hovering around. Look, there it is floating just above the ground," he wailed.

"Oh, Oakey, you've made a mistake. That's no ghost. It's just an old coat, hanging on the hook. Coats don't float!" laughed Mum.

Oakey's ears drooped and off he went. But he was back in a flash! "Why aren't you in bed, Oakey?" asked Mum.

"There's a great big lump beneath the sheets. It's waiting to get me. I'm scared it's going to pounce. Please come and see," sniffed Oakey.

"Oh, Oakey, you've made a mistake. The only thing underneath the sheets is your old teddy bear," smiled Mum.

Oakey's ears drooped and he got into bed. But he didn't close his eyes. "Why aren't you asleep?" asked Mum.

"There are huge creepy crawlies underneath my bed. And I can't get the thought of them out of my head," complained Oakey.

"They're just your slippers, Oakey, so there's no need to hide. They won't be creeping anywhere without your feet inside," grinned Mum. "That's it now, Oakey. Time to say goodnight."

Mum left the room, switching off the light. And then Oakey saw it by the door. The monster! It moved across the floor and walked straight towards him, with its arms stretched out. Oakey's mouth opened, but he found he couldn't shout. The monster leaned over him and Oakey closed his eyes. What happened next gave Oakey an enormous surprise.The monster picked him up and cuddled him tight. Monsters just don't do that.

This couldn't be right! Then Mum's voice whispered, "Don't worry, it's just me. When I said 'Goodnight' just now, I forgot to give you this." Then Monster Mum gave Oakey a goodnight kiss!

The Missing Scarf

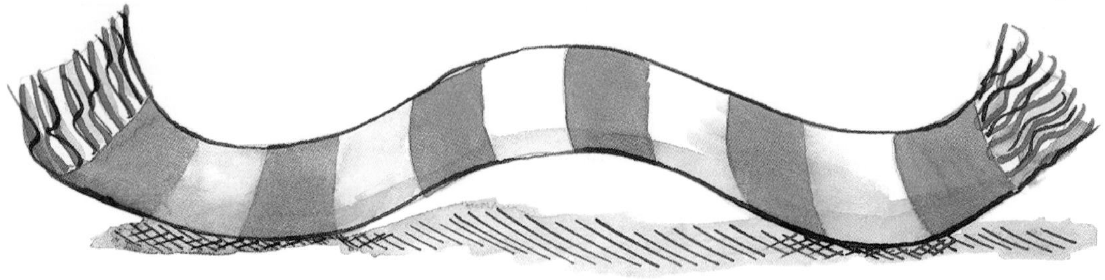

Kanga was very proud of her stripy knitted scarf. She had made it herself and she had also made a smaller matching one for her son, Joey. Kanga used to hop through the bush with her scarf streaming out behind her, while Joey's could just be seen poking out of the top of her pouch. Now Joey was older, he was too big for Kanga's pouch, but he still wore his scarf as he hopped along beside his mother.

Then one day Kanga woke up to find that her beautiful scarf was missing. She searched high and low but it was nowhere to be found. Eventually she decided that she would have to go out into the bush to look for it.

"Stay here," she said to Joey. "I'll try not to be long. I'm sure to find my scarf soon." Kanga hopped off into the bush and started to search among the roots of trees and under stones.

She had gone quite a long way when, looking up into the branches of a eucalyptus tree, she spotted Koala. Now Koala was usually asleep, but this time she was preparing a meal of eucalyptus leaves for her children. Kanga looked up at Koala and then her jaw dropped. For Koala was quite clearly wearing Kanga's scarf around her tummy. Then, to Kanga's horror, she saw Koala use the end of the scarf to wipe the teacups! "Koala," Kanga called. "Whatever do you think you're doing?"

Koala stopped cleaning the teacups and looked down through the branches of the eucalyptus tree at Kanga. "I'm wiping my teacups with my apron," she replied sleepily, "and I'll thank you not to interfere!" And with that, she yawned and moved several branches further up the tree.

Poor Kanga felt very embarrassed. How could she have mistaken Koala's striped apron for her own scarf? She hopped away and carried on further into the bush. After a while she heard Kookaburra's familiar laughing call nearby. "I know," thought Kanga, "I'll ask her. She'd be able to spot my scarf easily from the sky." She followed the sound of Kookaburra's call until she came to the tree where she lived. Kanga was about to call up when her jaw dropped again. For Kookaburra was quite clearly carrying Kanga's scarf in her beak. "Kookaburra," Kanga called. "Whatever do you think you're doing?"

"I'm lining my nest," mumbled Kookaburra through a beakful of stripy feathers. "And please don't interfere," she added as she arranged the feathers carefully in place.

Poor Kanga felt even more embarrassed. She carried on further into the bush. After a while she reached a wide, open plain and there she saw Emu running past with his baby chicks on his back. As he rushed past, Kanga's jaw dropped yet again. Emu quite clearly had Kanga's scarf tucked in amongst his chicks.

"Emu, whatever do you think you're doing?" called Kanga.

"I'm taking my chicks to safety," said Emu, glancing up at the sky as he sped away. "And you should do the same," he added. Kanga realised that what she had thought was her scarf were just the striped chicks on Emu's back.

Poor Kanga felt even more embarrassed. Then she felt a few spots of rain on her nose and, looking up, saw a huge black cloud overhead. There was no time to lose – she must find shelter. She made a dash to the edge of the plain and soon found herself by a stream. She wandered along feeling cold, wet, tired and miserable. Finally, she lay down in the wet grass beside the stream and tried to get to sleep. She shivered with cold and wondered how Joey was and whether he was behaving himself. She so hoped he hadn't got into mischief.

Just then there was a tap on her shoulder and there stood Platypus. "I could hear you in my burrow over there," she said pointing towards a hole beside the stream just above the water. "I thought you might like this to keep you warm," she added.

"My scarf!" exclaimed Kanga.

"Oh, *that's* what it is! I'm ever so sorry," said Platypus. "I've been using it as a blanket for my babies.

It's cold and damp in my burrow, you know," she added, rather forlornly. "It was stuck on some thorns and I know I shouldn't have taken it, but I just thought it would be so nice for keeping my young ones warm," blurted Platypus, and she started to sob.

"There now," said Kanga, "don't cry. You can keep the scarf. You need it more than me."

Platypus stopped crying and looked overjoyed. "Thank you," she said.

"No, thank you," said Kanga. "I've learned a lesson, which is not to get upset over a scarf, for I've ended up falling out with my friends."

Kanga made her way back home, but it took a long time because she apologised to all her friends on the way. When she explained what had happened Emu, Kookaburra and Koala all forgave her, and by the time she reached home she was feeling much better. Joey was there to greet her. "What have you been up to while I was away?" she asked.

"I made you this," he said. He handed her a scarf. It was a very funny-looking scarf, made out of twigs, grass and feathers, but Kanga loved it very much.

"This is much more special than my old scarf," she said. And she gave Joey an extra big hug.

Sniffle

A long way away, in a jungle no one had ever been to before, lived the Sniffle monster.

The famous explorer, Major Jolly, went into the jungle looking for new animals. First, he found a big, bright bird that strutted about showing everyone what a great tail it had. Then he found a new type of monkey that could knit socks! His greatest discovery, though, was when he came upon the MONSTER, in a tree, eating a banana. Major Jolly got very excited, the monster was intelligent! That means it could think like you and me. The monster was quite ugly, but then he would be, wouldn't he? He was big, ugly and covered in red fur.

Major Jolly decided to take him home to show his wife. They flew back together in a big plane and the monster sat on three seats. The famous explorer's wife met them at the airport.

"This is the monster I discovered, Maud," said Major Jolly. "How do you do?" Maud held out her hand.

"Howdeedoodee," repeated the monster. He took the lady's hand and sniffed it, and then danced her round the room in circles.

"I've already started to teach him English," said Maud, as they danced past for the third time.

Back home the monster wanted to dance with

everyone at first! But just a few weeks later he began to look ill and sad. He coughed and sniffed and spluttered. His coat turned green, and patches of fur fell out. And he had something really nasty running out of his nose.

When Maud visited, he wouldn't dance round the room with her. "My dear Monster," she said, "what's wrong with you?"

"I am Sniffle monster!" he said. "I was taken away from jungle without my friend. I must have this friend with me always, or I get ill! Stuff comes out of my nose! My friend is Hanky monster."

Maud thought she understood. "And you need this Hanky monster… umm… to wipe your nose for you?"

"No, no, no!" said Sniffle. "Hanky is a magician. He will make Sniffle dance again! Only Hanky monster knows the secret magic potion."

Major Jolly took Sniffle back to the jungle to find the Hanky monster. They found the place in the jungle where Major Jolly had camped. Suddenly, something that looked like a giant cabbage appeared and threw itself at Sniffle. Sniffle gave a whoop of joy! The cabbage was the Hanky monster, of course! It rushed back into the jungle.

"Gone to get magic potion," whispered Sniffle weakly.

The Hanky monster came back with a drink in a coconut shell. Sniffle drank it and went straight to bed. Next morning his colour was back to red and his nose had stopped running. He danced with everyone. Major Jolly was desperate to know the secret of the magic drink.

Hanky monster winked and whispered, "Hot lemon and honey!"

Hippo's Holiday

It was a warm, sunny morning in the jungle.

"A perfect time for a long, relaxing wallow," thought Howard Hippo. Wallowing in the river was Howard's favourite thing to do. He found a nice, cool, muddy spot and settled in. Howard was just drifting off into a delightful daydream, when… SPLASH! "Gotcha!" shrieked Maxine Monkey. SPLOOSH! "Gotcha back!" shouted Chico Chimp.

"Can't you monkeys and chimps play somewhere else?" Howard grumbled. "I'm wallowing here!"

"Oops! Sorry, Howard," Maxine apologised. But it was too late. Howard's wallow was ruined. That afternoon, as the hot sun beat down on his back, Howard slithered into the river to cool off.

"Aaah," he breathed, as he soaked in the cool water. "This is sooo lovely."

"Yoo-hoo! Howard!" called Penelope Parrot. "I've just learned to do a double-rollover-loop-the-loop! Want to see?"

"Sure, Penelope," sighed Howard. It didn't look as if he was going to have a chance to relax this afternoon, either! The next morning, Howard's cousin, Hilary, came to visit.

"You look exhausted, Howard," she said.

"That's because I never have a chance to relax and wallow any more," said Howard.

"What you need is a holiday," said Hilary. "I'm leaving for Hippo

Hollow this afternoon. Why don't you come with me?"

"That sounds like a good idea!" said Howard.

"You'll love Hippo Hollow," said Hilary, as the two hippos trundled through the jungle. "There's so much mud!"

Howard saw himself relaxing in a cool mud bath.

"And there are streams and waterfalls!"continued Hilary. Howard imagined having lots of cool showers.

"And everyone has lots and lots of FUN!" finished Hilary.

Howard thought about playing games with new hippo friends. At last Howard and Hilary arrived at Hippo Hollow. "It's even more beautiful than I had imagined!" Howard exclaimed.

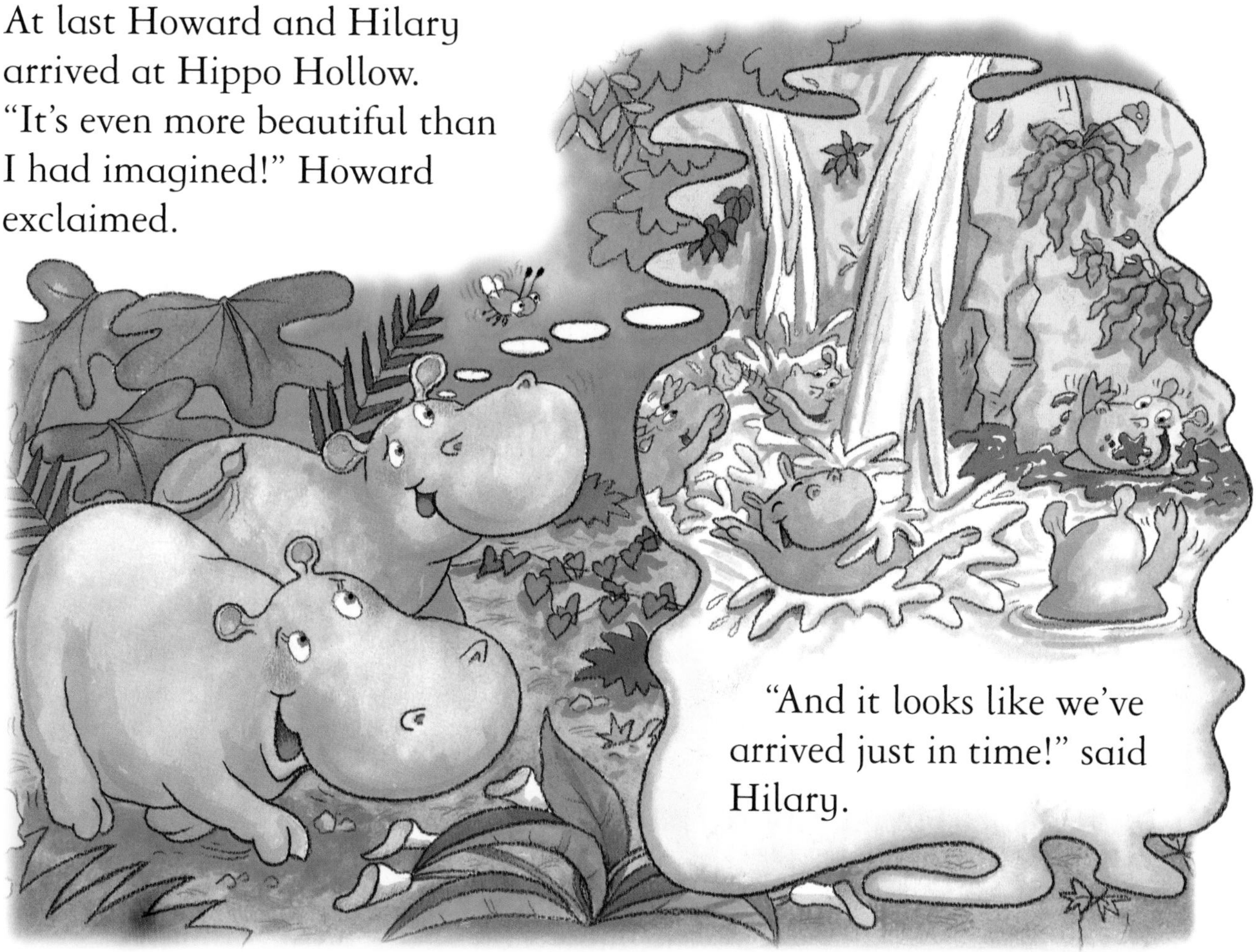

"And it looks like we've arrived just in time!" said Hilary.

"For what?" asked Howard. "A relaxing mud bath?" "No, silly!" laughed Hilary. "Hippo-robics!"

"Let's get moving, everyone!" called a sleek-looking hippo. Lots of other hippos galloped into the stream behind her.

"Come on, Howard," said Hilary. "Don't be a party pooper on the first day of your holiday!"

Howard had no choice but to join in. "Kick, two, three, four! Kick, two, three, four!" shouted the instructor.

Howard did his best and kicked with all the others. "Surely everyone will want a nice, long rest after all this exercise?" he thought. But he was wrong! After a quick shower in the waterfall, everyone rushed off to play Volley-Melon and Hilary wanted Howard on her team. Howard finally did get to have a rest after lunch – but not for long! "You're looking much more relaxed, Howard," Hilary called, as she led her junior swimming class right past him. "This holiday was just what you needed, wasn't it?"

"Er... I guess so," Howard replied, weakly. After his busy day, Howard was hoping for an early night. He was just getting settled, when he heard Hilary.

"Come on, Howard!" she bellowed. "You don't want to miss the Hippo-Hooray Cabaret! They are really good!"

"Oh – YAWN – how wonderful," sighed Howard. He could barely keep his eyes open.

The next morning, Howard was sliding into the river, when he heard Hilary calling.

"Is it time for Hippo-robics?" he asked.

"Oh, no," said Hilary. "Lots of good, fresh air is what you need. So we're going on a hike!" Howard huffed and puffed all through the exhausting hike. "I hope I can have a nice cool bath when this is over," he thought. Howard got his wish. But, as he was soaking his sore muscles, Hilary came by for a chat.

"The hike was fun, wasn't it?" she said.

"Oh yes," said Howard. "In fact, I enjoyed it so much, that I've decided to go on another one!"

"Really?" said Hilary. "That's great! Where are you hiking to?"

"Home!" said Howard. "I'm going home, where I can have a REAL holiday. And where there are no Hippo-robics, and no Volley-Melon games, no cabarets and no one to stop me wallowing as long as I like!" And so that's exactly what Howard did!

Shanty Goes to Sea

Shanty, the harbour kitten, just loved fish. He ate every scrap that the fishermen threw away. And sometimes, when nobody was looking, he even helped himself to a few whole fish that should have gone to market.

"Don't you ever get tired of fish?" asked his friend Gull. But Shanty just shook his head and continued nibbling on a tasty sardine. He just couldn't get enough fish!

One day, Shanty had a brilliant idea. "There's only one thing that would be better than being a harbour kitten," he told Gull. "And that would be being a boat kitten. Then I could eat all the fish I wanted."

So the next morning, when none of the fishermen were looking, Shanty crept aboard the *Salty Sardine*, the biggest of all the fishing boats in the harbour. Everybody was so busy that they didn't notice the stowaway hidden beneath an old raincoat.

The sea was calm as the boat chugged out to sea, and Shanty had a great time dreaming about all the fish that he was going to eat.

When the fishermen started pulling in the nets, Shanty couldn't believe his eyes. He was in kitten heaven. He'd never seen so many fish. There were mackerel. There were cod. There were haddock. And there were Shanty's favourite, sardines.

There were so many that nobody noticed when a few began to disappear under the old raincoat.

Shanty ate and ate, until he could eat no more. Then he curled up and settled down to sleep. But, just as he was dozing off, something strange began to happen.

The *Salty Sardine* began to creak and moan. Then it began to sway and rock. Water sprayed over the sides as it bounced over the waves then crashed back down again. Shanty's head began to reel and his stomach began to roll. Oh, how he wished he hadn't eaten so many fish! Oh, how he wished he'd stayed on dry land!

"We're going to drown," wailed Shanty, as a big wave crashed over the raincoat.

Soaked right through, Shanty peered out to see what the fishermen were doing. He couldn't believe his eyes. Instead of running about and screaming, they were carrying on with their work. One of them, who Shanty thought must be the captain, was even whistling. And another was eating a sausage roll. It seemed that for them, this was a normal day's work.

When the *Salty Sardine* finally got back to the harbour, Shanty couldn't get off fast enough.

"How is life as a boat kitten?" asked Gull, when he came visiting later that evening.

"Ah!" said Shanty, after he'd finished nibbling on a scrap of sardine. "Boats are all very well but give me the harbour any day. After all, how many fish can one kitten eat!"

This Little Froggy

This little froggy took a big leap,
This little froggy took a small,
This little froggy leaped sideways,
And this little froggy not at all,
And this little froggy went,
Hippity, hippity, hippity hop, all the way home.

Pitter-patter

Pitter-patter,
Pitter-patter
Listen to the rain!
Pitter-patter,
Pitter-patter,
On the window pane!

Bedtime

"Come, let's go to bed,"
Says Sleepy-head;
"Tarry a while," says Slow;
"Put on the pot,"
Says Greedy-gut,
"We'll sup before we go."

Good night

Good night, God bless you,
Go to bed and undress you.

Good night, sweet repose,
Half the bed and all
the clothes.

Come to the Window

Come to the window,
My baby, with me,
And look at the stars
That shine on the sea!
There are two little stars
That play bo-peep
With two little fish
Far down in the deep;
And two little frogs
Cry "Neap, neap, neap";
I see a dear baby
That should be asleep.

Hush-a-bye, Baby

Hush-a-bye, baby, they're gone to milk,
Lady and milkmaid all in silk,
Lady goes softly, maid goes slow,
Round again, round again, round they go.